MASSACHUSETTS DEPARTMENT OF AGRICULTURE
Dr. Arthur W. Gilbert
Commissioner

BIRDS OF MASSACHUSETTS

AND OTHER NEW ENGLAND STATES

BY

EDWARD HOWE FORBUSH

PART II. LAND BIRDS FROM BOB-WHITES TO GRACKLES

Illustrated with Colored Plates from Drawings by
LOUIS AGASSIZ FUERTES

AND

Figures and Cuts from Drawings and Photographs by Others

ISSUED BY AUTHORITY OF THE LEGISLATURE
1927

Norwood Press
J. S. Cushing Co. — Berwick & Smith Co.
Norwood, Mass., U.S.A.

PREFACE

THIS foreword is written for a single purpose. One can do no less than acknowledge herein the kindness and courtesy of those who have placed the author under obligations by giving valuable assistance or granting special privileges.

Acknowledgments are due to Mr. John A. Farley, who has edited the work; Mr. Arthur H. Norton of the Portland Society of Natural History who has furnished authentic information regarding Maine records, and to Mr. John H. Edmonds for an opportunity to examine ancient maps and records of Massachusetts preserved in the archives of the Commonwealth. Mr. P. A. Taverner of the Canadian National Memorial Museum at Ottawa, Ontario, Drs. Jonathan Dwight and Frank M. Chapman of the American Museum of Natural History at New York City, Dr. C. W. Richmond of the National Museum at Washington, D. C., Messrs. Samuel Henshaw, Outram Bangs, and James L. Peters of the Museum of Comparative Zoölogy, Harvard University, Cambridge, Massachusetts, and Mr. Winthrop S. Brooks of the Boston Society of Natural History have extended to the author the privilege of examining the bird collections under their charge. The Honorable John E. Thayer, and Messrs. A. C. Bent and F. H. Kennard have given the author permission to work in their private collections; Mrs. Grace P. Johnson and Mrs. Edna Ingalls of the Science Museum at Springfield, Massachusetts, have granted similar privileges there.

The author is indebted especially to Mr. Louis Agassiz Fuertes, the artist who illustrates this work, for helpful suggestions and advice; to Dr. John B. May who drew the maps, and who without adequate material with which to work has produced creditable drawings of some of the very rare birds not otherwise illustrated, and to the following persons for permission to quote from the publications set against their names: Drs. Frank M. Chapman and T. Gilbert Pearson, "Bird-Lore", and other publications; Mr. William L. Finley, "American Birds"; Houghton Mifflin Company, "Footing it in Franconia" by Bradford Torrey; Dr. C. W. Townsend, "The Birds of Essex County," and the Supplement to that work.

Special acknowledgments are due to Mr. J. H. Fleming of Toronto, Ontario, for revising the "ranges" of the different species and to the Biological Survey, Department of Agriculture, at Washington, and especially to Dr. H. C. Oberholser for supplying additions and corrections to the "ranges" from records not obtainable elsewhere.

President H. A. Obst of the Quadri-Color Company of New York City, makers of the colored plates, has taken an active personal interest in reproducing Mr. Fuertes' drawings and has given close, personal attention to the work.

iii

Dr. A. W. Gilbert, Commissioner of Agriculture, has given the project his cordial support and has continued to advocate before the legislative committees appropriations adequate for the work. His initiative and the support of the members of the Department has made possible the financing of the undertaking.

It now remains to express the most grateful appreciation of the author for the services rendered by several hundred observers and collaborators in the northeastern States and the maritime Provinces of Canada, who during the past ten years have corresponded with him and transmitted many thousands of notes on bird migration, unusual occurrences, descriptions of habits, molts, etc., many of which have been utilized in the preparation of this volume. Many excellent photographs also have been received, some of which are used for illustrating the work. Due credit for these is given in the captions under the illustrations.

Since the above was written Louis Agassiz Fuertes, the premier American portrayer of bird life, who painted the pictures which are reproduced in this volume, has passed into the Great Beyond. It is an irony of fate that he, having explored great wildernesses of North America, South America and Africa, having visited Europe and travelled many thousands of miles by sea and land in his favorite pursuits, should be instantly killed in his native state while driving his own car over a grade crossing. His untimely death came as a great shock. It was a poignant blow to a host of admiring friends.

When, as a young man, in 1897, he entered the field as an ornithological artist, that eminent American ornithologist, Dr. Elliot Coues, himself an artist of no mean ability, said of Fuertes' work, "I say deliberately with a full sense of my words that there is no one who can draw and paint birds so well as Mr. Fuertes, and I do not forget Audubon himself when I add that America has not before produced an ornithological artist of equal possibilities."

In all the years since then Mr. Fuertes has devoted his great talent to perfecting his art, and the paintings that he made for this volume and the succeeding one, Volume III, are the last of his illustrative work.

As Dr. Frank M. Chapman says in Bird Lore for October, 1927, — "Fuertes' drawings for the 'Birds of Massachusetts,' his last published work, are conceded to be finer than any illustrations he had previously painted." His loss to the art and literature of ornithology is great. He was remarkably versatile and excelled as a writer, lecturer, teacher and entertainer. He gave freely of himself, his time, his talent and his means to worthy projects and to his many friends. He was a lovable transcendent genius. He was kindly, hospitable, loyal and sincere. All in all we shall not look upon his like again.

EDWARD HOWE FORBUSH.

Boston, October 10, 1927

CONTENTS

vi CONTENTS

LIST OF ILLUSTRATIONS

PLATES

FIGURES

ix

MAPS

CUTS IN THE TEXT

INTRODUCTION

TOPOGRAPHY OF MASSACHUSETTS AND OTHER NEW ENGLAND STATES.

MASSACHUSETTS, lying across the south-central part of New England, extends on the coast from latitude 41° north to latitude 43° north. The distance from the coast of Westport, at the boundary between Massachusetts and Rhode Island, to the northeastern coast in Salisbury on the New Hampshire line is about 96 miles, but the shore line of Massachusetts, following the various indentations and points, is nearly 300 miles in length. Along the southern coast west of Chatham a number of deep bays enter the land. Along the eastern seaboard there are protected bays or harbors at Provincetown, Plymouth, Boston, Lynn, Salem, Gloucester and Newburyport, with numerous smaller estuaries or inlets between. A direct line from Chatham beach at the elbow of the peninsula of Cape Cod to the northwestern corner of the state at Williamstown would measure about 177 miles, and a line running north and south through the widest part of the western section of the state from the southwestern corner of Southwick to the northwestern corner of Colrain about 50 miles.

The long arm of Cape Cod and the islands of Nantucket, Marthas Vineyard, No Man's Land, the Elizabeth group and Block Island are composed very largely of glacial drift. Their surfaces show many glacial boulders and terminal moraines, marking the former location of the end of the great continental glacier. Apparently Nantucket, Marthas Vineyard, No Man's Land, Block Island and Long Island are the most southerly stations now remaining above water to indicate the southward extension of the continental ice sheet. Western Cape Cod and the Elizabeth Islands are largely formed of "drift" from the retreating glacier which, later, maintained its front along that line for a considerable period.

Nantucket and Marthas Vineyard, lying south of Cape Cod, together include over 100 square miles of land. The submerged continental shelf extending in comparatively shallow water 120 miles east of Cape Cod to Georges Bank cannot be considered biologically or politically as a part of Massachusetts.

From sea level at the tide-washed lands of the coast the general terrain of the state rises gradually, reaching its highest point at Mount Greylock, the peak of the great mass of Saddle Mountain, 3,535 feet above the level of the sea. Between these extremes the state presents a considerable diversity of physical conditions which fit the land to support a variety of forms of animal and vegetal life. The central and western parts of the state consist of a rather broken plateau divided by the low valley of the Connecticut River. Two mountain chains trend north and south along the plateau in the higher western end of the state—the Taconic Range with its summits near the western boundary, and the Hoosac Range occupying the eastern part of Berkshire County and the western part of Franklin, Hampshire and Hampden counties. The Taconic includes mountains in western Connecticut and western Vermont and those near-by along the eastern boundary of New York and near it. They may be regarded as a continuation of the Green Mountains of Vermont and the whole of these western New England ranges as an extension of the Appalachian mountain system. Among the highest peaks of the Taconic Range in Massachusetts are Berlin Mountain (2,804 ft.), the actual summit being just over the line in New York State, and Mount Everett (2,624 ft.).

Most of the land surface of Berkshire County is much higher than the other parts of Massachusetts, and its higher elevations also rise considerably more above sea level than those of the rest of the state. There are more than a score of mountains ranging between 2,000 and 3,000 feet. Toward the Connecticut Valley the land gradually lowers, while most of the valley near the river lies below 200 feet and much of it below 100 feet. The land in the northern part of Worcester County about Winchendon (about 1,200 ft.) may be regarded as a part of the height of land on which Mount Monadnock stands in southern New Hampshire.

Any treatment of the physical geography of Massachusetts would be incomplete without some reference to New England as a whole, a definite geographic region, of which Massachusetts is an integral part, its physical features being continued into other states to the north and south. New England is a well defined division, separated by definite boundaries from other regions. The eastern and southern coasts bound it on two sides, except on the easternmost boundary of Maine. Some of its physical features continue into neighboring territory, as the extension of certain northern mountains into Canada, but the Hudson-Champlain Valley is the natural boundary of the New England region on the west and the St. Lawrence Valley on the north.

New England is a rugged country. Its surface was built up, in remote times, largely of crystalline and old bedded rock. Through the ages this rock has been much disturbed and in places upheaved into mountains. Afterward it was tremendously eroded and worn down, and then in a later period again generally elevated. Probably there have been a number of elevations and depressions of the surface.

Geologists tell us that after the warm climate of the Tertiary period New England became as cold as Greenland is to-day, and that in the Quaternary period the entire region was glaciated and much of the surface was buried under glacial deposits. The great Quaternary sheet of ice was higher than Mount Washington. Much of its surface rose possibly a mile above the earth, and extended from higher lands in northern regions south into what is now the northern United States. This ice period is called the Pleistocene or glacial epoch.

The great ice sheet, moving slowly southward, ground off the tops of mountains, hills and ledges, scoured out valleys, and carried with it enormous quantities of boulders, small stones, gravel, sand and clay or till. These earthy materials, called glacial drift, were

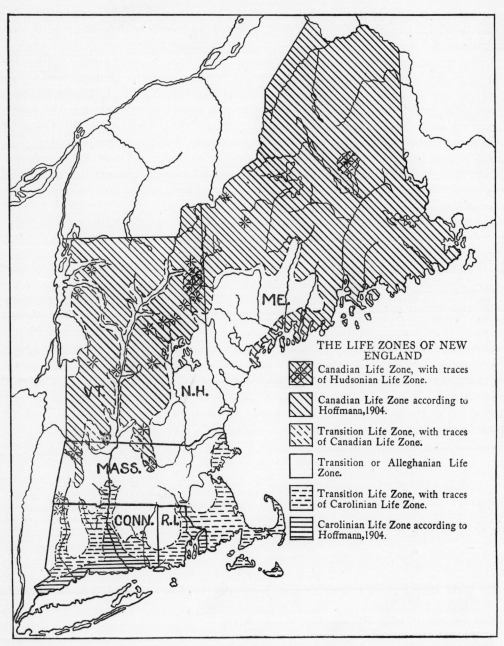

THE LIFE ZONES OF NEW
ENGLAND

Canadian Life Zone, with traces
of Hudsonian Life Zone.

Canadian Life Zone according to
Hoffmann,1904.

Transition Life Zone, with traces
of Canadian Life Zone.

Transition or Alleghanian Life
Zone.

Transition Life Zone, with traces
of Carolinian Life Zone.

Carolinian Life Zone according to
Hoffmann,1904.

In addition to the faunal areas shown above there are alpine spots at the summits of some of the higher
New Hampshire mountains and some small Maine areas, partly Hudsonian, not shown on the map.

Northward distribution, says Dr. C. Hart Merriam, is restricted "by the total quantity of heat during the season of reproduction," while distribution southward is governed "by the mean temperature of a brief period covering the hottest part of the year." Temperature depends largely on four factors — latitude, altitude, amount of moisture, and character of forests. Latitude and altitude have a like effect. Temperatures may be modified also by proximity to the sea, by the slope of the land and by prevailing winds. Other conditions being equal, however, the mean temperature lowers as we go higher up or farther north. Dr. Merriam, after long study and as a result of many exploring expeditions, divided North America into Boreal, Austral and Tropical "regions." New England, because of variations in latitude and altitude, has animals and plants of both Boreal and Austral regions. Dr. Merriam has divided these regions into life zones — the Boreal into the Arctic, Hudsonian and Canadian zones and the Austral into the Transition, Upper Austral and Lower Austral zones. The zones of the Austral region are again divided, the 100th meridian roughly separating the humid and non-humid divisions. The eastern (humid) subdivision of the Transition Zone is called the Alleghanian Faunal Area, the eastern (humid) subdivision of the Upper Austral Zone, the Carolinian Faunal Area, and the eastern (humid) division of the Lower Austral Zone the Austroriparian Faunal Area.[1] The Transition Zone is a temperate region in which both Austral and Boreal forms meet and mingle. Each region, zone, and area has animals and plants which if not peculiar to it are characteristic of it and probably thrive best within its limits. Migratory animals, such as migrating birds, which are regarded as characteristic of a faunal region, are those that breed there regularly in numbers.* Following the distribution of animal and plant life in New England we may draw a line from northeast to southwest through the territory to denote the southern edge of the Canadian Zone, but the line will have many sinuosities on account of variations in altitude (see map). Below this line (which is not fixed nor arbitrary) New England is Alleghanian, except that in southwestern Connecticut (with some extensions up the Connecticut and Housatonic Valleys), some Carolinian life may be found. Traces of this extend in a lessening degree along the southern and southeastern coasts and islands as far north at least as Essex County, Massachusetts.

A well-defined faunal zone, as the Canadian, usually shows traces of other faunal regions in the plants and animals coming into it from the north and the south. There is a broad belt along the northern and southern boundaries of any zone or faunal area which extends on either side of the boundary well into the contiguous zone, where forms of the two regions may be found more or less intermixed. Altitude also plays a part here. An isolated mountain in the Alleghanian area, because of its altitude and resulting soil and vegetation, may become a breeding place for such Canadian faunal birds as the Yellow-

---

[1] See Geographic Distribution of Life in North America. Smithsonian Institution Report, 1891, pp. 365–415; see also United States Department of Agriculture, Biological Survey Bulletin, No. 10, 1898, pp. 18–31.

* But plants and other animal life besides birds when occurring *in numbers* are just as important in determining the character of an area. Of these, plants, being stationary, are probably the most important in characterizing an area.

bellied Sapsucker or the Myrtle Warbler; or some high elevation in the Canadian Zone may prove to be a breeding place for the Bicknell's Thrush, a Hudsonian bird.

Oftentimes vegetation alone seems to be a potent factor in distribution, as in the spruce-grown country in Winchendon and Ashburnham in northern Worcester County, Massachusetts, where the general elevation, to be sure, is 1,200–1,300 feet (but with no great heights to be found anywhere) with breeding White-throated Sparrows, Juncos, Olive-sided Flycatchers, Winter Wrens, Golden-crowned Kinglets, Myrtle and various other Canadian faunal warblers, or the more elevated Colrain, Heath and Rowe in Franklin County, on the Vermont line, with their breeding Kinglets, Myrtle Warblers, Sapsuckers and Olive-backed Thrushes.* All these towns have a very strong trace of the Canadian faunal bird and plant life.

The Alleghanian Faunal Area (in which most of southern New England lies) being the eastern part of the Transition Zone is, naturally, the chief region in which northern and southern forms may be expected to mingle. Massachusetts, lying east and west across this region, therefore is mainly Alleghanian. Strays from the Carolinian Faunal Area sometimes penetrate up river valleys even to the borders of the Canadian Zone, but such occurrences, being the exception, do not invalidate the rule. Although the Fauna and Flora of Massachusetts is so largely Alleghanian, certain Carolinian and Canadian faunal birds breed in various parts of the state, many of the latter group being found on the western and northern elevations as far east at least as eastern Worcester County. If one wishes to find straggling Carolinian birds in Massachusetts in the breeding season, he will naturally seek them near sea level in the southeastern parts along the coast or in the valleys of the Connecticut or Housatonic Rivers. In these sections he *may* find the Fish Crow, the Yellow-breasted Chat and the Carolina Wren.† On steep, cool, northern mountain sides he might expect to find more breeding birds of the Canadian Zone than on their warmer southern slopes. If he were looking especially for "Canadian" birds, he would go to the higher lands of the northern part of the state (in Worcester County or farther west), where he might find the Golden-crowned Kinglet, Yellow-bellied Sapsucker, Winter Wren and Olive-backed Thrush, together with several Canadian faunal warblers. In the lowlands of southern Connecticut he might expect to find the sweet gum and the tulip tree, and those typical Carolina birds the Worm-eating and the Hooded Warblers; but on the higher hills of Berkshire County, Massachusetts, where in a higher altitude he would find spruce woods and other northern plants, he might look with confidence for nests of Myrtle and Mourning Warblers, the latter in sprout-land.

Vegetation plays a great part in the distribution of animals. Dense woods of white pine, spruce and hemlock tend to reduce somewhat the summer temperature within their limits, and are generally inhabited by birds of both Canadian and Transition zones, but

---

* Of the above birds, two species — the Kinglet and the Thrush — cling most closely to the spruce and may, therefore, be regarded as most typical of the Canadian Zone.

† But the Fish Crow has been found also in the breeding season in numbers as far east as Wareham, the Carolina Wren breeding still farther north and east, while the Chat breeds regularly though rather rarely in southern Essex County, and also more rarely in Worcester City to which it may have had access by the valley of the Blackstone.

rarely if ever by birds of the Carolinian Fauna. In certain well-wooded towns in northern Worcester County, situated on the central plateau that stretches across the state from New Hampshire to Connecticut, there occurs an interesting mingling of "northern" and "southern" trees. Red pines (more in the past than the present), canoe and yellow birches, beech and basswood, sugar maple and a little spruce (in swamps chiefly) stand mingled with trees quite characteristic of southern Connecticut, as the hickory, tupelo, sassafras, pitch pine and various oaks. Yet this region cannot in any sense be considered within the Canadian Zone — nor the Carolinian Fauna either, as the "Canadian" birds that breed there are few both in numbers and species.* The prevailing trees — white pine, hemlock, red oak and white ash — are, like the prevailing birds, Alleghanian, and acquire their greatest development in this and other parts of the Transition Zone.

While the boundaries of the regions, zones and areas are, in general, fairly well marked, the altitude, exposure and vegetation of Massachusetts lands are so varied that it may be possible to find Carolinian, Alleghanian, and Canadian birds breeding within a short distance of one another, as in the Webster laurel and black spruce swamp where the Hooded Warbler was in full song close to a nesting Canada Warbler, with a pair of Myrtle Warblers nesting in a white pine not far away; and in the Berkshire, Franklin, and Hampshire County localities where Wood, Hermit, Olive-backed, and Wilson's Thrushes may be heard all singing at once. Mourning Warblers, Sapsuckers and Winter Wrens may be found there also with occasionally, in some valley, a Louisiana Water Thrush — a typical Carolinian or Upper Austral bird. † Sometimes we find the usual conditions reversed. A moist forest lowers the summer temperature. A low swamp with a cold, springy bottom and a dense growth of coniferous trees may be so cool in summer that some "Canadian" birds, as the Canada Warbler, Northern Water Thrush and Brown Creeper, will breed in this Canadian island, while on near-by highlands that have been denuded of their native coniferous forests and turned into farms with deciduous woodlots, Alleghanian birds alone will be found nesting. A deep, wooded, watered ravine in a farming country may serve as a breeding place for "Canadian" forms which do not nest in the surrounding summer uplands.

The Carolinian Faunal Area or humid division of the Upper Austral Zone reaches the Atlantic seaboard chiefly in the region between Virginia and southeastern New York. It is represented in southern New England in the breeding season by such birds as the King Rail, Black Rail, Florida Gallinule, Barn Owl, Acadian Flycatcher, Fish Crow, Orchard Oriole, Rough-winged Swallow, Cardinal Grosbeak, Blue Grosbeak, Seaside

---

* As the Goshawks found breeding in 1922, 1923, 1924 in Petersham by Mr. Farley.

† It must be always borne in mind that cutting off timber has changed most markedly the countryside in Massachusetts. Thus the little spruce left standing in the state to-day (outside the scattering black spruce in eastern cedar swamps) is to be found here and there from northern Worcester County west, mostly at the tops of elevations which, by reason of their relative inaccessibility, as well as by their generally poor soil which grows poor timber, stunted by strong winds, have hitherto escaped the axe. The axe has been swung to so good purpose on the lower and easier (from the viewpoint of the teamster) slopes of these same elevations, as well as in the relatively flat valleys between elevations (which also were originally spruce grown) that nothing practically has been left to show that conifers ever grew there. In this connection note the extensive cutting of spruce carried on for so many years on Greylock (and the Saddleback Range generally) which was only stopped when the state stepped in and saved some of it by right of eminent domain.

Sparrow, White-eyed Vireo, Blue-winged Warbler, Hooded Warbler, Worm-eating Warbler, Louisiana Water Thrush, Yellow-breasted Chat, Carolina Wren and Mockingbird. These species have occurred in the breeding season principally along the southern and southeastern coasts of southern New England and up the river valleys into Connecticut and in most cases into Massachusetts.

The Alleghanian Faunal Area of the Transition Zone which is, as hereinbefore stated, the region where northern and southern forms meet, mingle and overlap, lacks distinctive birds. Southern species in the attempt to extend their range farther north meet and pass here northern species pushing southward. For example, the Mockingbird of the Carolinian Fauna appears to have been pushing northward and eastward in recent years to Maine, while the Herring Gull of the Canadian Fauna, under protection with increasing numbers, has gradually extended its summer range southward, from Maine to southeastern Massachusetts.

The common birds of Massachusetts, derived as they are mainly from either boreal or austral regions, may be ascribed to the Alleghanian Faunal Area. The Canadian Fauna is confined mainly in New England to the higher or more northern lands where normally it may be distinguished in vegetation from the other faunal areas by the development of spruce and fir forests. Characteristic birds of this Canadian Zone are the Spruce Grouse, the Canadian Ruffed Grouse, Northern Raven, Canada Jay, Acadian Owl, Goshawk, Yellow-bellied Flycatcher, Pine Siskin, Red Crossbill, White-winged Crossbill, Yellow-bellied Sapsucker, Rusty Blackbird, Golden-crowned Kinglet, Red-breasted Nuthatch, Brown Creeper, Winter Wren,* Tennessee, Myrtle, Mourning, Bay-breasted, Blackpoll and Canada Warblers, Acadian Chickadee, and Olive-backed Thrushes. Not all of these breed in Massachusetts and some others only rarely. Their nesting here seems to depend nearly as much upon vegetation, and in the case of birds of prey, on extensive wooded districts and available food, as on altitude.

The Hudsonian Zone marks the northern or highest limit of the forests of spruce and fir. There are some traces of its fauna near the treeless alpine summits of the highest mountains of New Hampshire, as in the Presidential Range — also the highest summits in Maine and possibly local limited areas in certain river valleys and along the coast from Mt. Desert east. A Hudsonian bird, the Pine Grosbeak, breeds in New Hampshire and also in Maine at altitudes of about 3000 feet. Characteristic birds of the Hudsonian Zone are the Rough-legged Hawk, Great Gray Owl, Pine Grosbeak, Northern Shrike, White-crowned Sparrow and Gray-cheeked Thrush.

CHANGES IN THE BIRD LIFE OF NEW ENGLAND.

Many changes have taken place in the numbers and distribution of birds since the settlement of New England. Some have been due to natural causes, while more have

---

* The Winter Wren, like the White-throated Sparrow, seems to be so adaptable a bird that it does not depart after the cutting of the spruce, but still nests along its favorite brooks shaded now only, alas, by broad-leaved trees, just as the White-throated Sparrow continues to frequent the "slash" in pastures formerly spruce-grown.

been caused by man and his satellites. Among the changes occasioned by natural causes are the westward movements of the Dickcissel and the Red-headed Woodpecker, also the eastward extension of the range of the Prairie Horned Lark, the recent increase northward of the Meadowlark, the recent eastward and northward increase of the Mockingbird, the increase and spread of the Rose-breasted Grosbeak and the Golden-winged Warbler, the recent push northward in numbers of the House Wren and the eastward winter migration of the Evening Grosbeak during the past half century.

Along the coasts of New England there are many islands and points on which seabirds breed or have bred safely in the past. The changes in topography constantly taking place along the coast and their effect on bird life may best be understood by a description of the action of the wind and sea upon our sandy shores.

ENCROACHMENT OF THE SEA UPON THE LAND.

Along most of the New England coast the restless sea constantly wears away the shore. Great changes take place continually wherever wave meets sand, gravel, or clay. Maps of the coast soon become obsolete so frequent are the changes. At Peaked Hill bars near Provincetown a storm may change in a single night the shape and location of a bar, but where wave meets rock the changes are exceedingly slow.

The region included in Cape Cod and the islands south of it, the soil of which is largely composed of sand and gravel with some deposits of clay, may be used to exemplify the action of the sea upon the land of New England and its effect upon bird life. Doubtless there were once in this region many islands inhabited by myriads of sea-birds where now the waves break over submerged shoals.*

The Destruction and Elimination of Islands.

The destruction of islands which goes on off-shore, and to a less degree in harbors along the coast, has a marked effect on the breeding of sea-birds, which can nest in comparative safety on islands, but which cannot persist long on the coast, because of excessive destruction by man and the many enemies which soon find the breeding places of fowls that nest in communities on the ground.

When in 1602 Bartholomew Gosnold discovered Cape Cod and landed at what is now Provincetown there were many sandy islands about the end of the Cape. The last one to disappear, Home Point near the west end of Provincetown Harbor, has been washed away within the lifetime of men now living.

The little sand bar now known as Billingsgate Island lying off Wellfleet harbor, was either once a part of a long point extending out across the entrance of the harbor, or one of a chain of islands which at one time must have extended to a point about three miles farther south than the present islet. Early in the nineteenth century Billingsgate was still a large island, later broken in two by the sea. A government lighthouse stood on the

---

* Proofs of the existence formerly of such islands cannot be given here in full for lack of space, but research has unearthed much evidence in support of the statements herein advanced.

outer end of the southernmost island. In spite of a stone breakwater erected by the government, this island and the lighthouse were swept away. Another lighthouse was then built on the inner island, and that has since been destroyed by the sea, together with another retaining wall built by the government to protect it. Probably the remnant of the island will not last many years.

CAPT. CHAMPLAIN'S MAP OF A PART OF WHAT IS NOW CHATHAM (1606).   UNITED STATES COAST SURVEY MAP OF CHATHAM SHORE (1872).

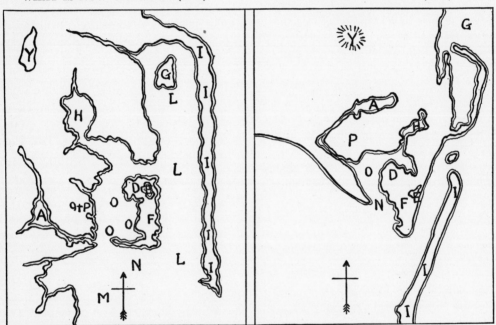

CAPTIONS, ONE FREELY TRANSLATED AND BOTH ABRIDGED.

A.	A pond of salt water.	A.	Salt Pond.
D.	Low hills on the island covered with trees.	D.	Hillocks (Stage Island).
E.	A fresh water pond with quantities of wild-fowl.	E.	Island Pond (fresh).
F.	A prairie on the island.	F.	"Morris Island," so called.
G.	A wooded island within a large bay.	G.	Site of Ram Island (now washed away).
H.	A salt water pond with many shell-fish and oysters.	H.	Mill Pond.
I.	Sand Dunes on a tongue of land.	I.	Sand Dunes (on Monomoy).
L.	A land-locked bay.	M.	Roadstead.
M.	Roadstead where we anchored.	N.	Bar.
N.	Entrance to harbor.	O.	Stage Harbor.
O.	Harbor.	P.	Stage Neck.
P.	The cross which we planted.	Y.	Great Hill.
Y.	A low hill which appears inland.		

Captain John Smith found a large island off the east coast of Orleans that he named "Ille Nausett." Early in the nineteenth century this disappeared entirely. Webb's Island, which lay east by south from Chatham, distant about 9 miles, contained about 15 acres and was wooded when the Cape was first settled; it has disappeared. The only vestige of the island remaining now is a large sunken rock known as Crabbs Ledge.[1] Another ledge known as Island Ledge still may be found off Chatham on a direct line off the beach toward Crabbs Ledge but much nearer shore.

Several of the older inhabitants of Wellfleet speak of Egg Island in Wellfleet Harbor. Many birds nested there about the beginning of the nineteenth century and people then visited the island to gather eggs. Remains of this island are still visible at very low tides.

Many years ago there was an islet off the end of Monomoy called Egg Island. Its name indicates that formerly it was high enough above the water to serve as a breeding place for sea-birds. There is no island there now. Mr. Henry Mitchell, of the Coast and Geodetic Survey, evidently believed Shovelful Shoal to be the remains of Egg Island shifted to an advanced position and nearly submerged. This seems a reasonable explanation. This shoal has moved southward toward Nantucket.[2]

Champlain's Map of the Cape, where the present town of Chatham lies, shows an island about half a mile in length and about a quarter of a mile wide lying east of the present site of the town and a peninsula several miles long extending east about a mile from the shore and thence southward, thus forming a harbor in which lay the island. The island, tradition has it, was named Ram Island by the settlers and there is a legend that out beyond it there were once some larger islands upon which people lived and where cattle were kept. The peninsula probably was what is now known as Monomoy and the outer islands* (not shown on Champlain's Map) probably are now represented only by ledges and shoals. On the map of Nickerson's Purchase made at least fifty years after Champlain's Map, Monomoy is no longer connected with the mainland but is shown as an island, extending farther south, narrower and much nearer both the shore and Morris Island, so-called (see map), while Ram Island appears under its Indian name of Cotchpinicut and much reduced in size. All this accords with what has happened since. Ram Island has disappeared and Monomoy has been extended southward and pushed back upon the coast. As an example of another island destroyed in a harbor there is Nix's Mate in Boston Harbor, once a considerable islet, now merely a shoal supporting a lighthouse.

The Destruction or Shifting of Barrier Beaches.

The action of the sea in changing the outline of the coast is exemplified along the shores of Marthas Vineyard, Nantucket and Cape Cod, particularly on the outer coasts, and also on the sandy shores north of Cape Ann, on those of Massachusetts and Cape Cod

---

[1] See Massachusetts Magazine for December, 1790; also New England Genealogical and Antiquarian Register, 1864, pp. 43, 44.

[2] Report of the superintendent of the United States Coast and Geodetic Survey, 1886, p. 258.

* These islands may have been a part of the peninsula, broken up by the sea after Champlain's visit.

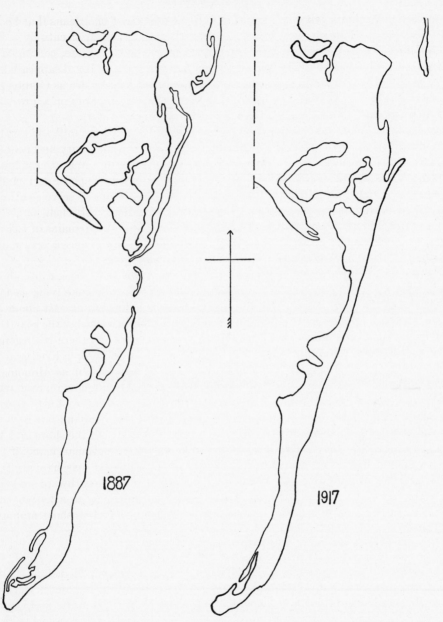

1887

1917

RECENT CHANGES IN THE SHORE LINE OF CHATHAM AS SHOWN BY COAST SURVEYS.

Monomoy which was a short peninsula in Champlain's day had become a long island with two long sand bars north of it in 1887, but now it is a still longer peninsula. It has been driven west by wind and sea.

Bays, even in Boston Harbor and on other parts of the New England coast.   The waves tear down the land along the sea-coast and swift tides carry the wave-borne sand and other material along the beaches to build up shoals or new land elsewhere.

In some early maps of Massachusetts, the outer barrier or beach ridge protecting the bays and harbors of Chatham, Orleans and Eastham from the sea is represented as a long narrow island about 12 miles in length, lying far to the eastward of its present position, with several small islands north of it and outlets to the ocean at either end — the northern one at Eastham and the southern lying between the end of this beach ridge and the Chatham shore.   In the great harbor protected by this barrier were several islands, some of which have now disappeared.   In 1854 during the great storm that wrecked the lighthouse on Minot's Ledge, the sea broke through the barrier into Orleans waters at Nauset, and afterward much of Nauset Harbor near the entrance filled partially with shifting sands.   Great changes have taken place in Chatham Harbor.   Since Gosnold's voyage the outer barrier has been pushed back perhaps a mile against the coast north of Pleasant Bay and is now connected with the mainland at its northern end also in Eastham.   In 1871 that part of it in front of the town of Chatham began to break up.   A channel still remained open between Morris Island and the mainland and in the 80's boats could sail through this from the Atlantic to Stage Harbor.   In 1908 I was obliged to wade to reach this island and Monomoy at low tide.   In 1917 I found that the channel between Morris Island and the mainland had been filled by sand thrown up from the sea, and now the "Island" is solidly connected with Cape Cod by a barrier beach.   Within the past three centuries Monomoy must have moved bodily westward to connect with Morris Island as it now does (see maps).   The junction of Morris Island with the mainland and the extension of Monomoy to the island make both Monomoy and Morris Island a part of a peninsula.   Most present day maps show Monomoy as an island, but this is incorrect.   Monomoy and Morris Island, now connected, might become one continuous island should the sea break through the barrier into Stage Harbor. Champlain's Map shows that in his day Morris Island was a real island with a channel between it and the Chatham shore, and a pond containing a quantity of game.   Now the island is connected with the mainland and the pond is a swamp with little water.*

Shaler held that an area on the eastern coast of Truro and Wellfleet amounting to not less than thirty square miles had been carried off by the sea, but believed that the maximum recession of the eastern coast here since the land came to its present altitude could not amount to more than three or four miles.[1]   The recession of the beach bluffs here still continues, and once has necessitated the removal of Highland Light.   Similar necessary removals of lighthouses have occurred at Chatham and at Cape Poge, at the east end of Marthas Vineyard.   At Cape Poge the lighthouse has been moved more

---

* Monomoy, like the barrier beach in front of Chatham, seems to have moved westward at least half a mile to a mile since Champlain saw it in 1606, and thus has reached its present position, joined to Morris Island.

[1] Shaler, N. S.: Eighteenth Annual Report of the U. S. Geological Survey, Part II, 1897, p. 570.

than once. A part of the foundation of an old Chatham lighthouse still exists on the very verge of the bluff above the harbor.

There is no place on the coast of Massachusetts where the erosive action of the sea is more plainly evident than on the south shore of Marthas Vineyard. There is a tradition that a barrier beach or causeway once extended from that island to No Man's Land so that the Indians could cross from one to the other. The northward movement of the barrier beach south of Katama Bay is remarkable. Professor Whiting found that in 25 years, between 1846 and 1872, it had shifted a distance of 450 feet.[1] Probably in recent years the movement has been quite as rapid. The continual shifting of such beach ridges is not caused entirely by the action of wave and tide, although in storms the surf frequently washes over parts of the beach carrying sand from the outside to the inside. This continual recession at Katama Beach takes place in great part by reason of the shifting of the sand from the sea side to the bay side in dry weather, under the influence of sea winds which continually drift it northward. Doubtless north winds sometimes blow sand over the beach into the sea, but this is carried away by the tide. The sand drift from the beach ridge is continually filling in along the southern shores of all the lagoons or ponds that, like Katama Bay, are separated from the sea by mere barrier beaches. These ponds are also filled on their northern sides by sand which in winter is driven across them on the ice by south winds. Some small ponds and a creek between Edgartown Great Herring Pond and Katama Bay have filled with sand since the early part of the nineteenth century.

The south shore of the island of Marthas Vineyard lies but little above sea level, except near the west end where the cliffs of Nashaquitsa and Squibnocket rise high above the sea. From Katama Bay on the east to Chilmark on the west a series of low ridges runs southward from the higher land of the interior, gradually sloping toward the sea as they near it. There are good reasons for believing that these ridges once extended out into the sea, which then filled the bays or small fiords between them, but in time the ocean formed from the sea sands a barrier beach, which, driven by wind and sea, moved northward until it met the ends of the ridges, encroached upon them and shut out the sea entirely, thus forming landlocked basins.* These basins between the ridges then filled up with fresh water from the interior, which, in seasons of extreme high water, overflowed the barrier beach and cut through it, thus in time washing out the salt water. In this way fresh-water ponds were formed inside the barrier reef.† Some of the inhabitants now excavate channels in spring and autumn from one of these ponds to the sea so that the alewives may enter, breed, and return to the salt water. Heavy surf from seaward soon fills up these outlets with sand, which must be opened later to let the alewives out.

---

[1] Whiting, H. L.: Quoted by Shaler in Geology of Marthas Vineyard. Seventh Annual Report, Director U. S. Geological Survey, 1885–86, p. 348.

* There is a tradition that early in the last century people could go in boats from Katama Bay to Chilmark Pond in summer, passing between the barrier beach and the ends of the ridges which now separate these lagoon ponds from each other, and could skate the whole distance in winter. Some of the old maps indicate this passage.

† A number of similar lagoons have been formed on Cape Cod in the same way.

Maps published early in the last century show Squibnocket Pond in the south part of the town of Gay Head as a bay connected with the sea by an outlet through the west shore. This former bay is now a fresh-water pond, slightly brackish, with an artificial outlet on the south shore above high tide, and a small stream running from it into Menemsha Pond. Squibnocket Pond now has a fresh-water marsh connected with it. There are a number of large fresh marshes on Cape Cod toward its end, formerly salt but now shut off from the sea by ridges or dunes. This change has made a corresponding change in bird life. The beach ridges on the south side of the Marthas Vineyard ponds are similar to Katama Beach which shuts off Katama Bay from the sea on the south. Wind and wave tend to bare such barrier beaches and keep them in excellent condition for breeding places for the Least Tern and the Piping Plover, which thrive there. The bays or fiords which once existed on the south side of the island doubtless were favorite feeding-grounds for sea-birds and sea-fowl, such as Scoters, Old-squaws, Red-breasted Mergansers, and Eider Ducks, but now as fresh-water ponds within the barrier, they produce a great quantity and variety of pondweeds and other aquatic plants which attract more valuable fowl (largely pond and river ducks and geese), than can be found on any equal area of fresh water in southern New England. The rapid wearing away of the cliffs on the south side of the west end of the island is evidenced by the overhanging of turf and fences. United States Coast Survey experts ascertained that in forty years, from 1846 to 1886, the shore in the central part of Nashaquitsa cliffs retreated northward 220 feet, an average of five and a half feet a year. Sometimes a panel of a fence may be seen overhanging the cliff for several feet. In severe winter weather the upper part of the cliff freezes, while at its foot it is cut away by the surf until the great weight of the earth above causes it to topple into the sea, which soon disintegrates it and carries it away. I am told by residents that at one time within recent years, after a great storm, a section of the cliff, nearly a quarter of a mile in length, fell into the sea, taking with it a horse in a pasture near the verge, and that after the storm there was a depth of ten feet of water at that point. In 1908 I photographed there a small cliff of colored clay similar to that at Gay Head but not so high. In 1923 no vestige of this cliff remained. These cliffs doubtless wear away most rapidly during winter storms. The western end of the island where these bluffs are located is (as hereinbefore stated) higher than the rest of the island and more hilly. Undoubtedly all these hills once sloped gradually down to the sea, which, rapidly advancing and eating out their slopes, cut them down nearly vertically to sea level, thus forming the cliffs. These heights now offer breeding places for hundreds of Bank Swallows, which could not have bred on the island before the bluffs were formed.* The prevailing eastward drift of the tide currents along the south coast of Marthas Vineyard which carries the washed-out material continually to the east is shown by the eastward movement of the various southern outlets at Katama Bay. Many times during the last century an outlet has been formed either by the sea breaking through the barrier beach, or by artificial means. Some of the old maps show two outlets, making

---

* The cliffs of Truro, similarly formed, also provide a breeding place for these birds.

Professor Whiting, writing in 1886, says in effect that the island had been little more than a shoal for the "last twenty years," but that recently it had risen somewhat from the sea and for the first time in fifty years beach-grass and weeds were growing on its surface. This island is situated in the midst of shoals and troubled waters and the pounding of the sea frequently changes its contour. In 1886 according to Whiting, it was 1200 feet long, 290 feet wide in its widest part, and contained four and a half acres. I have watched its changes since 1908 when it presented high banks and no vegetation, and have seen it change from a long, banked-up sand-spit with a lagoon in the center to an oblong island more or less covered with vegetation. Some years in great winter storms the sea makes a clean breach over it, sweeping away all vegetation. At other times the sea divides it, forming two islands, and once in December there were three islands, two in the next May and only one in the following July, when I sailed over a sunken islet to reach Skiff's Island. In 1903 the island disappeared for a time but later rose again. It is not known just when sea-birds began breeding on this island, but many terns bred there in 1908 and Herring Gulls joined them later. The island now makes a comparatively safe breeding place for these birds, although its surface may be washed occasionally by some exceptionally severe summer storm.

Dry shoal off Eel Point near the west end of Nantucket appears as an island on the latest coast survey charts. Mr. Isaac Hills, 3d, informs me that recently some beach-grass grew upon it and a number of terns attempted to breed there. Now (1927), however, Mr. George Mackay informs me that it has been reduced to a mere shoal showing at half-tide.*

An island is made now and then by the sea breaking through a long point or barrier beach and separating it from the mainland. Recently a part of the barrier beach at Cotuit on the south side of the Cape has been cut off from the mainland and has become the breeding place of many birds. In Nauset Harbor there existed about seventy-five years ago a tiny salt-marsh islet which gradually increased in size until it was about three-fourths of a mile in length and filled a considerable part of the harbor. Wind-blown sand accumulated at its southern end, raising it above the level of the marsh. This end was occupied until 1903 by a large colony of terns. In 1903 the waves washed away much of the accumulated sand and greatly reduced the breeding ground of the birds. An island, probably formed in a similar manner, now accommodates a great colony of terns in Chatham Harbor. These islands, however, may be rendered untenable for the birds in time by the filling up of these harbors which may connect the islands with the shore.

The Filling of Harbors and Estuaries.

The general tendency of the action of water on the land is leveling. By erosion hills are lowered and hollows filled; islands and shores are broken down and washed away, while the waters become shallower. Harbors and estuaries are choked with sand, carried by wind and tide, and by current-borne silt. Nauset and Pamet harbors and the Powder

---

* Mr. Laurence B. Fletcher tells me that this shoal has since risen, is larger than ever before, and that terns are breeding upon it.

Hole at Monomoy once sheltered fleets of fishing schooners. Now these harbors have filled so that they are accessible only to small boats. As tide flats are built up, sand is mixed with silt brought into the estuaries and harbors by the streams and tides. In time eel-grass grows and collects more sediment and finally as the land continues to rise from the waters, salt-marsh is formed. Later wind-driven sand covers the marsh and the former harbor or estuary becomes dry land. This, in brief, is the process by which shallow harbors and estuaries are filling up except where stream channels are kept clear by swift currents or by dredging. Many a salt-marsh was once a shallow bay, but protected by a barrier beach thrown up from the sea it gradually filled with sand. Such marshes often eventually become fresh and finally dry land unless the land itself sinks to a lower level. "Islands" in the salt-marsh are now islands only at high tide. Before the marsh filled in, they were real islands, surrounded by water at all times, and were safe breeding places for water-birds.

The Subsidence of the Land.

Evidence has been presented by geologists to support the theory that the land along our sea-coast has subsided within recent times. The stumps still to be seen on sunken Egg Island in Wellfleet Harbor apparently indicate a recent sinking of that island. In the harbor of Hyannis stumps of cedar trees may be found standing under water three or four rods from the shore. I incline to the opinion, however, that such phenomena do not always indicate a sinking of the land but merely a subsidence of the soil caused by the washing out of the sandy subsoil beneath by the action of the waves. This I have repeatedly observed. The sea undermines the sandy shore, carrying away the subsoil and leaving turf, rocks, interlacing roots and stumps without support. Turf, stumps and rocks overhanging the sea are thus undermined until they sink beneath the water. The rocks and turf carry down with them the stumps, which become water-logged and remain on the bottom. A great boulder thus undermined may sink with the surface soil until its top no longer shows above high water. Nevertheless there is other evidence of subsidence. Dr. C. W. Townsend gives some evidence which seems incontestable in his book "Sand Dunes and Salt Marshes." Possibly some of the slight earthquake shocks felt occasionally along the New England coast may have resulted in settling some of our shores. There are legends indicating that once there was land on Georges Shoal one hundred miles off Cape Cod. We know that many islands have disappeared since the country was settled and that most of those now in existence are doomed. If the land on which they rest should sink but a few feet so that waves could wash over them, they would soon disappear. Rocky islands, such as some off the coast of Maine, will outlast all the rest. In a comparatively brief period probably all the small sandy or earthy islands off the New England coast will have disappeared. Then the sea-birds will have no place on the coast of Massachusetts where they can breed in safety, except possibly Egg Rock off Nahant and Penikese Island, both now owned and protected by the Commonwealth.

The Filling of Shallow Ponds.

A filling process is taking place in shallow fresh-water ponds. Along the coast as on Marthas Vineyard, Nantucket and Cape Cod where the forest has been cut off and dunes have formed, numbers of small ponds have been filled with sand. In the interior of Cape Cod where the forests and the soil have been destroyed by fire many small ponds have dried up. In the forested interior of New England shallow ponds gradually fill up with vegetal matter and become first quaking bogs and then muck meadows. These eventually become dry land. About one-third of a small pond that I watched, filled up in this manner in twenty-six years and another "pond hole," in which I caught fish as a boy, is now nearly "dry." All over New England many such ponds have dried or filled up and thus the land that they occupied is gradually fitted first for swamp birds and finally for land birds. The destruction of muskrats for their fur hastens this process as these animals tend to check too rank a growth of vegetation in such ponds.

CHANGES IN BIRD LIFE CAUSED BY MAN.

The settlement of a country, the advance of civilization, the operation of the agriculturist, lumberman, hunter, trapper and fisherman inevitably bring about considerable changes in the wild life of any region, and especially in the bird life. The bird fauna of a country cannot be preserved intact without special care; and during the settlement of a country and the organization of its communities, such care never is exercised. It is well known now that since the settlement of New England, nine bird species have disappeared from its territory. Three of these, the Great Auk, Labrador Duck and Passenger Pigeon are believed to be extinct; one, the Eskimo Curlew, is either extinct or so nearly so that any attempt to preserve it seems hopeless; two, the Trumpeter Swan and the Whooping Crane, are nearing extinction; they inhabit now only the wilder parts of North America and may yet be saved; two, the Wild Turkey and the Sandhill Crane, are still common in some of the wilder and more remote parts of the United States; and one, the Avocet, has disappeared from the Atlantic coast and from most of the western region which it formerly occupied. The food value of most of these birds was the chief factor that brought about their extirpation. Many other species have been greatly reduced in numbers for the same reason. Chief among these are the Marbled Godwit, the Hudsonian Godwit, the Upland Plover and the Golden Plover.

There are other causes which have reduced the numbers of birds and extirpated them from localities. Chief among these are man's satellites — dogs, cats, hogs and rats. The effect produced by these animals readily may be observed on sea islands. An Arctic explorer turns loose some Eskimo dogs on a Maine island inhabited by a great colony of terns and the birds disappear from that island. A vessel is wrecked on another Maine island. The rats leave the wreck and destroy a great breeding tern colony. A house cat hunting over an island kills or drives away all the Petrels nesting there; and a dog is similarly destructive in another island; hogs are pernicious whenever they are allowed to roam where ground-nesting birds breed, but in New England hogs are kept in pens or enclosures.   Terns formerly nested in considerable numbers on islands on the coast of Essex County, Massachusetts, but the increase of the summer population drove them away.   Egg Rock off Nahant formerly held a bird colony, but the government established a lighthouse there and the birds disappeared.   With the increasing popularity of the New England coast as a summer resort the time will come when there will be no spot along these shores where sea-birds can breed in safety unless certain points can be fenced off, guarded, and kept for their use during the summer.

When New England was settled, it was a forested region.   The settlers of necessity cut away more or less of the forest and transformed the land into cultivated fields and pastures, driving out the forest birds but increasing the birds of the open.   It seems probable that there are in New England to-day more sparrows, orioles, robins, bluebirds and other birds which feed in the open than were here when the country was settled. The cultivation of the soil brought in numerous earthworms and greatly increased insects that feed on farm lands such as grasshoppers and cutworms, thus providing an accession to the food supply of the field-birds.   On the other hand woodpeckers and other forest birds may have decreased somewhat in numbers as the forest area was reduced. During the last fifty years, however, many New England farms in rough and rocky regions have been abandoned and are now overgrown with forest trees thus adding to the breeding area for forest birds.   There is more wild land now than there was 75 years ago, even in Massachusetts.

The character of the forest has changed, however, and with it the character of the bird life.   The great demand for the lumber of coniferous trees, especially of white pine, spruce and hemlock, has resulted in a dearth of these trees.   They have been cut, and deciduous trees have sprung up in their place.   This has resulted in largely replacing birds of the Canadian Fauna which formerly bred in our coniferous forests, with birds of the Alleghanian Fauna, most of which prefer deciduous woods.   The cutting of deciduous coppice causes only a temporary change in the bird life of the woodlot.   When such wood is cut, birds that nest in trees, *i.e.* tanagers, grosbeaks, thrushes, wood warblers, vireos, etc., must go elsewhere to breed, and other birds that nest among the sprout growth soon take their place.   Later, as the trees grow larger, the wood birds come back.

The drainage of swamps and shallow ponds brings about local changes in the character of bird life.   Many swamps in southeastern Massachusetts have been drained, ditched, graded and sanded by cranberry cultivators.   Some of these swamps were wooded, others were open and grassy; some contained shallow ponds, the haunts of Black Ducks and Wood Ducks; others were formerly inhabited by blackbirds, sparrows, rails, marsh wrens, etc.   Drainage drives out all these birds and no bird can nest in safety in a well-kept bog devoted to the cultivation of cranberries.

City waterworks have drained wooded swamps which formerly were inhabited by water-birds and swamp birds.   In such cases the Ruffed Grouse and Ring-necked

Pheasant now roam in the former haunts of the wild duck. A mania for the drainage of swamps, marshes and shallow lakes seems to have swept the country in recent years. We are told that over seventy-five millions of acres have been drained in the United States. A large part of the area to be relieved of its excess water included swamps, marshes and shallow lakes, which formerly were breeding places and feeding-grounds of wild-fowl and marsh birds. Some of these areas when drained have proved worthless for any agricultural or other purpose. Others have produced excellent crops. In either case the water-birds have been driven out. New England and, in fact, most lands elsewhere are being gradually unfitted for water-birds and prepared for an increased number of land birds.

THE NATURAL ENEMIES OF BIRDS.*

As this volume includes the New England birds of prey and as predatory birds frequently become victims of unreasoning prejudice, this section of the introduction has been prepared for the purpose of exhibiting the utility of native natural enemies of birds and to show the misfortunes that might follow their extermination, as well as to set forth the conditions under which they may need restraint. The present strong sentiment for game protection, commendable as it is, has resulted in a war of extermination against the enemies of game-birds. This destructive policy may, in time, defeat its own ends. Bounties are paid on the heads of predatory creatures by individuals, towns, counties and states. Farmers, sportsmen, gunners, gamekeepers, game commissioners and wardens and many bird protectionists persecute indiscriminately all creatures that kill birds or destroy their eggs or young, and the increased prices now paid for furs offer an incentive to the trapper to pursue the fur-bearing animals as never before. It must be conceded that some of the more crafty birds and mammals, such as the fox and the Crow, may under some conditions become too numerous and too destructive to bird life, and that certain natural enemies of birds introduced by man from foreign countries, such as the domestic cat, persecute birds excessively, and should be reduced in numbers; but the majority of the larger and more destructive native enemies of birds are held in check by the gunner, the farmer and the trapper, through self-interest, and with the constant increase in the numbers of game preserves and bird preserves there is danger that we shall overdo the destruction of so-called vermin and thereby bring about serious consequences.

In the preparation of this paper much time, thought and care have been given to a study of the relations of birds and their enemies, and the experience of many observers has been drawn upon. Nevertheless, it will be noted that the statements herein set forth are supported by comparatively little evidence. Thus they lack the apparent authority that a fuller presentation of the evidence would give. If the original plan had been followed, many more pages might have been filled with matter fully justifying

* Most of the material included here under the foregoing heading was written originally for Economic Biology, Bulletin No. 3 of the Massachusetts State Board of Agriculture, 1916, now long out of print. The part of it that appears herewith has been revised and rewritten especially for this introduction.

the conclusions arrived at, but the limits of space forbade. Therefore the statements and recommendations made and the conclusions drawn should be taken as the judgment of an observer who, having opportunity, has endeavored to inform himself fully, and who is confident that his conclusions have value as guides to all who seek to protect birds.

It is well known to biologists that in a state of nature the natural enemies of any species are as essential to its welfare as are food, water, air and sunlight. Unthinking people are slow to realize this, as they see only the apparent harm done by the so-called rapacious creatures, and fail to perceive the benefits that such creatures confer upon the species on which they prey.

Insect-eating, fish-eating, and flesh-eating animals are essential in the great scheme of nature, as they serve to check the increase and regulate the numbers of other species, which in turn, when so regulated, tend to perform a similar office for vegetation. Thus these predatory creatures may be regarded as among the chief regulators of life upon this planet. Savage man, of course, must be included among them, and civilized man, if guided by reason and wisdom rather than greed or folly, may exercise a beneficial control over many lower animals.

Natural Enemies Regulate the Numbers of Animals and Keep Them Fit.

All organic beings naturally produce a superabundance of offspring and thus tend to increase in numbers. This is a provision of nature tending to prevent the extinction of species. The rate of multiplication varies greatly in different animals, but should any form increase without check, it would become so numerous eventually that it would devour its entire food supply and become extinct from starvation, or it would compete with other forms which feed on similar food until all became extinct for lack of nourishment and from diseases that accompany crowding, starvation and weakness. Natural enemies tend to prevent this by disposing of surplus individuals.

Darwin says, truly, that the struggle for existence is greatest between individuals or varieties of the same species. Natural enemies protect a species against itself by keeping its numbers low enough to prevent serious competition for food. Natural enemies also preserve the fitness of a species, (1) by acting to check the spread of disease and (2) by operating to preserve by selection the strongest, most active, cautious or otherwise efficient and fit individuals.

The spread of epidemics or contagious diseases is checked by the natural enemies of a species, which readily capture and destroy individuals which are weakened by disease, as such animals are slower to act or react than those in robust health. Sick birds, for example, readily are captured, not only by enemies sly, swift, or strong enough to catch healthy birds, but also by an additional number of slower enemies, which birds in full vigor would escape with ease. The buzzard hawks, such for example as the common Red-shouldered Hawk, feed mainly on mice and reptiles as they are too slow to catch most active vigorous birds; but if a swift bird should become slow and incautious, owing to weakness or disease, it might be seized by one of these hawks. Crows are able to overtake or overcome birds weakened by starvation which could readily escape or defend themselves if well nourished.

On this subject Professor Spencer F. Baird of the Smithsonian Institution wrote as follows: — "It has now been conclusively shown, I think, that hawks perform an important function in maintaining in good condition the stock of game birds by capturing the weak and sickly, and thus preventing reproduction from unhealthy parents. One of the most plausible hypotheses explanatory of the occasional outbreaks of disease amongst the grouse of Scotland has been the extermination of these correctives, the disease being most virulent where the gamekeepers were most active in destroying what they considered vermin." [1]

The following quotation from Mr. W. Woods Smyth of Maidstone is taken from an English newspaper, the Morning Post: "Eagles prey on the weak birds, as a rule, and thereby profit the survivors — it is the destruction of the unfit. It is well known that birds on unprotected moors are finer and stronger than those where protection reigns. I knew of a grouse moor in Ireland where the birds were almost lost by the complete destruction of the eagles in the neighborhood. The weak birds being allowed to remain and breed into the others brought on disease, decay, and inability to survive."

Mr. James Henry Rice says that in South Carolina the Bob-white sometimes is attacked by a deadly contagious disease [probably bird pox] which affects the head of the bird in such a way that it becomes stupid, comes out in the open, and stands or lies in the sun. There it is readily detected and killed by hawks, and thus the progress of the contagion is stayed. Mr. Rice says that he has known preserves to be denuded of these birds, because of the trapping of hawks which had previously kept down the disease.

A similar selection is seen in the removal and destruction by natural enemies of the dull, slow-witted, deformed, or otherwise unfit individuals which, in the long run, are the first to be caught and killed, while the active, quick-witted, strong and symmetrical individuals are more likely to escape. A Sharp-shinned Hawk dashed into a flock of Juncos feeding on the ground. All escaped by flight but one, which seemed to have lost its wits or failed to make use of them, and crouched close to the ground while its companions were already in flight, and thus fell a victim to its swift, rapacious enemy. Individual birds which vary widely from the protective coloring of the species to which they belong are more easily seen, followed and destroyed by their enemies. Thus albinos (or partial albinos) which are conspicuous because of their complete or partial whiteness are weeded out, and the protective color of the species is kept true.

Evidently, then, the tendency to increase is serviceable in maintaining a species, provided only that there exist effective checks to regulate its increase and to preserve its fitness. Natural enemies provide such checks.

---

[1] Letter from Prof. Spencer F. Baird to Mr. J. W. Shorton, published in the Journal of the Cincinnati Society of Natural History, Vol. V, 1882, pp. 69, 70.

Natural Enemies Regulate One Another.

There is another way in which natural enemies benefit the species on which they prey and that is the regulation, by some of them, of the numbers of certain other of these natural enemies. One must count among the foes of birds, for example, hawks, owls, crows, jays, shrikes, foxes, weasels, minks, squirrels, snakes, rats and mice; but certain large hawks destroy smaller hawks; large owls destroy smaller owls; hawks and owls kill crows, jays, shrikes, weasels, minks, squirrels, snakes and rats; weasels destroy squirrels and rats, snakes eat other snakes, and all catch mice, as also do gulls, herons, ravens and crows. If rats, ground mice, climbing mice and shrews, lacking these and other checks, were allowed to increase too much in numbers, they might exterminate most birds by destroying their eggs and young, and so might squirrels and weasels or crows and jays.

Few people in this country realize how serious would be the consequences of an excessive increase of rats and mice. The experts of the Biological Survey have experimented with the common meadow mouse *Microtus pennsylvanicus*. A single pair of these creatures produced within a year 83 young in 17 litters. The young begin to breed when about 46 days old, and it is estimated that if all the progeny of one pair lived and bred, their descendants would number over a million at the end of the first year.[1] Mr. Vernon Bailey who reports the result of these investigations estimates that only ten of these mice to the acre on the hay land of the 38 states in which they live would cause a loss to the farmers of $30,000,000 a year in hay alone. Such a loss, much increased by the profits of merchants, would be borne eventually by the consumers of milk, meat, etc.

In 1922 the estimated yearly loss to the people of the United States due to rats and mice in buildings and on farms and other lands was estimated at $500,000,000.[2] As the numbers of mice increase, owing to the destruction of their natural enemies, the loss that they cause must increase in due proportion, and where such natural checks are reduced seriously, the mice destroy practically every green thing on the face of the earth. There is then no breeding ground left for game birds, and should any such birds produce eggs or young, the mice would eat them. All excessive killing of hawks, owls or other enemies of game birds will tend therefore to make the country uninhabitable for such birds.

Rats and mice, although they must be classed as enemies of birds, do not constitute a serious menace to bird life if themselves held in check by their own enemies, and thus they perform a service to birds by maintaining their own numbers at such a point that they furnish a great surplus of individuals, and become the main food supply for most of the hawks, owls and other enemies of birds. Therefore rats and mice, while thus serving as food to maintain the numbers of birds' enemies, also attract the attention of these enemies sufficiently away from birds, and therefore tend to keep them from becoming too destructive to bird life. As Professor Forbes says, the whole series of forces pressing one on

---

[1] Bailey, Vernon: Journal of Agricultural Research, 1924, p. 528.
[2] United States Department of Agriculture, Bulletin No. 1091, 1922, p. 2.

another is like an arrangement of springs, working one against another, keeping all in place, thus maintaining the general equilibrium and safeguarding the general welfare.

USEFUL SPECIES MAY BECOME HARMFUL IF NOT HELD IN CHECK.

Certain bounds are set by nature to the numbers of each species. Within these bounds they serve a useful purpose, but whenever through any fortuitous circumstance, such as may arise by reason of man's interference, a species overflows this high water mark, normal habits may change and severe injury to other species, even to man himself or his property, may result. Animals considered serviceable to mankind, such as insectivorous birds, toads, bats, shrews, etc., are useful if they are kept within certain limits. The injurious species, so-called, are those, mainly, which tend to increase beyond normal bounds. Then, by reason of abnormal multiplication and consequent shortage of food, they become destructive. Under such circumstances the so-called useful species may become harmful by changing their food habits when they outrun their usual food supply. Birds, mammals or insects, which usually are insectivorous, may then attack grain, fruits or other products of man's industry. No one can tell what any animal may eat in case of necessity. Carnivorous creatures then may devour grass, leaves or fruit. Vegetable feeders may prey on other animals. No mammal is considered more carnivorous than the wolf, yet, at times, it feeds voraciously on berries. My son saw a mink eating the bark and foliage of fruit trees. Wallace says that the carnivorous sable feeds partially on fruits or seeds in winter.[1]

It is a well known fact that grain-eating birds have strong, muscular stomachs or gizzards lined with a hard, corrugated membrane which, with the assistance of sand or pebbles, swallowed for the purpose, triturates or grinds up the grain or other seeds eaten, thus virtually masticating them in the stomach. Nevertheless, most birds provided with such stomachs readily turn to animal food. It is well known, also, that flesh-eating birds have soft stomachs not fitted for grinding grain, but many of them will eat grain at need. Hon. John E. Thayer informs me that the Hooded Merganser (*Lophodytes cuculatus*), a fish-eating duck, readily learns to eat corn. In the Shetland Islands the Herring Gull (*Larus argentatus*) is said by Dr. Edmonstone to live on grain in summer and fish in winter.[2] In America our closely allied race of this species has not been recorded as a grain-eater, but where too numerous it becomes destructive to the blueberry crop. A change of food may even transform the lining of the stomach. Dr. Hunter fed a gull for a year on grain and at the end of that time the appearance and structure of the stomach had so changed that it resembled the gizzard of a pigeon, and Dr. Edmonstone asserts that the Herring Gulls of the Shetland Islands thus produce a change in the structure of the stomach twice a year as they shift from grain to fish. Similar transformations have been observed in the stomach of a raven and that of an owl, and Dr. Holmgrén has proved by experiment that the stomachs of pigeons, fed for a long time on meat, gradually come

---

[1] Wallace, Alfred Russell: Darwinism, 1890, p. 191.
[2] Semper, Karl: Animal Life as Affected by the Natural Conditions of Existence, 1881, p. 61.

to resemble those of rapacious birds.[1]   When it is shown how all animals tend to increase in numbers, and how readily some of the most useful may change their feeding habits and become injurious under the spur of necessity and competition, it becomes plain that the creatures which prey on such species and so keep their numbers within normal bounds are essential to the welfare of all.

Natural Enemies Supplement One Another.

When we examine broadly the relations of birds and their enemies, we find that some species appear far more destructive than others to bird life.   Certain swift hawks, for example, seem to feed very largely on birds whenever they can obtain them, while other slower hawks rarely take any except helpless, sick or disabled birds, but feed largely on small mammals, such as squirrels and field-mice, and on reptiles.   Thus one species takes an excess of birds while the other takes an excess of their enemies, the effect of the activities of one tending to balance those of the other.   Again, a mammal may be a destroyer of certain birds and a protector of others.   The skunk, for example, is known occasionally to destroy the eggs and young of grouse and other birds which nest on the ground, as well as those of domestic fowls.   On the other hand, the skunk is a guardian and protector of young water-birds, which are unsafe except in shallow waters, where there are no great fish to eat them.   Therefore they frequent such waters, and there their greatest enemy is the snapping turtle (*Chelydra serpentina*).   Wherever these great turtles are numerous, practically no young water-birds can be raised, as these cold-blooded monsters hide in the mud of the bottom or swim under water, and pull down the young birds by their feet.

During four summers I watched many of these turtles depositing their eggs and burying them in the earth near the shores of a river, and in every case, within twenty-four hours, the skunk unearthed and ate every egg laid.   Where skunks are numerous, it seems impossible for any snapping turtles' eggs to hatch, but where skunks have been extirpated, turtles increase rapidly in numbers and in time prevent the multiplication of wild ducks or geese.

Although this tortoise is an enemy of wild-fowl, it may unwittingly befriend the ground-nesting birds by providing the skunk with a tempting supply of turtle eggs and thus so attract it away from birds'-egging as to save many early broods of birds.

The Marsh Hawk feeds to some extent on marsh birds and their young, but a much larger part of its food consists of meadow mice and frogs.   These mice certainly would be very destructive to birds' eggs and young birds were they not held in check, and large frogs are known to swallow the young of water-birds, as well as the young of land birds that are learning to fly.   Marsh Hawks and other enemies prevent most frogs from reaching a size at which they would be dangerous to young birds.   A roosting place of Marsh Hawks was found on a southern "quail preserve."   About half of the thirty hawks frequenting the place were shot before their status as alleged enemies of Bob-white was

---

[1] Semper, Karl: Animal Life as Affected by the Natural Conditions of Existence, 1881, pp. 67, 68.

investigated. On gathering regurgitated pellets from this roost the remains of only four Bob-whites were found in them, while 935 pellets contained remains of cotton rats which in the south rank among the greatest enemies of Bob-white.[1]

The larger buzzard hawks feed commonly on snakes, which are known to be destructive to birds. Even the rattlesnake is a common prey of the Red-tailed Hawk.

Natural Enemies Tend to Keep the Number of Birds Normal.

Under natural conditions, wherever man and his satellites — cats, rats, dogs, hogs, goats, etc. — have not interfered with the balance of natural forces, the native natural enemies of birds do not tend, on the whole, to reduce the numbers of any species to a point much below that at which its normal food supply will maintain it. Any species having an excess of food constantly tends to increase rapidly in numbers, and natural enemies and meteorological checks are necessary to keep its increase below the limit of its supply of food.

A school of writers has risen of late who refer to the natural enemies of birds as far more destructive than the hunter, and assert that it is useless to attempt to protect birds and increase their numbers anywhere unless natural enemies (which they denominate as vermin) be first destroyed. It even is asserted positively that if a certain tract of land is set aside, and all shooting upon it stopped for a series of years, the game and birds will lessen rather than increase, because of the unrestrained destructiveness of their natural enemies. This contention apparently is not supported by facts.

If we go back to the times of the early settlers of this country, we find that most birds and game were remarkably numerous, far more so than now, and that not only were eagles, hawks, owls, skunks, weasels, raccoons and other foes of birds far more abundant then than now, but there were also pumas, wolves, lynxes, bears and ravens, which are now rarely or never found in southern New England. It must be accepted as a fact that the natural enemies of birds did not then tend to diminish their numbers. Going back only to the days of the Civil War we find that in the southern states, when white men were practically all in the army, when negroes had no guns and when very little hunting was done, game increased to enormous numbers in spite of its natural enemies.

In 1877–78, when I was on the Indian River, Florida, game was more abundant than I have ever seen it anywhere since. Hosts of wild-fowl blackened the waters. Bob-whites and Wild Turkeys were plentiful and myriads of herons, egrets, shore birds and land birds were seen, some of which are now nearly extinct. But Eagles were more than common, so common that a collector secured nearly 100 sets of their eggs. Seven nests of the Great Horned Owl were found in a limited region on Merrit's Island; Barred Owls and hawks were numerous and breeding; raccoons, lynxes and opossums were abundant; while bears, panthers and alligators were so common that, allowing such creatures to be game exterminators, it would seem that no game could have lived in that region. All these animals have been much reduced in numbers now, but the game also has decreased

---

[1] Bureau of Biological Survey. Report on the Coöperative Quail Investigation (1925–26), 1926, pp. 38–39.

enormously. We are told that in France, in 1916, when nearly every able-bodied man was in the army and little was done to protect the game or to destroy vermin, game had increased so after the war began in 1914 as to become a menace to agriculture. These instances tend to disprove the contention that the natural enemies of birds, and not the hunters and other influences of civilization, are responsible primarily for the decrease of birds and game. Birds breed rapidly under natural conditions when undisturbed by man. If birds and game are below their normal numbers in any region, they will increase if *protected from poachers, lawbreakers, cats, dogs* and other inimical influences of civilization (or savagery) under a law prescribing a long, close season. If they do not, it is a sure indication that *adverse human influences are at work.* But it must be borne in mind that whereas the natural enemies of a species tend to allow an increase in its numbers up to nearly the limit of its food supply, they tend to decrease them after that limit has been reached, as the birds that first feel the effects of want, being weak, are first caught and killed, while well-nourished individuals survive. If nature is undisturbed, therefore, about all the birds that the land will support are reared and maintained, but where man steps in and disturbs the natural balance, there the natural enemies of birds may become unduly destructive.

Whenever man, in poultry raising or gamekeeping, attempts to produce, by excessive feeding or other artificial means, more birds to the acre than the land otherwise would support, nature brings her destructive forces to bear against the project. The natural enemies of game and poultry, finding in the crowded birds a numerous, easily accessible source of food, attack eggs, young and adults, and unless every resource is used to protect them, the poultryman, the sportsman or the gamekeeper will reap neither pleasure nor profit from his venture in propagation.

Bearing in mind that only when man steps in and in some way disturbs the biologic balance does it become necessary for him to reduce the numbers of the natural enemies of birds, let us inquire under what circumstances such reduction may be necessary.

When Man Should Reduce Natural Enemies.

Man must reduce (not exterminate) certain natural enemies of birds: (1) when he attempts to rear poultry or game-birds in excessive numbers; (2) when, because of the disturbance of the biologic balance caused by extensive agricultural operations, he wishes to increase the number of insectivorous birds beyond what the land naturally would support; (3) when the most sagacious natural enemies of birds, like the fox and the Crow, — their own enemies having been reduced or exterminated by man himself, — take advantage of the extra protection and food afforded them in civilized communities and thus become too numerous and too destructive; (4) wherever man hunts and destroys wild game, he may also reduce somewhat the numbers of the enemies of the game and thereby relieve the game of a part of the pressure brought to bear against its increase; (5) when by reason of a periodical scarcity of game in the fur countries, Goshawks and Horned Owls migrate south into the United States in excessive numbers, these numbers should be reduced in order to protect native game. In all such cases discrimination should be used, and it is unsafe to deplete too far the numbers of any but the most powerful and dangerous predatory animals.

An Economic Question.

The destruction of poultry or game-birds upon game farms or preserves by the enemies of birds is a direct economic loss to the property of the individual poultryman or game farmer, and through him to the community. This should be prevented if possible, even if it is necessary to destroy the actual culprits, but the indiscriminate setting of traps upon poles for long distances about a game farm is an unnecessary, cruel and pernicious practice which destroys not only the actual culprits but also many innocent victims; among them such species as the Rough-legged Hawk, a very useful bird (not known to kill any appreciable number of birds, poultry or game), and many insect-eating birds such as flycatchers and swallows which casually perch upon the traps. The excessive, indiscriminate killing of hawks in migration for sport, for bounties or for food, when many hundreds are killed in a day, should be prohibited, for some of these birds are essential to the general welfare.

The destruction of song birds by hawks, owls and other native natural enemies is not a direct economic evil but is a salutary and necessary provision for the welfare of such species, and should not weigh in the balance against native bird or mammal enemies since such restraints on the increase of small birds are required, as hereinbefore stated, to prevent their undue increase. This, of course, is not true of additional interloping enemies introduced from foreign countries. Therefore we may even tolerate the Sharp-shinned Hawk, for example (except in bird preserves), so long as it does not prey upon young chickens and young game birds, while we should eliminate if possible the wild house cat and the unrestrained hunting dog.

Man's Misdirected Activities.

The activities of civilized man in the destruction of predaceous animals are not always well directed and regulated. Often these activities are guided more by prejudice than by knowledge and reason. We destroy the Great Horned Owl, the greatest enemy of the Crow, and Crows become unduly numerous and injurious. If we seriously reduce crows, robins, on which they prey, probably will become so abundant as to do great injury to small fruit, as they have already in some western states. The indiscriminate destruction of herons, hawks, owls, crows, skunks, weasels and other enemies of rats, mice, and the larger insects is sure to result in great periodical increases of such creatures, which are far more dangerous to man's interests than are their enemies, and he often is powerless to check their devastating hordes. They never can be checked by humans without great effort and expense. In a region devastated by field-mice what will happen to the eggs and young of game birds that breed upon the ground? The climbing wood mice destroy eggs and young of small arboreal birds and take birds' nests for their own use. Birds can rear no young where swarming insects ruin every green leaf and blade. If we kill off all the large birds, the small birds are powerless before any great irruption of insects. When such insects become numerous, the larger wading and rapacious birds feed upon them almost exclusively and because of the much greater quantity of food that they require are then far more beneficial than the smaller birds ; also while feeding on abundant, easily obtained insects or rodents they have little incentive to prey on smaller birds which are left more free and unmolested also to feed on such pests as they can master. Most people will agree that it is imperative in settled regions to extirpate such baleful creatures as the wolf or the rattlesnake, but the views of the well meaning but misinformed man who advocates the extermination of the lesser native natural enemies of birds or even their general and indiscriminate slaughter should be given no serious consideration.

EXTERNAL PARTS OF A BIRD.

As the first volume (Part I) of this work went out of print long before the present volume (Part II) could be issued many persons who will obtain the latter will be unable to secure the former. Therefore the following cuts and explanations are necessary here, although some of them duplicate in some respects certain cuts and captions published in Volume I.

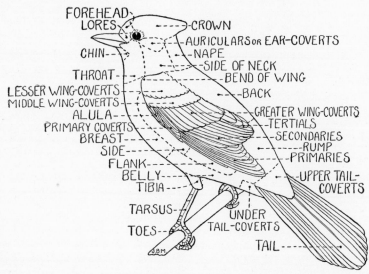

TOPOGRAPHY OF A JAY, drawn to show the names of the principal external parts used in this work in describing species and subspecies.

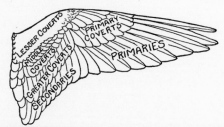

TOPOGRAPHY OF THE UPPER SIDE OF THE WING OF A FALCON, drawn to show the principal divisions of wing plumage as used in describing species and subspecies in this work.

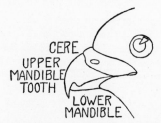

DIAGRAM SHOWING THE DIFFERENT PARTS OF THE TOOTHED BILL OF A FALCON and terms used in this work in describing the bill of a bird. The nostril opening is in the cere as in all hawks and eagles.

INTRODUCTION

MEASURING BIRDS.

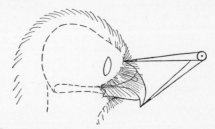

BILL OF A HAWK SHOWING MEASUREMENT. Bill measurements of hawks, eagles and vultures are taken from the tip of the upper mandible to the front edge of the cere.

DIAGRAM OF THE HEAD OF AN OWL showing nostril opening at the front edge of the cere, and the manner of measuring bills of owls and all other land birds in this work, except diurnal birds of prey (hawks, falcons, eagles and vultures) and except where otherwise stated in the text. In Part I (Volume I) the bills of water birds are measured by taking the chord of the culmen or ridge from the tip of the upper mandible, to the center of the frontal feathers of the forehead, except where otherwise stated in the text. In the succeeding parts (Volumes II and III) bills are measured for the most part by taking the chord of the culmen or ridge from the tip of the upper mandible to the point where front center of forehead (skull) and base of bill meet, as shown above, regardless of the feathers, except where otherwise stated in the text.

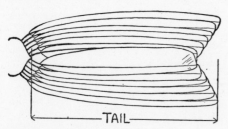

Method of measuring tail.

In measuring the tail when the outer feathers are longest the distance is taken *between the insertion of the two central quills and the end of the longest outer tail-feather* — a measurement *longer* than the span between the two vertical lines.

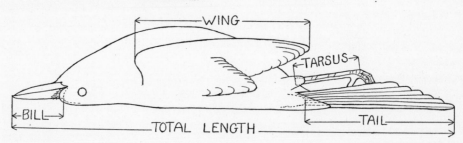

DIAGRAM SHOWING METHOD OF MEASURING ALL PASSERINE BIRDS INCLUDED IN THIS WORK EXCEPT WHERE OTHERWISE STATED IN THE TEXT. The bird is extended at full length with neck straightened and in taking the spread the wings are fully extended. The chord of the culmen is taken from the point of the upper mandible to the point where the base of the bill meets the front center of the skull. The tarsus is measured in front from upper to lower joints inclusive. The tail is measured from the insertion of the two middle feathers to the tip of the longest feather, the measurement in this case is the exact span between the two vertical lines in the tail measurement shown in the cut.

BIRDS OF MASSACHUSETTS

AND OTHER NEW ENGLAND STATES

PART II

ORDER GALLINÆ. GALLINACEOUS BIRDS.

Number of species in North America 25; in Massachusetts 7.

This is an order of ground-dwelling, scratching game birds. The head is small compared with the heavy body. The bill is stout and obtuse; the wings short, arched, rounded and strong; the tarsi generally broadly reticulated or feathered; in most cases the front toes are slightly webbed or connected at base; the hind toe is elevated; the claws are short and blunt. Members of this order generally are polygamous, though some are not. They nest on the ground, produce numerous eggs, and the young are able to run about soon after they are hatched. Members of this order are found in every continent, but only one suborder, *Phasiani*, is represented by birds indigenous to the United States.

ECONOMIC STATUS. The birds of this order are of great economic consequence. From among its representatives man has selected the most important and productive of his domesticated fowls. As poultry, birds of this order the world over annually produce food products worth many millions of dollars. Some furnish valuable ornamental feathers. Members of the order rank among the most important of game birds. Bob-whites, quails, partridges, grouse, pheasants and wild turkeys are hunted annually by millions of sportsmen. The aggregate sum expended annually for guns, ammunition, outfits, dogs, guides, gamekeepers, etc. is enormous. The presence of these game birds also adds to the value of the land. Large sums are expended for shooting rights and privileges, and the value of the flesh of the birds killed as food is surprising when computed. Some of the species are exceedingly useful also as destroyers of injurious insects.

1

Suborder PHASIANI. Pheasants, Grouse, Partridges, Quails, etc.

Number of species in North America 25 ; in Massachusetts 7.

This suborder includes birds differing widely in appearance, but having structural affinities indicating close relationship. Its members are more or less terrestrial, with three toes in front and one behind, the front toes not always webbed at base. The tarsi often are feathered and sometimes the toes ; but usually both are naked, scaled and reticulated, sometimes spurred. In some families the nostrils are feathered, in others naked, each partly covered by a scale. In some cases the head is naked with fleshy appendages. The short arched wings are capable of rapid, whirring flight. The tail varies in the different genera from extremely long to quite short.

Family ODONTOPHORIDÆ. Bob-whites, Quails, etc.

Number of species in North America 7 ; in Massachusetts 1.

This family is set off by American ornithologists as indigenous to the New World. The so-called true quails and partridges belong to the eastern hemisphere. Their native representatives in this country are the Bob-whites and the so-called American Quails. There are seven native species in the United States, of which the common Bob-white is the only one normally native to New England. All are rather small in size with heads completely feathered and in some cases crested ; the nostrils are covered with a scale ; the lower mandible is more or less toothed in some species ; legs stout ; tarsi and toes naked ; toes not pectinated ; front toes webbed at base ; hind toe rather small, and tail short. It seems doubtful whether all members of this family can always be distinguished by any structural character from the partridges of the Old World. Apparently the so-called quails of America are true partridges and should be included with the Old World partridges under family *Phasianidæ*, but this cannot be done consistently by one who follows the third edition of the Check-list of the American Ornithologists' Union.

Colínus virginiánus virginianus (Linnæus). Bob-white.

Other names: quail; bob-white quail.

Plate 34.

Description. — Lengthened and erectile feathers on top of head hardly forming a true crest ; tail short, about three-fifths as long as wing, 12-feathered ; plumage variable because of interbreeding with introduced southern birds. *Adult male:* Forehead, broad stripe before, over and behind eye ; chin and throat white, bordered black ; upper plumage mainly reddish-brown, mottled and barred more or less with blackish and bluish-gray ; scapulars and wing-coverts with dark centers and lighter edges and tips ; rump slightly variegated ; upper tail-coverts with dark or black shaft-streaks ; top of head, neck all round and upper breast reddish-brown, feathers about sides of neck marked with white and black ; under

PLATE 34

PLATE 34

BOB–WHITE
Page 2

CANADA SPRUCE PARTRIDGE
Page 23

ADULT MALE ADULT FEMALE

ADULT FEMALE

ADULT MALE

EUROPEAN PARTRIDGE
Page 12

ADULT

All about three-eighths scale.

plumage from breast to tail-coverts whitish, with sides and flanks broadly striped reddish-brown (sometimes plain reddish-brown), marked with irregular, narrow, black bars often U-shaped or V-shaped; flight-feathers plain grayish, under wing-coverts and axillars usually grayish or grayish and white; tail-feathers chiefly plain bluish-gray more or less finely mottled with brownish and black; under tail-coverts mainly brown with black central streaks and often with tips broadly much paler; bill dark brown or black; iris brown or hazel; feet bluish-gray to brownish-gray, sometimes greenish. *Adult female:* Similar to adult male but duller and browner, with throat patch and line over eye deep buff, and dark markings of head replaced by brown or rusty. *Young in juvenal plumage (sexes alike):* Ear-coverts and top of head dusky or grayish, rest of head dull whitish with broad, dark streak below eye and light streak through it; above mainly dull, rusty brownish, more or less spotted with blackish and streaked with whitish shaft-lines; rump pale brownish; wings and tail brownish-gray more or less barred with pale brownish, and usually with some fine blackish mottling; sometimes back, flanks and wings very sparingly barred and striped with dusky; breast grayish-brown with whitish shaft-streaks; abdomen often whitish. *Downy young:* Head dirty buff, paler or much paler on chin and throat; a narrow blackish stripe or line behind eye and a small spot of same above gape; patch of chestnut on back of head extending forward and narrowing to a line on middle of forehead; above mainly chestnut, striped and mottled with buff and sometimes mottled with dusky; below pale grayish-buff darkening to brownish on sides.

NOTE. Albinistic specimens either pure white or with white markings are noted, and very rarely black or melanistic birds.

MEASUREMENTS. — Length 9.50 to 10.75 in.; spread 14.00 to 16.00; folded wing 4.25 to 5.10; bill .50 to .65; tail 2.40 to 3.00; tarsus 1.20 to 1.50. Weight commonly about 6 oz., rarely 8 to 9; largest southern birds nearly 7 oz. Female averages larger than male.

MOLTS. — Complete molt of natal down is succeeded by juvenal plumage, which develops piecemeal during summer, beginning when bird is quite small; in autumn (September to November) complete postjuvenal molt occurs, except outer primary in each wing which is not renewed; limited prenuptial molt in May (chiefly about head) produces first nuptial plumage; after complete postnuptial molt (August to October) young bird takes on second (or adult) winter plumage; second nuptial plumage is acquired by limited molt as in young bird. In adults most of the plumage succeeding postnuptial molt is worn through the year.

FIELD MARKS. — Much smaller than Ruffed Grouse. Slightly larger than Woodcock, but distinguished from it in flight by small head, extremely short bill, and different motion of wings; in rising, whirrs loudly and flies at no great height with high speed and fast beating wings, then scales with wings sharply curved downward; does not flutter and sail alternately like the smaller Meadowlark, which is sometimes called Marsh Quail, and which in flight shows white outer tail-feathers; black and white markings on head of male Bob-white are conspicuous at some distance; similarly placed buff markings of female not so noticeable.

VOICE. — Common call, an interrogative whistle *wha-whoi?* or *wha-wha-whoi?* the last note with a rising inflection. Usually translated as *Bob-white, ah Bob-white* or *buck-wheat-ripe, more-wet* or *some-more-wet*, head thrown upward and backward on the final interrogative note; the gathering cry, *ka-loi-kee? ka-loi-kee?;* the reply, *whoil-kee;* also "queer responsive caterwaulings more unbirdlike than those of the Yellow-breasted Chat, suggesting now the call of a cat to her kittens, now the scolding of a caged gray squirrel, now the alarm notes of a mother grouse, blended with the strident cry of the Guinea-hen" (Judd); many low chatterings by way of conversation when the company gets together; "a rich, powerful, double note, the first about one octave above the last and about four times the value of the last, both notes pitched low, constituting a strong, clear whistle of extraordinary power" (C. L. Whittle); "a Quail very near us prefixed the usual '*Bob-white*' with two notes, the first higher than the second. To put it in words — '*high-low Bob-white*,' repeated six or seven times before a long pause. At no time did this particular quail utter simply '*Bob-white*' as all other quail are doing here daily. The first two notes resemble the sad, plaintive notes of the Piping Plover when she runs before the intruder on the beach.

The two notes had no resemblance to the autumn notes, uttered to call a scattered bevy together" (H. W. Abbott); the female clucks and twitters to her young.

BREEDING. — Usually on farm land in or near fields of grass or grain or in undergrowth. *Nest:* On ground, sometimes in a grassy field, often along bush-bordered fences of stone or wood, by roadside or in the edge of woods, concealed in thick tuft of grass or under bushes, often arched over at top with grasses; well hollowed and lined chiefly with grass, straw or strips of bark; sometimes a covered passage is constructed leading into it. *Eggs:* 7 to 42, often 10 to 17 (the larger numbers found probably the product of at least two females); 1.12 to 1.22 by .92 to .96 in.; short ovate, pointed at small end, very blunt at large end; pure white. *Dates:* May 20 to September 2, southern New England; latest date October 10, Rhode Island (G. M. Allen); eggs found at various places in the range of this bird in every month but December. *Incubation:* Period 23 to 24 days; chiefly by female. One brood yearly.*

RANGE. — Upper Sonoran and all but upper part of Transition zones of eastern North America, ranging through the northern tier of states and southern Ontario; resident and breeds from eastern Wyoming, South Dakota, southern Minnesota, northern Michigan, southeastern Ontario, southern New Hampshire and southwestern Maine south to southeastern and northern Texas, the Gulf coast and northern Florida and west to eastern Colorado and northwestern New Mexico. (A smaller, darker race inhabits most of Florida and closely allied species and subspecies are found in Arizona, Texas and Mexico.) Introduced into central Colorado, Utah, Idaho, California, Montana, North Dakota, Oregon, Washington and Bermuda.

DISTRIBUTION IN NEW ENGLAND. — *Maine:* Formerly common resident in some seasons in southwestern counties; possibly native only to York County, but reported at times also from Oxford, Cumberland, Androscoggin, Franklin, Penobscot and Waldo counties, probably in most cases introduced; now uncommon, local, rare or wanting. *New Hampshire:* Formerly common resident in southern counties, now uncommon, local, rare or wanting there; found occasionally as far north as the southern valleys of the White Mountains, where possibly introduced. *Vermont:* Rare resident, chiefly in valleys of southern counties, where introduced, but does not last long. *Massachusetts:* Formerly common resident except at higher altitudes, now locally common where introduced and protected, otherwise uncommon or wanting. *Rhode Island:* Common resident generally. *Connecticut:* Common resident generally, especially near coast, rather rare in northwestern parts. Introduced from the south or west occasionally in all these states. No permanent northern boundary to the range in New England can be given. A succession of mild winters may extend its range northward; then a severe winter may kill or drive southward the more northern birds.

SEASON IN MASSACHUSETTS. — Resident throughout the year.

HAUNTS AND HABITS. During my boyhood the cheery, heartening "call of the quail" was one of the most common and welcome sounds of spring and summer. The plowman resting his team gave ear to the gladdening sound and it mingled with the ring of the whetstone on the scythe. Since those days many hundreds of the birds have been introduced from the south; others have been artificially reared and liberated, but by 1915 the note had become a rare one near the city of Worcester where much of my boyhood was passed. Bob-whites were very abundant in southern New England when the country was settled. Thomas Morton (1632), who located in what is now a part of Quincy, Massachusetts, records that he saw 60 of these birds in one tree. They contin-

---

* Sportsmen often advance the opinion that this bird sometimes *raises* two broods in a season, but I have seen no conclusive proof of this. Young of different sizes have been seen with the female. When eggs or young of the first brood are destroyed, a second brood usually is produced. It is said that the Florida Bob-white raises two broods commonly and some southern birds may do so when introduced to northern regions.

ued abundant up to about the middle of the nineteenth century. Mr. George Linder says that, many years ago, he once knew of the killing of 96 in Massachusetts by two men in two days.

Many sportsmen naturally attribute the decrease of the birds to "hard winters." Occasionally a severe winter destroys the greater part of the Bob-whites in New England, left over from the shooting season. Within easy motoring distance of the large cities, however, too many gunners roam the fields, and Bob-white has a small chance to survive unless protected at all times by law, as now in Ohio. The late Charles E. Bailey, living in Billerica, took pains to tramp through the snow one severe winter to feed several broods of these birds. About half of them survived and mated and nested in spring on near-by farms. The broods did well except one where the first set of eggs was taken by a farmer and put under a hen. The bereaved pair later produced some young birds, which were about half grown on the opening day of the shooting season. That day two men and two dogs from the near-by city of Lowell found them and followed those half grown chicks until they had killed them all. The next day there were six men and four dogs in the fields and those men and others followed the coveys day after day until the birds were exterminated. The "call of the quail" was not heard again in that section for years. Many such instances of local extirpation have been reported.

A hard winter will not destroy all the New England Bob-whites, though it may kill off all the most northern outposts and 90 per cent of the others, but if these prolific birds could have sufficient protection after such a winter, they would soon recover their former numbers. It is well to record here that 106 of my correspondents, chiefly gunners, attribute the decrease of these birds mainly to the gun. They are right. Overshooting, if allowed, will exterminate the birds. There need be no fear, however, of the extermination of this useful and highly valued bird. The sportsmen of the country must take care of it, and see that its numbers are replenished. If they do not, the people will put it on the list of song birds, and give it perpetual protection, as they have in Ohio.

There is an old saying among the gunners that if the coveys are not shot into and thus broken up, the birds will not pair and breed. This old saw came to us from England. The birds would breed faster if no gun was ever fired at them. During the Civil War when practically every southern able-bodied hunter was in the army, and when the negroes had no guns, Bob-whites increased enormously. Their numbers in South Carolina were much greater at that time than they have ever been since.

It is a well-known fact that the greatest danger faced by Bob-whites in winter is a hard crust on the surface after a heavy fall of snow. When heavy snow comes, the bevy gathers in its usual circle on the ground near some thicket or under some sheltering branch, and soon is covered deep by fast-falling snow. If then rain comes, followed by freezing cold, a crust which they cannot break forms above the birds. Imprisoned thus under the snow they may be able to move about a little, and get some food from the ground, but if the crust does not thaw, they must eventually starve, and during severe winters large numbers sometimes perish in this way. At a meeting under the direction of the Massachusetts Department of Conservation, Mr. Lindley Collins, of Marshfield, said that he was feeding a "bunch of twelve Quails" one winter. There came a snow-storm followed by thaw and rain, then frost which formed a crust over the snow. The next day and for ten days the birds did not come to feed. Mr. Collins believed that they were imprisoned under the snow, and he went to places where he knew that they had slept at night and broke the crust. The next day they came to feed, and by searching he soon found where they had come out from under the snow where he had broken the crust. They had cleared a space under the crust "about the size of a bushel basket," and had worn away the feathers on their heads somewhat in trying to get out. He had broken the crust quite near where they were imprisoned, and they had found the way out. Another observer tells of a similar instance where the birds had worn the feathers and skin off their foreheads in their efforts to break through the crust. One of them was so badly injured in this way that it died, but the others recovered. In this case the length of their imprisonment was not known.

The home life of the Bob-white has much of human interest. It is rare to find among the polygamous *Gallinæ* a species the domestic affairs of which are ordered so much like those of mankind. Bob-white appears to be a cheerful, good-natured, little fowl, but does not hesitate to do battle with his rivals for the favors of his chosen mate. He is a good husband and father, as he has been seen to engage in nest building, and although the female alone probably usually attends to the duties of incubation, the male has been known to incubate the eggs long and faithfully after the death of his mate and to care for and raise a brood bereaved of its maternal parent.

Sometimes a female will lay a remarkable number of eggs. The late George O. Welch said that he had experimented once by taking the eggs one by one from a Bob-white's nest. The bird laid forty and then died. In confinement one female has been known to lay 102 eggs in a season, another 106, and another 124,[1] nearly all of which proved fertile. Sometimes a very large number will be found in one nest. The eggs are packed in solidly with the small ends down, and if the number is very large, they are arranged in two layers. It is said that if the eggs are handled or disturbed, the bird will desert them. The incubating bird normally leaves her eggs every afternoon in pleasant weather for rest and recreation, often not returning to her duties for several hours. Usually the vitality of the eggs is not injured by this seeming neglect, but if the eggs become addled, the female continues to incubate for a long time. In one case she was known to sit for 56 days. In leaving the nest the bird ordinarily flies directly from it and comes back to it in the same way.

When hatching time comes, each chick breaks a hole through the shell, using for the purpose the little horn or spur near the end of the upper mandible (which drops off about three days after the chick is hatched). Next it breaks the shell in a line all around the egg so that the shell separates as if it had been cut in two with a knife, and the struggling, little chick pops out into the world. All the birds of a brood hatch at nearly the same

---

[1] Game and Fish Conservationist, Richmond, Virginia, Vol. VI, No. 3, September–October, 1926.

Fig. 36. — Bob-whites in Roosting Formation

A time exposure at night, Courtesy of William C. Adams, Director Division of
Fisheries and Game, Massachusetts Department of Conservation

Page 7

Fig. 37. — Nest and Eggs of Ring-necked Pheasant

Photo by courtesy of Mr. Adams

Page 17

time, and they are active and able in case of necessity to run away almost at once. Mr. George Davis tells me that his grandfather mowed over a nest one morning when the young were hatching, and that the old gentleman called to him to come quickly and see them come out of the eggs and run away and hide in the grass. The young, like their parents, are adepts at hiding. They usually seek shelter, then squat and become indistinguishable, and such is their apparent confidence in their invisibility that they will actually remain until trodden upon. The driver of my slow-moving, heavy farm team on seeing a female Bob-white fluttering before him in the road stopped the team, and found several tiny young ones in the ruts. Two had already been crushed by the wheels. Often when the young are in danger, one or both parents simulate lameness or helplessness so artfully as to draw off a dog or a cat and lead it away from the little ones.

The young ones grow rather slowly, and their little wings do not develop quite so fast as in the Ruffed Grouse or the Spruce Grouse, but they begin to use them at an early age. Wings are needed indeed, as the little ones must run the gauntlet of many enemies. Storms are fatal to many, as they soon get chilled in the wet grass, and chills are deadly to young birds. As soon as they are large and strong enough to dispense with the maternal brooding, they learn to squat in a close circle on the ground at night, usually near some cover, and there, tails together, heads out, alert for trouble in any direction, they pass the night, with the parents usually in the circle or near by. The circular formation gives them the advantage of mutual contact and warmth, and in case of an alarm with one simultaneous spring forward and upward every bird in the flock gets wing room. Probably when the alarmed birds alight, they squat, each by itself, where they strike the ground, and thus when under the influence of fright with their feathers drawn close to their bodies some individuals seem to give out no scent, and so long as they remain quiet it is exceedingly difficult for dog or fox to find them. Others do not seem to be able thus to retain their scent, but it may be that these move after alighting and so leave a trail. There is a mystery here which calls for careful investigation. Often Bob-whites will lie extremely close when resting on the ground in their circular formation. Once I almost trod upon such a gathering when, happening to look at the ground at my feet, there they were in the usual ring and under very slight cover. Another step would have brought my foot into their midst. They did not wait for me to take it, but scattered in flight. Sometimes when alighting after a sudden fright, some one of the bevy goes into a hole in the ground or a foot track in the snow. Mr. A. W. Higgins found one dead in a steel trap which had been set well down in a woodchuck's hole. Occasionally a bird is said to dive directly into the soft snow, going far under the surface, and if pursued it will burst out again in full flight. When first flushed the birds of a bevy often go away in company, but if started a second time, they are likely to scatter widely. Not infrequently they alight in trees. When they feel that the immediate danger is past, they begin to sound the rallying call which brings them together.

In the year 1908 there were 25 Bob-whites on my farm. In the winter of 1910–11, owing to the severe season and destruction by hunters and other enemies, there was but one bird left — a male.   This bird we fed, thus keeping him about the farm-house most of the winter, where his actions could be readily watched.   The children called him Bob.

Bob's readiness in finding places of concealment and eluding his enemies was remarkable, and yet his strategy was extremely simple.   In artifices of concealment he was a perfect success.   His grays and browns, the black and white markings of his head and his mottled breast were, on the approach of danger, combined and blended into the semblance of a clod.

He was running lightly around the yard one day when a dog appeared in the distance plunging along at full speed.   The yard was flat and open; there seemed to be no place of concealment, and, to make matters worse, most of the ground was whitened with a thin layer of drifted snow, being entirely bare only in patches.

Did Bob take wing and fly to safety?   Not he!   A slow, quiet settling of his whole body was followed by a widening of the shoulders and an indrawing of the head, and shaking out his feathers, he squatted on the snowy ground "as flat as a pancake."   The white markings of the throat and head were cunningly concealed, the top of the head projecting barely enough beyond the general outline to allow him a comprehensive view of his surroundings.   There he sat, while the blundering dog lunged past within a few feet, unaware of the bird's existence.   When the dog had passed, Bob raised himself cautiously, and then went about his business as if nothing had happened.

A little later a daughter of the household, going out for a walk, left the house by the front door.   Across the yard there is a grove of white pines.   As soon as Bob saw who was coming, he ran to a little hollow at the foot of one of the pines and there effaced himself.   By keeping my eye upon him I witnessed the whole performance.   But our young pedestrian never saw him at all.

She came back, inquired where he had gone, and went out again but could not see him. When she had gone, I looked out but could not find him.   I focused my glass on the butt of that tree, not forty feet away, and still could see no sign of him, when suddenly he "grew" out of the ground, and calmly walked directly into the center of my field of vision.

As a member of the family left the woodshed and walked toward the barn, Bob made a quick short run and disappeared.   This happened where once had stood a pine tree within thirty feet of the window.   This tree was partially uprooted by the terrific gale of November, 1898, and was afterward sawed off close to the ground.   Through its stump ran a wide cleft.   The bird had merely run to the stump, and throwing its body forward landed in the cleft, where with head down, it disappeared from sight.   My position was such, however, that looking downward and directly through the cleft the bird was in full view.   Still it seemed to bear no resemblance to a bird, having become apparently a part of the stump.   Only when it raised its head a little to watch could anything resembling a bird be distinguished, although the cleft was less than three inches deep.

Another time when someone went out, the Quail was caught unawares on the snow in plain view.   While the door was opening, he ran until he was behind a tree, quietly squatted on the snow, and remained there unseen by the intruder.

He did not fly unless forced to do so, and seemed to have the utmost contempt for a dog. Indeed he once fed about on bare ground twenty feet to leeward of the dog, merely keeping a watchful eye on the stupid beast that never saw him. Many dogs are almost as blind as most people. When the dog moved about, Bob showed a little excitement by raising his crest as he did when running away to hide.

By watching this bird in the spring, we noted that when he called he did not stretch up his neck like a barnyard cock, in the manner that is frequently represented in books. He stood erect but not high on his legs, with head drawn down and not thrown forward. In whistling he threw the head back and opened the bill slightly, throwing the head farther back with each note, until when the third note was uttered it was thrown a little back of the perpendicular. All the time the neck was drawn in and the head held close to the body. In case of the approach of danger the bird lowered or softened the whistle until it seemed to come from far off. One morning a child walking toward the hen-house went past the bird, which sat in some raspberry bushes beside the path uttering its usual call. When the child opened the door, the bird so softened the whistle that it sounded as if an eighth of a mile away. After she had walked past, the bird gradually increased the volume of the sound until when she had passed to a distance of about six rods, he was whistling as loudly as before.

There is some evidence that where Bob-whites are abundant, some of them, possibly young birds, migrate short distances in autumn, going generally not far and southward, but I have seen no statement anywhere to indicate that they return in spring. Ordinarily Bob-white probably passes its life in or near one neighborhood, although at times some may be driven away from their home by persecution or lack of food. In such a case marked birds have been taken in a near-by town.

He who wishes to increase the number of the species should provide them with food and shelter in winter. For this purpose high brush piles should be built, and weeds should be cut as soon as the seeds ripen. A sheltered place should be selected on the south side of a little grove or thicket, where a pile of weeds should be laid down to a depth of about a foot; a layer of strong brush should be added, then another layer of weeds, another of brush, and a cap over the whole composed of a deep layer of weeds or boughs from a coniferous tree. There should be a rock or two on the heap or a few slanting stakes to hold it against strong winds. The brush allows the sun and wind to enter the pile and makes a refuge into which the birds can creep. The brush must be strong so that no layer of heavy snow can crush it down. It may be necessary toward spring to add to the food supply barn sweepings, millet seed, or small grains. Probably no better feeding place and shelter than this can be devised.

The greatest possible attraction for this bird in summer is a fruiting mulberry tree and in autumn a field of buckwheat, and next to this a weedy potato patch or a field of small grain.

Bob-whites may be hatched in incubators and reared in brooders or under bantam hens, and may be taught to come at call to be fed until they are full grown. The usual successful method, however, is to rear them under bantam hens until they are somewhat more than half grown, feeding them largely on clabber, and then to give them free range. Artificial rearing of the species, however, has never been successful as a commercial enterprise.

Bob-white has many natural enemies. As it feeds mainly on the ground and passes the night there, no bird is more constantly menaced by prowling foes. Hawks, owls, crows, foxes, skunks, weasels, squirrels, rats, mice and snakes all destroy the birds or their eggs. Roaming dogs snap up the young or eat the eggs. The domestic cat is one of their most destructive enemies, often cleaning up a whole brood. The following from my bulletin on The Domestic Cat[1] gives some idea of the pernicious activities of this animal in relation to Bob-white:

"Mr. F. W. Henderson tells in the Rockland 'Independent' of a cat that brought her kittens an entire brood of Bob-whites. Dr. George W. Field, chairman of the Massachusetts Commission on Fisheries and Game, relates that a covey of Bob-whites which he was watching in Sharon was discovered by a cat and attacked at night, at intervals of two to seven days, until the number had become reduced from 16 to 8. They then left in a body for Canton, where they were recognized later. Mr. E. Colfax Johnson of Shutesbury says that he has known of entire flocks of young Bob-whites being destroyed by cats. Mr. John M. Crampton, superintendent for the Connecticut State Board of Fisheries and Game, writes that last fall (1914) a farmer requested that a special protector be sent to look after the Bob-whites on his land. When the warden arrived he found that the farmer had 15 cats, some of which had brought in three Bob-whites already that morning. Mr. B. S. Blake of Webster tells of a cat that took home three Bob-whites in one week. Mr. Edward L. Parker tells of a servant who saw a cat break up two Bob-whites' nests. Senator Louis Hilsendegen of Michigan asserts in the 'Sportsmen's Review' that Henry Ford bought 200 pairs of Bob-whites at \$3 a pair, and released them on his farm at Dearborn, Michigan. A stray cat, left by a farmer who had moved away, found them, and it was noticed that their numbers were decreasing rapidly. A watch was set for the cat; it was shot and found to weigh sixteen pounds. Under a rail shelter, where the birds had fed, a mass of feathers and other remains about a foot deep was found. That cat, says the senator, had killed more than 200 Bob-whites, which had cost the owner over \$300. Mr. E. R. Bryant of the Henry Ford farms writes me that this story is true except that it may be a little overdrawn in regard to the number of birds killed. He never knew exactly how many were slain by this cat."

Bob-white is so exceedingly prolific, however, that its many enemies make little impression on its numbers, and it readily may be increased by protection, winter feeding and control of its enemies. The Pennsylvania plan of catching a few bevies and keeping them in confinement through the coldest part of the winter has manifest advantages.

The food of Bob-white is largely vegetal, consisting of seeds of trees such as the maple, pine, oak and beech, numerous smaller seeds, many wild fruits, grasses and leaves; also

[1] Massachusetts State Board of Agriculture, Economic Biology Bulletin No. 2, 1916, p. 46.

many insects. The bird feeds on the seeds of at least 129 species of weeds, and eats enormous quantities of the seeds of the common kinds, such as ragweed, chickweed and sorrel. Among the wild fruits that it takes are bayberries, mulberries, the fruit of Solomon's seal, greenbrier and sassafras, thimbleberries, blackberries, strawberries, apples, wild and ground cherries, fruit of the sumacs, holly, black alder, climbing bittersweet, frost grape, flowering dogwood, sour gum, blueberries, huckleberries, nightshade, black haw, honeysuckle, wintergreen, elder and partridge berries, sarsaparilla and woodbine berries. These fruits are given by Dr. Sylvester D. Judd.[1] The bird is very fond of mulberries and will go into the trees for them, but eats comparatively little cultivated fruit. It eats more or less green food such as grass, clover, sorrel, plantain and the leaves of weeds. It is, however, a glutton for insects in spring and summer, and eats them in every month of the year whenever and wherever it can get them. The young seem to feed principally on insects. Among the insects taken are quantities of several of the most destructive insect pests such as cutworms, army worms, cabbage worms, Colorado potato beetles, chinch bugs and many other bugs, two species of cucumber beetles, May beetles, weevils, grasshoppers, locusts, flies and plant lice. In winter the bird eats whatever it can find, dried wild fruits, dried grasses and leaves of weeds, also weed seeds and insects living or dead, grass seeds and small grains wherever they can be found. Along the coast dried eel-grass is eaten. Bob-whites require gravel, and when snow covers this they suffer or even die. At that season flocks often learn to eat with poultry.

ECONOMIC STATUS. As a friend of the farmer Bob-white stands preëminent. The grain it eats is mostly waste grain picked up in the stubble fields and it is not known to injure appreciably any crop. It destroys many of the greatest insect pests of the farm. In some cases where spraying has not been done in season, or when it has been prevented by rain, broods of Bob-whites have kept potato fields so clear of Colorado potato beetles that there was no appreciable damage to the crop. This happened on my own farm. One farmer estimates that each Bob-white in his fields is worth at least five dollars a year, because of the good it does in destroying insects. A captive Bob-white ate 568 mosquitoes in two hours, another 5,000 plant lice in a day, another 1,532 insects in a day, 1,000 of which were grasshoppers.[2] In the stomach of one Bob-white 101 potato beetles were found, in another 30 locusts. The bird may render some economic service as a destroyer of weed seeds. Mrs. Nice found that Bob-whites in captivity ate from 600 weed seeds each a day to 30,000, according to the size of the seeds and the capacity of the individual, and Dr. Judd estimated very conservatively that the Bob-whites of Virginia consumed 573 tons of weed seeds between September 1 and April 30.

As a popular game bird of the open country Bob-white has no rival. Probably about 500,000 sportsmen now go out annually from cities east of the Rocky Mountains to hunt this bird. This necessitates a great annual expenditure for hunters' clothing, guns, ammunition, dogs and guides. It adds to the revenue of farmers and country hostelries.

[1] United States Department of Agriculture, Bureau of Biological Survey, Bulletin No. 21, 1905, p. 37.
[2] Nice, Margaret Morse: Food of the Bob-white, Journal of Economic Entomology, Vol. 3, 1910, p. 312.

In some of the southern states Bob-white pays the taxes on many farms where the farmers sell their shooting rights to sportsmen.   Many individuals and sportsmen's clubs own or lease large tracts of land which they maintain as shooting preserves.   In New England the birds are not now numerous enough to be so important economically, and in several counties of Massachusetts they are protected from time to time by law at all seasons with the expectation of increasing their numbers.

"Perhaps there is no bird to which the American people are more deeply indebted for both æsthetic and material benefits.   He is the most democratic and ubiquitous of all our game birds.   He is not a bird of desert, wilderness or mountain peak which one must go far to find.   He seeks the home, farm, garden and field ; he is the friend and companion of mankind ; a much needed helper on the farm ; a destroyer of insect pests and weeds ; a swift flying game bird, lying well to a dog ; and, last as well as least, good food, a savory morsel, nutritious and digestible." [1]

NOTE.   The American Ornithologists' Union has not included introduced species in its Check-list (1910), but two Old-World game birds seem to have become naturalized in New England.   Apparently systematists of various countries do not agree upon the order in which these birds should be placed in the scheme of classification, but as the European Partridge has now become American by introduction, it is included here with the American partridges (which structurally it closely resembles) without definite assignment to any family.   Eventually the committee on nomenclature of the American Ornithologists' Union may place it where in their judgment it belongs.

Pérdix perdix perdix (LINNÆUS).   European Partridge.

Other names: HUNGARIAN PARTRIDGE ; BOHEMIAN PARTRIDGE ; ENGLISH PARTRIDGE ; GRAY PARTRIDGE.

An introduced species.
Plate 34.

DESCRIPTION.* — Nostrils not covered with feathers ; a patch of bare skin behind eye ; tail normally of 18 feathers, short and rounded, tips of tail-feathers also rounded ; tarsus bare, without spurs.   *Adult male in breeding plumage:* Variegated with brown, chestnut, buff and gray, and finely cross-waved or vermiculated with blackish ; sometimes a few black feathers at base of upper mandible ; forehead, space before eye, stripe over it, chin and throat light yellowish chestnut, paler on throat, often a small white or very light patch below eye ; top of head, nape and ear-region dark brown, crown feathers with narrow shaft-streaks of buff near their tips ; hind neck, sides of neck and back mainly brownish-gray, with fine wavy bars of black ; lower back, rump and upper tail-coverts becoming buffy, or, in some cases, reddish-brown, usually with pale shafts and rather narrow chestnut and blackish sagittate bars alternating near tip of each feather, these bars becoming wider on rump and upper tail-coverts ; tail chestnut with narrow buff tips, its four middle feathers pale buff with fine wavy cross-lines and barred black, each feather with chestnut shaft-streaks ; the next two (sometimes more) have edges and tips vermiculated ; flight-feathers mainly dark brown with bars and tips of buff ; scapulars, lesser, middle and greater wing-coverts mostly

[1] Game Birds, Wild-Fowl and Shore Birds, 1912, p. 369.   Part of this history of the Bob-white was written in slightly different language, originally for a leaflet published in Bird-Lore by the National Association of Audubon Societies.

* As Partridges have been introduced from both the British Isles and continental Europe and as no Massachusetts specimens were available for examination, the above description is composite and applicable more to the species than to any race.

The description was taken from specimens taken in this country.   The ancestry of the specimens examined may have been English or continental or both.   No attempt was made to determine the subspecies.

darker than back, the latter with buffy bars, edges and tips and buff shaft-streaks; lesser and middle wing-coverts have central buff streaks and no bars, but, instead, dark spots and fine dark vermiculations; fore neck and breast gray, with fewer bars than on sides of neck; feathers of sides and flanks heavily barred dark chestnut, with paler or buffy margins and tips and fine pale shaft-lines, a large horseshoe-shaped dark chestnut patch in middle of lower breast, partly surrounding a gray patch that is finely vermiculated black; axillars and wing linings white, speckled dusky, except inner under wing-coverts; bill blackish-brown to greenish horn color; iris brown; legs and feet bluish-gray. *Adult male in winter plumage:* Similar, but generally less gray and more buffy above. *Adult female in breeding plumage:* Somewhat similar to male, but chestnut markings usually paler and crown more spotted; browner above, and horseshoe mark on breast often nearly white with few black tips, but sometimes (especially in young females) resembling that of males; lesser and middle wing-coverts have the buff shaft-stripe slightly broader and two or three buff bars on each web of each feather. *First winter plumage:* Like adults, but tips of first (outer) and second primaries more pointed; feet of male in this plumage yellowish-brown or clay color changing to bluish horn color or bluish-gray before spring. *Juvenal plumage:* Top of head blackish-brown with buff shaft-streaks; sides of head dark brown, streaked whitish; from back of head to tail buffy-brown with pale shaft-streaks, varying from pale buff to white, the feathers slightly margined blackish; tail much like that of adult, tipped buff, but often with subterminal dusky bar and central feathers speckled dusky; flight-feathers brown, barred pale buffy; scapulars and tertials lighter than flight-feathers, with brownish-black bars and mottling, and pale shaft-streaks widening toward tips; chin, throat and middle of abdomen whitish; breast, sides, flanks and under tail-coverts slightly paler than back, with whiter shaft-streaks, flank feathers with faint brown margins; legs and feet yellow. *Downy young:* Top of head dull chestnut, spotted and sometimes lined sparsely with black; rest of upper surface pale buff; a wide central blackish line down back of neck, sides of neck marked blackish; some rufous and black marking ill defined on back; small spot of dull chestnut at base of wing and large one of same on rump; forehead and sides of head pale yellowish-buff with small black markings; chin and throat same, but unmarked; elsewhere below slightly yellower.

MEASUREMENTS. — Length 12.00 to 14.00 in.; spread 18.00 to 22.00 in.; folded wing 5.90 to 6.20; tail 3.00 to 3.40; bill .50 to .55; tarsus 1.50 to 1.70; weight 12 to 15 oz. Average of English birds, male, about 14½ oz.; female, about ½ oz. less; heaviest male 16.37 oz. (F. M. Ogilvie).

MOLTS. — As the young bird grows, its down is replaced by juvenal feathers. This plumage is followed by an autumnal molt (sometimes not completed until January), and first winter plumage is assumed, which is practically as adults; adults acquire winter plumage by a complete postnuptial molt (July to December) and breeding plumage by an incomplete prenuptial molt (April to June) chiefly of neck and throat feathers.

FIELD MARKS. — Size about half-way between Ruffed Grouse and Bob-white. Usually found in cultivated grounds, gardens, grass fields or grain fields. Short gray neck, brownish-gray body. Flight swift, noisy and direct, the initial hurried wing-beats followed by a sail with down-curved wings like Bob-white, then if tail is spread, chestnut or reddish-brown tail-feathers are conspicuous.

VOICE. — Cry of male a loud hoarse "*caer-wit, caer-wit.*"

BREEDING. — In or about cultivated lands, fields, meadows or waste lands, especially on light soils. *Nest:* A hollow in ground, by roadside, hedge, bushy fence or wall, often in open field; lined with grasses and dead leaves and sheltered by a bush, growing grass, grain or other vegetation. *Eggs:* 9 to 20, a pointed ovate, olive color; slightly smaller than those of Ruffed Grouse. Numbers up to 40 rarely recorded, probably deposited by two or more birds. *Incubation:* Period variously given as 21 to 26 days, 24 or a part of the 25th in England (F. M. Ogilvie); by female. One brood yearly, sometimes two.

RANGE. — Greater part of continental Europe, the British Isles and eastern Asia; races of the species range east to foot of Altai Mountains. At least eleven races have been described; breeds throughout its range; introduced into various states of North America and in central southern and southwestern Canada.

HISTORY. The European Partridge was first introduced [1] in the Willamette Valley of Oregon in 1900, and in 1904 an importation was liberated in South Carolina, and another in British Columbia. In 1905, 20 were placed in a preserve in Massachusetts and 91 in North Carolina. Importations continued, and during the years 1908 and 1909 nearly 40,000 were transported from Europe to America. During that time and since the birds have been introduced into Alabama, California, Colorado, Connecticut, Delaware, Indiana, Illinois, Iowa, Kansas, Kentucky, Maine, Maryland, Massachusetts, Michigan, Minnesota, Montana, Nebraska, Nevada, New Hampshire, New Jersey, New York, North Dakota, Ohio, Ontario, Pennsylvania, Rhode Island, South Dakota, Texas, Utah, Vermont, Virginia, Washington, West Virginia, Wisconsin and Western Canada.

For a time, under protection, the birds on private preserves in Massachusetts increased and spread to some distance from the preserves, but when their propagation was discontinued, they died out, and at the present time (1925) the only birds known to exist at large within the state are a few that came in from Connecticut, where large numbers were introduced. In some cases, particularly where the birds were introduced in large numbers, in mild temperate regions and many in a place, they seem to have become established, especially when protected by law for five years. Under less favorable conditions they have died out in some states.

HAUNTS AND HABITS. The European Partridge frequents open and cultivated fields, grain fields, meadows and waste lands, all of which it prefers to the woods, though it will often seek cover in thickets. In spring after most of the weed seeds are gone it haunts clover fields. As a game bird in New England it has not proved a great success, as it has not had sufficient protection, and it often nests in grass fields and meadows where its nest and eggs are destroyed by early mowing. It seems to thrive best in light soils in a farming community where grain growing is the principal industry. In Bohemia it is said to live largely in the hop and beet fields. Like the Bob-white this Partridge sleeps on the ground, the individuals of a covey forming a circle with heads outward to guard against night prowlers, and like the Bob-white also it is not usually polygamous. When the mating season arrives, the birds may be seen pursuing each other in the fields. The males fight fiercely for the possession of their chosen females. The female is said to cover her eggs with leaves when she leaves the nest until all are laid. During the time of incubation the bird seems to give out no scent, and dogs rarely find the nests. When the young are hatched the male takes his turn in brooding them. The parents are very solicitous in their care, and endeavor to lure an enemy away by their cries and antics. The male often defends his mate and young against birds larger than himself. After the breeding season the partridge when alarmed crouches close to the ground, where, like the Bob-white, it is very difficult to detect, even on bare ground. It may lie thus until nearly trodden upon, so secure does it seem to feel in its invisiblity, but it is said not to lie so well to dogs.

---

[1] Oldys, Henry: Introduction of the Hungarian Partridge in the United States, U. S. Department of Agriculture, Year Book, 1909, p. 254.

The parents and young keep together during autumn and winter, and so long as they can find food they remain in the same locality, moving only in case of necessity. In spring their food consists largely of insects and succulent green vegetation. Shoots and blades of grass, clover and other plants are eaten. Many insects, including ants, plant lice, and beetles, are taken, ants being a favorite food. In summer and autumn they eat wild berries, seeds of grasses, weeds and grain also, but so far as records go there is little evidence that they injure cultivated fruit.

ECONOMIC STATUS. In Europe this partridge is looked upon as a very important game bird. In cultivated lands it is considered more beneficial than injurious. Its status in this country remains to be determined.

FAMILY **PHASIANIDÆ**. PHEASANTS AND THEIR ALLIES.

Number of species in North America, at least 4 ; number in Massachusetts 1.

This family includes the most gorgeous and magnificent fowls of the world. As it is usually constituted its members range in size from the little "true" quails and the larger "true" partridges of the Old World to that of the long-tailed pheasants, the jungle fowls (among them the progenitors of the domestic cock) and the peafowls. The tarsi, toes, nostrils and usually parts of the head (or the whole of it) are unfeathered, and the head often supports fleshy protuberances, combs, wattles, etc. In many cases the head is crested. The wings usually are short and concave. The tail and its coverts vary greatly in shape, but both are in some cases much elongated, the tail thus often extended. The males of many species develop spurs on the tarsi and many are polygamous.

ECONOMIC STATUS. The family has furnished the greater part of our domestic fowls and many highly valued game birds. Many of its members feed largely on grain, but also eat insects and weed seeds.

Phasiánus cólchicus torquátus GMELIN. **Ring-necked Pheasant.**

Other names: CHINESE PHEASANT; CHINESE RING-NECK; OREGON PHEASANT.

An introduced species.
Plate 35.

DESCRIPTION. — Bill stout, shaped somewhat like that of the domestic hen, upper mandible down-curved, edges and tip thin-edged, overlapping a nearly straight, obtusely pointed lower mandible ; wings strong, short and rounded ; outer webs of primaries very slightly serrated ; tail much graduated, folding narrowly, central feathers long and streaming, outer very short ; tarsus rather short and strong, with (in male) a small spur ; hind toe short, front toes slender, connected at base by small web. *Adult male:* Lower forehead black at base of bill, shading into green or greenish-gray on top and back of head ; stripe from black forehead over and behind eye white or whitish underlined with black and reaching nearly to base of an erectile tuft of iridescent black square-tipped feathers, extending above ear-region, which is brownish-black ; sides of face around each eye bare and red (except a few tiny, short, black feather tufts and a line or patch of feathers under eye), forming a wattle on each side of jaw below eye ; rest of head and neck shaded with iridescent greenish-blue, bluish-green and purplish ; broad collar around base of neck (not always complete) abruptly and conspicuously white; upper back yellowish with U or V-shaped markings connected with terminal central spots, all of iridescent black, the ground color shading into rich chestnut-red or deep burnished copper on middle back and scapulars, each feather with a submarginal black U or V enclosing a pale, yellowish-white, or more or less mottled or vermiculated white, area; lower back and rump *light grayish-green*, middle feathers with crescentic markings of black and buff; lateral feathers washed bluish with some rusty red tips; upper tail-coverts light grayish-green bordered laterally with rusty red; tail-feathers centrally yellowish-drab shading to pinkish-brown toward basal margins and barred conspicuously with black, the basal margins barred deep chestnut-red; wing mainly light ashy bluish with concealed arrowhead markings, flight-feathers largely grayish-brown with paler shafts and bars; breast deep, burnished copper-bronze, highly metallic, each feather with a narrow W-shaped end margin of purplish-black, giving the effect of scaled, polished armor; sides and flanks rich, deep yellow-buff, with large spots of blue-black; middle of lower breast and abdomen deep brown to blackish with bluish or purplish reflections; under tail-coverts varying from rather light brown to blackish, often with some darker markings or lighter tips; wing linings mainly pale buff to whitish; axillars same, barred dark grayish-brown; iris hazel; legs and feet brownish-gray; bill pale greenish-yellow. *Note.* The long, loose, hairlike feathers of the lower back and rump, which are mainly green in male Ring-necked Pheasant, are *maroon* in male English Pheasant. Birds having rump mixed maroon and green are regarded as English Ring-necks, having an admixture of the blood of the English Pheasant. *Adult female:* Forehead, top and back of head drab-brown each feather with blackish-brown center and wide, drab-brown or pinkish margin; whitish about eye, flecked dusky; sides of head elsewhere yellowish-brown with some irregular inconspicuous blackish barring under eye; chin and throat yellowish-white or light buff, sometimes pinkish; neck brown with feather tips next throat black and black subterminal spots or narrow black tips on larger feathers; feathers of upper back marked concentrically with rusty-red, black and pinkish-white; lower back, rump, upper tail-coverts and visible outer parts of closed wing with black feather centers fading to yellowish-brown near ends and margined white, buffy or drab; flight-feathers much as in male, but pale bars and end margins on secondaries and tertials; tail pointed like that of male, but shorter, and barred with blackish and brown or pinkish-brown; wing linings and axillars varied or barred with dull white or pale buff and pale brown; under body pale yellowish-brown or buff, lightening on belly, all finely cross-waved with dusky or brown, except sides and flanks which are coarsely marked with brownish-black. Some females (probably sterile) sometimes assume plumage similar to that of male. *Juvenal plumage:* Top of head and back of neck dark brown, feathers with subterminal pale buff or yellowish-brown spots; other upper plumage mainly brownish-black, growing browner towards tail, with central shaft-streaks and other margins yellowish to pale buff, some on upper back often tinged rusty; tail shorter than in adult female and buff, barred reddish-brown or blackish; wing like that of adult female; chin and upper throat white or buffy; lower throat often streaked with dark brown; breast yellowish-brown tinged rusty; sides and flanks marked concentrically buffy-brown, brownish-black and dull white; belly yellowish-white or pale buff; under tail-coverts pale buff. *Downy young:* buff or rufous buff to dark yellowish-brown above, with dark stripes on back and head and a dark spot on ear region; below fading gradually to yellowish-white, more buffy on breast, sides and flanks; some have a dark spot on thigh.

MEASUREMENTS. — *Male:* Length 33.00 to 36.00 in.; folded wing 9.00 to 10.50; bill 1.20 to 1.30; tarsus 2.75 to 3.00. *Female:* Length about 20.50; folded wing 7.56 to 8.30; bill about 1.15; tarsus 2.38 to 2.44. Weight 2½ to 4½ lbs. Female much smaller than male.

MOLTS. — Juvenal plumage, which is acquired by complete postnatal molt, is completely shed (beginning before the young are grown) excepting the two outer primaries; and first winter plumage, with exception of two outer primaries (which are more pointed), is as adult; adults have one complete molt annually, finished in September or October.

FIELD MARKS. — Largest of New England game birds; the only one with a long, streaming, folded, tapering, pointed tail; head of male appears black, breast bronze, sides yellow with black spots; tail barred blackish; female brown, slightly scaled on back, lighter below with a shorter, barred, pointed tail; flight noisy but not so much so as that of Ruffed Grouse.

VOICE. — Male a peculiar harsh crow, *kok-cack*, or *kock, kock*, followed by beating of wings; both sexes when suddenly alarmed have a harsh, rattling machine-like cackle, continued for several seconds; female clucks to her young.

BREEDING. — Usually in open country in bushy pastures, moorlands, or fields of grass or grain, sometimes in woods. *Nest:* Usually on ground; rarely in nest of some other bird in tree; built of leaves of deciduous or coniferous trees, grass, straws, etc. *Eggs:* 6 to 12; rarely 14 to 16; ovate; olive-brown to pale blue or pale bluish-green. The native Chinese Ring-necked Pheasant is said to lay pale bluish-green eggs spotted with a deeper tint. *Dates:* Late April to late June. *Incubation:* By female; period 23 to 25 days. One brood yearly, two may be raised rarely.

RANGE. — Normally "eastern and southeastern China from Canton to Hunan, north to the lower and middle Yangtse, up river at least to Ichang, north to Pekin Kalgan," and the Ordos country (C. Wm. Beebe). Its descendants are widely distributed. Introduced into various countries in Europe and America and many of the United States including Maine, New Hampshire, Vermont, Massachusetts, Rhode Island, Connecticut, New York, New Jersey, Delaware, Pennsylvania, Ohio, Indiana, Illinois, Kentucky, Oklahoma, Kansas, Utah, Virginia, Georgia, California, Oregon, Washington and other northern states and into Ontario and British Columbia also.

DISTRIBUTION IN NEW ENGLAND. — Generally distributed in the three southern states, mostly in the coastal region, the lower lands and valleys; not found on the higher elevations, sparingly distributed in the more southern valleys of Vermont and New Hampshire and in southwestern Maine.

SEASON IN MASSACHUSETTS. — Resident; most conspicuous in winter, spring and summer; secretive in the hunting season.

HISTORY. Pheasants, believed to have been normally Asiatic birds, have been introduced from Asia into Europe and the United States. Several species have been bred in many countries, either in captivity, or in partial or complete domestication, but only one has become generally acclimated. Among those most commonly introduced in the New World are *Phasianus colchicus colchicus*, the so-called English Pheasant, a Chinese subspecies *Phasianus colchicus torquatus*, the Ring-necked Pheasant, *Phasianus versi-color*, the Japanese Green Pheasant, and *Phasianus mongolicus*, the Mongolian Pheasant. Probably the first of these to be acclimated in Europe was the English Pheasant which, a native of Transcaucasia, is said to have been brought from the River Phasis in Colchis by the Argonauts of Jason's expedition in search of the Golden Fleece, hence the name *Phasianus colchicus*, derived from its native river and country. The pheasant now found on the banks of that river (now known as the Rion River) is the Rion Caucasian Pheasant *Phasianus colchicus colchicus*, which closely resembles the original English pheasant and gives color to the tale of its origin. Students of the collection of traditions, legends, sagas and inscriptions that passes for ancient history attribute the introduction of the bird into England variously to the Romans and the Normans. Newton in his Dictionary of Birds doubts the old accounts of its introduction into Europe and thinks it not impossible that the bird may be indigenous. It seems to have been acclimated in Europe 1250 years before the Christian era and in Britain in 1299 during the reign of Edward the First. The full-blooded English pheasant had no white ring around the neck, but it has interbred with the Ring-necked Pheasant (introduced later) until most of the pheasants now in England are of the strain called the English Ring-neck — a cross between the two races, with probably some admixture of the blood of others. They show either a partial or almost complete white ring around the neck.

Pheasants were introduced into the United States several times in the nineteenth century, but in most cases failed to become established. The first successful introduction was that undertaken by Judge O. W. Denny, then American Consul General at Shanghai, China, in 1881, when he sent a shipment of 28 Ring-necked Pheasants from China to Oregon. These birds were a pure (or nearly pure) strain of *P. c. torquatus*, and in the mild humid climate of western Oregon they soon established themselves and multiplied rapidly. Others were introduced later. The species increased so fast that in 1894 the state Game Warden of Oregon estimated that 13,000 birds were killed in three months in Linn County alone, and he learned that in the winter of 1892–93 1,200 dozens of these birds were sent to one dealer in San Francisco.

The first successful introduction of pheasants into the eastern United States was initiated by Rutherford Stuyvesant, who in 1887 brought over a number of the birds from England and placed them in charge of a Scotch gamekeeper. After several unsuccessful attempts the birds became established. The English Pheasant has been bred under artificial conditions so long that it does not do well in the wild, and the probability is that the blood of the Ring-neck predominated in the strain that finally became established there. In 1894 Mr. Sullivan Forehand of Worcester, Massachusetts, obtained a few pairs of breeding birds from Oregon, which he turned over to Commissioner Brackett, then chairman of the Massachusetts Commission on Fisheries and Game. Mr. Brackett established breeding pens at Winchester, Massachusetts, and having secured a small appropriation from the Commonwealth began rearing young pheasants. Thus the policy of game breeding by the Commonwealth of Massachusetts was begun. It has been extended since so that several farms have been devoted to the purpose, and many thousands of pheasants have been distributed throughout the state. I examined the original stock secured by Mr. Brackett. He called these birds Mongolian Pheasants, but they were all apparently full-blooded Chinese Ring-necks. There has been some interbreeding with other pheasants since that time. English pheasants, mostly English Ring-necks, also have been reared by commercial game breeders, but the great majority of wild birds now breeding in the state are the descendants of Ring-necked Pheasants liberated by the Massachusetts Commission on Fisheries and Game, or by their successors, the Division of Fisheries and Game of the Department of Conservation, which now has charge of the breeding of game birds for the Commonwealth. Wild specimens killed in Massachusetts and examined by me exhibit little more variation from the type than do specimens killed in China and also examined by me. So far as can be determined there are no typical specimens of any other species now running at large in Massachusetts, and *P. colchicus torquatus*, the chief progenitor of our pheasants, is the only race of pheasants the descendants of which have been able to establish themselves in a wild state in New England. With special care and protection they seem to hold their own in the more open lands where the

Ruffed Grouse cannot long survive, and where the pheasant has become a valuable acquisition to our supply of feathered game.

HAUNTS AND HABITS. The Ring-necked Pheasant is a proud, stately, handsome bird, active, daring and aggressive; well adapted to sustain itself in a mild climate even under adverse circumstances, but not quite hardy enough to endure the severe winters of the higher and more northern parts of New England. In its native land it is a dweller chiefly in river valleys, grain fields, flats, meadows, marshes and low rolling scrubby or forested hills, and it thrives best here in such situations. It enters woodlands and commonly finds shelter in tracts of low bushes and briers. It frequents open woods with a thick undergrowth of shrubbery, briers and grasses, with open glades and streams. It is rather rarely seen in trees as it roosts more or less on the ground in summer, but in autumn and winter it roosts much in trees, and in winter when food on the ground is covered with snow, it has been seen in trees feeding on buds or wild berries.

In speaking of the habits of this species, I refer to wild birds and not to half-domesticated pheasants reared on game preserves. The bird is not so well adapted to our climate as is the Ruffed Grouse, for it feeds chiefly on the ground and needs a continuous supply of grain or weed seeds to carry it through the winter. After sleet storms pheasants have been found attached to the ice by their long tails which have "frozen in." This seems to indicate that possibly some of them roost more or less on the ground even in winter. A severe winter with deep snows makes life hard for the pheasants, as most of their accustomed food is then covered with snow. When the snow becomes crusted, they can find little food, and, unless they have learned to subsist on buds, they may require to be fed at such times with grain. When deep snows come, they search diligently for food, often approaching farm-houses and even coming into the outskirts of villages to hunt for garbage or anything edible that may be thrown out by the inhabitants.

As a game bird in the fields the pheasant is inferior to the Ruffed Grouse and the Bob-white, as usually it does not lie so well to the dog and is given more to skulking and running. As it can move fast and close to the ground, it can conceal itself in grass or grain and keep far in advance of the sportsman. Under some circumstances, however, an entire covey will lie close and spring up almost underfoot. The female and young can hide in short grass where, by "lying low," they become almost invisible, and when thus concealed, they sometimes remain until almost trodden upon. The cock is more conspicuous than his mate, and likely to be more shy and to fly or run off before the sportsman gets within easy range, but with a few tufts of grass or bushes for cover, he may crouch and remain invisible. It is astonishing how readily this conspicuous and handsome bird can conceal himself in very scanty cover. Wounded birds sometimes escape by running and hiding. They do not hesitate to cross water, as they can swim well, and may thus throw a slow dog off the scent.

In the mating season the cock has a habit of strutting, crowing and flapping his wings in a manner somewhat similar to the crowing of the familiar barn-yard fowl, but it has no such clarion call as that of the domestic bird. The following observations on the crowing and "drumming" of the pheasant were sent to me by Mr. Henry E. Childs:

"Just before starting the first syllable the forward portions of the wings were drawn forward a few inches and beaten sideways toward the body and one another. I could hear no sound from the wings while this was being done. I think there was a jerk of the neck at the start of the call. As he swung into the second syllable the tail was wagged violently up and down once while the wings were being stretched straight upwards to full length. They were as high or a little higher than the head. They were then beaten rapidly toward one another. I am not sure whether they struck one another or not. The sound was just beginning to come from the wings when the second syllable of the call was finished. The roll of sound from the wings continued for just about as long a time as the call itself had taken. It grew in volume during the first few beats and then diminished quickly. It was without the slow preliminary beats of a drumming Ruffed Grouse, was not so deep in tone, gave an impression of 'suddenness,' and diminished more quickly. The individual sounds seemed to be a succession of faster notes or blows than that of the first two-thirds (at least) of a Partridge's drumming, and the ending died out instead of being sharply marked off with emphatic notes as in the grouse."

The Ring-necked Pheasant is polygamous, and a single cock is likely to sport a harem of several hens. The cocks are vigorous powerful birds, and, like the males of other polygamous species, they fight viciously for the possession of their chosen females. In autumn as the young birds begin to develop and to imitate the crowing of their elders, they commence fighting, and in early spring, beginning even in February in some places, fighting and mating go on apace. While in winter the sexes keep largely apart, in spring they begin to intermingle, and during the strutting and crowing of the mating season the males become quite noisy and conspicuous. The bare skin about their heads becomes a deeper red, they carry their wings lower and their tails higher, and appear more proud and stately. Like the domestic cock whenever they find some choice store of food, they gallantly call up the females to the feast. At this season the amorous male, lacking mates, may mate with any other species of pheasant and even with domestic fowls, including the turkey. Battles in the hen yard between wild pheasants and domestic cocks, in which the pheasants are said to come off the victors, sometimes take place.

When the young pheasants are hatched, they soon leave the nest, never to return. Like the Ruffed Grouse the mother broods them here and there and takes them under her wings at night wherever darkness overtakes them. She leads her brood about as does the domestic hen, finds food for them and calls them to it. At first they get their water from their food, the rain and the dewdrops, but later they seek water at some pool, lake or stream. When the mother is surprised by an enemy, she flies up with a sudden uproar of wings, making herself conspicuous and inviting pursuit, while the young run and hide. They are adepts at the game of sneaking away to safety and some usually manage to escape the attacks of their many enemies, of which the domestic cat, the weasel, and the Great Horned Owl are particularly destructive. In winter the Goshawk is perhaps the greatest enemy of the full-grown birds. This pheasant is remarkably intelligent and makes good use of all its keen faculties to preserve its life. It may become accustomed to the presence of the farmer in the fields and seem quite unsuspicious, but let the sportsman appear with gun and dog, and its behavior is soon altered. It is a swift flier and knows a few tricks by which it often makes out to elude the hunter and his dog.

On account of limited space I have purposely omitted any description of the habits of the pheasant in the breeding-pen or any reference to methods of artificial propagation. There are a number of excellent published treatises on the subject. Two of the more recent ones are "Pheasant Raising in the United States," as described by Henry Oldys in Farmers Bulletin No. 390, issued in 1910 by the United States Department of Agriculture, and "American Pheasant Breeding and Shooting," by E. A. Quarles, published by the American Game Protective Association of New York. The methods of pheasant raising are described also in the Propagation of Wild Birds by Herbert K. Job.[1]

The vegetal food of the Ring-necked Pheasant consists of flowers, fruit seeds, buds, leaves, stems, shoots and roots or tubers. Its animal food includes many insects, worms and other small forms of animal life; its vegetal food is comprised very largely of parts of wild plants including great quantities of the seeds of pernicious weeds and a considerable amount of grain which often makes up from 14 to 17 per cent of the food for the year. Most of the grain, however, is either waste grain picked up in the stubble or in corn fields, or grain fed to them by people interested in their preservation.

In 1913 the Massachusetts Commissioners on Fisheries and Game were directed by the Legislature to investigate the habits of the introduced pheasants with special reference to their injurious and beneficial food habits. In the report made in pursuance of this purpose the Commissioners give the following list of insect pests eaten by these birds:[2]

Pests of the Market Garden	Fruit Pests	Tree Pests and Others
Tomato or tobacco worm (*Sphinx*)	Codling moth, adults and larvæ	Tussock moth
White grub, adults and larvæ	Apple maggot, adults and larvæ	Elm-leaf beetle
Striped cucumber beetle	Tent caterpillar, adults and larvæ	Tent caterpillar
Black squash bug	Tussock moth, adults and larvæ	Mosquitoes
Parsnip web worm	Cherry lice	Flies, house, adults and larvæ
Wire worms, adults and larvæ	Plant lice	Flies, blow, adults and larvæ
Cut worms, adults and larvæ	June bug	Gypsy moths and larvæ
Potato beetle	Adults of tree borers	Brown-tail moths and larvæ
Green cabbage worm, larvæ	Curculio on plum, peach and apple	Rose bugs
Corn louse ant		
Asparagus beetle, adults and larvæ		

[1] See also United States Department of Agriculture Bulletin No. 521 by W. L. McAtee of the Biological Survey.

[2] Special Report of the Massachusetts Board of Commissioners on Fisheries and Game, under Chapter 70 of the Resolves of 1913, relative to the habits of those birds commonly known as Pheasants. House No. 2049, 1914, p. 7.

In spring the species feeds principally on insects and succulent green food, in summer on insects, green food and grain, and in autumn on grain and seeds.   During winter it takes such hibernating insects as it can find, and supplements its grain food with weed seeds, buds and garbage.   In addition to the above these pheasants feed greedily on grasshoppers and crickets and eat several species of plant lice and other undetermined insects, snails, slugs and earthworms.

ECONOMIC STATUS.   Pheasants are known to injure some farm crops.   Many complaints of such injury have been made to the Massachusetts Department of Agriculture and the Department of Conservation.   These complaints refer chiefly to damage done to corn or tomatoes, and in lesser degree to garden truck, peas, fruit and potatoes.   The most serious injury is due to the habit of pulling or digging up seed sweet corn after it has been planted.   The farmer who is looking for high prices for early sweet corn must suffer considerable loss if he has to replant several times so that the corn gets into the market too late to give him the advantage of high prices.   The late J. L. Ellsworth, former Secretary of the Massachusetts Board of Agriculture, estimated that he lost $600 in one season by such depredations.   The tomato crop on a small farm is sometimes considerably reduced by pheasants which peck the fruit.   The birds rarely dig up and eat potatoes, though they eat the green shoots of the plant in spring.   I have known but one case where they destroyed half a bushel of potatoes.   Peas are sometimes attacked.   Impartial investigations show, however, that the good done by the pheasants among crops overbalances the depredations committed.   Miss A. F. C. Eveshed investigated the food of pheasants in England for years.   She found, after an examination of 303 crops of pheasants, that the principal damage was done to grain, but that while the grain taken in the fields was only 10.69 per cent of the food (and much of this was waste grain picked up in the stubble), insects composed 16.41 per cent, and the fruit and seeds of weeds composed about 20 per cent, the other food being rather neutral in character.   She concluded that: "On the whole the balance seems decidedly in favor of the pheasant."

The eminent English economic ornithologist, Dr. Walter E. Collinge, who quotes Miss Eveshed's conclusions, examined the contents of the stomachs of 188 birds, and tabulated them in 1913.   After four years' further study of the species he finds that his later investigations confirm his first results, when he said that "apart from their value as game, they merit the protection of all interested in agriculture." [1]   In the investigations made by the Massachusetts Commission on Fisheries and Game in 1914, wardens were sent to farms where complaints of injury originated, and were instructed to kill pheasants in the act of destroying crops.   Even under such circumstances the contents of 17 pheasants' stomachs submitted to the Biological Survey for observation showed that tomatoes and corn made up 27 per cent of the food, while weeds and insects totaled 37 per cent.   The remaining items were practically neutral.   The conclusion arrived at by the Commissioners was that as a rule pheasants were more beneficial than injurious, and that where substantial injury was done upon farms by these birds, fostered and pro-

---

[1] Reprint from the Journal of the Land Agents' Society, June, 1917, p. 5.

tected by the state, the farmers should be reimbursed therefor. Outside of their utility as destroyers of insects the tribe of pheasants is one of the most important economically. Most of our domestic poultry belongs in this family, and as game birds and as food there are no more valuable birds in the world than the pheasant family. The amount of money expended in their pursuit in many countries is enormous, and in New England the rearing and sale of pheasants must become eventually an important industry.

FAMILY **TETRAONIDÆ**. GROUSE, SPRUCE PARTRIDGES, PTARMIGANS, ETC.

Number of species in North America 14 ; in Massachusetts 4.

Birds of this family are larger than those comprising the so-called American quails and smaller than the pheasants. The head is feathered, excepting usually a bare strip over each eye. The legs are more or less fully feathered, sometimes to the toe tips. The toes when naked are provided in winter with horny fringes or comb-like processes (pectinations). The tail is variously shaped, but never folded as in pheasants, never very long, and composed of 16 to 22 feathers. The sides of the neck often have tufts of feathers, either elongated or modified into ruffs, or bare skin capable of distension, or both. Birds of this family lack brilliant plumage such as is seen in most pheasants. The colors usually are inconspicuous and harmonize with their surroundings. The flight is rapid and often noisy, though seldom much protracted, and most of the members of the group undertake no extended migrations. The family contains about 25 species, scattered through the northern hemisphere, and is well represented in North America.

ECONOMIC STATUS. Among the grouse are some of the most prized game birds of the world, and most of them do little injury to crops or trees.

Canachítes canadénsis cánace (LINNÆUS). Canada Spruce Partridge.

Other names: SPRUCE GROUSE; SPRUCE PARTRIDGE; SWAMP PARTRIDGE; HEATH HEN.

Plate 34.

DESCRIPTION. — Head not fully crested, but crown feathers capable of erection into a slight subcrest; no feathered appendages on neck; a distensible naked colored patch over each eye, which when fully distended in the breeding season is bright red with a comb-like appearance; tail rather short, somewhat rounded, of 16 broad feathers; legs feathered to toes which grow pectinations in autumn and shed them in spring. *Adult male:* Forehead black or blackish, with small white spot on each side and another slightly below and before eye; elsewhere above marked with irregularly crescentic bars of black and gray, often with tawny or rusty tinge on back and wings; a few white shaft-streaks on scapulars, broadening toward tips; tail black, its tip barred rather broadly light rusty or orange-brown, this often narrowly margined and tipped black; chin and throat chiefly black (which usually extends up under eyes), bordered more or less completely and narrowly with white; lower neck and breast black, many feathers on sides of breast rather broadly tipped white; sides and flanks variegated with brown, black and white, the white mostly in broad shaft-streaks; abdomen and under tail-coverts black and white, tail-coverts with broad white tips; wing linings and axillars brownish-gray, the larger lower wing-coverts more grayish, and axillars and some of wing-coverts with white shaft-streaks and white tips; bill dark gray or blackish; iris brown; feet dusky. *Adult female:* Quite different in color from male except for white shaft-streaks on scapulars, sides and flanks; mostly barred above with irregular bars of black, gray and tawny or rusty; tail irregularly barred rusty and black, a broad terminal rusty bar, with each rusty feather-end margined and tipped very narrowly black; black and buff barring predominate on upper breast, and black and white on lower breast and abdomen. *Young in first winter plumage:* Similar in each sex to that of adult of same sex, but perhaps a trifle duller, black areas not so solidly black and white, edges broader. *Young in juvenal plumage:* Both sexes resemble adult female but somewhat duller in color, browner above, rustier on crown, neck and breast, whiter on chin and upper throat, and pattern of flank feathers different. *Downy young:* Buffy, darkening to brown above and lightening to brownish-yellow or "pale straw yellow" below; some dusky spots and stripes on head and rump; a rusty patch on top of head, bordered black.

MEASUREMENTS. — Length 15.00 to 17.00 in.; folded wing 6.50 to 7.00; tail 3.75 to 5.00; bill from nostril .40 to .45; tarsus 1.10 to 1.50.

MOLTS. — Juvenal plumage gradually succeeds natal down, wings being developed first; a complete or nearly complete postjuvenal molt (August and September) is followed by first winter plumage; two outer primaries are not shed until postnuptial molt in next autumn, after which young birds become as adults; in some cases there may be limited molting chiefly about head and throat during first spring when bird assumes first breeding plumage; adults have complete postnuptial molt (August) and some individuals may have a limited prenuptial molt about head in spring, sometimes beginning in February.

FIELD MARKS. — *Male:* Slightly smaller than Ruffed Grouse; recognized by barred black and gray upper plumage and black and white under plumage. *Female and young:* Brownish, barred black and brown above where Ruffed Grouse is *spotted* and mottled.

VOICE. *Immature male:* A low wailing whistle, *weeo-weeo-weeo.* *Female:* When disturbed with young, *kruck, kruck, kruck, kr-r-r-uck,* almost incessantly (Brewster); also a cluck like that of Ruffed Grouse, but "hoarser and rougher."

BREEDING. — Chiefly in swampy, coniferous woods. *Nest:* On ground, usually at foot of tree or under bush, well concealed; made of twigs, leaves and grasses. *Eggs:* 8 to 16, usually about 12; 1.68 to 1.90 by 1.18 to 1.26 in.; long oval; color variable, usually deep buff, spotted and speckled with varying browns; purplish-brown and burnt sienna often occur. *Dates:* May 24 and early June, Maine; June 2, Nova Scotia. *Incubation:* Period 17 days (Bendire); by female. One brood yearly.

RANGE. — Wooded regions of Canadian Zone of central eastern North America from southern Manitoba, southern Ontario, southern Quebec and New Brunswick south to northern parts of Minnesota, Wisconsin, Michigan, New York and New England and in Nova Scotia. Breeds throughout its range; accidental in Massachusetts.

DISTRIBUTION IN NEW ENGLAND. — *Maine:* Uncommon to rare resident locally in Somerset, Franklin, Oxford, Knox, Piscataquis, Penobscot, Waldo, Hancock and Washington counties, very rare or wanting in southern Maine; less uncommon but local in Aroostook County. *New Hampshire:* Not uncommon resident locally in northern part of Coos County, uncommon farther south in that county, and rather rare above 3,000 feet in the White Mountains south to Mt. Passaconaway. *Vermont:* Uncommon to rare resident in northernmost parts. *Massachusetts:* Formerly accidental. Records: Gloucester, bird recorded September 1851, by S. Jillson;[1] Roxbury, bird shot in November, prior to 1869.[2]

HAUNTS AND HABITS. In the dense spruce, fir, cedar and tamarack swamps of the great Maine woods the Spruce Grouse dwells. Where giant, moss-grown logs and stumps of the virgin forest of long ago cumber the ground, where tall, blasted stubs of others still project far above the tree-tops of to-day, where the thick carpet of green sphagnum

[1] Putnam, F. W.: Proceedings of the Essex Institute, Vol. 1, 1856, p. 224.
[2] Allen, J. A.: American Naturalist, Vol. III, 1870, p. 636.

moss deadens every footfall, where tiny-leaved vinelets radiate over their mossy beds, there we may find this wild bird as tame as a barn-yard fowl. In the uplands round about, there still remain some tall primeval woods of birch and beech and rock maple where the moose and bear have set their marks upon the trees. In winter the deer gather in the swamps, and there their many trails wind hither and yon. Gnarled, stunted trees of arbor vitæ, some dead or dying, defy the blasts of winter, while the long, bearded Usnea droops streaming from their branches. Black-capped Chickadees, Brown-capped Chickadees and Red-breasted Nuthatches curiously gather about the intruder.

One day in early September while following a trail through such a swamp which borders Sandy Stream, and hurrying to reach camp before dark night closed down, we almost stumbled over a male Spruce Partridge standing in the trail. The bird was somewhat startled and flew heavily up into a near-by spruce, alighting near the tip of a little limb about 20 feet from the ground. As the limb drooped under his weight, he walked up it to the trunk, hopped up a branch or two higher, and immediately began to feed on the foliage. After a few minutes of this he moved a little into another tree and continued feeding. Pounding on the trunk with an axe did not alarm him, and it was only after several sticks had been thrown and one had hit the very limb on which he sat that he was induced to fly.

The Canada Spruce Grouse is disappearing from the inhabited regions of northern New England, although it holds its own fairly well in some of the wilder tracts. It is a bird of the Canadian Zone, and may have been a casual visitor long ago to some of the mountains of western Massachusetts, but as there are only two records of its occurrence within the limits of the state, and as the spruce growth such as it frequents has nearly all been cut, probably it will not occur here again. It is a forest recluse, much more arboreal than the Ruffed Grouse, confined rather closely to spruce, larch and cedar swamps and thickets in densely wooded regions, though found also among firs, hemlocks and other trees and on higher, dryer lands, but rarely in open meadows or clearings.

It is said to be non-migratory, but as it occurs in winter in swamps in the southern part of its range where it is not found or seldom found in summer, there may be some southward migration in autumn. Often it is so unsuspicious that it may be killed with a stick or captured by means of a noose on the end of a pole. Young birds have been taken by hand when sitting on a limb, and the little chicks may be picked up from the ground. After much persecution, however, the few survivors become more cautious. Many escape notice by retiring to dense coniferous thickets and refusing to fly unless almost trodden upon.

The male in courtship struts about with the red comb-like patches above the eyes distended, breast feathers ruffled, wings lowered and tail up-raised and spread; he drums also, making a sound somewhat like the more rapid part of the drumming of the Ruffed Grouse, but less loud and resonant. This sound is produced by the wings, which beat upon the air with quick nervous strokes, while the bird is fluttering up ten or fifteen feet into a tree, or flying down from a branch. He has been seen to drum also while climbing the leaning trunk of a tree, while hovering in the air, and while merely flying up or down to or from the top of a stump. The usual flight of an unhurried Spruce Grouse is rapid and comparatively noiseless. The bird has been seen to start up silently from the ground and to drum during the latter part of the flight, and occasionally he drums when leaving the ground, but stops before the flight is completed. When this grouse is flushed suddenly from the ground, the sound of the wing-beats resembles that made by the wings of the Ruffed Grouse under similar circumstances, but is not quite so loud.

The female bravely defends her nest. Mr. E. O. Grant tells of finding a nest with only two eggs left and with many feathers of the mother scattered about, but she was still on the eggs. The next day another egg was gone, but the brave bird was still holding the nest and incubating her one egg. The enemy was supposed to have been a skunk. Mr. Grant says that when he has knelt upon the ground and imitated the squeal of the young bird, the mother has flown directly at his head. Wet weather in May and early June is fatal to most of the young birds. Like the young of the Ruffed Grouse, they are extremely susceptible to wet and cold.

Ordinarily this grouse is seen singly or in small groups, rather smaller than those of the Ruffed Grouse. Some of the earlier writers told of the former abundance of this bird. Mr. Manly Hardy said, according to Bendire, that a "pack" of many thousands was utilized by a tribe of Indians in Nova Scotia to "feed the whole village."

The food of the Spruce Grouse consists largely of wild berries in late summer and autumn and of shoots, foliage and buds of spruce, larch and fir in winter. It is fond of insects and eats many, including grasshoppers, in spring and summer, and also parts of low-growing plants. The young are said to subsist mainly on insects and spiders. Dr. C. W. Townsend says that in July in Canadian Labrador the Spruce Grouse was eating curlew berries, snowberries, the leaves of blueberry and the seeds of sedges.[1]

ECONOMIC STATUS. In winter when the Spruce Partridge feeds chiefly upon the "spills" and buds of coniferous trees, its flesh becomes bitter and unpalatable. It may be of some economic service in the forest in summer because of the large number of insects that it destroys.

Bonása umbéllus umbellus (LINNÆUS). Ruffed Grouse.

Other names: PARTRIDGE; "PATRIDGE"; PHEASANT.

Plate 35

DESCRIPTION. — Head crested; a wide, partially concealed ruff of about 30 feathers on each side of neck, capable of erection, the skin beneath them naked; tarsi rather sparsely feathered above, naked below; toes with deciduous pectinations, shed in spring; tail normally of 18 square-tipped feathers, longer than in Canada Grouse and much more barred; very variable, with two distinct color phases, the red and the gray. *Adult male:* Top of head with many narrow bars or spots of rusty brown, black and sometimes whitish; rest of upper plumage mottled and variegated rusty brown and whitish or buffy, with some black marks; inner secondaries and wing-coverts commonly edged or tipped buffy-whitish, often spotted with black; primaries dark brownish-gray, marked and spotted with buffy or whitish on

---

[1] In Audubon's Labrador, 1918, p. 226.

PLATE 35

PLATE 35

RING–NECKED PHEASANT
Page 15

HEATH HEN
Page 39

ADULT MALE

ADULT MALE

RUFFED GROUSE
Page 26

ADULT FEMALE

ADULT MALE

All about one-fourth scale.

Louis Agassiz Fuertes

narrow outer webs; back and rump with numerous oblong or lance-shaped pale, black-edged shaft-spots; neck ruffs usually black with green and purplish reflections, in some cases reddish-brown; tail bright reddish-brown to gray, barred regularly with from 6 to 11 narrow blackish bars and one broad subterminal black bar; chin and throat buff, lower and lateral feathers often tipped dusky; wing linings and axillars brownish-gray and white; rest of lower plumage whitish, grayish-white or buffy-white, usually tinged buffy on lower neck and breast, with many bars of deep buff, brown or black, all darkest on sides and flanks, often fading and obscure on breast and belly; buff and white predominate on under tail-coverts; bill dark brown; iris hazel; feet dark horn. *Adult female:* Similar but duller, with somewhat lesser ruffs and shorter tail; iris, bill and feet as in male. *Juvenal plumage:* Sexes practically indistinguishable; similar to that of adult female but browner, with barring usually paler, not so distinct; chin and often upper throat white or whitish; outer webs of flight-feathers wider, more mottled, ruffs wanting. *Downy young:* Chestnut-buff above, variegated with paler buff, paler on top of head; a black line behind eye, sometimes interrupted; below pale buff or pale yellow, brightest on chin, with faint brownish band on lower neck.

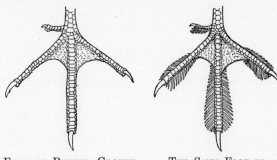

FOOT OF RUFFED GROUSE IN SUMMER THE SAME FOOT IN WINTER

MEASUREMENTS. — Length 15.50 to 19.00 in.; spread 22.00 to 25.00; folded wing 6.90 to 7.50; tail 5.50 to 7.00; bill from nostril .50 to .53; tarsus 1.50 to 1.60. Weight 16½ to 27 oz. (B. H. Warren). Male said to weigh rarely 29 oz. Female smaller than male.

MOLTS. — Juvenal plumage slowly replaces natal down (June to August); flight-feathers develop very early; tail-feathers come later; this plumage quite fully developed when bird is not more than three-fourths grown; first winter plumage acquired by postjuvenal molt (September) complete except outer primaries; slight prenuptial molt about head in spring, when bird becomes practically a breeding adult. Adults have prenuptial molt about head and throat in spring (most extensive in males), and complete postnuptial molt in autumn.

FIELD MARKS. — Largest brown, native, ground-bird of woodlands in southern New England; sudden spring from ground with extremely noisy whirring flight is characteristic; female Ring-necked Pheasant resembles it somewhat in flight, but has longer, more pointed tail, and when rising in flight its wing-beats are slower and not so loud; drumming of male is distinctive.

VOICE. — Squirrel-like chitterings and snickerings; a low, soft *coo-coo-coo-coo*, reminding one of the subdued murmuring sound which muskrats make in early spring; call of female to young *crut-crut-car-r-r-r* (William Brewster); also various subdued clucks and a wild squeal or whine when attacking an enemy in defense of young; common alarm note *quit quit*.

BREEDING. —Usually in wooded uplands, but sometimes in low damp woods. *Nest:* A shallow depression in soil, lined chiefly with dead forest leaves, often in a dense thicket or at foot of tree, and usually concealed by log or logs, overhanging leafy plants, shrubbery or low tree branches, very rarely in trees, in abandoned nests of Crows. *Eggs:* 7 to 14; rarely 15, 16 or 17; 23 found in one case; 1.26 to 1.65 by 1.00 to 1.30 in.; ovate; whitish to dark cream, pale pinkish-buff or pale brown, sometimes faintly and finely spotted or blotched with darker shades of ground color or with reddish-brown. *Dates:* April 1 to late July, southern New England; eggs commonly found in May. *Incubation:* Period 24 days; by female. One brood yearly; small young have been seen as late as September 14.

RANGE. — Eastern United States, from southern Minnesota, southern Wisconsin, southern Michigan, southern New York and southern Massachusetts south to eastern Kansas (formerly northern Arkansas),

Missouri (rarely), Tennessee and Virginia, and in the Alleghanies to northern Georgia and northern Alabama.

DISTRIBUTION IN NEW ENGLAND. — Typical birds of this race occur on Cape Cod and Marthas Vineyard and in southern Connecticut. Elsewhere in New England most of the birds found are intermediates between the two races in numerous variations or else typical Canadian Ruffed Grouse.

SEASON IN MASSACHUSETTS. — Permanent resident.

HAUNTS AND HABITS. How quickly memory leaps athwart the years to the day long ago when as a child I flushed my first "Partridge." I can see now those dim and windless woods at break of day. The woodland songsters were awake and tuneful, and the woods rang with the staccato notes of the Oven-bird, when I started little bunny from the undergrowth. As I sprang forward hoping to catch the furry thing, a large bird, whose thundering pinions seemed to fill the air with their sudden breath-taking roar, rose almost beneath my feet and sped away through flying leaves and bending twigs into the shadowy recesses of the forest. My heart seemed to stop beating as I stood amazed, while little Molly Cottontail made good her escape.

An old cock grouse treading his native forest floor is a sight to gladden the eye. Can you not see him? There, near the foot of that great white birch! He stands erect, his raised ruffs with their dark metallic sheen glistening in a ray of sunlight that sifts in through the tree-tops. With crested head erect and carried high, with bright and banded tail held clear and widely spread, he turns, pauses, listens, now turns again, throws forward his proud head, and steps lightly along, raising his feet well up, moving over the inequalities of the ground with a gently undulating motion, his broad tail raised or lowered at will, his dark wild eye flashing on all around; his frame instinct with electric life and vigor drawn from rugged New England hills. A perfect full-winged bird he stands, decked in his nuptial plumage, ready for love or war. Now his keen senses have detected the presence of his chief enemy, man. With a quick flirt of wings he has slipped over a low stone wall and is gone — hidden in friendly, sheltering thickets. This grouse is the king of New England game birds, and doubtless has no superior among the grouse of the world.

In my early days the grouse often lay close and rose almost under foot, but now many of them have learned caution by sad experience and rise farther and farther away. When the country was first settled, this bird was one of the most tame and unsuspicious of the fowls of the air. It was known as the "fool hen." It was so tame that many were killed with stones or knocked over with sticks. They were then fair game for the small boy. Forty-five years ago in the wilderness I saw birds of this species that walked boldly up to within a few feet of the hunter, or even sat on a limb just over his head. An occasional unsophisticated bird may be seen now even in southern New England that will seek human companionship, and even allow itself to be picked up and handled, but such birds are rare and usually are short-lived. Where they are hunted, the survivors have become "educated," and they resort to all kinds of tricks to escape the hunter and his dog.

The Ruffed Grouse often out-guesses the sportsman by swinging behind a tree as it flies off, by lying close until he has passed or by doubling back on its trail and then escaping behind his back. It may run quietly away and rise beyond gunshot. To befool man and dog it may fly into a thick pine tree, or it may leave the woods and alight far out in a pasture while the sportsman and his dog search the thickets in vain. A hard-pressed bird has been known to go into shoal water, apparently for concealment. Mr. L. Barber tells us that a grouse that was startled by his dog alighted in the water. She was entirely under water except her head which was covered by a projecting bush.[1] Mr. W. L. Bishop writes that he killed a Goshawk near a brook, and afterward discovered by traces on the snow that the hawk had been pursuing a Ruffed Grouse. He found the frightened bird in the brook entirely submerged with the exception of its head. Though the Ruffed Grouse seems to drink mostly the dew and raindrops from the leaves, it is not afraid of water, and if winged over water can swim fairly well.

When frightened and in full flight this grouse seems reckless. It does not, like the Wood Duck, so control its movements as to avoid the twigs and branches of trees, but dashes through them. I have seen one in such a case strike bodily against a limb and fall to the ground. This bird had been fired at in a neighboring wood, and had crossed the open with tremendous speed to another wood where it struck the limb. Aside from the shock the bird was unhurt. Mr. Albert A. Cross of Huntington sent me a Ruffed Grouse that in full flight had collided with the forked and broken end of a dead limb, driving one of the prongs three inches into its breast and the other into its vitals, and tearing the head and neck from the body. Often in autumn (the so-called "crazy" season) the swift flying birds dash against houses or through windows, and some have been known to go through the glass of moving motor cars or trolley cars and even into locomotive headlights. So careless are they of obstructions that a high wire fence around a covert is likely to kill all the Ruffed Grouse within its confines. From September to November, whether hunted by man or not, some of them rush wildly about from place to place by day or by night. At this time they may be found in the most unlikely places, and some individuals kill themselves by striking against buildings far from the woods. This mad desire to get away somewhere, to fly into strange places, may be due to an inherited instinct of migration. Mr. Ernest Thompson Seton says that it is a trait of the young birds, which they exhibit during the first season and sometimes in the second, but never afterward. Dr. A. O. Gross found that three birds which had been killed by flying against obstructions were infected by internal parasites, and he suggests the possibility that the irritation caused by such parasites may be the initial cause of the "crazy" behavior commonly observed.

The Ruffed Grouse is a woodland bird. It may at times go far afield, but almost always it keeps within easy reach of cover. The rocky wooded hills of southern New England are its favorite summer home. In winter it seeks shelter in valleys and swamps under the protection of thickets or coniferous trees.

In early spring the drumming of the "Partridge" is one of the every-day sounds of the forest or thicket, although it is said to have been heard in every month of the year and

---

[1] American Sportsman, Vol. IV, 1874, p. 203.

in every hour of the day and night. It is less common in autumn than in spring, and in winter is very rarely heard. The deep toned *thump, thump, thump,* like the muffled beating of a great heart, followed by a quickly accelerated, drumming roll, like far-distant thunder, is produced by the wings, and probably by the concussion of swift blows upon the air, although the wings seem to strike against the feathers of the breast. The bird stands erect on log, stump, fence, mound or rock, with ruffs more or less raised and spread and tail trailing behind. The wings are raised quickly until they almost come together over the back and then are struck forward until they nearly touch the breast. The drumming is not produced by striking the wings together over the back, as such a contact would make a sharp crack like that heard when the wings of a domestic pigeon come together in this way. The sound seems pervasive and ventriloquial. Sometimes it appears to be more plainly audible at a distance of half a mile than when heard near-by. Often it is exceedingly difficult to locate the drummer, but if the observer can find the drumming log, he may be able to approach the bird while it drums. However, he must be very quiet between times, as the bird is very watchful while on the drumming log, except during the act of drumming. My friend, the late Charles E. Bailey, one of the best woodsmen I have ever known, has actually sat on one end of a log while the "Partridge" has drummed on the other. This drumming has to do with the mating season; it denotes virility and combativeness. Then, it is at once a call to the female and a defiance to rival males, and often results in a meeting of the sexes or a fight between two cock birds. At other seasons the action is mainly an expression of the extreme vitality and vigor of the male, though the bird has been known to copulate in autumn.

There is some evidence of polygamy in the relations of the sexes, as more than one female has been seen to come to a drummer and accept his caresses.

In the mating season the male often struts like a turkey-cock with wings lowered, head and neck drawn back, and tail, crest and ruffs raised high. The ruffs and tail are then fully spread — the tail a perfect fan, the two ruffs almost encircling the neck and merging into one. The female also, under excitement, sometimes struts in the same way, although her ruffs are smaller and less conspicuous. After mating, the female steals away and makes her nest, apparently hiding it from the male, whose behavior if he finds it is said to resemble that of the traditional "bull in a china shop." On stormy days the female sits closely; but during continuous severe weather she must leave at times to get food. Ordinarily she is absent from the nest for hours at a time, but this does not seem to affect the vitality of the eggs, except during cold storms.

The incubating female often covers the eggs with dead leaves when she quits the nest, if not too suddenly startled. This is done in some cases, when the bird is hurried, by quickly sweeping leaves over the eggs with the wings or feet; * often the bird when not hurried picks up leaves and lays them gently on her back and tail, and then rises, moving

---

*Mr. J. A. Farley tells me of a grouse's nest that he found in 1925 in Prescott, Massachusetts, where the hen went off her eggs with the usual burst of speed and without a second's delay; yet she succeeded in covering her eggs so carefully and so completely that at first no nest was suspected, and the eggs were only found by brushing away the leaves. Just how and when she did it is a matter of conjecture.

Fig. 38. — Nest and Eggs of Ruffed Grouse

Courtesy of William C. Adams, Director Division of Fisheries and Game, Massachusetts Department of Conservation

Page 27

Fig. 39. — Ruffed Grouse on Nest

forward, so that the leaves slide down her back and off her tail, thus covering the eggs. Some individuals apparently do not cover the eggs at all, especially if the nest is well concealed under protecting foliage, or if the bird is startled so suddenly that there is no time to conceal the eggs.

Like the eggs and young of all ground-nesting birds those of this grouse are subject to the attacks of any prowler of the woods. Occasionally a wandering cat finds the nest, steals on the mother bird at night and makes a meal of her. Once I saw a skunk eating the eggs in a nest while the bird fussed about in an ineffectual attempt to drive him away. The fox also is an unwelcome visitor. It seems probable that the bird on her nest gives out no scent, and that when a dog or a fox finds it, the brute merely stumbles upon it as humans often do. Dr. C. F. Hodge assured me that both pointer and setter dogs which he utilized in a test could not find the sitting bird, and quite often a nest situated near the den of a fox is unmolested, though foxes kill and eat grouse whenever they can catch them, as the feathers around their burrows and the traces left on the snow in winter plainly testify.

Mr. Farley tells me that he once found a grouse's nest "chock-full of eggs" at the foot of a medium sized white pine, where there was no cover whatever, and a Sharp-shinned Hawk's nest with five eggs at a moderate height above in the same tree. In climbing the pine he had to take care not to step in the grouse's nest, and from the hawk's nest he could look straight down into the nest on the ground and see the ten eggs therein. He says that he could easily have dropped the hawk's eggs down into the nest below.

When the eggs are hatching as well as when the young are very small and unable to fly, the mother on the approach of danger simulates a crippled condition, and attempts to lead the enemy away in futile pursuit of herself, while the little ones, if out of the shell, scatter and hide beneath the undergrowth or the dead leaves on the ground.

Mr. C. E. Bates says that a grouse flew at him in this way, passed him and turning, ran directly between his feet and back into the undergrowth. Mr. C. W. Vibert relates that a small boy wandering about in a tobacco field was attacked by a Ruffed Grouse. The men in the field heard the boy cry out in fear, and looked up to see him running wildly across lots and "yelling at the top of his voice," with the old grouse at his heels. The venerable Governor N. S. Berry, of New Hampshire, used to tell a similar story of some little boys in New Hampshire who came out of the woods once with a terrible tale of the awful creature that had suddenly attacked them. An investigation revealed a "hen partridge" and her chicks.

Mr. C. E. Ingalls, writing of an experience at Templeton, stated that he saw a fox approaching the nest of a Ruffed Grouse near the edge of the woods. "A big ball of feathers," writes Mr. Ingalls, "flew out at that fox and drove him some distance into the grassland." The fox, nevertheless, returned to the attack only to die in his tracks by a well directed bullet from the rifle of the watcher, not, however, until the brute had filled both mouth and throat with egg contents from the nest of the devoted mother.

When all goes well, the young remain for a short time in the nest, then at the call of their parent they leave it, never to return. They roam through the woods, scattering about, picking up insects from ground and foliage and drinking dewdrops from the leaves. The mother accompanies or follows them with head held high, alert for any enemy that may be creeping upon their trail. Thus they travel wild and free, but never go very far from the place of their nativity. When they become wet or chilled, the mother gathers them under her wings, and broods them quietly on the forest floor under the sighing trees. At evening she settles down, wherever night overtakes her, and calls them to her to sleep. If during the day she hears some faint suspicious sound near by, she coos very gently to the young as if to attract their attention. They seem to disregard the cooing; but if she discovers an approaching enemy, she utters a quick warning cry, and in an instant the young are hidden; they dart into near-by cover or creep under the dead leaves on the ground. Sometimes, if not greatly alarmed, the mother will strut before the intruder with fan-like tail raised high, and ruffs and crest erect, crying and clucking to attract the attention of the enemy to herself; she may act like a wounded bird to tempt the intruder to pursue her, or she may merely run away squealing loudly. Her behavior at such times is very variable. Once I saw a fracas between the ordinarily inoffensive rabbit and a grouse hen, defending her chicks. She "bristled up" and struck at bunny, but he apparently tried to leap upon her. In the ensuing running fight he drove her about a rod. Her chicks having hidden in the meantime, she then flew away. Very rarely, when the young are in danger, the male bird appears and takes his turn at running toward and strutting near the intruder, and he has been known to care for a brood after the death of the mother bird. When all danger is passed, the mother calls and assembles her brood and leads them quickly away. The young usually seem to keep silent but sometimes utter a piping cry. The little wings grow rapidly, and after the first week the chicks can flutter short distances. In ten days the wings are quite well developed, and soon, under favorable conditions, the chicks will fly 50 to 100 yards.

In June, 1904, rains continued to fall much of the time for about two weeks. This rainfall so raised the Musketaquid that the meadows were flooded, and the eggs and young of many birds were destroyed. For some time I had been watching three broods of Ruffed Grouse in the woods along the river, and one of these broods had been reduced to a single chick. On the 20th this grouse and her chick came to the cabin that I occupied. The mother halted within about twenty feet of the window, but the young bird "crying" plaintively came on, accompanied by a Song Sparrow. This sparrow attended the chick wherever it went, either hopping or running along with it on the ground or keeping near it on low branches. The chick could fly readily, but in its flights it was always accompanied by the attentive sparrow. At a slight sound in the cabin the mother became suspicious, and retired behind the log-built woodshed whence she took a path leading up the steep hillside at the rear. When she had reached a point on the hill that was higher than the roof of the shed, she called the young bird which immediately flew up to the front corner of the shed, alighting on the end of one of the logs and from there fluttered up to the roof from which it rejoined its mother on the steep hillside above. The Song Sparrow accompanied it on every step of its journey. For fifteen minutes while the birds were in sight, the sparrow never left its little companion, and the mother grouse seemed to take the escort as a matter of course. The two little birds wandered about together, going where they pleased, but always responding to the call of the mother. The Song Sparrow may have lost its brood in the freshet and found consolation in the company of its little companion.

In warm days the grouse hollows out saucer-shaped depressions by the roadside or in some dry, dusty place in the wooded upland, and resorts to these places for dust-baths to rid itself of vermin. As the summer wanes and wild fruits and seeds develop, the young birds change their diet from insects and succulent green vegetation to fruits and seeds. Late in August, if not before, the old male may join the flock, which now consists of four to twelve birds. As autumn comes on, they frequent the vicinity of oak and chestnut trees, hazel bushes, wild apple trees and wild grape vines to feed on the fruit. Then comes the hunting season, when the birds are driven and scattered far and wide among the hills. They are now putting on their snow-shoes — growing the pectinations on both sides of each toe which so broaden the sustaining surface of the feet that the snows of winter will better bear their weight.

During summer and autumn they have learned to roost high in the trees, but with the coming of snow and cold they stay on the ground at night under shelter of low branches, and in storm and darkness allow the snow to cover them. Later, as the snow grows deeper, some fly and dive directly into and under it at nightfall, thus leaving no trail. In this snug shelter they pass the night. Even here, however, the prowling nocturnal fox sometimes finds them and catches them unawares by a swift pounce and a plunge into the drift, where his tracks and the feathers of the victim tell the tale. Sometimes a hard crust forms over the snow at night and imprisons the birds beneath the surface, but their strength and endurance usually enable them to break out; again, a crust may form in the daytime and thus shut the birds out from their sleeping quarters. Then they sleep on the surface, beneath the low and sheltering limbs of spruce, hemlock, pine or juniper, often in a hole hollowed in light snow, fallen on the crust. Here again the crafty fox sometimes surprises the sleeping bird. Some of these birds drop into the soft snow and pass the night in snug depressions made by their bodies, from which by raising the head they can see an approaching enemy. I have seen the Ruffed Grouse dive into soft snow on a winter day to escape pursuit. In such a case it sometimes emerges in full flight after having passed for several feet under the snow. I once found a small cave in the rocks where several of these birds had sought shelter on winter nights, feeding on sumach berries near by.

The Ruffed Grouse is a hardy bird. It can withstand extreme cold and privation, and can subsist if need be on twigs and dead leaves. The stomach seems to digest the bark off the twigs, leaving them white and bare. In very severe winters with heavy snow crusts when the trees for long periods are covered with ice, some of the weaker birds may succumb, but ordinary winters have no terrors for them. Their pectinated toes serve as snowshoes to bear their weight on the lightest crust or on packed drifts.

The Ruffed Grouse is not known to migrate far, though some local movements in numbers have been noted. Their seasonal movements are mainly those of individuals which wander about after the breeding season, and of others that nest on the mountains and come down into the valleys on the approach of winter. Otherwise they are supposed to pass their lives near the place of their nativity, except when forced to move for lack of food.

The species has decreased much in numbers since the country was settled. Practically it has disappeared from the Dakotas, Kansas, Arkansas, and Missouri, and parts of some of the older northern states. This is due in great part to the increase in the number of hunters, the improvement in firearms, the extension of railroads and highways and the increase of motor cars; but the destruction of the forest, the use of woodlands for grazing purposes, and the prevalence of forest fires, all have had much to do with the decrease of this bird. Forest fires in spring kill many females on their nests, and at any season of the year great fires seem to attract the grouse, as they have been seen to fly directly into the burning woods.

The Ruffed Grouse has periodical seasons of decrease, due probably to a combination of adverse conditions. Among the primary causes of periodical scarcity may be named, first, long, cold rains in late May or early June which starve, chill and destroy the tender young; next, a dearth of rabbits and grouse in the fur countries, which always causes an unusual winter influx from Canada of hawks, owls and other enemies of grouse. Internal parasites, external parasites (such as ticks or blood-sucking larvæ), contagious intestinal diseases, pulmonary mycosis and tuberculosis, all have been named as contributory causes, but there is little known regarding the conditions which bring about these extreme reductions of the race.

This grouse has been bred to the third generation in confinement, and becomes as tame as the most confiding domestic fowl; but as a commercial undertaking the breeding of forest grouse in confinement has never been profitable.

The food of the Ruffed Grouse in spring and summer consists very largely of insects and young growing plants. Tender grass is eaten freely. Perhaps the plant most sought after in the New England coastal region is the cow-wheat, a low growing plant with small white blossoms which thrives almost everywhere that this bird is found. Ruffed Grouse in confinement are so fond of it that they eagerly eat quantities of it, consuming the entire plant, root and branch. Edible mushrooms are taken eagerly. Fern leaves which remain green in swamps under the snow of winter are eaten then as well as at other seasons. The grouse is extremely fond of grasshoppers, locusts and crickets, and often seeks them in their season in fields and meadows near the woods. Ants, beetles, cutworms and other caterpillars, also bugs, including leaf hoppers and tree hoppers, are eaten.

The Ruffed Grouse is known to eat in winter many leaves of sheep laurel, *Kalmia augustifolia*, and mountain laurel, *Kalmia latifolia*. These leaves have poisonous properties, and there are tales of serious poisoning resulting from eating the flesh of the birds. Dr. J. Somers describes how he suffered the well-known symptoms of such poisoning as a result of eating a grouse that had fed on laurel foliage.[1] Such poisoning, however, seems to have been caused long ago and only by birds taken in winter. It is illegal now to kill them at that season.

The following list of the vegetal food of this grouse, largely compiled from a Biological Survey Bulletin by Dr. Sylvester D. Judd on the Grouse and Wild Turkeys of the United States, was given in the volume entitled "Useful Birds and Their Protection," issued by the Massachusetts State Board of Agriculture. As this publication is now out of print, the insertion of the list here may serve a useful purpose for those who desire to increase the numbers of this fine game-bird. *Nuts or Seeds:* Hazelnuts, beechnuts, chestnuts, acorns. Seeds of tick trefoil, hornbeam, vetch, hemlock, pitch pine, maple, blackberry, lily, beggar's ticks, chickweed, sheep sorrel, sedges, violet, witch-hazel, beech drops, avens, persicaria, frost weed, jewel weed. *Buds, Blossoms or Foliage:* Poplar, birch, willow, apple, pear, peach, alder, hazel, beech, ironwood, hornbeam, blackberry, blueberry, spruce, arbor vitæ, Mayflower, laurel, maple, spicebush, partridge berry, sheep sorrell, aster, green ovary of bloodroot, clover, purslane, wood sorrel, yellow sorrel, heuchera, chickweed, catnip, cinquefoil, buttercup, speedwell, saxifrage, live-forever, meadow rue, smilax, horsetail rush, azalea, false goat's beard, dandelion, cudweed. *Fruit:* Rose hips, grapes, smooth sumac, dwarf sumac, staghorn sumac, scarlet sumac, poison ivy, partridge berry, thorn apple, cockspur thorn, scarlet thorn, mountain ash, wintergreen, bayberry, blackberry, huckleberry, blueberry, cranberry, sarsaparilla berries, greenbrier, hairy Solomon's seal, smooth Solomon's seal, black raspberry, raspberry, domestic cherry, cultivated plum, wild black cherry, wild red cherry, elder, red elder, black haw, nannyberry, withe rod, maple-leaved arrow wood, high-bush cranberry, mountain cranberry, snowberry, feverwort, black huckleberry, black alder, flowering dogwood, bunchberry, cornel, silky cornel, pepperidge, mulberry, bittersweet, manzanita, barberry, Virginia creeper.

Those who wish to bring about conditions favorable for the increase of the Ruffed Grouse may do so by planting or protecting fruit-bearing plants from the above list.

ECONOMIC STATUS. As a game bird the Ruffed Grouse is an exceedingly valuable asset to New England. Its insect food is such that it must be classed among the useful species. Its one fault from the viewpoint of the fruit grower is its tendency to destroy the buds of fruit trees. Where Ruffed Grouse are numerous, considerable loss to the fruit crop may result. Maynard tells us that at one time a bounty of 25 cents a head was offered for these birds in certain Massachusetts towns. He also says that he took 180 apple buds from the crop of a bird that he shot at ten o'clock in the morning.[2] Many more buds have been found in crops of birds taken earlier in the day or at evening when

---

[1] Proceedings and Transactions, Nova Scotian Institute of Natural Science, Vol. VI, 1886, pp. 81–84.
[2] Maynard, C. J.: The Birds of Eastern North America, 1896, p. 232.

they have finished their last meal.   Mr. Charles Hayward reports that he found in the crop of a grouse 140 apple buds, 134 pieces of laurel leaves, 28 wintergreen leaves, 69 birch buds, 205 blueberry buds, 201 cherry buds and 109 blueberry stems.   Another bird had 610 apple buds in its crop and a third had more than 300.   Weed and Dearborn found in the crop of a female Ruffed Grouse 347 apple buds, 88 maple buds and 12 leaves of sheep laurel.[1]   During the winter of 1922–23 and the succeeding winter considerable injury was done by grouse to orchards in several northern states and in Canada, west to British Columbia.   The two summers had been hot and dry, producing much less wild fruit and seeds than usual, thus reducing the natural food for grouse, and the birds had bred well and were abundant.   The damage in New Hampshire during the first winter was estimated at $5,000.   Doubtless when grouse become abundant, considerable injury may be done to the fruit crop of orchards near woods.   Mr. Wilfred Wheeler, former secretary of the Massachusetts State Board of Agriculture, informed me in 1923 that at Hatchville in Falmouth the grouse absolutely denuded of buds a wild apple tree in the woods so that it died, and I have heard from farmers and orchardists very many complaints of injury done to their trees.   However, in ordinary years when the grouse are not very abundant, probably their budding is more beneficial than injurious to the trees. It must be borne in mind that many apple trees in New England that grow near woods are wild and worthless.   For twenty years one or two birds customarily "budded" on an apple tree near my farmhouse window.   This tree seemed to be their favorite, but notwithstanding the "budding," or because of it, the tree bore a good crop of large apples nearly every year, while other trees not "budded" by the grouse often bore none.   Apparently the thinning of the buds by the birds was a benefit to the crop.   Mr. William Brewster had a similar experience at his farm at Concord.   To sum up — the Ruffed Grouse is useful by reason of its appetite for destructive insects, invaluable as a game bird and practically harmless except when unduly numerous.

Bonasa umbellus togáta (Linnæus).   Canada Ruffed Grouse.

Other names: NORTHERN RUFFED GROUSE;   PARTRIDGE;   BIRCH PARTRIDGE.

DESCRIPTION. — Like Ruffed Grouse but averages a little larger, distinctly darker and usually grayer above, with more black in upper plumage, in most cases, and less reddish, especially on upper back and back of neck where *umbellus* always appears "sandy"; brown markings below very conspicuous, usually heavier and more distinct.   Has a red and a gray phase as in *B. u. umbellus*.   This bird is almost identical with *umbellus* but can be distinguished from it by comparison (red-tailed birds are not considered as typical *togata*).   There is a slight (average) superiority in size and a difference in shade which have induced ornithologists to regard it as a northern race; weight may average greater than in *umbellus*, running rarely up to 2 lbs.   Sequence of molts and plumages, voice, field marks and breeding as in *umbellus*, except that the eggs may average a little larger.

RANGE. — Canadian Zone of North America from James Bay south to northern Michigan, central New York, northwestern Connecticut, northern and western Massachusetts, Vermont, New Hampshire and Maine, and in mountains south to North Carolina; "birds indistinguishable from the eastern form

---

[1] Birds in Their Relation to Man, 1903, p. 226.

occur from east central British Columbia south to eastern Oregon and central Idaho" (A. O. U. Check-list, 1910).

DISTRIBUTION IN NEW ENGLAND. — Common resident throughout most of Maine, New Hampshire and Vermont, in wooded regions, and south through the mountains of western Massachusetts and north-western Connecticut; in southern New England, many intermediates between *umbellus* and *togata* may be found, most of them approaching *togata* in coloration.

SEASON IN MASSACHUSETTS. — Permanent resident.

HAUNTS AND HABITS. Deep in the Maine woods a long ridge slopes steeply down to a gentle stream where trout break the still surface and where the beaver builds its house. The rotting wrecks of forest trees are strewn along the ledges, their great gnarled roots flung high where the storm winds have thrown them. Beside these symbols of decay there springs the perennial life of the earth. From the forest floor rises a new wood of little spruces and firs, interspersed with dainty wood plants; seedlings spring up even from the tops of moss-grown stumps and logs. Thus from the primitive richness of the earth the forest ever renews itself. Great trees of birch, beech and rock maple stand guard over all. They have secured a firm foothold by clasping their clinging roots around great rocks and thrusting them down deep into the crevices of the ledge.

Here in the forest shades a Canada Ruffed Grouse, "quitting" softly, runs up the face of the ridge, pauses to look back, and then disappears in the deeper shadows.

Near the summit of Mt. Greylock, Massachusetts, picturesque wrecks of old spruce trees burned by fire, seared and scarred by lightning and broken by ice storms still stand defying the winter gales that sweep the mountain, their tops high above the thickets. The undergrowth is composed largely of northern shrubs and dwarfed trees such as the moosewood and mountain maple. There in the shelter of the thickest shrubbery we shall find this grouse. In these shades nearly three thousand feet above sea-level, it finds a safe retreat. In summer we find this bird often on the higher elevations. In winter it may retire into the lowlands, but it makes no extended migrations. The Canada Ruffed Grouse is really the typical forest grouse of New England, as it occupies the greater part of the territory, and haunts regions similar to those occupied by the Ruffed Grouse, but it is more typical of the Canadian faunal region, and is found commonly in most of the forested region of northern New England.

Its habits and food are similar to those of the Ruffed Grouse, but it feeds to a greater extent on the foliage, seeds and fruit of northern plants and on northern insects.

ECONOMIC STATUS. See under Ruffed Grouse, page 35.

Lagópus lagopus lagopus (LINNÆUS). Willow Ptarmigan.

Other names: WILLOW GROUSE; WILLOW PARTRIDGE.

DESCRIPTION. — Bill short and convex; tail rather short, somewhat rounded, normally of 14 feathers; tail-coverts very long, the two longest reaching end of tail; legs and feet densely feathered to toe tips; a red comb over each eye. *Adult male in breeding plumage:* Head and all foreparts chestnut, orange-brown, or reddish-cinnamon, becoming more tawny on back, scapulars and rump, with many indistinct whitish feather-tips; barred sparsely on foreparts and more closely and heavily on back, scapulars and rump with black, where the feathers also have heavy black shaft-streaks; lesser and median wing-coverts much like back; rest of wing mainly white, but outer surfaces of shafts of some outer primaries blackish; breast and sides usually darker below; middle of belly, region about vent, and under tail-coverts white; bill blackish; iris brown. In the far north, adults retain considerable white in summer, some males having dark feathers only on head, neck and tail. In Greenland the males are said to remain white all summer. *Adult female in breeding plumage:* Similar but more tawny or paler than male, irregularly marked with black.

WILLOW PTARMIGAN

Summer   Winter

Adults in winter (sexes alike): Entirely white except outer surfaces of several primary shafts and tail which are blackish, tail tipped white, the blackish ordinarily concealed by long white tail-coverts; legs and feet so heavily feathered as to resemble those of northern hare. *Young in first winter plumage:* Similar to adults, except that some birds may retain some brown feathers. *Young in juvenal plumage:* Somewhat resemble female but smaller; primaries chiefly grayish-brown (except two outer which are white) sometimes speckled dull black toward end; tail dark brown, barred reddish-brown and narrowly tipped white. *Downy young:* Rusty brown or olive-buff above, mottled with black; head, back, wings and rump striped with same; crown chestnut, edged black; below sulphur-yellow, or pale buffy, deeper on fore neck and upper breast.

MEASUREMENTS. — Length 14.00 to 17.00 in.; folded wing 7.00 to 8.00; tail 4.90 to 5.50; bill from nostril .40 to .45; tarsus about 1.50.

MOLTS. — Molt of natal down is completed when young bird is about half grown, and juvenal plumage is assumed; then, apparently, a double molt taking place (August and September), in many cases gives bird a mixed brown and white plumage (abdomen, flanks and feet always white); this is succeeded by molt into white winter plumage; this is worn until April when prenuptial molt takes place (April to June) and bird takes on first nuptial plumage; double molt occurs (July to September) succeeded by adult winter plumage. Adults have similar double molt.[1]

FIELD MARKS. — Near size of Ruffed Grouse, with shorter tail; when seen in the United States in winter or early spring is white or largely white.

VOICE. — Male, a crowing or barking note, also a sound similar to the Indian word "*chŭ-xwan*" repeated several times (L. M. Turner); a series of notes like *kû-kû-kû-kû*, and a hard rolling *kr-r-r-r* (E. W. Nelson).

BREEDING. — On higher parts of Arctic tundra, in Barren Grounds, and in wooded and mountainous regions. *Nest:* A hollow in ground or moss, lined with a few leaves or feathers and stalks of grass, often among dwarf brush or sedge. *Eggs:* 6 to 15, rarely 16 to 20; 1.15 to 1.35 by 1.60 to 1.85 in.; ovate to elongate ovate; deep reddish-cream with conspicuous confluent blotches of dark purplish-brown or other shades of brown which sometimes cover entire surface. *Dates:* Late May to middle July in various parts of Arctic America. *Incubation:* Period probably about 24 to 26 days; by female. One brood yearly.

RANGE. — Arctic regions. In North America breeds from northern Alaska, northern Banks Island and central Greenland south to central Mackenzie, southern Keewatin and southern Ungava (Quebec), also south in the mountains to west central Alberta and central British Columbia; migrates south in winter to southern Alberta, southern Saskatchewan, central Ontario and southern Quebec; accidental in North Dakota, Montana, Wisconsin, Michigan, New York, Massachusetts and Maine.

---

[1] Condensed from a description of the molts of ptarmigans given by Dr. Jonathan Dwight in The Auk, Vol. XVII, 1900, pp. 147–159.

NOTE. The above range includes that of *Lagopus lagopus ungavus* Riley, to which race some or all New England ptarmigans may be referable.

DISTRIBUTION IN NEW ENGLAND. — Accidental spring visitant. Records: *Maine:* Kenduskeag, bird taken April 23, 1892.[1] *Massachusetts:* Manchester, bird taken May 10, 1859,[2] and now in collection of Essex Institute, Salem.

HAUNTS AND HABITS. Ptarmigans are dwellers in Arctic wastes or high mountain ranges where Alpine conditions prevail. The Ptarmigan is a bird of the snow — white as the snow itself in winter. When it desires to rest during the day, it scratches a hole in the snow as a refuge from the cold wind. At night, to get shelter from the storm, it flies down into the snow and sleeps there. It is a bird of great vitality, of strong and swift flight. It has been known to distance a pursuing Goshawk. In autumn many birds of this species leave their breeding grounds and fly south for hundreds of miles. No one knows how far they can fly without resting, but many of them cross Great Bear Lake and Great Slave Lake, though some are unable to make the passage and are drowned on the way. In these winter migrations a straggler here and there reaches the northern United States, but these are mere accidental wanderers, venturing far south of the main body of their kind. These Ptarmigans, like the northern hare, change color with the season, becoming white in winter and brown in summer. In the transition stages when the snow occurs more or less in patches on the ground, their plumage looks like patchwork.

In the northern summer they feed on berries, foliage and insects. Mr. Edward A. Preble gives leaves of wild rosemary and a small vetch, catkins of dwarf birch, blueberries, crowberries and the fruit of *Andromeda polifolia* as a part of their summer food.[3] In winter they subsist largely on the twigs of willows, alders and other shrubs and in the spring they eat the buds of willows, birches, alders, poplars, mountain ash and other trees or shrubs, also grass, insects and spiders.

ECONOMIC STATUS. Willow Grouse often gather in immense "packs" after the breeding season. They are killed then in large numbers by northern peoples and form a part of the staple food supply of the scattered population of the fur countries.

Tympanúchus cupído (LINNÆUS). Heath Hen.

Other names: HETHEN; EASTERN PINNATED GROUSE.

Plate 35.

DESCRIPTION. — Head with a slight crest; sides of neck with tufts of rather loose erectile elongated feathers, one on each side, beneath which is a tympanum or sac of loose, naked skin, capable of great inflation and when distended resembling half of a very small orange; legs feathered to toes; tarsi bare behind; toes webbed at base; tail short, rounded, normally of 18 broad feathers; sexes nearly alike. *Adult male:* Above light reddish-brown, variegated with irregular blackish-brown or dull black marks

---

[1] Merrill, Harry: Auk, Vol. IX, 1892, p. 300.
[2] Coues, Elliott: Proceedings Essex Institute, Vol. V, 1868, Communications, p. 289.
[3] North American Fauna, No. 27, 1908, pp. 342–343.

which form irregular bars on back and wing-coverts; scapulars tipped white; chin, throat and cheeks buffy; cheeks marked with dark brown or dusky spots; a dark brown stripe running from base of bill below eye across upper ear-coverts; below rusty whitish or whitish, heavily barred dark reddish-brown; general color much like that of Prairie Hen but rustier and more strongly marked underneath; neck tufts of 3 to 5 sharp-pointed, long, narrow feathers; flight-feathers brownish or dusky drab, spotted either buffy or whitish on outer webs; under wing-coverts marked brown and white, axillars white, sparsely spotted brown; neck sac bright yellow or orange when inflated, often edged with pink; tail colored like flight-feathers, but unspotted and with whitish tip; under tail-coverts conspicuously white, with some marks of rusty and dark brown or dull black; iris hazel; "bill horn brown; feet yellow" (C. E. Hoyle). *Adult female:* Similar to male, but neck tufts very short, neck sacs rudimentary and tail-feathers dark clove-brown, with many light brown or rusty bars; bill and eye as in male; feet brownish-orange above, the under sides brownish-yellow. *Young in juvenal plumage:* Similar to female but smaller and neck-tufts lacking. *Downy young:* Mottled above with rusty brown and large spots of dull black, with several small spots of black on top of head and one or two behind eye; below bright yellowish.

MEASUREMENTS. — Length 15.00 to 18.00 in.; spread 26.60 to 29.00; folded wing 7.93 to 8.75; tail 3.75 to 5.00; tarsus 1.63 to 1.75; bill .55 from nostril, .70 from feathers. Weight about that of Canada Ruffed Grouse, or somewhat heavier.[1] Female slightly smaller than male.

MOLTS. — According to Dr. Dwight juvenal plumage is acquired very early, and postjuvenal molt begins before young birds are half grown; succeeding first winter plumage is acquired by complete molt and closely resembles that of adult; there is partial prenuptial molt about head, and in spring young bird assumes first nuptial plumage; after complete postnuptial molt young in the next autumn become as adult; adults have partial molt about head in spring and complete postnuptial molt in autumn.

FIELD MARKS. — Somewhat larger than Ruffed Grouse, but tail shorter and more rounded; male in mating season often holds tail erect showing white under tail-coverts, lowers wings, and with head and body thrown forward, raises neck tufts, shows "round orange" neck sacs, and "toots" (see Fig. 39). In flight rises gradually with wing-beats less noisy than those of Ruffed Grouse, and alternately flutters and sails like Meadowlark, sometimes flying several hundred yards; rarely seen in woods.

VOICE. — Male, "when in air emits peculiar cacaphonous call or cackle which when heard at a distance gives the impression of a hearty burst of laughter" (G. W. Field); female, in flight, a cackling call; young chicks, a peeping or piping call. See also page 47.

BREEDING. — On sandy plains covered with a low growth of shrub oaks and other shrubbery, with scattering pitch pines. *Nest:* On ground, a depression lined chiefly with leaves. *Eggs:* 6 to 10; 1.25 to 1.27 by 1.72 to 1.75 in.; ovate; yellowish-green or creamy yellow with a greenish tinge, unspotted. Illustrated in Bendire's "Life Histories of North American Birds," Vol. I, Plate III, Fig. 2. *Dates:* May and early June. *Incubation:* By female.

RANGE. — Formerly southern New England from Cape Ann or southern New Hampshire along the seaboard, including Long Island to Pennsylvania, New Jersey, Maryland and probably Virginia; now confined to Marthas Vineyard and in danger of extinction.

SEASON IN MASSACHUSETTS. — Resident throughout year; most conspicuous in March and April, in mild, pleasant weather.

HISTORY.   The Eastern Pinnated Grouse, or Heath Hen, probably was formerly an eastern race of the Prairie Hen, but as all intergrading birds in the region between Massachusetts and the west have been destroyed, leaving no connecting link between the two races, it has been regarded as a distinct species.[2]   Dr. A. O. Gross who has examined most

---

[1] Wilson says that specimens have been taken up to three pounds in weight but I find no corroboration of this statement.
[2] Brewster, William: Auk, Vol. II, 1885, pp. 80–84.

of the specimens in American Museums believes the bird to be entitled to subspecific distinction only. We have no very definite information regarding the former geographical distribution of this bird. The bird described by Linnæus in 1758 was said to have come from "Virginia." It may have been taken there, as the late C. S. Wescott of Philadelphia spoke of it as having occurred (according to tradition) "in Maryland and Delaware, on the shores of Chesapeake Bay, and on the peninsula of Maryland and Virginia." [1] Mark Catesby included this bird in his "Natural History of Carolina, Florida, and the Bahamas" (1826). Audubon was told that the species was found at Mars Hill, Maine, and also on the island of Mt. Desert, but the bird now known at Mars Hill under the name of Heath Hen seems to be the Canada Spruce Partridge. It is possible that the species may have been found in some part of Maine, as we know that the Prairie Hen thrives in the Canadian Northwest, but there is no good evidence to that effect. There is no authentic account of the Heath Hen in Maine, although the southwestern corner of the state may have been included in its range. Belknap (1792) said that the Grouse, a bird larger than the Ruffed Grouse or Partridge was "rare" in New Hampshire. Probably he referred to the Heath Hen. It is believed to have bred formerly from Cape Ann, Massachusetts, or southern New Hampshire along the Atlantic seaboard in Connecticut, New York (Long Island chiefly), New Jersey and Pennsylvania, and may have extended south through Delaware and Maryland to northern Virginia. Alexander Wilson in his biography of the "Pinnated Grouse," quotes from a letter of Dr. Samuel L. Mitchell, who describes fully and interestingly the habits of the Heath Hen. Wilson says it always avoids the woods. That part of its history which follows is taken from one of my former works, written in 1910:

"Many early American writers speak of this bird, and it is designated by some of them as the 'grous,' 'pheisant,' 'Heathcocke' or 'Heath Hen.' Thomas Morton in his New English Canaan (1632) says of the 'pheisants' that they are formed like the Pheasant Hen of England, and that they are delicate meat, 'yet we seldome bestowe a shootte at them.' Wood in his New England's Prospect (1629–34) says, 'Heathcockes and Partridges bee common; hee that is a husband, and will be stirring betime, may kill halfe a dozen in a morning.' Nuttall (1834) states that according to Governor Winthrop this Grouse formerly was so abundant on the bushy plains in the neighborhood of Boston that laborers and servants stipulated in agreements with their masters that they should not have it 'brought to table oftener than a few times in the week.'

"As the Heath Hen is not primarily a forest bird, the settlement of the land and the clearing away of the forests favored its increase, and had it been properly protected it might have been plentiful now in southern New England; but this was not to be. In early times it probably was confined mainly to the more open lands along the coast and to the river valleys; but the settlers cleared land and sowed grain and grass, thereby adding largely to its feeding grounds and increasing the supply of seeds and insects. This naturally would have increased the numbers of the species; but it was pursued, trapped,

---

[1] Grinnell, George Bird: American Game Bird Shooting, 1910, p. 211.

and shot at all seasons; the young were destroyed by dogs and cats, and thus the Heath Hens soon were reduced in numbers and driven to dense thickets which hunters and dogs found it difficult to penetrate. In such regions this grouse persisted in considerable numbers until the nineteenth century. It never has been adequately protected by law until recent years, for, although some States passed laws for its protection, such laws rarely were enforced. Nuttall (1834) asserts that it is still met with in New Jersey, Long Island, Marthas Vineyard, and at Westford, Conn. Peabody (1839) states that it is found in Massachusetts only on Marthas Vineyard and one small island near it, and the same year Lewis rated it as 'very rare and almost extinct in the northern and middle states; but within a few years quite abundant in portions of Long Island. . . . A few,' he says, 'are still found on the Jersey Plains,' and 'every year we hear of the extermination of a small pack.' Giraud states (1844) that on Long Island it is very nearly if not quite extinct, and that occasionally it is seen near Schooly's Mountains, New Jersey, and in Pennsylvania and Kentucky. According to William Dutcher the last specimen recorded from New York was killed in the Comac Hills in 1836. Turnbull (1869) says, 'It is now very rare; a few are still met with in Munroe and Northampton Counties, Pa.; within the last year or two it has been found on the Jersey plains.'

"The Heath Hen seems to have been exterminated earlier in the neighborhood of Boston than elsewhere; but Brewster quoting notes of a conversation with Mrs. Eliza Cabot, states that the assertion is made that Mrs. Cabot saw a 'prairie grouse' in Newton in her youth (probably about the beginning of the nineteenth century), and another (on Cape Cod), after her marriage (probably about 1812). Judd, in his history of Hadley, quotes the statement of Levi Moody of Granby to the effect that the Heath Hen had not been seen on the plains of Springfield for about fifty years. This would fix the date of its disappearance from that part of the Connecticut valley at about 1812 or 1813. Dr. Timothy Dwight published the statement in 1821 that the Grouse was no longer common in New England. Between that date and 1840 it disappeared from the mainland of Massachusetts. Audubon (1835) quotes Mr. David Eckley, who says that 'fifteen or twenty years ago' it was common to see as many Heath Hens in a day on Marthas Vineyard 'as we now see in a week.' The Heath Hen was introduced by the Forbes family on the island of Naushon where it was not native, and it soon disappeared. About 1888 Mr. E. H. Thompson told me that he had seen the species in his early days at Falmouth, on the mainland, and that his father killed two, which were preserved and presented to Col. E. B. Stoddard of Worcester. Mr. William Brewster, however, believes that these birds were introduced Prairie Chickens. In 1876 Minot asserted that the Heath Hen was found no more on Naushon and probably was extinct on Marthas Vineyard. Subsequent inquiry proved that it was still extant. In 1877 foxes and raccoons were introduced on the island and probably helped to reduce the numbers of the Heath Hen. Brewster estimated in 1890 that there were from one hundred and twenty to two hundred birds on Marthas Vineyard, left over from the previous winter. Mr. C. E. Hoyle asserts that in 1892-93 men who had watched the birds closely stated that they had decreased seventy-five per cent during the previous few years. Since then the species narrowly has escaped extinction. In 1894 a fire swept over practically all the breeding grounds, and Mr. Hoyle states that in the fall of that year he spent two weeks going over the ground, and found the skeletons of many birds destroyed in the fire; that where he had started a hundred birds the previous fall, he failed to start five. He says that in 1897 he again went over the ground with a good bird dog and did not start a bird. Since then the foxes and raccoons are believed to have been exterminated. In 1902 three specimens of the Prairie Chicken (*Tympanuchus americanus americanus*) were liberated on Marthas Vineyard, but whether or not they survived is not known. A fire swept over the breeding grounds in 1906 and very few birds were reared that year; but, under protection, the birds have increased slowly. On May 2, 1907, the Commissioners on Fisheries and Game could find only twenty-one birds on the island. On January 11, 1908, the number was between forty-five and sixty.

"The history of legislation to protect the Heath Hen is interesting. I have found no record of any laws or regulations regarding it in any town or city, or in the Commonwealth generally, until 1831, when it had become very rare if not extinct on the mainland. Then the Legislature passed a special act to protect it *during the breeding season only*, from March 1 to September 1, with a penalty of *only two dollars*. Under this act the Heath Hen had been nearly, or quite, exterminated from the mainland, when in 1837 a close season of four years was declared, with a penalty of two dollars and a forfeit of the same sum to the landowner. This close season was extended five years more in 1841, but these acts permitted any town to suspend the law within its own limits by vote of any regularly called town meeting. Some towns took advantage of this, *thus nullifying the law in the only towns where the birds still existed*. On May 6, 1842, for example, the Tisbury town meeting voted to allow the townspeople (hunting without dogs) to take, kill or sell Grouse or Heath Hens from December 1 to December 10. In 1844 the close season was extended for five years more; but the birds evidently had decreased in their last stronghold on Marthas Vineyard, for on April 1, 1850, the town of Tisbury voted to suspend the law so as to allow hunting only on the '12th and 13th of November next.' In 1855 all protection was removed, but for five years the Heath Hen existed without it. In 1860 it was protected again by law at all times; but in 1870 the period of protection was limited to five years. Thus, under periodical juggling of the statutes, the species managed to exist, protected most of the time until the year 1907, when Mr. John E. Howland of Vineyard Haven, finding it in imminent danger of extinction, agitated the question of establishing a Heath Hen reservation. Owing to the cordial and energetic coöperation of Dr. George W. Field, chairman of the Massachusetts Commission on Fisheries and Game, a protector was located in the breeding grounds of the birds. Dr. Field secured contributions from public-spirited citizens for the purchase of land for a reservation. The towns of Tisbury and West Tisbury contributed to the good work and the sum of $2,420 was collected. A bill was introduced into the Legislature by Representative Mayhew of Marthas Vineyard, placing under the control of the Commissioners on Fisheries and

Game such lands as might be leased, given or otherwise acquired for the purpose, and authorizing the commissioners to take not more than one thousand acres in the name of the Commonwealth.   The bill was advocated by the Audubon Societies and sportsmen's organizations, and was passed with an appropriation of two thousand dollars for carrying out its provisions.   The commissioners soon secured sixteen hundred acres, by donation and purchase, which has now (1911) been increased to over two thousand.   Fire stops were made, the birds were guarded carefully and fed, and by the year 1909 they had increased in number to about two hundred." [1]

With special care the future of the species in its island home now seemed assured. From that time the numbers of the Heath Hen, fluctuating, increased slowly, until in April, 1916, I was satisfied by personal observation that there were at least 800 of these birds on the Island, and Mr. William Day, the superintendent of the reservation, who has charge of their protection, estimated that there were then about 2,000.   An unsuccessful attempt was made to introduce the species on Long Island, New York, and Dr. John C. Phillips attempted a similar experiment at Wenham, Massachusetts, but this also failed.

In May, 1916, a great fire swept practically the entire interior of Marthas Vineyard, and though it was checked on the Heath Hen reservation, a large part of that was burned over.   This fire destroyed the natural cover and food of the birds over most of their habitat.   Many of them were consumed in the fire, and the rest were scattered about over the island, wherever they could find food.   During the succeeding autumn great flights of Goshawks and other hawks came down from the north.   These hawks killed some of the surviving Heath Hens.   In the spring of 1917 less than 100 Heath Hens could be found. The breeding season of 1917 was cold and rainy, but in April, 1918, 155 birds were accounted for.   They continued to increase and in 1921, 414 were located, but that year the breeding season was exceedingly cold and wet and in 1922 only 117 birds could be found. Heavy rains occurred during the breeding season of 1922 and later a few full-grown Heath Hens were found dead and dying, apparently diseased, and after that until 1925 the decrease of the species was progressive.   In 1923 there seemed to be not more than 50 birds.   In 1924 the number seemed to have decreased still more.   In April, 1925, it was difficult to find any.   I saw but four birds during a stay of three April days on the island and heard none.   Dr. Alfred O. Gross saw but three during a longer stay.   During the breeding season only three broods were reported.   In June some very heavy rains occurred on the island, and after that no young birds were seen.   Mr. McLeod, the Federation Warden, who goes over the region daily, told me September 25 that he had seen but three birds.   The species then seemed on the verge of extinction.   The Federation of Bird Clubs of New England, realizing this condition, raised a fund to assist in protecting the few birds remaining, and in 1926 it was reported that there probably were about 50 birds on the island.

The protection of the Heath Hen by the Commonwealth has been continued since 1911.   Ever since then a superintendent has been kept on the reservation in a dwelling

---

[1] Game Birds, Wild-Fowl and Shore Birds, 1912, pp. 385–390.

provided for him by the Commonwealth. Land has been cultivated and clover, grass, sunflowers and grain have been grown especially for the birds. After the great fire of 1916, a fire tower commanding a view of the island was erected on the highest ground of the reservation, and the Department of Conservation has kept a watcher there during times of fire danger. Many natural enemies of the Heath Hen have been killed, and the reservation has been guarded against poachers. Mr. William C. Adams, Director of the Division of Fisheries and Game, of the Massachusetts Department of Conservation, informs me that up to April 30, 1925, the Commonwealth had expended $56,912.07 in the attempt to save the species from extinction, but now, even with the assistance given by the Bird Clubs, its future seems problematical. If, however, we accept the account of Mr. C. E. Hoyle, the situation in 1897 was even more hopeless and the birds, notwithstanding, increased afterward.

HAUNTS AND HABITS. If the accounts of early writers are trustworthy, the Heath Hen always has inhabited bushy plains, and they dwell on such plains now on the Island of Marthas Vineyard, where they rarely are seen in the woods. Several more recent writers assert that they are forest birds. Much of the region on Marthas Vineyard which they now inhabit was once covered with a forest growth. Old residents affirm that lumbermen worked there within the last century. Lumbering and fire destroyed the forests, but since then repeated fires have burned away the soil and kept down the tree growth, so that the entire region now supports only shrubbery and a few stunted trees. The growth is largely bearberry, chinquapin and shrub oaks, with some stunted oaks of other species and scattered pitch pines. The scrub varies from two to six feet in height.

The Heath Hen may possibly have been to some extent a forest bird when the forest was intact. If so, it has since changed its habits. This seems unlikely, however, as the Ruffed Grouse has not done so. It still inhabits the wooded parts of the island and avoids the shrubby home of the Heath Hen. Mr. Hoyle says that the Heath Hens are driven to the woods by deep snow sometimes in winter, where they eat acorns; but usually the shrub oaks on the plains will supply them with acorns. From their chosen breeding-places in the scrub they sally out in spring on the farms, where they frequent grassy fields or cultivated ground. The following account was written by me in 1918 from notes taken in 1916, when the Heath Hens were abundant on Marthas Vineyard:

"A wide plain covered with diminutive leafless shrubby oaks and low bushes, with stunted pines showing here and there; to the west low rolling hills; to the south on the far horizon the wide Atlantic; such is the prospect on an April morning from the fire tower on the plains of Marthas Vineyard where the few remaining Heath Hens now make their last stand. Here in the gray dawn a strange, weird sound fills the air. It swells and dies upon the ear, but never rises or falls, and becomes intermittent or ceases only when the sun rides up the sky. Apparently it is not a vocal effort. It is neither whistle nor call; there is no other sound quite like it in nature. One might imagine it the

wail of the wind spirit, but no man understands just what it is or how it is made.*
We know only that it emanates from strutting, dancing heathcocks, and is one of their
customary mating sounds. Heard from a distance, borne on the sea wind, it swells to
the fullness of a grand undertone, mingling with the ordinary nearer sounds of the rolling
plain. Like the trilling of the toads in a million pools, like the morning chorus of bird
song on a thousand hills, it is a vital, virile expression of the fecundity of old Mother
Earth. It is a rune of reproduction, foretelling the renewal and multiplication of the
species in the coming spring awakening. It is a pæan of hope and joy, a forerunner of
the pulsating, vigorous life of summer.

"No satisfactory explanation has been advanced regarding the means by which this
sound is produced. As we listen to its volume the wonder grows; fifty birds seem to
make noise enough for a thousand, and this they do apparently without opening their
mouths or using their vocal organs. The sound may be heard under favorable conditions
for about two miles. Some future investigator may solve the riddle of its production.

"The most remarkable and interesting habits of this bird are those of the mating season. These are not unique, as other American grouse give more or less similar manifesta-
tions of the mating instinct, but they are worth going far to see. My opportunities for
watching their mating antics have been all that could be desired. Some of my observations have been made from a blind raised about two feet above the surface of the ground
so that the birds could pass not only all about but underneath, and they not infrequently
alighted on top of the blind, thus affording chances to view them from all directions.

"The male birds begin to 'toot' and strut about four o'clock, or even earlier on bright
mornings. Many gather on certain open fields or cleared spots that have served as their
assembling places for many years, and there the dance goes on apace until about seven
o'clock, when it begins to subside, and the birds scatter. The 'tooting' however may be
heard at intervals during the day. Again toward sundown there is another gathering
that lasts until the dusk of evening. My observations, therefore, have been made early
in the morning, or toward sunset, and were possible only through the courtesy of the
Massachusetts Commissioners on Fisheries and Game and their superintendent on the
reservation, Mr. William Day.

"In April, 1917, I went to the reserve in Company with Mr. A. C. Bent. On April
25, at three in the afternoon, I entered a 'blind' in a cornfield where the birds were accustomed to dance and where corn had been thrown out to attract them. The standing
corn had been cut and removed, providing an unobstructed view. At first no heath hens
appeared. Red-winged blackbirds came and alighted on the blind, then descended and
fed on the corn. A robin came, and it was interesting to listen to the timbre of its well-
known notes at a distance of less than three feet. At 4 : 40 the first heath hen appeared,
and soon the show began, but no bird came very near the blind until about five o'clock.
Then for an hour the dance went on all about me until the superintendent appeared. This

---

* Since the above was written Dr. A. O. Gross has described in his report on the Heath Hen the manner in which (as he
believes) the sound is produced.

FIG. 40. — HEATH HEN CHICK

From a mounted specimen, Courtesy of William C. Adams, Director Division of
Fisheries and Game, Massachusetts Department of Conservation

Page 40

Photograph by Dr. George W. Field

FIG. 41. — HEATH COCK DANCING AND TOOTING

Courtesy of Mr. Adams

Pages 47–48

was the signal for the end of the performance. The day was clear, the light excellent, and all conditions for observation were of the best. Only four females came within my range of vision, but from twenty to twenty-five males were in sight constantly. Occasionally a female picked up a little corn, but the males did not feed. They seemed to be obsessed with their own antics and devoted themselves with great enthusiasm to the dance. This exercise consists of running, strutting, bowing, posturing, cackling, calling, flapping up and turning about in the air, and even fighting a little from time to time. All in all it is a great and exciting expression of the abounding energy of the species. While the male is dancing the body is inclined forward, the neck stretched out horizontally with the bill pointed downward, the plumage is fluffed, the tail erected and spread more or less, the wings drooping or partly spread downward but the lowest of the separated primary quills rarely reaches the ground. The pinnates, or 'necktufts,' are erected like rabbit's ears, or thrown away forward, over and in front of the lowered head, with the points together like an inverted V. In this position the bird inflates the orange air sacs on the sides of the neck, which sometimes show pinkish or flesh color around the edges, or even purplish at the upper edge, but look much like small oranges and are about the size of a tennis ball. In some cases they appear more triangular than round, but usually they seem globular when seen in profile, and project considerably on either side of the neck. The yellow combs over the eyes are enlarged also at the same time and become turgid, while the bird seems to increase in size. The white tips of the tail coverts show like the 'white flag' of a deer. With all his beauties thus displayed the heath cock is a handsome fellow, but seems bizarre and unbirdlike to human eyes.

"The booming or 'tooting' sound is produced, not when the air is expelled from the sacs, but while they are swelling, and stops then until they have been more or less deflated. It is not so deep and resonant as is that produced by the prairie chicken, and never resembles 'the distant croaking of bullfrogs or the grunting of buffaloes,' resemblances which Nuttall ascribes to the booming of the prairie chicken. It may be likened to the soughing of the wind, or the noise produced by blowing gently into a small bottle or phial, but is more musical. It is commonly a double *woo'-doo*, or at times a triple *oo-oo'-woo*, with the accent on the second syllable and all on the same pitch.* There is no perceptible final falling inflection, but it ends in the air like a Scotch ballad. Rarely the last note comes on a lower pitch than the others, and a few birds sound a deeper tone all through it, but most of them maintain the same pitch, and when forty or fifty are engaged in the dance a great volume of sound is produced lasting almost continuously for two hours or more. It has something of the quality of the subdued and distant echo of many medium pitched steam whistles. Above this can be heard a medley of vocal notes, some like the squeal of a frightened rabbit, some regular war whoops, such as *wooow* or *waugh*, others flatter, snarling calls given when two males are facing each other. There are many cackling and laughing sounds, some resembling those emitted by gulls, others

---

*The sound varies from time to time in pitch, number of syllables and accenting, but the general effect produced by a large number of birds is always the same.

those given by barnyard fowls. There are queer clucking and chuckling noises. The conversational character of some of these sounds recalls similar notes heard in more subdued tones from a flock of bob-whites. There are others resembling the whine of a puppy and one of the calls of a jay. Cooing also is heard, but no billing is seen. When close at hand the cries are more striking than the continued chorus of the 'tooting,' but at a distance of a mile or more, where the booming was plainly audible, only one of the louder vocal calls could be heard.

"The males danced much of the time while producing these sounds. The dance reminds one of similar performances by Indians. The bird bows or leans forward with muscles tense and rigid, lifting the feet stiffly but quickly and striking them down hard and very fast upon the ground, so that the sound may be heard for rods. Sometimes he stands in his place while dancing or merely wheels a little to right or left. Again he runs forward five or ten feet, or makes short rushes around the female in segments equaling about one third of a circle, sometimes circling her in three or four runs, but never seeming to approach very near her. I have never seen one caress or molest a female during these mating antics. How the happy pair perform when finally mated no one seems to know. The dancing is accelerated at the end until it somewhat resembles the quick tapping of a muffled drum, ending in a roll. This rapid stamping causes the whole body and especially the wings to quiver in unison with the drumming feet. The roll of the drumming can be heard continuously as it mingles with other sounds of the dance, but two hundred yards away it is inaudible. While dancing the male keeps the sacs, and the combs over his eyes more or less distended, but in the 'tooting' which usually precedes or follows the dance the sacs are fully inflated. They swell with each toot or syllable and contract more or less between each. I watched four birds perform thus at distances varying from five to eight feet. Audubon, experimenting with the prairie chicken, found that the bird could not produce the sound if the sacs were punctured. Evidently it is emitted in some way during the intake of the air.

"Sometimes a male seems to challenge all creation by flying up a few feet, cackling meanwhile, and turning to different points of the compass so that upon alighting he faces in another direction from that in which he started. Two males sometimes, after posturing, dancing and blowing on the way, charge toward each other for many rods as if urged by the frenzy of battle, and then squat on the ground facing each other, open their beaks, and utter a variety of cries, as if trying to intimidate each other or to muster up sufficient courage to fight. Sometimes one turns and runs away, or backs off, or they may fly at each other like domestic cocks, or one may leap over his opponent, or they may even flutter up a few feet in actual combat, but I never saw blood spilled in any of these contests. Often they strut, dance and toot without even offering to fight. Withal there is great excitement, constant sound and motion, each bird acting 'as the spirit moves,' and performing his part with ludicrous seriousness and self-importance. In the midst of all this commotion the females move about, calm and cool, apparently interested only in looking for something good to eat. Indeed they seem so unconcerned and indolent as to squat or lie down to eat corn rather than take the trouble to reach down and pick it up.

"As night comes on the birds become more quiet and gradually steal away into the shades. It is remarkable how quickly and silently they can disappear in case of an alarm. They can hide in stubble where it would seem difficult to conceal a mouse, but if flushed they fly swiftly, fluttering and sailing much after the manner of a meadow lark. In this way they can quickly cover a mile. A flock of fifty birds thus speeding across country is an inspiring sight. . . .

"When the downy young are hatched they are ready to follow the mother within a few hours, and she broods them under her wings wherever night overtakes her. They frequent dry and sandy plains and never have been seen to go to the water to drink or bathe. Probably they get what moisture they need from their food or from the dew or rain, but captive birds have been known to take water supplied to them. During the hotter part of the day they seek dusting places in the dry sand along the roads, where they wallow and work the dust into their plumage. They feed upon green vegetation, such as grass, buds, clover, and alfalfa, also on berries, acorns, grain, weed seeds, and insects. They seem to roost on the ground or in low shrubbery, but sometimes alight on trees, fences, and buildings."[1]

Apparently they pass the night either upon the ground or in small shrub oaks, though during the day they sometimes alight on the tops of shrubs, fences, or small trees, or even on the roofs of buildings. The young leave the nest and follow the mother about as do domesticated chickens. She broods them whenever they need it, and calls them under her wings at night. If suddenly startled with her brood she may fly off cackling, or, feigning lameness, may try to lead the intruder away, while the young squat on the ground, trusting to their protective coloration for concealment.

The Heath Hen seems fond of sorrel and clover, and may be found in early spring in fields where these plants grow. According to Mr. Hoyle, who has examined the crop contents of a considerable number of Heath Hens taken at all seasons of the year, their food in spring consists largely of tender shoots, blades and leaves, and many insects. In summer it consists largely of grasshoppers, crickets, other insects, and spiders. I have seen about 20 birds of this species following an invasion of army worms and evidently feeding on the worms. Sometimes they attack young sunflowers, eating almost the entire plant. Mr. Hoyle has found few berries except "wild cranberries" and cranberry leaves, "of which," he says, "they seem to be very fond." This so-called "wild cranberry" is the bearberry, *Arctostaphylos uva-ursi*, which is common on the Island. Probably the fruit of this plant is the one referred to by early writers on the food of this bird as "cranberries" or "barberries," as neither cranberries nor barberries grow naturally on the kind of soil frequented by the Heath Hen. In summer the Heath Hens eat blueberries and wild strawberries. In autumn they take some small grains and seem fond of

---

[1] Forbush, Edward Howe: The Heath Hen of Marthas Vineyard. The American Museum Journal, Vol. XVIII, 1918, pp. 279–285.

sunflower seeds.   I found the crop of one bird distended with 204 seeds of the giant Russian sunflower.   In winter they consume corn, bayberries, partridge berries, sumac berries, seeds of weeds and grasses, rose hips and acorns.   They also eat the buds of the pine and alder, and the remains of other unidentified buds and leaves have been found by people who have dissected the birds.   Heath Hens formerly gathered in large flocks in winter, and then at morning and evening they visited any open land where they could find grain or other food.   We have few data regarding the food of the young, but what we have indicates a large percentage of insects in the diet of the little ones.

ECONOMIC STATUS.   The Heath Hen formerly was an important game bird and furnished a great quantity of palatable food.   Its flesh was excellent until winter, when necessity compelled it to eat bitter acorns which imparted their bitter flavor to the flesh. There have been some complaints from farmers regarding depredations in their gardens. The crops attacked by the birds were beans, peas, beets, turnips and carrots (the tops of which were bitten off in the spring), strawberries and corn.   Beans were shelled and eaten by the birds when nearly ripe.   Most of the complaints regarding corn referred to corn on the ear.   The damage in all cases was small.

ORDER COLUMBÆ.   PIGEONS AND DOVES.

Number of species in North America 14 ; in Massachusetts 3; one of
these believed extinct.

The names pigeon and dove have exactly the same meaning, as they denote closely related birds and may be applied properly to any bird of this order.   The name Passenger Dove might be correctly applied to the Passenger Pigeon or the Mourning Dove might be as properly called the Mourning Pigeon, but for the excellent reason that the latter name is not customary.   All pigeons or doves may be known by their bills, which resemble somewhat those of plovers, as they have a convex horny tip and are somewhat contracted toward the middle, but unlike those of the plovers there is a tumid membrane at the base of the upper mandible in which the nostrils open.   The head is small, wings ample and strong, legs short, tarsus (partly feathered) scaled before and behind, sometimes on the sides, the front toes are cleft to base or with a slight membrane between the outer and middle toes and the hind toe is usually on a level with the front toes, fitting the birds for both arboreal and terrestrial life.   The plumage is strong and dense but easily detached from the tender skin.   Pigeons feed mainly on seeds, grain and fruit, and drink, unlike other birds, by immersing the bill to the nostrils and steadily drawing in the fluid until satisfied.

The eggs of pigeons number one or two and the young are hatched naked, except for scattered bits of matted down, and are fed at first with a white curd, sometimes called "pigeons' milk," secreted in the internal organs of both parent birds, but not as milk is secreted in the mammary glands of mammals.   In the pigeons the male produces more of the nourishment than the female, and takes a larger share in feeding the young. When the young grow too large to be nourished by the parental secretions, they are fed by partially digested food regurgitated by the parent. Pigeons are generally monogamous, but some males are somewhat fickle.

Contrary to the general impression the dove is not altogether a bird of peace. The males of some species are very pugnacious in the breeding season, and bloody combats sometimes occur.

Pigeons are found throughout the Temperate and Tropical regions of the world. About 475 species have been described.

FAMILY **COLUMBIDÆ.** PIGEONS AND DOVES.

Number of species in North America 14 ; in Massachusetts 3.

The characters of the family are, in general, substantially those of the Order. We have two distinct types in New England. The square-tailed terrestrial dove introduced from the Old World, and the indigenous long-tailed arboreal type with shorter tarsus.

ECONOMIC STATUS. The chief economic value of pigeons and doves, which is great, lies in their usefulness as poultry and game.

Colúmba doméstica LINNÆUS. **Domestic Dove.**
Other names: PIGEON; STREET PIGEON; ROCK DOVE; BLUE ROCK.
Introduced species.

DESCRIPTION. — *Adults variable (sexes alike or different):* variability probably caused by more or less unnatural conditions or by descent from or interbreeding with fancy pigeons; plumage usually bluish-gray, bluish-slate, or various shades of slate, usually barred on wings with different shades of same or black, and in most cases with glossy iridescent reflections on the head and neck; axillars and under wing-coverts usually much paler, or white with some gray towards edges of wing; some doves have the lower back or rump light or white, and a wide black bar on end of tail; others are pure white; others a mixture of white and slaty. The original progenitor of most domestic pigeons is the Rock Dove of Europe and Asia. A bluish-gray bird with a white patch on lower back; neck and upper breast dark lavender purple showing iridescent metallic green and purple reflections; two broad black bars on wing, one on greater wing-coverts, the other on secondaries; another across end of tail; bill usually blackish-brown, turgid nostril membrane red sprinkled thickly with white; iris reddish or reddish-orange with an inner yellow ring; legs and feet pale purplish-red or dull red. *Juvenal plumage:* Similar to adult, but whole head and neck and sometimes body dark, dull, brownish-slate, all without iridescence. *Nestling:* Hatched naked, except for a little stringy down; slaty nestling plumage gradually develops, chin and gape remaining bare.

HEAD OF DOVE

MEASUREMENTS. — Length about 11 in.; folded wing 8.50 to 8.75; tail 4.35 to 4.60; bill .70 to .80; tarsus about 1.20 to 1.30.

MOLTS. — Young bird molts juvenal plumage during first autumn and assumes plumage as adult; adult acquires winter plumage by complete molt (June to November or December).

Voice. — *Male:* A varied cooing, usually *coo-roo-cooo* or *cock-a-war* (C. W. Townsend). *Young:* a thin peep.

Breeding. — *Rock Dove (in Europe):* Usually in caves or dove-cotes. *Domestic Pigeon (in America):* Usually on, in or about buildings under some shelter. *Nest:* A platform of sticks and straws, slightly hollowed. *Eggs:* Two; nearly oval; white, smooth and glossy; about 1.52 to 1.55 by 1.12 to 1.14 in. *Dates:* Every month in the year, except January, in different parts of New England, but most commonly from March to June and from August to November. *Incubation:* Fourteen days (O. W. Knight); by both parents. *Broods:* Two or more yearly.

Range. — The original Rock Dove, *C. livia*, is a native of Europe; closely allied forms of the species extending into Asia as far as India and Lake Baikal and south into northern Africa; in domestication its descendants have been introduced into most civilized countries of the world and many have become feral.

Distribution in New England. — Common in all the larger cities and towns and not rare in many rural districts in a wild or partly domesticated state.

History. The Rock Dove was domesticated in the Old World and introduced into the New. The bird normally bred in caves in rocky precipitous cliffs, and in holes or under overhanging rocks, and was most common near the seashore in localities where caves hollowed out by the sea in great cliffs were numerous. On such cliffs along the coast and on rocky islands of western Europe the eagle may build her lofty eyrie, the young Peregrine Falcon may nestle on the ledges, or gulls and guillemots may rear their broods, — while the dim caves below resound with the cooing of the Rock Doves. In a state of nature all varieties of domestic doves tend to revert to a type resembling the original Rock Dove. Some of those on our streets resemble this dove very closely, but many have lost the white rump. These are the birds known as Blue Rocks, formerly used in pigeon shooting at traps. The species was kept in domestication by the Greeks and Romans, and the birds were used as carriers of messages in very early times. This is the bird known to the ancients, which from time immemorial has been regarded by mankind as the emblem of gentleness and affection. It was sacred to Venus because of the affectionate intercourse between its sexes, and was represented as her constant attendant. The ancients learned that if dove-cotes were built with shelves projecting from the inner walls and so constructed as to prevent the inroads of cats, rats, weasels and other climbing enemies, the doves would occupy them. These dove-cotes soon produced a supply of toothsome young birds for their owners at little expense, for the doves picked up most of their own food wherever they could find it. Thus the domestication of the species was begun. Young birds kept in confinement thrived under domestication and by segregation and inbreeding all the domestic varieties have been produced. Not very long after the settlement of this country, doves and other poultry were brought here from England, and later as cities, offering nesting places about buildings, were established, many doves left the premises of their owners and became habituated to a life of freedom.

Haunts and Habits. The Domestic Dove or Pigeon is usually bred in captivity, but numerous individuals have escaped from their owners, and their offspring are virtually wild birds. These are most numerous in the larger cities where they have the best opportunity for breeding unmolested, and for picking up waste food in winter, and where also many kindly disposed people feed them during the inclement season. In rural districts their chances to secure sufficient sustenance in winter are less, but a few manage to exist by roosting in the cupolas of barns or the steeples of churches or in unoccupied buildings, and by securing food in weedy gardens, about barn-yards and hen-yards, from droppings in the roads, and from waste grain spilled from cars along the railroads or at stations or stores where grain is unloaded. These birds are wild and shy, but they often feed with domesticated birds and sometimes mate and nest with them. Those domiciled in cities are more tame, and some individuals will perch on the shoulder or eat from the hand of anyone accustomed to feed them, but they still possess the normal timidity of the race, and any sudden noise like the firing of a gun, or any quick and unusual movement on the part of a spectator is sufficient cause for quick and startled flight. The strutting, billing, and cooing of the male when mating are familiar to everyone. Doves are believed to mate for life, but when one of a mated pair dies, the survivor will mate again. The apparent affection that the mated pair bestow on each other, and the solicitude and loving care with which the young are fed and tended by both parents has secured the dove an established place in literature, and the bird has become the emblem of peace, notwithstanding the fierce and bloody combats which occur between the males which sometimes result in the complete exhaustion or death of one of the combatants. In the stone, brick and concrete buildings of New England cities, the doves find sheltered recesses such as occur in the native cliffs of their wild progenitors, and here they build their nests, high up on ledges, under windows, verandas, or porticos, under bridges or wherever they can find reasonable safety, and support and shelter for their nests about any large structure erected by man.

They are regarded as a nuisance about human dwellings, because of the filth they occasion, the vermin they bring, and their noisy early morning wooing and fighting, which is not appreciated by many city dwellers who turn night into day, and wish to sleep away the morning hours undisturbed by noisy, amorous birds.

When a pair is mated, both birds labor together in all the domestic duties. There is no shirking on the part of the male, and often he is even more assiduous than the female in feeding the young. He also feeds the female frequently by inserting his bill in hers and regurgitating the food, hence the term billing. The young remain in the nest three or four weeks, sometimes a little longer; and sometimes before they leave it, the female lays another set of eggs in another nest.

In winter the doves gather in large flocks, sitting on the sunny roofs of buildings, where they huddle together as if for warmth, while watching for food in the streets or parks. A flock gathers daily on the mall on Boston Common before the Park Street Subway station, where the doves have learned by experience that some people among the station crowds will feed them. These doves drink from fountains or park ponds, and if they cannot reach water readily otherwise in hot weather, some will alight on the surface of the water to drink. They can rise from it with ease. In the city they have not many destructive enemies. Certain active cats know how to catch them. One of these beasts is able now and then to creep near enough to a bird on the ground so that with three quick springs she reaches the escaping pigeon in the air, and strikes it down in flight. Occasionally a few Barred Owls hang about the city in winter, and probably get some pigeons. Rarely a Duck Hawk establishes his headquarters high on some tall tower, from which he sallies forth and decimates the doves, but perhaps their greatest enemy in Boston is the common Crow. A few Crows have found safe nesting places in some tall trees in Boston, from which they explore the buildings in all directions for pigeons' eggs and young, of which they destroy considerable numbers.

The food of the pigeons is largely vegetal, consisting of grain, grass, the seeds of numerous weeds and grasses and those of clover, tender grass roots, a few berries, bread crumbs and pieces of garbage from the table. In spring they are said to eat a certain proportion of animal food, such as earthworms and snails, but I have not observed this.

ECONOMIC STATUS. As the progenitor of many varieties of domestic pigeons and doves, the Rock Dove has conferred great benefits on mankind in the way of food, profits, and recreation. As a wild bird in city or country in New England it has some esthetic and humanitarian value, but no economic importance, being rather detrimental than otherwise. On seeded fields of grass, grain, or clover, it not only picks up seeds on the surface, but uncovers and devours many more, and thus sometimes necessitates reseeding.

Ectopístes migratórius (LINNÆUS). Passenger Pigeon.

Other name: WILD PIGEON.

Plate 36.

DESCRIPTION. — Longest of native American doves; wings long and pointed; tail long or nearly as long as wing, of 12 tapering feathers, much graduated, narrow and pointed at tips; tarsus short, feathered part way down in front. *Adult male:* Above and head all round slaty-blue, darker on upper back and lesser wing-coverts, and shaded with olive-gray on back and wings, but not on rump; some small, black spots on scapulars and wing-coverts; sides and back of neck with rich metallic golden, violet or reddish-purple luster; two middle tail-feathers dark brown or blackish, others blackish at base, but shading from bluish on outer web to white on inner, outer web of outer tail-feathers pure white; flight-feathers blackish, bordered whitish or bluish, with an inner tinge of rufous; below from throat light, purplish, brownish-red, paling gradually below breast, and shading into violet on abdomen and white on region of vent and on under tail-coverts; feathers of tibia bluish-violet; axillars and under wing-coverts light blue; under side of tail chiefly white, middle feathers and bases mostly brown, but blackish next to body; bill black; bare space around eye livid flesh color or purplish-red; iris scarlet or scarlet vermilion; legs and feet lake red. *Adult female:* Similar to adult male, but much duller; tail shorter; browner or more olivaceous above; head brownish-gray; pale ashy or whitish below with a tinge of reddish on neck and breast; scapulars and wing-coverts more heavily spotted black; iris orange or orange-red; bare skin around eye slaty; feet paler than in male. *Juvenal plumage:* Similar to that of adult female, but scapulars and feathers of head, neck and upper breast tipped whitish, giving bird a mottled appearance, and primary feathers margined rufous. *Nestling in down:* Dark slate color (Ruthven Deane).

MEASUREMENTS. — Length 15.00 to 18.00 in.; spread 23.00 to 25.00; folded wing 8.00 to 8.60; tail 8.00 to 9.00; bill .70 to .75; tarsus 1.00; female smaller than male. Weight about 12 oz. (E. H. Eaton).

MOLTS. — The juvenal plumage is shed (July to October), after which the young bird assumes a plumage closely resembling the adult of its sex, but may require another molt to become as adult. Adults molt completely and rapidly once a year, usually in September.

PLATE 36

PLATE 36

PASSENGER PIGEON
Page 54

Adult Male

Young in
Juvenal Plumage

Adult Female

MOURNING DOVE
Page 82

Adult Male

Young in
Juvenal Plumage

All about one-half scale.

Louis Agassiz Fuertes.

FIELD MARKS. — About as large as domestic pigeon, but longer, with longer and pointed tail; much larger than Mourning Dove; otherwise much like it but more bluish; male has a much redder breast, while female is much paler below than female Mourning Dove; no twitter or whistle like that of Mourning Dove when rising, and no black spot on side of neck, such as marks Mourning Dove.

VOICE. — *Male:* A loud, harsh *keck* sometimes high-pitched, a chattering series of *kucks*, and the "vestigial coo," a weak, musical strain sounding like *keeho*. *Female:* A clucking sound, almost toneless, and croaking sounds of five or six notes (W. Craig).[1]

BREEDING. — In wooded uplands or swamps. *Nest:* In either coniferous or deciduous trees, hardwoods preferred; a frail platform of sticks and twigs, at heights from 9 to 50 feet. *Eggs:* 1 usually, often 2 in a nest; about 1.47 by 1.02 in.; elliptical; pure white, glossy. *Dates:* Feb. 15 to Sept. 15 in captivity, April to July in the wild. *Incubation:* Period 14 days (Daniel Whitaker); by both sexes. *Broods:* Two or more yearly.

RANGE. — Formerly eastern North America; chiefly in forested regions, from northwestern Mackenzie, northern Manitoba, northern Ontario, central Quebec, New Brunswick and Newfoundland south to the Gulf coast and west to eastern Montana and western Texas. Bred from western Mackenzie, northern Manitoba, Quebec, New Brunswick and Nova Scotia south to Kansas, northern Mississippi, Kentucky (casually Tennessee) and Pennsylvania; wintered principally from Arkansas and North Carolina south to central Texas, the Gulf coast and Florida; casual in eastern Mexico, Guatemala and Cuba; accidental in Nevada, Wyoming, eastern Oregon, western Washington, British Isles, France, Austria, Norway, Russia and Bermudas. Now generally believed to be extinct.

DISTRIBUTION IN NEW ENGLAND. — Formerly abundant migrant and common local to abundant local summer resident in all New England States. Now apparently extirpated.

SEASON IN MASSACHUSETTS. — March 10 to October 21 (winter).

HISTORY. The Passenger Pigeon was in some respects the finest pigeon the world has seen. It is now regarded generally as extinct, and it would not be included in this volume were it not that several recent observations by responsible persons have led some people to hope that, as in the case of the Eskimo Curlew, some few individuals may have continued to exist until the present day.

Naturalists are prone to say and believe that the extinction of this species has never been satisfactorily explained; but when once its history is known, the story of its extirpation reads like an open book. The marvelous numbers of the Passenger Pigeon which once was believed to be the most numerous bird in the world caused no more wonder than did its comparatively sudden disappearance. The tales of its former abundance read like those of the romancer. Yet they are well attested and there are men even now living who have seen the countless multitudes of these birds that once wandered over the land. Their abundance in the forests west of the Appalachian Mountain chain during the 19th century is well known, but the vast numbers that roamed over the Atlantic Seaboard, during the early history of the country, have been forgotten. To show the former great hosts of the species in this region, it will be necessary to have recourse to the accounts of many early writers.[2]

---

[1] For a full description of the notes of the Passenger Pigeon, see Wallace Craig's paper, Auk, Vol. XXVIII, 1911, pp. 408–427.

[2] The account which follows is based upon my history of the Passenger Pigeon, published in 1912, in "Game Birds, Wild Fowl and Shore Birds." This in turn is taken largely from the writings of many early writers, from Mershon's work entitled "The Passenger Pigeon" and from the writings of ornithologists. Included in the present account also are items obtained from "The Passenger Pigeon in Pennsylvania" by John C. French and notes taken from the Auk (particularly those of Albert Hazen Wright in the Auk for 1910 and 1911), and some of the sportsmen's journals.

These relations are scattered generally through the literature of the centuries, many of them doubtless now lost or inaccessible, and they are mostly brief and sporadic, throwing a little light here and there on the movements and habits of this bird which for centuries was one of the most important periodical sources of food supply in the land.

The Passenger Pigeon was described by Linnæus in the latter part of the eighteenth century (Syst. Nat., 1766, ed. 12, Vol. I, p. 285); but it was well known in America many years earlier. In the "First Relation of Jaques Carthier of S. Malo (1534)," [1] "Stock Doves" are recorded at Cape Kildare. In his second voyage up the St. Lawrence (1535) he mentions "Turtles" and "Wilde Pigeons." In July, 1605, on the coast of Maine, in latitude 43° 25', Champlain saw on some islands an "infinite number of pigeons," of which he took a great quantity.[2]

Many early historians, who write of the birds of the Atlantic coast region, mention the pigeons. The Jesuit Fathers, in their first narratives of Acadia (1610–13), state that the birds were fully as abundant as the fish, and that in their seasons the pigeons overloaded the trees.[3]

The Baron de LaHontan, in a letter dated May 28, 1687, from Boucherville, describing a flight of these birds in the vicinity of Lake Champlain, says: "One would have thought, that all the Turtle-Doves on Earth had chose to pass thro' this place. For the eighteen or twenty days that we stayed there, I firmly believe that a thousand Men might have fed upon 'em heartily, without putting themselves to any trouble. . . . The trees were covered with that sort of fowl more than with leaves." [4]

P. Campbell in his "Travels in New Brunswick in 1791 and 1792" (published in 1793) says: "Of pigeons, in the season, may be seen from any eminence 10,000 flocks, or as far as the eye can reach."

Isaac Weld, Jr. (1799), relates that a resident of Niagara, while sailing from that town to Toronto (forty miles), saw a great flight of pigeons coming from the north which continued throughout the voyage, and the birds were still coming from the north in large bodies after he reached Toronto.[5]

These great flights of pigeons in migration extended over vast tracts of country, and usually passed in their greatest numbers for about three days. This is the testimony of observers in many parts of the land. Afterward, flocks often came along for a week or two longer.

W. Ross King (1866) speaks of a flight at Fort Mississisaugua, Canada, which filled the air and obscured the sun for fourteen hours. He believed that the flight must have

---

[1] Burrage, Henry S. (Editor): Original Narratives of Early American History. Early English and French Voyages, 1906, pp. 17, 71.

[2] Champlain, Samuel de: Publication of the Prince Society, 1878, Vol. II, pp. 68, 69.

[3] Thwaites, R. G. (Editor): Jesuit Relations and Allied Documents, 1896, Vol. I, p. 253.

[4] LaHontan, Baron de: Some New Voyages to North America, Vol. I, 1703, pp. 61, 62.

[5] Weld, Isaac, Jr.: Travels through the States of North America, etc., during the years 1795, 1796, 1797, London, 1800, Vol. II. p. 43.

averaged three hundred miles in length by a mile wide. An immense flight continued for some days thereafter.[1]

Passing now from Canada to Florida, we find that Stork (1766) asserts that the pigeons were in such numbers there for three months of the year that any account of them would seem incredible.[2]

Lawson (1709) speaks of prodigious flocks of pigeons in 1701–02, which broke down trees in the woods where they roosted, and cleaned up all the food in the country, scarcely leaving one acorn on the ground.[3]

The early settlers in Virginia found the pigeons in winter "beyond number or imagination."

Strachey (1612) says: "A kind of wood-pidgeon we see in winter time, and of them such nombers, as I should drawe (from our homelings here, such who have seene, peradventure scarse one more than in the markett) the creditt of my relation concerning all the other in question yf I should expresse what extended flocks, and how manie thousands in one flock, I have seene in one daie . . . but there be manie hundred witnesses." [4]

Hamor (1615) says: "My selfe haue seene three or foure houres together flockes in the aire, so thicke that euen they haue shaddowed the skie from vs." [5]

Professor Kalm found the pigeons in numbers "beyond conception" in the middle states and in Canada.[6] He says in his monograph of the Passenger Pigeon, that there are certain years when they come to Pennsylvania and the southern English provinces in such indescribable multitudes as to appall the people.[7] The year 1740 was one of the years when they came to Pennsylvania and New Jersey in incredible multitudes. He also asserts that Dr. Colden told him that he had twice seen similar great flights between New York and Albany.

In 1803 Rev. T. M. Harris made a tour into the State of Ohio and at Waterford, Washington County, there was, he remarks, "a large forest of several hundred acres" which had been killed as a consequence of the vast flocks of pigeons alighting upon it, and he was informed by the Rev. Mr. Story that he had visited two large pigeon roosts, one supposed to cover a thousand acres and the other larger, where the destruction of timber and brush was incredible. This destruction of timber by the pigeons in the great roosts was a common occurrence.[8]

Hinton (quoted by Buckingham [9]) says that the trees for thousands of acres in the pigeon roosts were killed as completely as if girdled with an axe, and that numerous

[1] King, W. Ross: The Sportsman and Naturalist in Canada, 1866, p. 121, 122.

[2] Stork, William: An Account of East Florida, 1766, p. 51.

[3] Lawson, John: History of Carolina, 1860, pp. 232, 233.

[4] Strachey, William: The Historie of Travaile into Virginia Brittannia, printed for the Hakluyt Society, 1849, p. 126.

[5] Hamor, Raphe: A True Discourse of the Present Estate of Virginia, 1615, p. 21.

[6] Kalm, Peter: Travels into North America, first English edition, Vol. II, pp. 82 and 311.

[7] Kalm, Peter: A Description of the Wild Pigeons which visit the Southern English Colonies in North America during Certain Years in Incredible Multitudes. Translated by S. M. Gronberger from Kongl. Vetenskaps-Akademiens Handlingar för ar 1759, Vol. XX, Stockholm, 1759; Auk, 1911, pp. 53–66.

[8] Mason, Thaddeus: The Journal of a Tour into the Territory northwest of the Alleghany Mountains, 1805, pp. 179–180.

[9] Buckingham, J. S.: The Slave States of America, Vol. II, p. 332.

places could be pointed out where for several years scarcely a single vegetable made its appearance.

John Lyman, one of the settlers in the great forests of Pennsylvania, estimated that in 1805 there were 20,000,000 pigeons nesting in the valleys along the Allegheny River. In 1810 John Lyman and Francis King passed along this river again and concluded that an estimate of 20,000,000 pigeons would be conservative for that year. At the same time other immense nestings are recorded on the eastern slope of the mountains in New York and Pennsylvania; also in Indiana, Ohio and Kentucky. Each man who recorded these great nestings probably believed that he was telling about all the Passenger Pigeons in existence.[1]

Many chroniclers tell of great pigeon roosts or nestings in New York State during the first part of the nineteenth century. In 1835 there was a great roost near Norwich, Chenango County; in 1867 a large nesting in Clinton County. The last great nesting in New York was in 1868 along Bell's Run, near Ceres, Allegheny County, on the Pennsylvania line. The nesting was about 14 miles in length. In 1875 there was an immense roost at Coopers, Steuben County.[2]

In 1866 and 1870 there were great pigeon nestings in Potter County, Pennsylvania. "Each morning," says Mr. John C. French, "a valley a mile wide between the hills was filled strata above strata, eight courses deep at times, for about an hour with the multitude of birds flowing westward at the rate of a mile a minute, going for food. The roar of wings was like a tornado in the treetops and the morning was darkened as by a heavy thunder-shower." "The nesting in 1870," says Mr. C. W. Dickinson, "was from one-half mile to two miles wide and about 40 miles long, running through an unbroken forest"; this nesting extended over parts of Potter and McKean Counties.

In early times the pigeons were abundant in New England. Hollister, in the History of Connecticut (1855), says that pigeons were innumerable in spring and autumn and were startled from the thickets in summer.[3] Early Massachusetts authors make brief but numerous references to the species. Wood (1629–34) records the migration through eastern Massachusetts in the following words: "These Birds come into the Countrey, to goe to the North parts in the beginning of our Spring, at which time (if I may be counted worthy, to be beleeved in a thing that is not so strange as true) I have seene them fly as if the Ayerie regiment had beene Pigeons; seeing neyther beginning nor ending, length, or breadth of these Millions of Millions. The shouting of people, the rattling of Gunnes, and pelting of small shotte could not drive them out of their course, but so they continued for four or five houres together: yet it must not be concluded, that it is thus often; for it is but at the beginning of the Spring, and at Michaelmas, when they returne backe to the Southward; yet are there some all the yeare long, which are easily attayned by such as looke after them. Many of them build amongst the Pine-trees, thirty miles to the North-

---

[1] French, John C.: The Passenger Pigeon in Pennsylvania, 1919, pp. 24–27.
[2] Eaton, E. H.: Birds of New York, Vol. I, pp. 382–383.
[3] Hollister, G. H.: History of Connecticut, 1855, Vol. I, pp. 33–34.

east of our plantations; joyning nest to nest, and tree to tree by their nests, so that the Sunne never sees the ground in that place, from whence the Indians fetch whole loades of them."[1] This nesting must have been somewhere near the coast of Essex, or, as Dr. Townsend puts it in his Birds of Essex County, in the Essex woods.

The following is an extract from a letter written by Governor Dudley to the Countess of Lincoln, March 12, 1630: "Upon the eighth of March from after it was fair daylight, until about eight of the clock in the forenoon, there flew over all the towns in our plantations, so many flocks of doves, each flock containing many thousands and some so many that they obscured the light, that it passeth credit, if but the truth should be written."[2]

Higginson, writing of Salem about this date, apparently makes the same statement in nearly the same words. In Charles Brooks's History of Medford, Mass. (p. 37), we find the following occurrence recorded on March 8, 1631: "Flocks of wild pigeons this day, so thick they obscure the light." Apparently these were the first large flights of pigeons of which we have definite record in New England.

The Plymouth colony was threatened with famine in 1643, when great flocks of pigeons swept down upon the ripened corn and beat down and ate "a very great quantity of all sorts of English grain." But Winthrop says that in 1648 they came again after the harvest was gathered, and proved a great blessing, "it being incredible what multitudes of them were killed daily."[3]

Hubbard in his General History of New England (1680) says that the pigeons came in multitudes every summer "almost like the quayles that fell round the campe of Israel in the wilderness."[4]

Lewis and Newhall, writing of those early days in the History of Lynn (1866, p. 46), state that a single family "has been known to have killed one hundred dozens of these birds with poles and other weapons."

Roger Williams (1643) says that the pigeons bred abundantly in Rhode Island in the "Pigeon Countrie." Josselyn (1672), who had a general acquaintance with the New England colonies, and who lived in Massachusetts and Maine for some years, writes that of pigeons there were "millions of millions; I have seen," he asserts, "a flight of Pidgeons in the spring, and at Michaelmas, when they return back to the Southward, for four or five miles, that to my thinking had neither beginning nor ending, length nor breadth, and so thick that I could see no Sun. . . .[5] But of late they are much diminished, the English taking them with Nets."

The latter statement shows that the extirpation of these birds began in New England within fifty years after the first settlement at Plymouth. It went on for more than two hundred years. Nevertheless, they were still quite numerous about the beginning of the nineteenth century.

---

[1] Wood, William: New England's Prospect, Pub. Prince Society, 1865, pp. 31, 32.
[2] Coll. Massachusetts Historical Society, Vol. VIII, 1st series, p. 45.
[3] Winthrop, John: The History of New England from 1630 to 1649. James Savage, editor, 1825–26, Vol. II, pp. 94, 331, 332.
[4] Massachusetts Historical Society Collections, second series, Vol. V, 1815, p. 25.
[5] Josselyn, John: Two Voyages to New England, 1865, p. 79.

Belknap (1792), in his History of New Hampshire, says that the pigeons came in the spring, from the southward, in large flocks, and bred "in our woods, during the summer months." Richard Hazzen, who surveyed the Province line in 1741, remarks: "For three miles together, the pigeons nests were so thick, that five hundred might have been told on the beech trees at one time; and could they have been counted on the hemlocks, as well, I doubt not but five thousand, at one turn round." This was on the western side of the Connecticut River and eastward of the Deerfield River (and probably extended into Massachusetts). "Since the clearing of the woods" he says "the number of pigeons is diminished." [1]

One of the earliest settlers at Clarendon, Vt., asserted that immense numbers of pigeons nested there. The trees were loaded with nests, and the noise made by the birds at night was so troublesome that the traveler could get no sleep. Settlers often cut down trees, and gathered a horse-load of squabs in a few minutes. [2]

In the History of Wells and Kennebunk, Me., it is stated that from the first settlement up to about 1775 pigeons in innumerable numbers haunted the woods near the sea, and "pigeon stands" were still in use there until after 1840. In their season they furnished food for many families. [3]

Wild Pigeons are not mentioned in Hampshire County, Mass., records until after 1700, but undoubtedly they were there when settlement began. They had a breeding place near the line between Hampshire County and Vermont, and their nests on the beech and hemlock trees extended for miles. They were noted in Hampshire County before 1740, and many were shot. Levi Moody is given by Judd as authority for the statement that they were caught in such numbers in Granby that not all could be sold or eaten, and after the feathers had been plucked from them, many were fed to the hogs. Pigeon feathers were much used for beds. In August, 1736, pigeons were sold in the Boston market at twopence per dozen, and many could not be sold at that price. In Northampton, from 1725 to 1785, when they could be sold, they brought usually from threepence to sixpence per dozen. In 1790 they brought ninepence per dozen, and a few years after 1800 one shilling, sixpence. After 1850 they were sold at from seventy-five cents to a dollar and a half a dozen. [4]

In the History of the Sesqui-centennial Celebration of the Town of Hadley, Mass., it is recorded that before 1719 Wild Pigeons in their migrations roosted in countless numbers in the oak and chestnut groves on the plains.

Thompson asserts that when the country was new there were many of their breeding places in Vermont; also, that they were much less abundant (1842) than formerly; "but," he says, "they now, in some years, appear in large numbers." [5]

Great nestings became few and far between in New England as the pigeons decreased;

[1] Belknap, Jeremy: History of New Hampshire, 1792, Vol. III, pp. 171, 172.
[2] Williams, Samuel: The Natural and Civil History of Vermont, 1809, Vol. I, p. 137.
[3] Bourne, Edward E.: History of Wells and Kennebunk, 1875, pp. 563, 564.
[4] Judd, Sylvester: History of Hadley, 1905, pp. 351, 352.
[5] Thompson, Zadock: History of Vermont, 1842, p. 100.

but there were many small breeding places regularly occupied during the first half of the nineteenth century, and scattered pairs bred commonly. Mr. Clayton E. Stone sends an account of the nesting site of a flock of Passenger Pigeons, furnished by his father, Mr. Stillman Stone, who was well acquainted with the birds. It was situated on the side of Mt. Sterling, in the towns of Stowe and Hyde Park (formerly Sterling), in the northern part of Vermont. Mr. Stone was acquainted with it from 1848 to about 1853. It occupied a tract of twenty acres or more of old-growth maple and yellow birch. There were often as many as twenty-five nests in a tree, and sometimes more. The number of eggs in a nest was one or two, usually one. Most of the time during the nesting season large flocks of these birds could be seen coming and going in all directions to and from the nests. The people from this and neighboring towns went to the place with their teams to take up the squabs that had fallen to the ground; they took them away by cartloads. The squabs were distributed free, to be used as food by all their friends and neighbors.

In 1848 Mr. Stone and Madison Newcomb sprung a net over forty-four dozens, or five hundred and twenty-eight birds, at one cast, and they thought that only about one bird in four of the flock was taken. Many escaped while they were taking out the forty-four dozens. Pigeons were abundant in that locality until the fall of 1865, when a man could shoot in half a day all that he could use. Mr. Stone says that hawks ravaged the birds continually. He left Vermont in 1866, and does not know how long afterward the pigeons continued plentiful. At that time there were still many pigeons in Massachusetts. There were bough houses and roosts erected for shooting pigeons, "pigeon-beds," nets and stool pigeons in almost every town. Old men remember this even now. Thoreau speaks of the arrangements for pigeon shooting in Concord in the 50's.

There are not many exact records of the flights of pigeons in Massachusetts during the early part of the nineteenth century. They were of such regular occurrence that no one thought of recording them. Dr. Samuel Cabot told Mr. Brewster that from 1832 to 1836, while he was in college at Cambridge, pigeons visited the town regularly, both in spring and autumn, sometimes in immense numbers.[1]

Mr. Clayton E. Stone writes that Mr. M. M. Boutwell, brother of the late Governor George S. Boutwell, knew of a nesting place of the Passenger Pigeon in the northern part of Lunenburg, Massachusetts, from his earliest recollection until 1851 or 1852. He says that an old gunner, Samuel Johnson, used to visit this place every year to get squabs. It was situated in the northern part of the town, on a tract of land which up to 1840 or 1845 was almost an unbroken forest for miles. It is said to have comprised something like five acres. Mr. Boutwell says that anywhere in any fall until the year 1860, a man could get in an hour all the pigeons he could use.

Mr. James W. Moore of Agawam, Massachusetts, writes that after 1850 great flocks of pigeons still visited that region; and that as a boy he was sent to drive them from the newly sown rye. "We boys," he says, "had pigeon beds, and caught them in nets."

---

[1] Brewster, William: Memoirs, Nuttall Ornith. Club, No. IV, Birds of the Cambridge Region of Massachusetts, 1906, p. 176.

About this time indications of the disappearance of the pigeons in the east began to attract some notice. They became rare in Newfoundland in the 60's, though formerly abundant there. They grew fewer in Ontario at that time; but, according to Fleming, some of the old roosts there were occupied until 1870.

Mr. C. S. Brimley wrote to me in 1910 that they were seen in some numbers near Raleigh, N. C., up to about 1850. For thirty years he had not seen one, which would fix the date of their disappearance there about 1880. Dr. Witmer Stone believes that they became rare in New Jersey about that time.

During the ensuing decade they became rare in Massachusetts; but Mr. August B. Ross writes that the pigeons were "quite plenty" in rye fields on the plains at Montague, about 1879; and Mr. Robert O. Morris asserts that a small flock was seen in Long-meadow in the spring of 1880; nevertheless there is no authentic record of a pigeon seen or taken in that vicinity since 1884. This seems to mark approximately the time that the bird disappeared from the Connecticut Valley.

Brewster records a flock of about fifty pigeons on September 2, 1868, in Cambridge; and he remarks that a heavy flight passed through eastern Massachusetts between September 2 and September 10, 1871, and that he was assured that thousands were killed, and that the netters in Concord and Reading used their nets as of old.[1]

My first experience with the pigeons was in 1872. Many flocks went through Worcester County during the fall of that year, and I saw small flocks passing rapidly over the northern end of Lake Quinsigamond. Friends saw them in Spencer, Mass., and in other towns near Worcester. At that time the Pigeons were still breeding in Pembroke, N. H., about five miles from Concord, where I passed the summer.

About 1870 a flock came into a tree at Lanesville, Mass., under the shade of which General Benjamin F. Butler stood delivering an address to a gathering of some two thousand people. Birds alighted "on every part of the tree."[2]

I have found no records of any very considerable flights of Passenger Pigeons in Massachusetts since 1876. Hundreds of thousands of pigeons then appeared in the Connecticut Valley.[3]

In 1876 Minot wrote that in many places the pigeons were already comparatively rare. He stated also that in a low pine wood within the present limits of Boston, flocks of several hundred have roosted every year.[4]

During the decade from 1880 to 1890 the pigeon seems virtually to have disappeared from Massachusetts. Many birds were seen and shot as late as the year 1878; after that they were scarce. The species was seen by Mr. C. E. Ingalls at Winchendon, Mass., in 1889; and several were reported by Mr. Ralph Holman at Worcester in August, September and October of that year. He also reports one killed by a Mr. Newton, janitor

[1] Brewster, William: Birds of the Cambridge Region, 1906, p. 177.
[2] Leonard, H. C.: Pigeon Cove, Mass., 1873, p. 165.
[3] Morris, Robert O.: Birds of Springfield and Vicinity, 1901, p. 17.
[4] Minot, Henry D.: The Land Birds and Game Birds of New England, 2nd edition, ed. by William Brewster, 1895, p. 396.

of the Worcester high school, on September 23, 1889. The last published authentic record of a Passenger Pigeon taken in Massachusetts is given by Howe and Allen as 1889; [1] but Mr. Neil Casey of Melrose has an adult female bird mounted, which he shot there on April 12, 1894; and he says that two days later a friend saw another, apparently its mate, in the same woods. According to Perkins and Howe a few were to be seen near Essex Junction, Vermont, and about Fort Ethan Allen each season up to the date of their publication (1901),[2] and Dr. Perkins wrote to me in 1910 that he believed that there were a few still about Stratton Mountain in that State where formerly they nested in great numbers, but no one has been able to obtain a specimen.

Unfortunately, there is no detailed published account of the migrations or the nesting of the Passenger Pigeon in Massachusetts or New England written when they were numerous; and to get any adequate idea of their numbers, and the causes of their disappearance, we must turn to the writings of Wilson, Audubon and others, who observed the bird in the south and west.

Peter Kalm (1759), who witnessed flights of pigeons in Pennsylvania, characterizes them as marvelous, enormous and incredible! He says that on the 11th, 12th, 15th, 16th, 17th, 18th, and 22nd of March, 1740, such a multitude of these birds came to Pennsylvania that a flock alighting to roost in the woods filled both great and little trees for seven miles, and hardly a twig or branch could be seen which they did not cover. On the larger limbs they piled up in heaps. Limbs the size of a man's thigh were broken off by their weight, and the less firmly rooted trees broke down completely under their load.[3] This reads like the tale of a romancer; but similar occurrences all over the land are recorded by many credible witnesses.

Alexander Wilson, the father of American ornithology, tells of a breeding place of the Wild Pigeons in Shelbyville, Ky. (probably about 1806), which was several miles in breadth, and was said to be more than forty miles in extent. More than one hundred nests were found on a tree. The ground was strewn with broken limbs, eggs, and dead squabs which had been precipitated from above, on which herds of hogs were fattening. He speaks of a flight of these birds from another nesting place some sixty miles away from the first, toward Green River, where they were said to be equally numerous. They were traveling with great steadiness and rapidity, at a height beyond gunshot, several strata deep, very close together, and "from right to left as far as the eye could reach, the breadth of this vast procession extended; seeming everywhere equally crowded." From half-past 1 to 4 o'clock in the afternoon, while he was traveling to Frankfort, the same living torrent rolled overhead, seemingly as extensive as ever. Taking no account of several strata of birds in the air above the lowest, he estimated the flock that passed him to be two hundred and forty miles long and a mile wide — probably much wider — and to contain 2,230,272,000 pigeons. He considered this estimate to be far below the actual

---

[1] See also Thayer, H. J.: Forest and Stream, Vol. XXXIII, October 31, 1889, p. 288.
[2] Perkins & Howe: A Preliminary List of the Birds found in Vermont, 1901, p. 17.
[3] Auk, 1911, pp. 56, 57.

numbers.   Assuming that each bird consumed only half a pint of nuts and acorns daily, he reckoned that this column of birds would eat 17,424,000 bushels each day.

Audubon asserts that in the autumn of 1813 he left his house at Henderson, on the banks of the Ohio, a few miles from Hardensburgh, to go to Louisville, Kentucky.   He saw that day what he thought to be the largest flight of Wild Pigeons he had ever seen. The air was literally filled with them ; and "the light of noonday was obscured as by an eclipse."   Before sunset he reached Louisville, fifty-five miles from Hardensburgh, and during all that time pigeons were passing in undiminished numbers.   This continued for three days in succession.   The people were all armed, and the banks of the river were crowded with men and boys, incessantly shooting at the pigeons, which flew lower as they passed the river.   For a week or more the people fed on no other flesh than pigeons. The atmosphere during that time was strongly impregnated with the odor of the birds. Audubon estimated the number of pigeons passing overhead (in a flock one mile wide) for three hours, traveling at the rate of a mile a minute, allowing two pigeons to the square yard, as 1,115,136,000.   He estimated, also, that a flock of this size would require 8,712,000 bushels of food a day, and this was only a small part of the three days' flight.

Mr. John C. French gives an estimate based on these and other figures that there were nearly five billion pigeons in Kentucky, Ohio, and Indiana about this time.

Great flights of pigeons ranged from the Alleghenies to the Mississippi and from Hudson Bay to the Gulf of Mexico until after the middle of the nineteenth century.   Even two decades later enormous numbers of pigeons nested in several states.

Their winter roosting places almost defy description.   Audubon rode through one on the banks of the Green River in Kentucky for more than forty miles, crossing it in different directions, and found its average width to be rather more than three miles.   He observed that the ejecta covered the whole extent of the roosting place, like snow ; that many trees two feet in diameter were broken off not far from the ground, and that the branches of many of the largest and tallest had given way.*

The birds came in soon after sundown with a noise that sounded "like a gale passing through the rigging of a close-reefed vessel," causing a great current of air as they passed ; and here and there, as the flocks alighted, the limbs gave way with a crash, destroying hundreds of the birds beneath.   It was a scene of uproar and confusion.   Others have described the noise made by the arriving birds as louder than the loudest freight train, a sound that could be heard from four to six miles, according to the situation of the listener and the direction of the wind.

The nesting places sometimes were equal in size to the roosting places, for the Pigeons congregated in enormous numbers to breed in the northern and eastern states.   When food was plentiful in the forests, the birds congregated in large numbers ; when it was not, they scattered in smaller groups.   Mr. Henry T. Phillips, a game dealer of Detroit, who

---

* Audubon's statement that trees were broken off by the birds has been questioned, but it is corroborated by others.   James Mease (1807) quotes a Rev. Mr. Hall who saw a hickory tree bent over by the birds until its top touched the ground and its roots were started, and he states that brittle trees often were broken off by them.   (A Geological account of the United States, 1807, pp. 348–349) Kalm and Lawson also observed this breaking down of the trees by the birds. ·

bought and sold pigeons for many years, says that one season in Wisconsin he saw a nesting place that extended through the woods for a hundred miles.[1]

The last immense nesting place of which we have adequate records was in Michigan, in 1878. Prof. H. B. Roney avers in the American Field (Vol. 10, 1879, pp. 345–347), that the nesting near Petoskey, that year, covered something like one hundred thousand acres, and included not less than one hundred and fifty thousand acres within its limits. It was estimated to be about forty miles in length and from three to ten miles in width. It is difficult to approximate the number of millions of pigeons that occupied that great nesting place.

Audubon, who described the dreadful havoc made among these birds on their roosting grounds by man, says that people unacquainted with them might naturally conclude that such destruction would soon put an end to the species; but he had satisfied himself, by long observation, that nothing but the gradual diminution of the forests could accomplish the decrease of the birds, for he believed that they not infrequently quadrupled their numbers during the year, and always doubled them. The enormous multitudes of the pigeons made such an impression upon the mind that the extinction of the species at that time, and for many years afterwards, seemed an absolute impossibility. Nevertheless, it has occurred.

How can this apparent impossibility be explained? It cannot be accounted for by the destructiveness of natural enemies, for during the early years when the pigeons were the most abundant, their natural enemies were most numerous. The extinction of the pigeons has been coincident with the disappearance of bears, panthers, wolves, lynxes and some of the larger birds of prey from a large part of their range.

The aborigines never could have reduced appreciably the numbers of the species. Wherever the great roosts were established, Indians always gathered in large numbers. This, according to their traditions, had been the custom among them from time immemorial. They always had slaughtered these birds in great quantities; but there was no market among the Indians, and the only way in which they could preserve the meat for future use was by drying or smoking the breasts. Thus they cured large numbers. Some were accustomed to kill great quantities of the squabs and try out the fat, which was used as we use butter. Lawson writes (1709): "You may find several Indian towns of not above seventeen houses that have more than one hundred gallons of pigeon's oil or fat";[2] but it was not until a market demand for the birds was created by the whites that the Indians ever seriously affected the increase of the Pigeons.

When the white man appeared on this continent, conditions rapidly changed. Practically all the early settlers were accustomed to the use of firearms; and wherever pigeons appeared in great numbers, the inhabitants armed themselves with guns, clubs, stones, poles and whatever could be used to destroy the birds. The most destructive implement was the net, to which the birds were attracted by bait, and under which vast numbers of

---

[1] Mershon, W. B.: The Passenger Pigeon, 1907, p. 107.
[2] Lawson, John: History of Carolina, 1860, p. 78.

them were trapped. Gunners "baited" the birds with grain. Dozens of birds sometimes were killed thus at a single shot. In one case seventy-one birds were killed by two
shots.[1] A single shot from the old, flint-lock, single-barreled gun, fired into a tree, sometimes would procure a backload of pigeons. The Jesuit Relations of 1662–64 tell of a
man who killed one hundred and thirty-two birds at a shot.[2] Kalm says that frequently
as many as one hundred and thirty were killed at one shot. Shooting in the large roosts
was very destructive. Osborn records a kill of one hundred and forty-four birds with
two barrels. An engine of destruction often used in early times was an immense swivel
gun, loaded with "handfuls of bird shot." Such guns were taken to the roosts and fired
into the thickest masses of pigeons, killing at one discharge "enough to feed a whole
settlement."

As cities were established in the east, the Indians, now armed with guns and finding a
market for the birds, became doubly destructive; but as the white man moved toward
the west he destroyed the Indian as well as the game, until comparatively few Indians
were left in most of the country occupied by the pigeons.

The pigeons were reduced greatly in numbers on the whole Atlantic seaboard during
the first two centuries after the settlement of the country, but in the west their numbers
remained apparently the same until the nineteenth century. There was no appreciable
decrease there during the first half of that century; but during the latter half, railroads
were pushed across the plains to the Pacific, settlers increased rapidly to the Mississippi
and beyond, and the diminution of the pigeons in the west began. Already it had become
noticeable in western Pennsylvania, western New York, along the Appalachian Mountain
chain and in Ohio. This was due in part to the destruction of the forests, particularly
the beech woods, which once covered vast tracts, and which furnished the birds with a
chief supply of food. Much of the land on which beech woods grew was considered excellent for farming and the great beech forests of the north were rapidly cleared away
by settlers. Later, the primeval pine and hemlock forests of the northern states largely
were cut away. This deprived the birds of another source of food, — the seed of these
trees. The destruction of the forests, however, was not complete; for, although great
tracts of land were cleared, there remained and still remain vast regions more or less
covered by coppice growth sufficient to furnish hosts of pigeons with food, and the cultivation of the land and the raising of grain provided new sources of food supply. Therefore, while the reduction of the forest area in the east was a factor in the diminution of
the pigeons, we cannot attribute their extermination to the destruction of the forest.
Forest fires undoubtedly had something to do with reducing the numbers of these birds,
for many were destroyed by these fires, and in some cases large areas of forest were ruined
by fire, thus for many years depriving the birds of a part of their food supply. Nevertheless, the fires were local and restricted, and had comparatively little effect on the vast
numbers of the species.

---

[1] Leffingwell, W. B.: Shooting on Upland, Marsh and Stream, 1890, p. 228.
[2] Thwaites, R. G. (Editor): Jesuit Relations and Allied Documents, Vol. XLVIII, 1896, p. 177.

The main factors in the extermination of the pigeons are set forth in a work entitled *The Passenger Pigeon*, by Mr. W. B. Mershon (1907), which will well repay perusal, and in which a compilation is made of many of the original accounts of the destruction of the pigeon during the nineteenth century. From this volume many of the following facts are taken.

In early days the Allegheny Mountains and most of the vast region lying between them and the Mississippi River were covered largely by unbroken forest, as was also much of the country from the Maritime Provinces of Canada to Lake Winnipeg. The only inhabitants were scattered bands of Indians. The pigeons found a food supply throughout this vast region, and also nesting places which were comparatively unmolested by man; but as settlement advanced, as railroads were built, spanning the continent, as telegraph lines followed them, as markets developed for the birds, an army of people, hunters, settlers, netters and Indians, found in the pigeons a considerable part of their means of subsistence, and the birds were constantly pursued and killed, wherever they appeared, *at all seasons of the year*. They wandered through this vast region, resorting to well known roosting places and nesting places, containing from a million or two of birds to very many more; and there were many smaller colonies. Wherever they appeared, they were attacked immediately by practically all the people in the region. At night their roosts were visited by men who brought pots of sulphur and burned it, to suffocate the birds and bring them to the ground. An assortment of weapons was brought into service. When the birds nested in the primeval birch woods of the north, the people set fire to the loose hanging bark which flamed up like a great torch until the whole tree was ablaze, scorching the young birds, and causing them to leap from their nests to the ground in their dying agonies. Before the great markets became accessible by means of railroads, "millions" of fat squabs were roasted to try out the oil, which was stored in barrels. In Pennsylvania hundreds of acres of trees were felled to get the squabs. Quantities of pigeons, young and old, were dried, smoked, salted or pickled for winter use. At the great nesting places both Indians and white men felled the trees in such a way that the larger trees, in falling, broke down the smaller ones, and threw the helpless squabs to the ground. The squabs were gathered, their heads pulled off, their bodies thrown into sacks, and large droves of hogs were turned in, to fatten on those which could not be used.

Sometimes, when the pigeons flew low over a hill-top, they were knocked down with poles and oars swung in the direction of their flight or across it, and in early days thousands were killed with poles at the roosts. Pike, on a trip from Leech River to St. Louis, on April 28, 1806, stopped at a pigeon roost, and in about fifteen minutes his men knocked on the head and brought aboard 298 pigeons.[1]

As soon as it was learned in a town that the pigeons were roosting or nesting in the neighborhood, great nets were set in the fields, baited with grain or something else attractive to the birds. Decoy birds were used, and enormous number of pigeons were taken by springing the nets over them; while practically every able-bodied citizen, men,

---

[1] Pike, Zebulon Montgomery: The Expeditions of, during the years 1805–07, by Elliott Coues, Vol. I, 1895, p. 212.

women, children and servants, turned out to "lend a hand" either in killing the pigeons or in hauling away the loads of dead birds.

Not only at each roost or nesting but for thousands of square miles around it wherever the multitudes of the pigeons alighted or passed in search of food they were shot down, decoyed, trapped and netted without mercy.   Kalm, in his account of the species (1759), states that several extremely aged men told him that during their childhood there were many more pigeons in "New Sweden" during summer than there were when he was there.   He believed that the pigeons had been "either killed off or scared away."   In either case their decrease was evident at that early date.

The net, though used by fowlers almost everywhere in the east, from the earliest settlement of the country, was not a great factor in the extermination of the pigeons in the Mississippi Valley states until the last half of the nineteenth century.   With the extension of railroads and telegraph lines the occupation of the netter became more stable than before, for he could follow the birds wherever they went.   The number of men who made netting an occupation after the year 1860 is variously estimated at from four hundred to one thousand.   Whenever a flight of pigeons left one nesting place and made toward another, the netters learned their whereabouts by letter or telegraph, packed up their belongings and moved to the new location, sometimes following the birds a thousand miles at one move.   Some of them not only made a living, but earned a competency, by netting pigeons during part of the year and shooting wild-fowl and game-birds during the remainder of the season.   In addition to these there were many local netters, who plied the trade only when the pigeons came their way.

From the time of Audubon and Wilson, even before the railroads had penetrated to the west, there was in the east an enormous destruction of pigeons for the markets. Wagon-loads were sent to market, where the birds were sold at from twelve cents to fifty cents per dozen, according to the exigencies of supply and demand.   Audubon tells of seeing schooners loaded in bulk with pigeons in 1805 that were killed up the Hudson River and taken to the New York market.   He says that from ten to thirty dozens were caught at one sweep of the net.   Daniel Ott of Snyder County, Pennsylvania, tells of netting and killing 1300 in one day and Stephen Sherwood and J. P. Lyman are said to have taken 1,500 one morning before 11 o'clock.   In the early days the farmers destroyed large quantities of pigeons for salting, and people were employed about the roosts plucking the birds for their feathers (which were used for beds) and salting down the heaps of bodies which were piled on the ground.   Birds and beasts of prey got their share.   Audubon in describing a great roost in Kentucky, says that the birds took flight before sunrise, after which foxes, lynxes, cougars, bears, opossums and polecats were seen sneaking off, and the howlings of wolves were heard ; while eagles, hawks and vultures came in numbers to feast on the dead or disabled pigeons which had been slaughtered during the night. He says that in March, 1830, the pigeons were so abundant in New York City that piles of them could be seen on every hand.

Great nesting places of pigeons occasionally were established in the eastern states after the middle of the nineteenth century, when vast numbers were killed for market. In 1848 eighty tons of these birds were shipped from Cattaraugus County, New York.

Possibly the last great slaughter of pigeons in New York, of which we have record, was some time in the 70's. A flock had nested in Missouri in April, where most of the squabs were killed by pigeoners. This flock then went to Michigan, where it was followed by the same pigeoners, who again destroyed the squabs. The pigeons then flew to New York State, and nested in the mountains near the upper Beaverkill in the lower part of Ulster County. It is said that tons of them were sent to the New York market from this nesting place, and that not less than 15 tons of ice were used in packing the squabs.[1]

The wholesale slaughter in the west continued to increase until 1878. There were very large nestings in Michigan in 1868, 1870, 1872, 1874, 1876 and 1878. In 1876 there were at least three of these great breeding-places in the state, one each in Newaygo, Oceana and Grand Traverse counties.[2] The great killing of 1878 in Michigan is said to have yielded no less than 300 tons of birds to the market. Various figures are given regarding the number of birds killed in a few weeks at this great nesting place near Petoskey, Michigan. Professor Roney estimates that a billion birds were destroyed there. This is evidently an excessive approximation. Mr. E. T. Martin, one of the netters, gives what he calls the "official figures" of the number marketed as 1,107,866. His "figures" are largely estimates, but he states that 1,500,000 would cover all the birds killed at the Petoskey nesting that year. This is apparently a very low estimate. Mr. W. B. Mershon shows that some of Mr. Martin's figures are very far below the actual shipments.

Professor Roney watched one netter at the Petoskey nesting place, who killed 82 dozens of pigeons in one day; and who said that he had caught 87 dozens, or 1,044 birds in a day. The law regarding shooting and netting the birds at their nesting places was ignored. Professor Roney says that the sheriff drove out 400 Indians from the nesting in one day, and turned back 500 incoming Indians the next; and that people estimated that there were from 2,000 to 2,500 people at this nesting place, engaged in the business of trapping, killing and shipping pigeons. Mr. H. T. Phillips, a provision dealer at Cheboygan, Michigan, says that from 1864 until "the pigeons left the country" he handled live pigeons in numbers up to 175,000 a year. He asserts that in 1874 there was a nesting at Shelby, Michigan, from which 100 barrels of birds were shipped daily for 30 days. At 40 dozen birds to the barrel, this would total 1,440,000 birds.

During the 70's most of the pigeons concentrated in the west. In the autumn of 1877 Mr. James V. Bennett, a famous pigeoner, left Pennsylvania for Arkansas in search of a pigeon roost there. He found at Highcove, Indian Territory, a roost estimated to be 15 miles wide by 40 miles long. The pigeons often passed the winter in Texas, Arkansas, Missouri, Indian Territory and contiguous regions, and nested in Michigan and adjacent States and in great Canadian forests. At that time some very large nets were

---

[1] Van Cleef, J. S.: Forest and Stream, 1899, Vol. 52, p. 385.
[2] Mershon, W. B.: The Passenger Pigeon, 1907, p. 77.

used, grain beds were made, and the birds were allowed to come and feed there until from 200 dozens to 250 dozens were taken sometimes at one haul. Mr. Mershon gives many records of large catches, and the largest number caught at one spring of the net (3,500 birds) is attributed to Mr. E. Osborn; but Mr. Osborn himself says that it was 250 dozens, or 3,000 birds. It was made by fastening three large nets together, and springing them all at once. Mr. Osborn states that his firm alone shipped in 1861, from a roost in the Hocking Hills, Ohio, 225 barrels of birds. Sullivan Cook asserts in Forest and Stream (March 14,1903), that in 1869 in about 40 days there were shipped from Hartford, Michigan, and vicinity, three carloads a day, each car containing 150 barrels, with 35 dozens in a barrel, making the daily shipment 24,750 dozens. Evidently there is a typographical error here, as it would require 55 dozens in a barrel to make the daily shipment 24,750 dozens, or 11,880,000 birds for the season. Thirty-five dozens of domestic pigeons would fill an ordinary sugar barrel; and possibly it required 55 dozens of Passenger Pigeons to fill such a barrel, as they were not quite as large as domestic pigeons, and often were packed without wings or heads. Mr. Cook's figures seem to be based on 55 dozens to a barrel. In three years' time, he says (which may mean three years later), there were shipped 990,000 dozens or about 11,000,000 birds. In the two succeeding years it is estimated that one-third more than this number, or 15,840,000 birds, were shipped from Shelby, Michigan. These estimates were made by men who killed and marketed the pigeons. The figures may be excessive, but, if reduced one-half, they still would be enormous (taking no account of those killed elsewhere).

It is claimed by Mr. C. H. Engle, a resident of Petoskey, Michigan, that "two years later" there were shipped from that point five carloads a day for 30 days, with an average of 8,250 dozens to the carload, or 14,850,000 birds. Mr. S. S. Stevens told Mr. William Brewster that at least 500 men were netting pigeons at Petoskey in 1881, and thought they might have taken 20,000 birds each, or 10,000,000 pigeons. Still, people read of the "mysterious" disappearance of the Passenger Pigeon, wonder what caused it, and say that it never has been satisfactorily explained. The New York market alone would take 100 barrels a day for weeks, without a break in price. Chicago, St. Louis, Boston and all the great and little cities of the north and east joined in the demand. Need we wonder why the pigeons have vanished?

Most of the above calculations are founded on statements derived from Mr. Mershon's work. A little volume entitled "Etna and Kirkersville," by General Morris Schaff, gives some of the history of the destruction of the pigeons in Ohio; and there are many short articles on this subject in sportsmen's papers, particularly in Forest and Stream and the American Field. The birds that survived the slaughter at Petoskey in 1878 finally left the nesting place in large bodies and disappeared to the north, and from that time onward the diminution of the pigeons was rapid and continuous. Some of the netters asserted that this great flight was swallowed up in Lake Michigan, and that the pigeons then became practically extinct. This statement had no foundation in fact, as will presently appear. It is probable that when they left Petoskey in 1878 they retired into inaccessible regions of Canada, beyond reach of rail or telegraph, to breed again. In April, 1880, (also in 1881) they again passed through Michigan. The late Professor Walter B. Barrows quotes John Sims, county game warden, to the effect that on that date "millions" of pigeons passed over Iosco, going westward, but were never seen there afterward. In 1880 or 1881 there was a large nesting in Benzie County.

It has been stated that the Wild Pigeon "went off like dynamite." Even the naturalists failed to secure sufficient specimens and notes, as no one had an idea that extinction was imminent. Practically the same thing has been said about the extermination of the Labrador Duck, the Great Auk, and the Eskimo Curlew.

People never realize the danger of extirpating a species until it is too late; but the "sudden" diminution and extermination of the Passenger Pigeon was, like that of the other species mentioned, more seeming than real. Professor Walter B. Barrows of the Michigan Agricultural College, who collected much information regarding this bird, says that it was abundant in Michigan until 1880, fairly common from 1880 to 1890, but steadily decreasing in numbers, and was by no means rare in 1891, 1892 and 1893. Then it rapidly became scarce, and finally disappeared. There were many nestings for years after the Petoskey nesting of 1878, though the records are meager, for apparently no naturalist visited these nestings, but the pigeoners found them. The Petoskey nesting of 1878 was unusually large for that time, for the reason that the birds at three large breeding places in other states or regions were driven out by persecution, and joined the Petoskey group. After this the pigeons exhibited a tendency to scatter and to nest in regions where they were least molested. There seem to have been two great nestings in Michigan in 1881. Mr. Brewster quotes Mr. S. S. Stevens of Cadillac, Michigan, as saying that the last nesting of any importance in Michigan was in 1881, a few miles west of Grand Traverse. It was perhaps eight miles long. Pigeons were common in Iowa in 1884 (Anderson: Birds of Iowa). In 1882 Mr. Otto Widmann saw several large flocks, February 5 and 6, going northward at St. Louis. (Birds of Missouri, p. 84.) Mr. A. S. Eldredge writes that he saw a flight of pigeons near Lampasas, Texas, in the winter of 1882–83, that was three and one-half hours in passing; and that he saw a roost among the post oaks where every tree was loaded with birds.

In the spring of 1886 "millions" came to Pennsylvania, as is attested by "many reputable citizens." Pigeons were scattered over three or four counties at first but later they gathered in one great roosting place. Many men went there one night with guns and shot into the treetops as long as they could see or hear a bird. It was a clear moonlit night, and before morning the remaining birds left, making toward Canada. This was the last great attempt at nesting in Pennsylvania, but there was a smaller one the same year near Blossburg where thousands of squabs were killed with poles, according to Mr. Oscar Huff.[1] This account seems authentic, but the numbers may be exaggerated.

Our late Canadian records of the species are meager. Mr. Ernest Thompson Seton says that it bred in Manitoba in considerable numbers as late as 1887; but he also says

[1] French, John C.: The Passenger Pigeon in Pennsylvania, 1921, pp. 59–61. (See also Cassinia, No. XVI, 1912, p. 21.)

(Auk, 1908, p. 452) that the last year in which the pigeons came to Manitoba "in force" was 1878.   The next year they were comparatively scarce, and each year since they have become more so.   In 1881 MaCoun saw large flocks there, and large numbers were shot for food; the eggs of this species were taken by Miles Spence at James Bay as late as 1888. The species was recorded in Montreal and other localities in eastern Canada in 1883, 1885, 1886, 1888 and 1891.[1]

Up to 1886 live pigeons came into the Chicago market in great numbers, and were shipped all over the country for "pigeon shoots."   All the "live pigeon shoots," organized by shooting clubs, were supplied with an abundance of Passenger Pigeons.   I well remember how boys and men surrounded some of the shooting grounds to shoot the birds that escaped alive.   In 1881, 20,000 live Passenger Pigeons were killed at one trap-shooting tournament on Coney Island, held under the auspices of the New York Association for the Protection of Fish and Game.   Many of these birds were too young or too exhausted to fly.   Thus, sportsmen who could not participate in the slaughter of the birds on their nesting grounds had them brought alive to the doors of their club houses, and unwittingly shared in exterminating the species.   Mr. Ben O. Bush of Kalamazoo, Michigan, says that the last pigeons that he saw used for this purpose were obtained by John Watson of Chicago.   They came from Indian Territory in 1886; but this did not end the traffic.   It seems probable that many birds still gathered in inaccessible regions of that territory during the winter.

Mr. James O. Bennett, pigeoner, of Williamsport, Pennsylvania, received a letter from a friend in Indiana in 1884, who had just returned from Indian Territory, informing him that a heavy flight of pigeons was then moving up the Missouri River.

In the spring of 1888 Mr. William Brewster and Dr. Jonathan Dwight, Jr., visited Michigan in search of the Passenger Pigeon, and found that large flocks had passed through Cadillac late in April, and that similar flocks had been observed in nearly all the southern counties.   This flight was so large that some of the netters expressed the belief that the pigeons were as numerous as ever; and Mr. Brewster himself opined that the extermination of the species was not then imminent, and that it might be saved, but considered it unlikely that effectual laws could be passed before its extinction.   The birds moved somewhere to the north to breed, and were not known to nest in any numbers in Michigan.   One of the netters brought intelligence of a flock at least "eight acres" in extent, and many other smaller flocks were reported.   Many birds were found scattered about in the woods, but no large nesting place was seen anywhere.   After that date comparatively few birds are recorded at any one locality.

Quantities of birds were sent to eastern markets from the southwest during the decade from 1878 to 1888.   Mr. Herbert K. Job says that Passenger Pigeons were still coming into the Boston Market in 1888.

Professor George H. Beyer informed me that he saw several large flocks of Passenger Pigeons at Rayne Station, Louisiana, in 1888, from which he killed three birds.   There

---

[1] MaCoun, John: Catalogue of Canadian Birds, 1900, Part I, pp. 215, 216.

was said to be a large nesting in North Dakota in 1889 where "millions"[1] of birds were slaughtered and shipped to market in carloads. At that time there was said to be but one great flock left.[2]

There was said to be a great roost in Indian Territory (now Oklahoma) about 1889. Mr. N. S. Goss (1891) said that the species was then "fast disappearing, though still to be found in numbers within the Indian Territory and portions of the southern states."[3] Adolph Shurr said that there was a small nesting at the head of Young Women's Creek, Clinton County, Pennsylvania in 1892. Dr. P. L. Hatch (1892) writing of Minnesota said that in "late years" but few were seen in any of the districts which he had heard from.[4]

How many barrels of pigeons were shipped to the markets during these final years? At least one shipment of several barrels was condemned in New York City as late as November, 1892,[5] and several hundred dozens came into the Boston market in December, 1892, and in January, 1893. I saw some pigeons in barrels there in 1892 or 1893, which probably were some of the lot recorded by Brewster and noted by Fleming, who records the New York shipment. All of these were from the Indian Territory. Mr. H. T. Phillips of Detroit, market hunter, stated (1907) that he used to see and kill pigeons every spring, "up to ten years ago," from the middle of March to the middle of April, on the Mississippi bayous. This must have been in the latter years of the nineteenth century, at the time when the pigeons were on the verge of extinction. Dr. A. W. Butler reports that more were seen in Indiana in 1894 than for several years.[6] A flock was seen in Illinois in 1895, from which two specimens were taken. At that time the netting of the birds had been practically given up, and most of the dealers had seen no pigeons for two seasons. Netting finally ceased, on account of the virtual extinction of the birds.

Messrs. W. W. Judy & Co., marketmen, of St. Louis, wrote to Mr. Ruthven Deane, in 1895, that the last pigeons that they received came from Siloam Springs, Arkansas, in 1893; they had lost all track of the pigeons since that time, and their netters were lying idle.

The above paragraph epitomizes the history of pigeon extinction. Judy & Company were perhaps the largest dealers in pigeons in the United States. The story of where their netters and others worked after 1878, how many birds they took and what markets they supplied, would explain only too well the so-called "mystery" of the disappearance of the Passenger Pigeon. It is evident from the foregoing that, although the business of pigeon netting was reduced much after 1878, it was followed for at least fifteen years thereafter. The pigeoners pursued the birds as long as they could find a flock so large that they could make a "killing."

---

[1] Probably an exaggeration.
[2] French, John C.: The Passenger Pigeon in Pennsylvania, 1919, p. 108.
[3] Birds of Kansas, 1891, p. 238.
[4] Birds of Minnesota, 1892, pp. 171, 172.
[5] Fleming, J. H.: Ottawa Naturalist, 1907, Vol. XX, p. 236.
[6] Birds of Indiana, 1897, pp. 264, 265.

I tried to get some information regarding the netting of pigeons by Judy & Company and other firms, but the firms had dissolved or the partners were no longer living. Mr. Otto Widmann of St. Louis, who kindly undertook to learn what he could about the pigeon shipments, sent an interesting letter, from which the following extracts are taken: "In reply to your letter of September 9, I am sorry I could not get what you wanted. The firm was W. W. Judy & Company. Judy died twenty-five years ago, and the firm was dissolved. One of the partners, Mr. Farrell, died eight years afterwards, and there is at present only one of the partners living, Mr. Dave Unger. The only information that could be gotten from him was the interesting statement that the Wild Pigeons have flown to Australia. While trying to get the desired information, a game dealer, F. H. Miller, stated that eight years ago (1902) he received 12 dozen Wild Pigeons from Rogers, Arkansas, for which he paid $2.50 a dozen, and sold all to an eastern firm for $5.00 a dozen. His last Wild Pigeon, a single individual, among some Ducks, was received four years ago [1906], from Black River, Missouri. As he is an old game dealer, who has handled many pigeons, there is no doubt about the species; but exact dates were not obtainable." This closes the history of the Passenger Pigeon in our markets. For the rest we must look to the millions of shot guns in the United States, the natural enemies of the pigeons, and the accidents of migration. For every pigeon that was shot and recorded during the last part of the nineteenth century, probably 100, perhaps 1000, were shot and eaten. Who was there to record them? Ornithologists may not be rare in some of our cities, but they are very rare in the western forests. For all practical purposes the close of the nineteenth century saw the end of the Passenger Pigeon. Later we tried to save it, and rewards aggregating about $1,500.00 were offered for the undisturbed nest and eggs; but without result. They came twenty years too late.

A campaign of publicity was conducted for several years and a search for surviving Passenger Pigeons was begun under the energetic management of Professor C. F. Hodge, then at Clark University at Worcester, Massachusetts; the large rewards offered were published widely in the press of the United States and Canada, and a great public interest in the search was aroused. Passenger Pigeons were reported in numbers from many parts of North America, but investigation of these communications did not result in producing so much as a feather of the bird. This merely shows the unreliability of such statements, and how easily people may be mistaken. There were three reports in 1911 that seemed promising. In each case a single bird was seen and watched for some time at very close range; but all assertions regarding large flocks at this late date probably are based on observations of Mourning Doves or Band-tailed Pigeons.

A large correspondence and a careful search through literature leads to the belief that the pigeons were common and in some cases abundant in parts of the west from 1880 to 1890, though gradually decreasing. After 1893 the reports became more vague and less trustworthy, except in a few cases. Small flocks were seen and specimens taken in the last decade of the nineteenth century in Canada, and in Wisconsin, Nebraska, Illinois, Indiana and other western states, and even in some of the eastern states. Chief Pokagon reported a nesting of pigeons near the headwaters of the Au Sable River in Michigan in 1896.   In 1898 a flock of about two hundred birds was said to have been seen in Michigan; one was taken; and in 1900 about fifty birds were reported.

While the last immense nesting of Passenger Pigeons on record in Michigan was in 1878 the species did not become extinct then in a day or a year; it was not wiped from the face of the earth by any great catastrophe; the pigeons gradually became fewer and fewer for nearly 30 years thereafter.

Such records as I find of the last specimens actually taken (not merely seen) in the states to which they refer indicate how the species finally dropped out of sight.   It is probable that in most cases Passenger Pigeons were seen in the states referred to at dates later than most of those given, but owing to the many mistakes that have been made in identifying the birds in the field, it is unsafe to record "sight records."

1882–83. — *Texas*, a flight that was three and one-half hours in passing, seen in winter of 1882–83 near Lampasas.   Many killed.   No recent record (A. S. Eldredge).

1885. — *New Hampshire*, Concord (G. M. Allen, Birds of New Hampshire, 1903, p. 95).   General Battles killed one in 1885 near Concord, specimen now in the collection at the Dewey School (White, F. B., Birds of Concord, N. H., 1924, p. 37).   *South Carolina*, immature female Nov. 21 (Wayne, Arthur T., Auk, Vol. XXIII, 1906, p. 61).

1886. — *Rhode Island*, specimen taken by Walter A. Angell at Cranston, November 2, 1886, now in collection of Harry Hathaway (Auk, Vol. XXX, 1913, p. 553).   T. M. Flanagan took about a dozen at Warwick in 1885 or 1886 (John H. Flanagan).

1887. — *Alabama*, Greensboro, a lone bird shot by Edward Pasteur (American Field, Vol. 34, 1890, p. 584).

1889. — *Province of Quebec*, Tadousac, specimen taken July 20 [now in collection of Dr. Jonathan Dwight, American Museum Natural History, New York] (J. H. Fleming, Ottawa Naturalist, 1907, Vol. XX, p. 236.   See also (below) in this list Province of Quebec under 1907).

1890. — *Ontario*, two females, one taken September 20, the other October 11 at Toronto.   Latter now in the collection of J. H. Fleming.   (Fleming, Ottawa Naturalist, Vol. XX, 1907, p. 236.)

1891. — *Minnesota*, young male taken on the Root River in August; now in the collection of H. W. Shoemaker.   Recorded by him in the Passenger Pigeon in Pennsylvania, 1919, pp. 174, 175.

1893. — *Indiana*, pair and nest taken by C. B. Brown of Chicago in spring of 1893 at English Lake; nest and eggs preserved in his collection (Ruthven Deane, Auk, Vol. XII, 1895, p. 299).

Arkansas, Siloam Springs, last shipment of its pigeons to W. W. Judy & Company, St. Louis (Ruthven Deane, Auk, Vol. XII, 1895, p. 298).

Tennessee, Brownsville.   In the fall of 1893 a Mr. Riddick killed one of a flock of eight (S. N. Rhoades, "Zoology of Tennessee, No. 2, Birds," Proceedings of the Academy of Natural Sciences of Philadelphia, 1895, p. 476).

1894. — *North Carolina*, Buncombe County, female taken by J. S. Cairns, October 20 (C. S. Brimley, Forbush, Game Birds, Wild-Fowl and Shore Birds 1912, p. 461).

Massachusetts, an adult female taken by Neil Casey at Melrose, April 12; specimen preserved and mounted (Game Birds, Wild-Fowl and Shore Birds, 1912, p. 461).

1895. — *Louisiana*, Mandeville, near New Orleans, January 26, two taken out of a flock of five by Dr. J. H. Lamb (Professor George E. Beyer in Game Birds, Wild Fowl and Shore Birds, p. 461).

Illinois, Lake Forest, August 7, young female in collection of John F. Ferry (Ruthven Deane, Auk, Vol. XIII, 1896, p. 81).

Nebraska, Sarpy County, bird killed out of 15 or 20, November 9, by Hon. Edgar Howard of Papillion, five miles southeast of that place (Lawrence Bruner, " Some Notes on Nebraska Birds," 1896, p. 84).

Pennsylvania, Canadensis, Monroe County, bird shot, October 23, by George Stuart of Philadelphia, now in his possession (Witmer Stone). See Pennsylvania (1898) below.

1895–6. — *Indiana*, pair of wings seen by Prof. W. P. Shannon from bird killed in winter, 1895–6 or spring, 1896 (A. W. Butler, "Birds of Indiana," 22d report, Department of Geology and Natural Resources of Indiana, 1897, p. 764).

1896. — *New Jersey*, Englewood, June 23, immature female taken by C. Irving Wood, mounted by J. Ullrich (F. M. Chapman, Auk, Vol. XIII, 1896, p. 341).

Missouri, Altie (sic), pair killed from flock of fifty by Charles U. Holden, Jr.; in collection of Ruthven Deane (Auk, Vol. XIV, 1897, p. 317). (The place given here is spelled "Altie" in Mr. Deane's communication, and in other publications "Attie," "Attic" and "Attick," Oregon County. "Alton," the only town or postoffice in the county beginning with A, probably would be correct).

Iowa, Lee County, September 7, William G. Praeger shot an immature male near Keokuk (R. M. Anderson, "Birds of Iowa," 1907, p. 239). (See also Charles B. Cory, "Birds of Illinois and Wisconsin," 1909, p. 446, where the date is given as September 17.)

1898. — *Manitoba*, Winnipegosis, adult male taken, mounted by George E. Atkinson, Winnipeg, April 14 (J. H. Fleming, Auk, Vol. XX, 1903, p. 66). (Possibly the same reported by Ernest Thompson Seton, as taken by J. J. G. Rosser, April 13 (Auk, Vol. XXV, 1908, p. 452).)

Michigan, Detroit, immature bird shot by P. H. Clements of Detroit, mounted by C. Campion, September 14 (J. H. Fleming, Auk, Vol. XX, 1903, p. 66).

Kentucky, Owensboro, immature male taken July 27, now in Smithsonian Institution (J. H. Fleming, Ottawa Naturalist, Vol. XX, 1907, p. 237). Mr. Fleming says the bird was taken by J. G. Taylor of Owensboro.

New York, Canandaigua, September 14, male taken by Addison P. Wilbur (E. H. Eaton, "Birds of New York," Vol. I, 1910, p. 385).

Pennsylvania, adult female in collection of Carnegie Institute at Pittsburg, marked "Pennsylvania" August 15th, 1898; no locality given (J. H. Fleming, Ottawa Naturalist, Vol. XX, 1907, p. 237).

1900. — *Ohio*, Sargents, March 24, specimen shot by a boy and mounted by Mrs. C. Barnes (W. L. Dawson, "Birds of Ohio," Vol. II, 1903, p. 427). Recorded by W. F. Henniger (Wilson Bulletin, Vol. XIV, old series, 1902, p. 82).*

Vermont, seen every season near Essex Junction about Fort Ethan Allen and a few shot there "last season" (George H. Perkins and Clifton D. Howe, "A Preliminary List of the Birds Found in Vermont," 1901, p. 17).*

Wisconsin, Babcock, September, specimen not preserved, killed by Neal Brown, while hunting with Emerson Hough (W. B. Mershon, "The Passenger Pigeon," 1907, p. 154). See also Emerson Hough in "Out of Doors" (Saturday Evening Post, October 15, 1910).*

1902. — *Arkansas*, F. H. Miller of St. Louis received 12 dozen from Rogers, Arkansas (Otto Widmann, "Game Birds, Wild-fowl and Shore Birds," 1912, p. 462).*

1904. — *Maine*, one killed at Bar Harbor, mounted by J. Bert Baxter of Bangor (Journal, Maine Ornithological Society, Vol. X, 1908, p. 54).*

1906. — *Connecticut*, North Bridgewater, Fairfield County, bird shot August, 1906. Now in Daggett Collection, Museum of History, Science and Art, Los Angeles, California (L. E. Wyman, Auk, Vol. XXXVIII, 1921, p. 274).

Missouri, Black River, F. H. Miller of St. Louis received a bird at his market in St. Louis, shipped from Black River (Otto Widmann, "Game Birds, Wild-fowl and Shore Birds," 1912, p. 462). Last previous record for Missouri was 1896 (see above).*

---

*Where the asterisk appears in this list either date or authenticity of the record so marked may be questionable.

1907. — *Province of Quebec*, Bird taken by Pacificque Couture of St. Vincent, P. Q., Sept. 23,* mounted by A. Learo, taxidermist of Montreal and identified by him. Mr. Couture had left St. Vincent in 1912, and efforts to locate him have failed.*

1909. — *New York*, an adult male taken by J. L. Howard, a Justice of Clyde, about three miles from that city on the Clyde River and mounted by George L. Perkins of that place. Mr. Howard said that he shot the bird at a small pond near the Clyde River in 1909. The specimen is in the museum of Cornell University. Recorded by S. C. Bishop and A. H. Wright (Auk, Vol. XXXIV, 1917, pp. 208, 209). The date of capture is questionable. Mr. Howard was over 80 years old in 1917, when the bird was recorded as killed in 1909. Upon the bottom of the mount was written "Geo. L. Perkins, July 5, 1898." This date is more than two months earlier than the capture of the bird taken by Addison P. Wilbur, which is given above as the last bird taken in New York. The mount, however, may have been an old one used previously for some other bird. The question is whether Mr. Howard's memory of the date can be relied upon.*

I must admit the probability that many Passenger Pigeons were seen at later dates than some of those hereinbefore recorded. Where flocks, small groups or single birds were watched by competent observers for hours through glasses, as they were in some instances, there can be no question of identity; but the taking of the specimen is the only tangible proof that satisfies the ornithologist in the case of a disappearing species, and for that reason the above records are confined to those cases where at least one bird was taken.

I cannot leave this subject without referring to various canards, some of which have been taken seriously by too many intelligent people. Efforts have been made to account for the supposed sudden disappearance of the pigeons by tales of cyclonic sea disturbances or lake storms, which are supposed to have drowned all of them. Thousands of pigeons actually were destroyed occasionally, during their flights, by storms or fogs at sea or on the Great Lakes. There are many reports of such occurrences. The earliest of these is recorded by Kalm.

Giraud, in his Birds of Long Island (1844), states that he has "heard" of great numbers of pigeons floating on the water which were seen by shipmasters, and many such tales were published when the pigeons were abundant.[1] Nevertheless, these catastrophes did not wipe out the species, for it had too wide a range.

The following "sailors' yarn," probably refers to another species. Mr. G. C. Tremaine Ward says that Mr. S. D. Woodruff of St. Catherines, Ontario, Canada, asserts that several shipmasters say that immense numbers of Wild Pigeons perished in the Gulf of Mexico, "being exhausted by contrary winds and dense fogs." This gentleman also avers that Mr. Woodruff states that several shipmasters saw myriads of pigeons alight on their vessels, and had to cast them off into the sea. (Auk, 1901, p. 192, — no names or dates given.) This is too indefinite to be of any value as evidence. There is no authentic record that the Passenger Pigeon in its annual flights ever crossed the Gulf of Mexico and, although there is a single record of its occurrence in Cuba, it has not been seen in great numbers near the Gulf coast for 50 years. The pigeons which once commonly

* Mr. J. H. Fleming of Toronto, vice-president of The American Ornithologists Union and an authority on records of The Passenger Pigeon, has reasons to doubt records above marked with an asterisk.

[1] See also Game Birds, Wild-Fowl and Shore Birds, 1912, pp. 463–464.

crossed these waters from Florida to Cuba in large numbers, belonged to another species, the White-crowned Pigeon (*Columba leucocephala*). Such tales about the drowning of birds in the Gulf of Mexico may have referred to some of the Plovers or "prairie pigeons," as they were called in the west, hosts of which crossed the gulf annually.

The Passenger Pigeon was not exterminated, or nearly exterminated, by drowning, soon after the nesting at Petoskey, in 1881, as some people believed, for as hereinbefore stated, there was an immense flight in Texas the ensuing winter, a large flight crossed Michigan to the north in 1888, and they were seen and taken in numbers in many places in the United States and Canada for years subsequent to the date of the Petoskey nesting in 1881. The statement recently published in a magazine article, that the pigeons have gone to South America, is absolutely without any foundation in fact. This bird is unknown on the South American continent. The assertion that they have gone to Australia is puerile.

Tales of wholesale destruction of pigeons by snow-storms in the north may have some foundation. Northward migrations of pigeons often occurred very early in the season, and the first nests were sometimes completed while snow still remained. On March 25, 1830, a flight of pigeons was overtaken by a high wind and snow-storm near Albany, New York. Twenty-eight inches of snow fell, and the birds were overwhelmed, and taken "in great abundance" by the people.[1]

Some of the pigeons may have been driven by persecution to the far north to breed, in the latter part of the nineteenth century, where they may have been destroyed by unseasonable storms, for many species are subject to periodical reduction by the elements; but the whole history of the last thirty years of the existence of the Passenger Pigeon goes to prove that the birds were so persistently molested that they finally lost their coherence, were scattered far and wide, and were extirpated by man's constant persecution. While they existed in large colonies, the orphans were taken care of by their neighbors. Mr. E. T. Martin, in a pamphlet entitled "Among the Pigeons," published in full in the American Field, January 25, 1879, asserts that one of his men shot six female pigeons that came to feed a single squab in one nest. (Comment on this shooting is unnecessary.) This communal habit of feeding preserved the species (wherever the squabs were not killed in the nests) so long as the birds nested in large colonies; but when they became scattered, the little ones starved when their parents were killed.

The Passenger Pigeon was not a suspicious bird, as birds go; it was easily taken. It reproduced slowly, laid few eggs and could not stand continuous persecution at all times. When its innumerable multitudes were destroyed and its flocks dispersed, the end came rapidly.

The question often is asked, "how was it possible for man to kill them all?" It was not possible, nor was it necessary that he should do so in order to exterminate them. All that was requisite to bring about this result was to destroy most of the young birds hatched each year. This was done year after year and nature cut off the rest. She

---

[1] Munsell, Joel: Annals of Albany, 1858, Vol. IX, p. 206.

always eliminates a large proportion of the young of all creatures. The squabs were sought because they brought a high price in the market. The flock mentioned by Mr. Van Cleef (see page 69), which nested in Missouri, Michigan and New York the same year, was followed by the pigeoners, who killed about all the squabs at each nesting. Sometimes the Pigeons were so harassed that all their nestings were broken up, and no young were raised that season; thus the natural increase was cut off, and constant diminution was assured. Each female pigeon laid but one egg (possibly rarely two) at each nesting. If the young were destroyed, the species must soon come to an end. In the fall migrations young birds, being inexperienced and unsuspicious, were first to fall victims to the gunner. The younger birds so persistently destroyed would have been more fertile than the older pigeons which after a few years could not produce young enough in any case to perpetuate the race. Extermination must have resulted under such conditions, even if no man ever killed an adult Passenger Pigeon. The adults were not immortal. Even if undisturbed by man and their natural enemies they would soon disappear; but they were not undisturbed. No adequate attempt to protect them was made until they virtually had disappeared. Whenever a law looking toward the conservation of these birds was proposed in any state, its opponents argued before legislative committees that the pigeons "needed no protection"; that their numbers were so vast, and that they ranged over such a great extent of country, that they were amply able to take care of themselves. This argument defeated most measures that might have given adequate protection to the species until it was too late. Where laws were passed, they were not enforced. We did our best to exterminate both old and young, and we succeeded. The explanation is so simple that all talk of "mystery" seems sadly out of place. To sum up: — The pigeons were reduced by the destruction of the great forests that formerly fed them, destroyed by market hunters and netters and, finally, their vast flocks gone, broken up and scattered, the survivors roamed the country, targets for a million shotguns, until the inevitable end.

HAUNTS AND HABITS. The Passenger Pigeon was a peculiarly graceful and elegant bird, formed for powerful, swift, long-continued flight. It was a native of the great forested region of eastern North America. It nested in the unbroken forests which covered the land before the advent of the white man, and it fed mainly on the fruits of trees and shrubs. The location of the enormous and wonderful breeding colonies or pigeon cities and the extensive roosts was decided by temporary abundance of mast, such as beechnuts or acorns, either on the trees or beneath them on the ground. The pigeoners believed that the small flocks which first appeared at the sites of these colonies were scouts that reported to the main body, which soon followed. On the appearance of the birds at a nesting place, they were already mating or mated. Chief Pokagon, the last Pottawotami chief of the Pokagon band, thus described the arrival of the mighty army of pigeons at a chosen nesting place.

. . . "About the middle of May, 1850, while in the fur trade, I was camping on the head waters of the Manistee River in Michigan. One morning on leaving my wigwam

I was startled by hearing a gurgling, rumbling sound, as though an army of horses laden with sleigh bells was advancing through the deep forests toward me. As I listened more intently, I concluded that instead of the tramping of horses it was distant thunder; and yet the morning was clear, calm and beautiful. Nearer and nearer came the strange commingling sounds of sleigh bells, mixed with the rumbling of an approaching storm. While I gazed in wonder and astonishment, I beheld moving toward me in an unbroken front millions of pigeons, the first I had seen that season. They passed like a cloud through the branches of the high trees, through the underbrush and over the ground, apparently overturning every leaf. Statue-like I stood, half-concealed by cedar boughs. They fluttered all about me, lighting on my head and shoulders; gently I caught two in my hands and carefully concealed them under my blanket.

"I now began to realize they were mating, preparatory to nesting. It was an event which I had long hoped to witness; so I sat down and carefully watched their movements, amid the greatest tumult. I tried to understand their strange language, and why they all chatted in concert. In the course of the day the great on-moving mass passed by me, but the trees were still filled with them sitting in pairs in convenient crotches of the limbs, now and then gently fluttering their half-spread wings and uttering to their mates those strange, bell-like wooing notes which I had mistaken for the ringing of bells in the distance."

Most of the courtship of the pigeons was conducted in the trees, for the Passenger Pigeon was essentially an arboreal bird. Its legs were short and its tail long and it was not much given to strutting in the manner of the domestic dove. Its usual pose in the trees was quite erect and in courting the male made use of his vigorous half closed wings which were flapped toward the female of his choice. On reaching her he frequently hooked his head over her neck, as if trying thus to embrace her. The male flapped his wings a great deal during the mating and breeding season, while seated on a perch, and often nodded his head with a circular motion as if trying to hook his bill over the neck of the female. The billing between the sexes was not prolonged, but each grasped the other's bill, and with a quick perfunctory shake let go. The males seemed very pugnacious during the breeding season, were very jealous and exhibited the most threatening mien towards a rival, but their fighting was mainly confined to striking out with the wings, which did little injury to the combatants. The nests were crude specimens of bird architecture, often built in one day and occupied the next. Some were so thin and frail that the eggs could be seen through the interstices; others were more strongly built. All authorities agree that in captivity the pigeons laid but one egg in a nest, but many observers maintain that in the woods a certain proportion of the nests often contained two eggs, and the pigeoners who gathered the squabs tell a similar story. In some nestings, however, they admit that most or all of the nests contained but one young. It seems probable that where a great supply of food was available, many of the younger and more vigorous females deposited two eggs in the nest, and that where food was less plentiful, fewer eggs were laid. It is possible that two females might have been responsible for two eggs in one nest, but if so it is difficult to understand why three or more were never found. Many nests contained neither eggs nor young. There were often 50 or more nests in a tree, and during the activities of the swarming multitudes some eggs and young were accidentally thrown or pushed from the nests. In most cases hardwood forests seemed to be preferred for the great nestings, but when the pigeons nested in coniferous trees, the number of nests in a tree increased, as these trees provided better support for the nests. As soon as the eggs were laid, incubation commenced, and from that time onward the eggs were carefully guarded, turned and incubated night and day. The males left the nesting at daylight and went out to feed, returning about ten o'clock, when each female stepped off her nest as the male took his turn, while the females went off to feed, returning about three P.M., again the males went out, returning about sunset. Thus great flocks of one sex arrived at the nesting at these hours, while other great flocks left it, going out in numbers that actually darkened the sun, and flying sometimes so low that the strong current of air created by the swiftly moving mass swept the ground beneath. Usually they flew downward from the trees, first passing near the ground, and then, rising above the forest, they started for their feeding-ground.

Two methods of feeding are described. The first was ground feeding. In picking up mast the flock alighted on the ground with extended front and beating wings, moving rapidly forward, the rear rank continually rising in air and passing over those in front, thus forming the front line until the next rear rank had passed over. Thus, as the flock rolled along with a rotary forward motion, all were fed, and the ground in that place was swept bare of pigeon food. While a flock was feeding, sentinel birds on the watch gave the alarm at the approach of an enemy by clapping their wings together over their backs. This signal was repeated by every member of the great flock as they rose with a thunderous roar of wings.

They drank commonly as other pigeons do, but where steep banks offered them no footing they could light on the water with wings raised and partially extended, drink and rise again on flapping pinions.[1]

It was customary for the birds of a nesting to leave the food near their home for the later use of the fledglings, and to go long distances for their own sustenance. Sometimes in order to get the beechnuts off the trees before the frost had loosened them, the birds fluttered among the branches pecking off the nuts or beating them off with their wings, afterward gathering from the ground those that fell.

In about 27 days from the laying of the eggs (14 for hatching and 13 for rearing) the young birds found a plentiful supply of food as soon as they left the nest. The young now seemed to be able to feed themselves, and the adults, leaving the locality in a body, sought another nesting often hundreds of miles away, usually farther north, but always where food was plentiful. In this way they were able in less than four months to produce at least three broods of young and in seasons when food was plentiful, another brood may have been reared. In their later years the large flocks had little chance to rear any, but

---

[1] Lenketter, W. A.: Rod and Gun in Canada, Dec. 1920, p. 54.

in the early days when they were unmolested by civilized man, they might have produced about one brood each five weeks for four or five months of spring, summer, and autumn. The young developed so rapidly that in about six months after they were hatched, it was difficult to distinguish them from adults.

Their migrations were not the regular, periodical, long-drawn-out movements that characterize the seasonal flights of most birds. They were undertaken chiefly in search of food. The pigeons were so swift and tireless in flight, however, that they could pass from zone to zone in a day, and a great unseasonable snow-storm in the north, covering their food supply, might send them all south at once, or such a storm in the mountains might drive them to the coast. They migrated *en masse*. That is, the birds of one great nesting rose into the air as one body, and the movements of these immense hosts formed the most wonderful and impressive spectacle in animated nature. There were stirring sights in this and other countries when great herds of grazing mammals thundered over the plains, but the approach of the mighty armies of the air was appalling. Then vast multitudes, rising strata upon strata, covered the darkened sky and hid the sun, while the roar of their myriad wings might be likened to that of a hurricane; and thus they passed for hours or days together, while the people in the country over which the legions winged their way kept up a fusillade from every point of vantage. Where the lower flights passed close over high hilltops, people were stationed with oars, poles, shingles, and other weapons to knock down the swarming birds, and the whole countryside was fed on pigeons until the people were surfeited.

The food of the pigeons was very varied. In the spring earthworms, also caterpillars and other insects were not disdained. Indeed there are tales of large forests around the nestings of the pigeons being cleared of caterpillars by these birds. They were known to eat grasshoppers and snails but their main food was vegetal. Green shoots of vegetation and berries were eaten in their seasons; blueberries, huckleberries, raspberries, juneberries, wild cherries, tupelo berries, mulberries, holly berries, wild strawberries, cranberries and pokeberries were favorites and all were utilized. Acorns, beechnuts, chestnuts and other seeds of deciduous and coniferous trees were greedily eaten. Grains and the seeds of grasses and weeds attracted them.

ECONOMIC STATUS. Passenger Pigeons were useful mainly as a source of food supply of considerable value and harmful only by reason of the destruction of grain.

Zenaidúra macroúra carolinénsis (LINNÆUS). Mourning Dove.

Other names: WILD PIGEON; TURTLE DOVE.

Plate 36.

DESCRIPTION. — Bill small, slender; wing rather long, pointed, 2nd or 3rd primary longest; tail of 14 feathers nearly ¾ as long as wing, middle feathers longest and obtusely pointed, rest shorter, less pointed and graduated from middle to outer, and from ⅓ to ½ its length. *Adult male:* Above mainly light grayish brown, much shaded with olive, verging toward fawn on forehead and sides of head, passing into slate gray or mouse gray on top of head, and bluish-gray on rump, flight feathers and tail; middle feathers of tail colored like back, but sometimes darkening toward ends; rest of tail-feathers gray or bluish-gray with black subterminal bar and long white tip, outer web of outer feathers white; below vinaceous buff, often tinged purplish on breast, darkest on breast, lighter (sometimes pale buff) on chin, throat and under tail-coverts; wing-linings and axillars bluish ashy. *A small spot of black, glossed blue on side of head and upper neck beneath ear region;* sides of neck and sometimes back of neck glossed with metallic purple or purplish bronze; a few black spots on scapulars, tertials and middle wing-coverts; "bill black, tumid nasal part somewhat glaucous; iris dark brown"; bare space about eye "pale blue," tinged above with "pale green" (Ridgway); "legs and feet lake red; claws horn blue" (N. S. Goss). *Adult female:* similar to adult male, but smaller, duller and tail shorter. *Juvenal plumage:* Much duller than male, smaller and tail much shorter; more grayish brown above; paler below; feathers of fore neck, scapulars and wing-coverts (sometimes more of upper plumage) margined around ends with paler; no black spot under ear; tail more brownish.

MEASUREMENTS. — Length 11.00 to 13.00 in.; spread about 17.00 to 19.00; folded wing 5.40 to 6.00; tail 5.70 to 6.70; bill .49 to .60; tarsus .75 to .85. Female smaller than male. Weight about 3 oz.

MOLTS. — Nestling plumage is followed by juvenal plumage in summer or early autumn. This is succeeded by complete molt, in autumn and winter, into first winter plumage, which is virtually as adult. Adults have complete postnuptial molt in autumn and winter.

FIELD MARKS. — Length about that of small Sharp-shinned Hawk, size smaller than Domestic Dove; brown head with rather long pointed tail and wings, wings and tail when spread have a bluish cast, tail-feathers mostly with white tips and black marks, white conspicuous when tail is spread, showing white edges; small black spot below ear-coverts distinguishes bird from Passenger Pigeon, but this can be made out only close at hand in good light, with powerful glasses; much smaller than Passenger Pigeon and browner; usually rises with twittering whistle from ground in open land, grain fields, buckwheat fields or weedy gardens and flies swiftly like a small swift hawk.

VOICE. — A plaintive long-drawn cooing, *coo-ah, coo, coo, coo* or *ah-coo′-roo-coo*. Its recurrent whistle as it rises is supposed to be made by the wings, but I heard the sound once when the bird was sitting with wings closed.

BREEDING. — Almost anywhere, usually on upland but sometimes in a swamp or marsh. *Nest:* In woods, orchard or shade trees; sometimes in lower branches of pine, more rarely in bush or vine, more rarely still on ground (when usually no nest); a loosely constructed hollowed platform of sticks with few straws and weed stalks, occasionally leaves or little moss; usually from 3 to 10 or 12 feet from ground; sometimes the deserted nest of another species. *Eggs:* Rarely 1, usually 2, occasionally 3 and 4 reported; .98 to 1.23 by .75 to .90 in.; elliptical or elliptical ovate; white; *Dates:* April 17 to July 27,* New England. *Incubation:* By both sexes. Period 12 to 14 days (Burns): 14⅛ to 15½ days in confinement (M. M. Nice). Broods, 2 yearly, possibly more, in the south.

RANGE. — "Eastern North America, chiefly in Austral Zones." Breeds north to New Brunswick, Nova Scotia, southern Maine, southern Ontario, Michigan and Wisconsin, west to eastern Iowa, eastern Arkansas and Louisiana, and south to Gulf coast, occasional in Bermuda; casual in Quebec and accidental in Newfoundland[1] and on Labrador coast; resident more or less regularly from Potomac and Ohio valleys southward; winters irregularly north to Massachusetts and Maine, and west along the northern tier of states to Michigan; occurs occasionally in winter along Gulf and Caribbean coasts of Mexico and Central America to Panama; other forms of the species occupy western North America.

DISTRIBUTION IN NEW ENGLAND. — Occurs mainly in Alleghanian Faunal Region below 1200 feet, most common along southern coasts and in southern river valleys. *Maine:* Rare migrant and summer

---

* A late breeding record is that of fresh eggs, Sept. 15, 1897, near Verona, Oneida Co., N. Y. (See Bird-Lore, Vol. XVII, 1915, p. 132.)

[1] Lewis, Harrison F.: Auk, Vol. XXXIX, 1922, p. 107.

resident, chiefly in southern part, where recorded in winter (Jan. and Feb. 1920, C. E. Miller). *New Hampshire:* Rare migrant and summer resident, chiefly in southern part (recorded Dec. 15) may winter rarely. *Vermont:* Rare summer resident; seen Jan. 8, 1919 at Shaftsbury (Dr. L. H. Ross).[1] *Massachusetts, Rhode Island* and *Connecticut:* Rare or uncommon to common summer resident locally; rare and rather irregular winter resident, sometimes locally common in winter.

SEASON IN MASSACHUSETTS. — Resident irregularly throughout the year in eastern counties (has wintered in Worcester County); arrives in others about mid-March to mid-April, and departs in September or October (rarely November); in winter more common on Cape Cod than elsewhere.

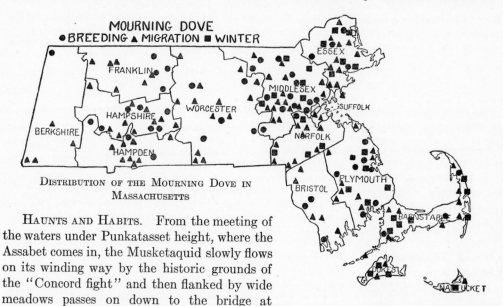

DISTRIBUTION OF THE MOURNING DOVE IN
MASSACHUSETTS

HAUNTS AND HABITS. From the meeting of the waters under Punkatasset height, where the Assabet comes in, the Musketaquid slowly flows on its winding way by the historic grounds of the "Concord fight" and then flanked by wide meadows passes on down to the bridge at Carlisle. With the first blush of day on still May mornings, up from the river valley comes the saddened cooing of the Mourning Doves. All along the valley the sad-voiced birds roam, as they did in the days when Thoreau found a nest in Sleepy Hollow. Formerly this gentle dove was abundant in that part of southern New England best suited to its needs, but it had decreased so much in numbers in the early part of the twentieth century that Massachusetts led the way in 1908 by giving it perpetual protection under the law, to save it from extirpation. Soon its numbers began slowly to increase. Many states now give the species entire protection, and in the northern states it is protected by Federal law also.

Up to 1912 I had not seen more than 12 in one flock in Massachusetts, but in 1921 I saw a flock of more than 100 birds on Cape Cod, and the species is beginning to appear not uncommonly in many of its ancient haunts elsewhere. It now seems to winter with more or less regularity on Cape Cod and Marthas Vineyard, as well as in Rhode Island and Connecticut, and I have known a large flock to pass most of the winter on Cape Cod.

---

[1] Joint Bulletins Vermont Botanical and Bird Clubs, 1919, p. 28.

It is now so well distributed over the lower lands of southern New England that the planting of a field of buckwheat usually suffices to ensure the presence of one or more pairs of the birds.

Mourning Doves may be said to belong to the open country, although in New England they nest usually in trees. In treeless regions the eggs are commonly found on the ground, except where reptilian enemies are numerous, and even in New England eggs have been found there, with little pretense of a nest. These doves feed mostly on the ground in grass fields, gardens, or grain fields, and are not seen often among forested hills, except in the clearings, though when frightened they often retire to the woods, and sometimes nest there. Nests have been built in peculiar situations, such as on a stump, in a tree cavity, on haystacks, and cliffs, on brush piles, rocks, woodpiles, fence corners, or even on a shed roof, but usually trees are preferred when available. Nests in trees are built mainly on horizontal branches, but often in crotches at heights of 5 to 50 feet. In New England the bird rather rarely nests at a height of over 20 feet and more commonly between six and 20. Often the deserted nest of some other bird is used for a foundation, such as that of the Robin, Brown Thrasher, Mockingbird, "English" Sparrow, Kingbird, Green Heron and even (rarely) the pensile nest of the Baltimore Oriole.*

The Mourning Dove like the Turtle Dove is very affectionate; mated pairs seem to remain together during the entire year. The male does not cease his attentions to the female when the eggs are deposited, but often brings sticks and straws for the nest and takes his share of the duties of incubation, feeding and brooding. Mrs. Margaret Morse Nice has made some interesting observations on the nests and nesting of the Mourning Dove in Oklahoma, from which some of the following facts are taken.[1] Sometimes the first nest may be used again for a second brood, but in most cases a new nest is built. As a rule, after incubation commences until the young are hatched, one or the other of the parents is continually on the nest, the female from evening till morning and the male from morning till evening. The young birds remain in the nest from twelve to fifteen days. When the adult bird is frightened from the nest by an intruder, she may drop to the ground and imitate so well a wing-broken bird as to lead the enemy away, or she may alight on the ground and flap her wings to draw attention. This is most likely to happen after the young are hatched, and in some cases both parents join in the ruse, but in many cases no such action occurs, and the bird flies quietly away to some other tree. The breeding season in Oklahoma, as in other parts of the south, lasts from six to seven months. Fresh eggs have been noted in Ohio every month in the year except December and January.

A common performance of the bird during the mating and nesting season is thus well described by Barrows. "An individual leaves its perch on a tree, and, with vigorous and sometimes noisy flapping (the wings seeming to strike each other above the back),

---

* In one case a Mourning Dove laid an egg in a Robin's nest with three eggs of the rightful owner. Another sat on the nest of a Boat-tailed Grackle on two eggs of her own and three of the owner (Oölogist, Vol. XXXV, 1919, p. 101, and Vol. XXXVI, 1920, pp. 136 and 188).

[1] Auk, Vol. XXXIX, 1922, pp. 457–474, and Auk, Vol. XL, 1923, pp. 37–58.

rises obliquely to a height of a hundred feet or more, and then on widely extended and motionless wings glides back earthward in one or more sweeping curves.   Usually the wings during this gliding flight, are carried somewhat below the plane of the body, in the manner of a soaring yellowlegs or sandpiper, and sometimes the bird makes a complete circle or spiral before again flapping its wings, which it does just before alighting." [1] It may glide downward in this way until very near the ground, but more often the soaring dove alights on a limb at a height of 20 feet or more.   Its soaring flight increases its resemblance to a small hawk (a resemblance often noted on account of the shape of the wings and the speed of its flight).   This peculiar evolution is sometimes repeated several times at brief intervals.

In courtship the male Mourning Dove sometimes strikes his feet hard on his perch one after another.   He also ruffles up the feathers of neck and rump, spreads his tail and droops his wings.

Mr. J. H. Fleming writes that in Tennessee he "observed a pair flying in wide circles; making a very loud droning sound with their wings, quite different from the usual whistle." [2]

Mourning Doves will live and nest in very dry regions, but they prefer the neighborhood of water, and if not nesting near water they fly long distances to it to drink and bathe, both morning and night.   Travelers in the desert in their search for water have learned to follow the morning and evening flight of the doves.   Gunners also take advantage of this habit to lie in wait for the birds near water at morning or evening.

Probably in New England Mourning Doves rarely, if ever, roost on the ground.   They are hardy birds and readily withstand a New England winter, provided they can find sufficient food.   Generally they are quite wild and shy while with us, but where unmolested they are less suspicious, and often learn to feed about the farm-yards with the poultry.

The young of Mourning Doves are fed at first on "pigeons milk" secreted by the adults, later they are fed worms, insects and seeds.   The adults feed very largely on seeds and grains.

Among the grains, buckwheat seems to be their favorite.   Wherever it is grown Mourning Doves may be found.   On January 9, 1924, Mr. Wilfred Wheeler, former Secretary of the Massachusetts State Board of Agriculture, told me there had been about 1,000 of these doves on a large farm of which he had charge in Falmouth, while the buckwheat, of which a great quantity was raised, was ripe.   One morning he said they perched on the telephone wires in such numbers that their line extended for nearly a mile.   They had nearly all disappeared however by the first of January.   They are known to eat corn and peas, but on the other hand they destroy enormous quantities of the seeds of weeds.   Investigators of the Biological Survey have examined the stomachs and crops of many Mourning Doves and find that over 99 per cent of the food materials consists of vegetal matter.   Wheat, oats, rye, corn, barley and buckwheat (mostly waste grain) made up 32 per cent of the food.   Weed seeds were the principal food and were eaten throughout

[1] Barrows, Walter: Michigan Bird Life, 1912, p. 253.   [2] Wilson Bulletin, Vol. XIX, 1907, p. 155.

the year.   In one bird were found 7,500 seeds of yellow wood sorrel.   In another 6,400 seeds of barn grass, and in a third, 2,600 seeds of slender joint-grass, 4,820 of orange hawk-weed, 950 of hoary vervain, 120 of Carolina cranesbill, 50 of yellow wood sorrel, 620 of panic grass, and 40 of other weeds, making a total of 9,200.   None of these plants is useful to mankind, and most of them are noxious.[1]   Mourning Doves take beechnuts and small acorns in winter.   They are said to eat some wild berries, some corn and peas, and Dr. B. H. Warren found apple seeds in the stomachs of two birds.

ECONOMIC STATUS.   In the south where the species is more numerous than in New England, Mourning Doves do some damage to grain and peas.   No complaints of injury to any crop by these birds in the north have come to my attention, and the destruction of weed seeds is an item in their favor.

ORDER RAPTORES.   BIRDS OF PREY.

Number of species in North America 59 ; in Massachusetts 31.

This order includes birds, mostly of large or medium size, which obtain much of their food by preying on other birds and mammals, although many species feed largely on batra-chians, reptiles and insects, and some of the larger species feed chiefly on carrion.   In birds of this order the bill is strong, hooked, and provided with a softer plate overlaying the base of the upper mandible and called the cere.   Parrots also have a hooked beak, but their feet are "yoke-toed"; *i.e.* two toes before and two behind, where birds of prey have three before and one behind, although some rapacious birds have one front toe so hinged that it can be turned backward at need.   The claws are weapons of offense or defense, large, long and strong.   They are curved, tapering and pointed talons, very flexibly jointed so that they may be bent strongly under the toes.   The legs and toes are large and powerful, well fitted for driving home the talons.   The wings and tail are ample and the breast-bone deep, supporting great muscles which with powerful wing muscles and strong wings fit the birds of the order for both protracted and swift flight.   Members of this order are found in every part of the world.   They are divisible into four suborders. The first is represented only by the long-legged Secretary-bird of Africa.   Of the other three, one, *Sarcorhamphi*, is confined to America, and the other two, *Falcones* and *Striges*, are well represented in the New World.

SUBORDER.   SARCORHAMPHI.   AMERICAN VULTURES.

Number of species in North America 3; in Massachusetts 2.

The birds of this group are widely separated from the Old World vultures.   When on the ground they walk instead of hopping, and some bear a slight superficial resemblance to turkeys.   They have comparatively little strength in their feet, and can attack suc-

---

[1] Pearson, T. Gilbert: Educational leaflet No. 2, National Association of Audubon Societies.

cessfully only much smaller and weaker animals or (rarely) those sick or dying. They subsist chiefly on carrion. There is nothing about them to suggest the hawk or eagle, except their great powers of flight and their telescopic sight. They are extremely timid and indolent. They have no perceptible vocal organs, and therefore their only attempt at vocal expression is a weak hiss or a feeble croak.

FAMILY **CATHARTIDÆ**. AMERICAN VULTURES.

Number of species in North America 3; in Massachusetts 2.

These vultures have the head and neck nearly bare of feathers, and the eyes are not overshadowed by a shield or overhanging brow as in the hawks and eagles; a comparatively weak and hooked bill; nostrils very large and completely perforated; wings long, wide and strong; tail medium; fore toes rather long, with basal webs; hind toe short and elevated; claws dull and little hooked; some have combs or wattles.

ECONOMIC STATUS. This family of scavengers is chiefly beneficial.

Cathártes aúra septentrionális WIED. **Turkey Vulture**.

Other names: TURKEY BUZZARD; BUZZARD.

Plates 37 and 38.

DESCRIPTION. — Head and a little of upper neck bare; plumage beginning as a circlet around neck; bare skin of head and upper neck more or less corrugated and sparsely set with bristly "hairs" (feather shafts); bill long, rather stout, somewhat hooked; nostrils very large and wide; wings extremely long and rather broad, third or fourth primary longest, outer four or five emarginate on inner web; tail not

TURKEY VULTURE

long, rounded; *naked skin of head livid crimson*, some have small wart-like excrescences between eyes and bill and on top of head. *Adults (sexes alike):* Neck and lower plumage dull black; upper surface of body, wings and tail blackish with some greenish and violet gloss; margins of feathers of back, scapulars and wing-coverts fading gradually and broadly into light grayish-brown or light ashy; shafts of flight-feathers and tail-feathers pale brown to yellowish-white; bill whitish, cere lake-red; iris grayish-brown or umber; legs and feet flesh colored or dirty whitish, tinged yellowish or flesh color. *Young in juvenal plumage:* Much as adult, but *naked skin of head blackish* or livid-dusky and more or less downy, and light margins to feathers of upper plumage less prominent. *Downy young:* Head mostly naked and dusky, long cottony down of other parts pure white above and below; some short white down extends forward on top of head; eyes almost black and open from their first day.

MEASUREMENTS. — Length 26.00 to 32.00 in.; spread 68.00 to 72.00; folded wing 19.00 to 25.00; tail 10.50 to 12.00; bill (without cere) 1.00 to 1.15; tarsus 2.23 to 2.30. Weight 4 to 5 lbs. (Coues). Sexes about equal in size.

MOLTS. — Juvenal plumage follows natal down; is acquired by a complete postnatal molt by August; young birds apparently in their first winter become as adults; not sufficient material available to determine whether one or two molts occur annually in adults; birds were seen to be molting more or less from April to October; apparently there is a single molt.

PLATE 37

PLATE 37

BALD EAGLE
Page 150
ADULT
About one-twenty-fourth scale

TURKEY VULTURE
Page 88
About one-thirtieth scale

RED–TAILED HAWK
Page 123
ADULT
About one-twelfth scale

DUCK HAWK
Page 164
ADULT
About one-twelfth scale

OSPREY
Page 182
ADULT
About one-twelfth scale

MARSH HAWK
Page 99
ADULT FEMALE
About one-twelfth sca

COOPER'S HAWK
Page 112
ADULT
About one-twelfth scale

ADULT MALE
About one-twelfth scale

Louis Agassiz Fuertes

FIELD MARKS. — Size of small eagle; a large blackish bird with long and rather broad wings, medium rounded tail and long, small, red head (*juvenal birds with blackish heads may be mistaken for Black Vulture*); sails and soars much with wings bent slightly upward and with separate upcurved tips of longest five or six primaries showing distinctly; tail usually closed; grayish patch on under surface of primaries and secondaries on each wing.

VOICE. — Its only vocal efforts a weak hissing, when angry or at bay; or a subdued croak, rarely uttered in flight.

BREEDING. — Usually in secluded places, near water, among rocks or cliffs or in woods. *Nest:* Virtually none; eggs laid on ground or ledges of rocks, in caves, hollow logs and stumps or hollow stubs, in deserted cabins or in old hogpens. *Eggs:* Usually 2, sometimes 1, rarely 3; 2.62 to 2.94 by 1.80 to 1.94 in.; elliptical to ovate, sometimes quite pointed at small end; creamy, yellowish-white or dead white, blotched and splashed irregularly with various shades of brown and usually with some spots of lavender, very variable, some unspotted. Illustrated in Bendire's "Life Histories of North American Birds." Vol. I, Plate IV, Figs. 1 and 3. *Dates:* March 1, Florida; April 3 to May 1, Virginia; April 25 through May, Indiana; May 30, Michigan. *Incubation:* By female. One brood yearly.

RANGE. — Austral zones (chiefly) from southern British Columbia, central Alberta, Saskatchewan, southern Manitoba, northern Minnesota, Wisconsin, Michigan, southeastern Ontario, western and southern New York and southern New England south to southern Lower California, Gulf coast of the United States and northern Mexico. Breeds over most of its range north in eastern half of United States at least to southern Michigan and Minnesota; occasional or casual in northern New York and northern New England; casual in northern Ontario (a James Bay-Moose Factory record, June, 1898), New Brunswick and Newfoundland; winters throughout most of its regular range on the Atlantic slope, but to the westward retires south to the Ohio Valley, Nebraska and California.

NOTE. The great slaughter of bison in 1883 (the northern herd containing about one million and a half being wiped out in that year) attracted in the fall thousands of Turkey Vultures to eastern Montana. Since then they have grown scarce until to-day they must be regarded only as accidental wanderers there. (E. S. Cameron, Auk, Vol. XXIV, 1907, p. 259.)

DISTRIBUTION IN NEW ENGLAND. — *Maine:* Occasional; nine records;[1] (another bird taken by Evander Andrews west of Bingham about August 1, 1916, reported by A. C. Bagg). *New Hampshire:* Occasional; Hampton Falls April 6 or 7, 1882, female taken by Frank Percell;[2] North Weare, spring of 1887, bird taken alive by a Mr. Felch;[3] Hampton Falls, May 15, 1898, bird seen by Wm. E. Cram.[3] *Vermont:* Accidental; Eutaw, prior to 1875, bird taken.[4] Woodstock, June 22, 1926, bird taken and in collection of Karl A. Pember;[5] *Massachusetts:* Occasional; in addition to 12 birds recorded by Howe and Allen in Birds of Massachusetts, we have other later records from various sections of the State. *Rhode Island:* Occasional; five records are given by Howe and Sturtevant in the Birds of Rhode Island and there are others. A late one is given by Miss Elizabeth Dickens who writes to me that a Turkey Vulture appeared at Block Island the last week in March, 1920, and remained for about 10 days. *Connecticut:* Occasional; formerly more common; fifteen birds are recorded by Sage, Bishop and Bliss in the Birds of Connecticut. Recently (June 8, 1925) the Turkey Vulture was found nesting in New York, north of Stamford, less than four miles from Connecticut line.

SEASON IN MASSACHUSETTS. — Records largely in spring, summer, and autumn, but one bird remained on Marthas Vineyard most of one winter; many *reports* of the species must be rejected because of possible mistaken identity.

---

[1] Norton, Arthur H.: Auk, Vol. XXVIII, 1911, pp. 263–264.
[2] Cory, Charles B.: Bulletin Nuttall Ornithological Club, Vol. VII, 1882, p. 184.
[3] Allen, Glover M.: Birds of New Hampshire, 1903, p. 96.
[4] Forest and Stream, Vol. IV, 1875, p. 5.
[5] Pember, Karl A.: *in litt.*

HAUNTS AND HABITS. The Turkey Vulture, or "Buzzard," as it is commonly called in the south, leaves the ground with a bound and a few flaps, unless gorged with carrion, when it must disgorge much of its filthy cargo in order to enable it to get away; but when once in air and gaining height it moves with the ease of a master. No other American bird is so generally celebrated for its perfect conquest of the aerial currents. It seems to sail and soar gracefully without effort and to gain altitude even in windless air with few motions of its widespread pinions, which carry it up as if by magic. It seems to material-ize the flight of the dreamer who imagines that he floats through the air by the mere effort of his will. In every state on the southern Atlantic coast and on the shore of the Pacific I have watched the vultures lazily wheeling in the summer sky and have envied them their apparently effortless flight. As Bradford Torrey says, "One might almost be willing to be a Buzzard to fly like that." Many people have sought their secret, but who has really found it? The Wright Brothers, pioneers in successful man-flight, studied the soaring buzzards on our southern coast, and apparently to some purpose.

There are, perhaps, not more than two or three Turkey Vultures to the square mile in their southern range, but on their aerial courses they patrol the land thoroughly, and probably there are few dead animals that escape their telescopic vision. Over hill and dale, lake and stream, farm, forest and village, the "Buzzards" wheel, adding life to the blue vault above, until one of the tireless birds sees some prospect of a feast. It may be that its keen eyes have spied a dead or dying animal, or a corpse rising to the surface of a stream, or even the village toper fallen by the wayside. Immediately the watchful fowl descends to the hoped-for feast, lowering its legs eagerly, long before it actually lights. Another, circling in the distant sky, sees that sudden "stoop" and follows. Others in all directions mark the descending twain and wing their way to the common center. As they go they are seen from afar by others still, and soon every vulture for miles around has assembled near the expected feast. Scores as they arrive alight on trees or fences, while a few of the boldest drop to the ground and with exceeding circumspection approach the object of their quest, for your "Buzzard" is a cowardly fowl and intends to take good care of his precious skin. They often gather thus, not only about dead animals but also about the sick or disabled when death seems imminent. Dr. T. Gilbert Pearson records that while working in a forbidding morass, he came upon a cow sinking slowly into what seemed to be fathomless mire. On the trees and bushes surrounding and above her, Turkey Vultures and Black Vultures were perched waiting for the end. The animal was doomed beyond any possibility of relief and the vultures were sure of their banquet. If the death of the victim seems assured they approach their prey. Over what follows let us draw the veil.

It is supposed that the "buzzards" find their food entirely by sight; they frequently have failed to locate it when it has been covered by so frail a substance as paper; but their nostrils are large, and probably they have a sense of smell, as often they have hung about malodorous decaying bodies, apparently searching for them, but unable to discover them when hidden from sight. There is some evidence to the effect that in some cases these birds have found carrion by scent. If, however, they have only the most ordinary and obtuse olfactory sense, it would seem impossible for them to enjoy some of their vile feasts, unless perchance their nostrils are so filled with the fetid stench of their own bodies and feathers that the odor of a rotting carcass is not noticed except perhaps as an agreeable change. They feed their young on carrion which is regurgitated from the stomach or gullet of the parent, and their nests become very foul. Such food as the ancient carcass of an alligator more or less macerated by long immersion apparently is relished by them. Probably the birds do not really prefer carrion, as they sometimes eat small animals, such as chickens, alive or freshly killed, but perhaps they have not sufficient strength in beak and talons to rend a large carcass until an advanced stage of decomposition has set in. However, they usually soon find a way to get at the softer parts.

Like the Black Vultures, the Turkey Vultures are always on the alert to pick up scraps of meat or bones with fragments of meat attached that may be thrown out. Dr. T. Gilbert Pearson says:

"One day, a lady of my acquaintance, while sitting alone in her room, was much startled when a beef-bone fell down the chimney and rolled out on the hearth. Going outside she discovered a Turkey Buzzard peering down the chimney in quest of his prize." "Chimney tops," he says, "are often occupied by Buzzards who expand their wings and stand in the smoke, undoubtedly enjoying the heat that comes from below. On two occasions I have seen these birds take such positions when their feathers were almost entirely frozen together by sleet that had recently fallen."

Turkey Vultures gather at night, often from considerable distances, to roost together in trees. Such a collection of trees is commonly known in the south as a "Buzzards' Roost."

When wounded or entrapped, the Turkey Vulture has two means of defense. It ejects at the enemy the putrid contents of its gullet, and if this is not enough, the bird can "play possum," apparently dying. Thus it simulates the dead in the hope, perhaps, of deluding its captor.

There is some evidence that this bird was once less uncommon in New England than it is now. In the west it ranges much farther to the northward. Probably it would be more common here to-day were it not for the fact that the moment one appears, several ignoramuses are likely to take after it with guns. Its killing can serve no useful purpose, as it is not fit food for a dog, but there are so many people who are anxious to kill anything large enough to serve as a target that the poor vulture has small chance for life in New England. It is reported that several years ago two Italians fought over the carcass of a "Buzzard" that they had shot, until one was wounded and the other had gone to his reward, leaving the poor victim of the marksman's shot a worthless carcass on the ground.

ECONOMIC STATUS. Vultures are useful scavengers, especially in southern regions where decay is rapid and where often the presence of these birds is welcomed, as they quickly dispose of carrion and garbage. Rarely this vulture feeds on dead fish on the ocean beaches. Occasionally it kills and eats small animals, and a flock has been known to feed on frostbitten pumpkins.[1] The present species has been accused of spreading such diseases as hog cholera, black-leg and anthrax, and in several states it has been proscribed on that account.   The bird has been convicted, however, on the weakest kind of evidence, while scientific investigation thus far seems to exonerate it.[2]

Coragýps úrubu urubu (Vieillot).   Black Vulture.

Plate 38.

DESCRIPTION. — Heavily built; wings and tail (tail especially) shorter than in Turkey Vulture; tail nearly even-tipped; bill strong, hooked, broad at base, but not so deep and stout as in Turkey Vulture; nostrils long and narrow, their front ends contracted and pointed. *Adults (sexes alike)*: Naked skin of head and upper neck blackish, feathering of neck extending up farther behind than in front; plumage dull black; primaries grayish toward bases on upper surfaces, under surfaces silvery gray,

BLACK VULTURE

shafts white; bill mainly dark brown or blackish, the end much lighter or whitish; iris and feet dark brown. *Young in juvenal plumage:* Similar to adult, but feathers less iridescent, and extending farther up on back of head. *Downy young:* Covered with light buffy down.

MEASUREMENTS. — Length 24.00 to 27.00 in.; spread 54.00 to 59.00; folded wing 16.00 to 17.50; tail 7.45 to 8.50; bill from front end of nostril .90 to .95, from front of forehead 2.10 to 2.35; tarsus 2.90 to 3.20. Weight, $4\frac{1}{4}$ to 6 lbs.

MOLTS. — Not enough molting material examined to determine; apparently there is a complete autumnal molt.

FIELD MARKS. — Smaller than Turkey Vulture, with shorter wings; tail shorter, not rounded, *head bare, blackish;* under side of wings silvery gray; wings wide at body, tapering toward tips which are gracefully and abruptly slender, *light colored area near ends* showing from above or below; less graceful in flight than Turkey Vulture, with much more flapping, but young of latter *with black head* has been mistaken for Black Vulture often.

VOICE. — Virtually none; produces puffing, snuffling and hissing sounds, and when disturbed "a low grunt" (F. M. Chapman).

BREEDING. — On islands or dry spots in swamps or marshes, chiefly on low ground, in river valleys or near sea. *Nest:* None; eggs deposited on ground, under logs, bushes, low palmettoes, etc. or in hollow logs or hollows of decaying stumps or trees, sometimes in caves or cavities in rocks. *Eggs:* Usually 2, rarely 1 or 3; 3.00 to 3.31 by 1.94 to 2.10 in.; elongate ovate or elliptical ovate, a few short ovate — rather more elongate than those of Turkey Vulture; pale grayish green, whitish, cream color or bluish-white, spotted with large blotches of dark reddish-brown or chocolate; some eggs have some smaller spots and some a few markings of lilac and purplish drab, markings often gathered about large end. Illustrated in Bendire's "Life Histories of North American Birds," Vol. I, plate IV, Figs. 7 and 10. *Dates:* Late February to third week in March, to May 26 in South Carolina. *Incubation:* Period about 30 days (W. Hoxie); by both sexes. One brood yearly.

RANGE. — Austral and Tropical zones from Arizona, western Texas, Kansas, Missouri, southern Illinois and southern Maryland south through southern states, Mexico and Central America, Cuba and Jamaica; occasional or accidental north to North Dakota, northern Indiana, southern Michigan, Ohio, Ontario, New York, New England, Quebec, New Brunswick and Nova Scotia; breeds locally throughout most of its regular range, which on Atlantic coast is not north of Maryland; rare in West Indies.

---

[1] Bird-Lore, Vol. XXIX, 1927, p. 117.
[2] McAtee, W. L.: Relation of the Turkey Buzzard to Diseases of Live-stock.   Auk, Vol. XXX, 1913, pp. 295–298.

Distribution in New England. — Accidental or occasional. *Maine:* Nine records.[1] *New Hampshire:* Randolph, April 17, 1926, bird shot by George H. Coulter and recorded by V. D. Lowe, game warden;[2] Whitefield, about May 1, 1926, bird seen.[2] *Vermont:* Woodbury, about July 10, 1884, bird reported by C. W. Graham.[3] Probably this is the mounted specimen in the Fairbanks Museum at St. Johnsbury which is labelled: "Only specimen known to have been killed in Vermont." Lunenburg,[4] reported by W. E. Balch, taxidermist, of that town. No date given. Pawlet, July 7, 1912, adult shot.[5] *Massachusetts:* Howe and Allen give several records in their "Birds of Massachusetts" (1901, page 60).

Later records: Taunton, Oct. 5, 1902, adult female shot;[6] Waltham, Sept. 15, 1905, immature bird shot by J. H. Storer, Jr. and now in his mounted collection;[7] Nahant, April 1, 1913, bird taken by Albert Richards;[8] Pigeon Cove, May 12, 1916, bird taken, now in collection of Charles R. Lamb;[9] Wenham, Aug. 20, 1917, female shot by Archer L. Pierce and sent to Boston Society of Natural History;[10] Chatham, March 31, 1923, female taken and sent to Boston Society of Natural History through kindness of Wm. C. Adams, Director Division of Fisheries & Game, Massachusetts Department Conservation;[11] Belchertown, about June 1, 1923, bird shot out of a flock of crows, and reported on June 2, 1923;[12] Pride's Crossing, June 17, 1923, male bird taken by Dr. Franklin Dexter;[13] Ipswich, Nov. 2, 1924, bird seen by Dr. C. W. Townsend.[14] *Connecticut:* Besides the doubtful record referred to by Merriam (Birds of Connecticut, p. 93) of three specimens killed by J. H. Hand at Westbrook, Aug. 10, Sept. 12 and 21, 1874, there are the following: East Lyme, July 6, 1901 [adult male] shot by Robert Payne and in collection of J. H. Hill (Auk, Vol. XIX, 1902, p. 94); Bolton Reservoir, Oct. 10, 1879, bird seen by Dr. Wm. Wood (M. S. note to John H. Sage).[15]

Season in Massachusetts. — July to November.

Haunts and Habits. The Black Vulture, a rare or uncommon straggler in New England, appears here now and then. Occasionally it wanders up the coast or along the river valleys where it flaps and sails in a less graceful manner than the Turkey Vulture. Its flight is more labored, with much more flapping. It is a foul carrion feeder, even more so than the Turkey Vulture. Carrion, offal, ordure and filth attract it. Its bill and claws are weaker than those of the larger bird, and therefore it is not so well fitted to attack living animals or the undecomposed dead. In the south its services are in demand as a scavenger, and wherever animal waste, scraps or garbage are thrown into the streets of cities, this bird is a common sight on the roofs, from which it watches, ready to pounce on anything that promises nourishment.

In the market district of Charleston, South Carolina, these birds hop about the streets, cleaning up all the scraps, and as they are not molested they become very tame. These

[1] Norton, Arthur H.: Auk, Vol. XXXIII, 1916, pp. 381–382.
[2] Means, William Gordon: *in litt.*
[3] Graham, C. W.: Random Notes, Vol. I, No. 9, 1884, p. 4.
[4] Perkins, George H. and Howe, Clifton D.: A Preliminary List of the Birds of Vermont, 1901, p. 17.
[5] Pember, F. T.: Auk, Vol. XXX, 1913, p. 112.
[6] Bent, A. C.: Auk, Vol. XX, 1903, p. 67.
[7] Auk, Vol. XXIII, 1906, p. 222.
[8] Townsend, Charles W.: Supplement to Birds of Essex County, 1920, p. 98.
[9] Lamb, Charles R.: Auk, Vol. XXXV, 1918, p. 233.
[10] Phillips, John C.: Auk, Vol. XXXIV, 1917, p. 478.
[11] Brooks, W. Sprague: Auk, Vol. XLI, 1924, p. 164.
[12] Jackson, J. W.: *in litt.*
[13] Frazar, M. Abbott: *in litt.*
[14] Auk, Vol. XLII, 1925, p. 130.
[15] Sage, J. H., Bishop, L. B., and Bliss, W. P.: Birds of Connecticut, 1913, p. 74.

city birds are half domesticated, like street pigeons, and do not hesitate to seek their food wherever it may be found, regardless of man and his many agencies of destruction.   In the waste lands and swamps where it breeds, it is much more shy.

Its migrations are merely movements in search of food, or wanderings possibly caused by the influence of storm winds.

My good friend, Arthur T. Wayne, notes a peculiar habit of the Black Vulture on its nesting grounds in South Carolina; almost invariably he finds "pearl, bone, and china buttons, as well as pieces of glass and figured china, around and under the eggs." [1]

ECONOMIC STATUS.   As a scavenger the Black Vulture has considerable value in southern states and countries.   Some of the great hotels in Florida make a practice of dumping their garbage daily at certain spots.   The dumps attract hundreds of vultures which dispose of all such matter very quickly.   This species is most useful because of its tameness.

SUBORDER FALCONES. VULTURES, FALCONS, HAWKS, BUZZARDS, EAGLES, KITES, HARRIERS, ETC.

Number of species in North America 36 ; in Massachusetts 19.

This large group, the diurnal birds of prey, includes the great majority of the *Raptores*. The nostrils are not connected at their external opening as in the American Vultures, nor is the hind toe elevated as in that group.   The head is bare only in some of the Vultures. The eyes are not placed so as to look directly forward as in owls.   Usually they are sunken beneath a projecting brow or shield, and there is no perfect facial disk of feathers as in owls.   The strong hooked bill is provided with a cere in which the nostrils open — not at its edge as in most owls.   The wings are strong and ample, with ten primaries, and the tail also is ample and usually of twelve feathers.   The upper leg is covered with long feathers which project well beyond the carpal joint.   The feet usually are very strong, with toes cleft to the base, or nearly so, their lower surface roughened, and with long curved claws or talons.   The food is chiefly or entirely animal, and the coarser indigestible parts are ejected from the stomach through the mouth in the form of pellets.

Diurnal birds of prey inhabit all parts of the world.   There are about 500 different forms, in most of which the sexes are alike or similar, with the female usually the larger. There are great changes in plumage from the fledgling to maturity, and some species have two or more color phases.   The eggs are spotted as a rule.   Three American families are included in this suborder — *Accipitridæ, Falconidæ* and *Pandionidæ*.

---

[1] Birds of South Carolina, 1910, p. 69.

PLATE 38

PLATE 38

1
TURKEY VULTURE
Page 88

8
RED–TAILED HAWK
Page 123
ADULT

15
BALD EAGLE
Page 150
ADULT

2
BLACK VULTURE
Page 92

16
BALD EAGLE
Page 150
IMMATURE

9
RED–SHOULDERED HAWK
Page 128
ADULT

3
SWALLOW–TAILED KITE
Page 95

10
RED–SHOULDERED HAWK
Page 129
IMMATURE

17
WHITE GYRFALCON
Page 158

4
MARSH HAWK
Page 99
ADULT MALE

11
BROAD–WINGED HAWK
Page 135
ADULT

18
DUCK HAWK
Page 164
ADULT

5
SHARP–SHINNED HAWK
Page 104
SMALL IMMATURE MALE

12
SWAINSON'S HAWK
Page 133
ADULT

19
PIGEON HAWK
Page 172

6
COOPER'S HAWK
Page 112
SMALL ADULT MALE

13
ROUGH–LEGGED HAWK
Page 141
IMMATURE
LIGHT PHASE

20
SPARROW HAWK
Page 178
MALE

7
GOSHAWK
Page 116
ADULT

21
OSPREY
Page 182

14
GOLDEN EAGLE
Page 145
IMMATURE

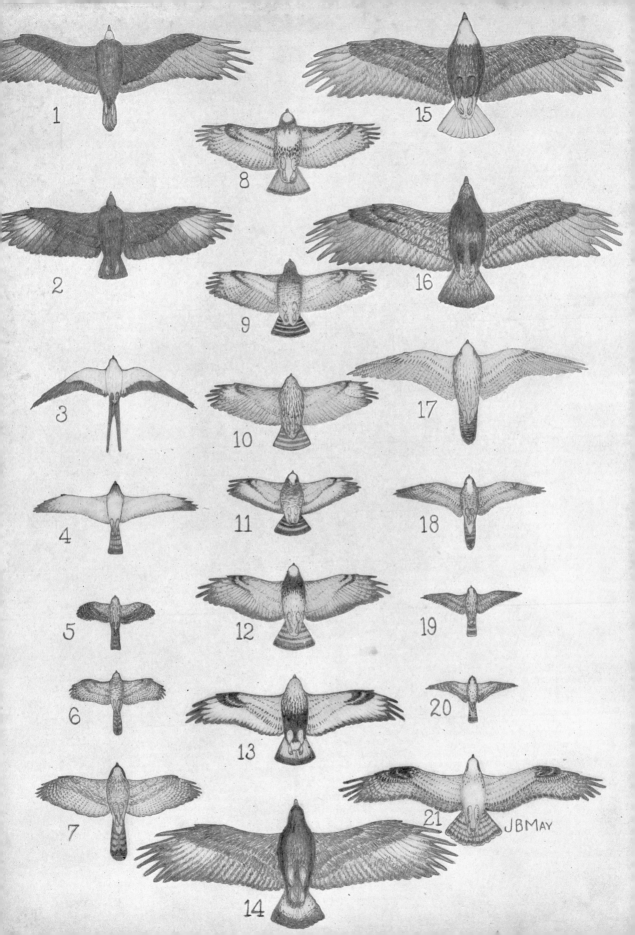

FAMILY **ACCIPITRIDÆ**. HAWKS, EAGLES, KITES, ETC.

Number of species in North America 36; in Massachusetts 19.

In general the characters of this family are the same as those of the order *Falcones*, but the head is feathered in all species. The *Accipitridæ* are separable at once from the *Pandionidæ* (Ospreys or Fish-hawks) by the position of their toes; the latter having the outer toe reversible while the *Accipitridæ* have three in front and one behind.

ECONOMIC STATUS. In the letter of transmittal, in which Dr. C. Hart Merriam, then Chief of the Division of Ornithology and Mammalogy, presented to the Secretary of Agriculture at Washington the report of A. K. Fisher on the Hawks and Owls of the United States, he asserted that only six of the 73 species and subspecies of hawks and owls in the country were injurious. This conclusion was arrived at after an examination of the contents of about 2,700 stomachs of these birds. Mr. E. H. Eaton in the Birds of New York tabulates the food contents of the common hawks of the eastern United States as follows: Species marked (g) in the table are supposed to be near the border line of the beneficial birds.

FOOD OF NEW YORK HAWKS.

PERCENTAGE OF STOMACHS EXAMINED CONTAINING VARIOUS KINDS OF FOOD.[1]

SPECIES EXAMINED	POULTRY OR GAME	OTHER BIRDS	REPTILES (Snakes, etc.)	BATRACHIANS (Frogs, etc.)	MICE	OTHER MAMMALS	INSECTS	CRAYFISH AND SPIDERS	EMPTY
Beneficial									
Rough-legged hawk	0	0	2	....	81	10	2	....	8
Broad-winged hawk	0	3	18	19	22	19	45	6	10
Red-shouldered hawk	1	6	10	19 (fish 2)	50	20	45	3	7
Sparrow hawk	$\frac{1}{3}$	17	..	4	28	4	7.1	sp. 9	9
Red-tailed hawk (g)	10	9	4	3	50	24	8	sp. $\frac{1}{5}$	16
Marsh hawk (g)	6	27	6	2	46	18	10	....	7
Injurious									
Goshawk	36	8	..	....	..	40	12	....	32
Cooper hawk	23	49	2	1	..	8	2	....	30
Sharp-shinned hawk	4	66	..	....	4	..	4	....	35
Duck hawk	35	45	..	....	5	..	10	....	20
Pigeon hawk	4	80	..	....	4	..	32	....	9

Elanoídes forficátus (LINNÆUS). Swallow-tailed Kite.

DESCRIPTION. — Head fully feathered to bill; wings very long, narrow and pointed; tail very long, slender and forked like that of a Barn Swallow; legs short, tarsus feathered part way down in front; feet rather small. *Adults (sexes alike):* Head, neck and all lower plumage white, including wing-lin-

[1] Eaton, E. H.: Birds of New York, 1914, Vol. II, p. 62.

ings; under side of basal half of secondaries more or less white, their ends black; upper plumage, except head, including upper surfaces of wings and tail, glossy black, with iridescence, chiefly of bronzy purplish or violet, on back, scapulars and lesser wing-coverts; rest of black plumage sometimes has a glaucous or bluish-green cast; tertials largely white, but black at ends; bill bluish-black, its edges, base, the cere and feet much lighter and bluish or light blue; iris black or very dark; feet often with a greenish tinge; "bill, cere and feet lead color" (C. K. Worthen). *Immature:* Similar but less lustrous, more brownish

above and iridescence more greenish; head and neck with narrow dusky shaft-streaks; flight-feathers and tail-feathers narrowly bordered white at tips. *Young in Juvenal plumage:* Similar to immature, but more or less brownish below and on head and neck. *Downy young:* Buffy.

MEASUREMENTS. — Length 19.50 to 25.50 in.; very variable; spread 45.00 to 50.00 (more or less); folded wing 15.00 to 17.98; tail 11.50 to 14.75; forked rather more than half its length; bill (without cere) .75 to .77; tarsus 1.25 to 1.65. Female averaging larger than male.

MOLTS. — Juvenal plumage acquired in nest by complete postnatal molt; young probably molt into first winter plumage in late summer and autumn, molting again into adult plumage the next summer. Adults apparently have one complete molt (postnuptial) in autumn and winter.

FIELD MARKS. — Size of Cooper's Hawk but wings much longer than in that species; unmistakable; much like a Barn Swallow in shape and flight, except that at times it soars in circles and spirals; black and white in contrasting masses; white head and under plumage, and black above.

SWALLOW-TAILED KITE

VOICE. — A shrill feeble cry (W. L. Ralph); call note, a high-pitched shrill *ke wee wee*, the first note short, somewhat like cry of Broad-winged Hawk (R. I. Brasher).

BREEDING. — Usually in great woods. *Nest:* In top of tall tree, commonly of sticks, lined with a little moss and sometimes a snake skin. *Eggs:* Usually 2, sometimes 1, rarely 3 or 4; 1.78 to 2.00 by 1.18 to 1.51 in.; rounded ovate; white or nearly so, sparsely to heavily spotted with varying browns, often with large blotches grouped more or less about large end, sometimes small lavender markings also; Illustrated in Bendire's "Life Histories of North American Birds," Vol. I, Plate V, Figs. 1 and 2. *Dates:* Varying from March to May in the south, to May or June in northern states. *Incubation:* By female. One brood yearly.

RANGE. — North temperate North America, east of Rocky Mountains, south to south temperate South America. Breeds locally from northern Minnesota, southern Wisconsin, southern Indiana (formerly Ohio, and probably southern Ontario and New York) and South Carolina south through eastern Mexico and Central America to Peru, Bolivia and Paraguay; winters chiefly in Central America and South America; casual or accidental in New Mexico, Colorado, southern Saskatchewan, southern Manitoba, Michigan, northern Wisconsin, Ontario and northeastern states — New York and New England and in Greater Antilles; recorded in the British Isles.

DISTRIBUTION IN NEW ENGLAND. — Accidental. Erroneously recorded from Maine. *New Hampshire:* Franklin, 1875, bird seen by George Stolworthy "within 100 feet" capturing a snake.[1]

NOTE. Ornithologists ordinarily will not accept a first record of a bird outside its regular range, unless substantiated by a specimen taken there; but this bird is so unmistakable that this record is given. *Vermont:* Waitsfield, April 26, 1913, one seen about town for "two weeks." [2] *Massachusetts:* Whately,

[1] Dearborn, Ned: A preliminary list of the Birds of Belknap and Merrimac Counties, New Hampshire, 1898, p. 13.
[2] Joint Bulletin of Vermont Botanical and Bird Clubs, No. 1, April, 1915, pp. 21 and 24.

one seen prior to 1870;[1] *Northampton* (near), 1880, bird seen by E. O. Damon;[2] West Newbury, one taken near Merrimac River about September 25, 1882.[3] *Connecticut:* Portland, one seen summer of 1861; Lyme, July 2, 1877, bird seen;[4] Saybrook, June 16, 1889, bird seen by John N. Clark.[5]

HAUNTS AND HABITS. The handsome, graceful Swallow-tailed Kite is preëminently a fowl of the air. In its chosen element it is supreme. It soars as gracefully as the Turkey Vulture and in speed it is not often excelled. Its flight resembles in lightness the erratic flight of the Barn Swallow. It appears like a gigantic swallow as it catches insects in the air or flutters above the tree-tops; but anon it circles and soars straight up to heights beyond the scope of the human eye, remaining at times at such altitudes for from half an hour to an hour. Again, it swoops suddenly downward in the manner of the Nighthawk or turns over and over in the air. No pen can adequately describe the beauty, elegance, and grace of its aerial evolutions. It is so much at home in the air that it devours its prey while on the wing, and it drinks by skimming rapidly like a swallow close to the surface of the water. I have seen it mostly flying over the wooded wildernesses of the south or perching on the tree-tops; but once seen it is not soon forgotten. Formerly it was a common bird as far north as the north-central states, where it was seen in small flocks, but now it is only a straggler in that region, and is decreasing rapidly in the south. It is too tempting a target to exist long in thickly settled regions. In future it will be confined chiefly to the few remaining wildernesses of the south. It migrates southward early to the southern Americas but returns early in the spring to Florida.

The food of the Swallow-tailed Kite consists largely of snakes and other reptilian forms of life, frogs and insects, such as beetles, moths, caterpillars, crickets, grasshoppers, locusts, wasps and hornets. Large insects are taken chiefly by this bird while on the wing, either high in air or sweeping along the surface of the ground, but it sometimes alights and walks about in pursuit of grasshoppers. It is said also to be destructive to the cotton worm. It hovers over forest fires in pursuit of insects that escape the flames. Also it takes the eggs of reptiles, and there is one instance recorded by Dr. Rufus Hammond where an individual had swallowed some whole eggs of the catbird.[6]

ECONOMIC STATUS. Apparently this bird does not pursue nor kill birds. It is a harmless, beautiful creature, and is considered beneficial because of the character of its insect food. It should be protected at all times by law, as it is now in danger of extirpation in North America.

[1] Allen, J. A.: American Naturalist, Vol. III, 1870, p. 645.
[2] Morris, Robert O. and Colburn, William W.: Birds of the Connecticut Valley in Massachusetts, 1891, p. 11.
[3] Chadbourne, A. P.: Quarterly Journal Boston Zoölogical Society, Vol. II, 1883, p. 16; Coues, Elliott: Bulletin Nuttall Ornithological Club, Vol. VIII, 1883, p. 61.
[4] Merriam, C. Hart: Birds of Connecticut, 1877, pp. 76–77.
[5] Ornithologist and Oölogist, Vol. XIV, 1889, p. 123.
[6] Proceedings Philadelphia Academy of Natural Sciences, Vol. VIII, 1856, p. 287.

Elánus leucúrus (Vieillot). White-tailed Kite.

Note. The following occurrence cannot be ignored. There seems to be no doubt that a bird of this species was actually seen. If seen once it may occur again and the account given by Mr. S. Prescott Fay shows how it may be recognized. It can hardly be included in the New England list without a specimen to substantiate the record, and so far as I know no specimen has been taken in this region. Nevertheless the account as written by Mr. Fay is well worth quoting:

"*A Massachusetts Record for the White-tailed Kite.* — As this bird is rare east of the Mississippi River, and in fact is scarcely much more than a straggler even in that region, its appearance on the Atlantic coast as far north as New England is very extraordinary. On May 30 last I saw an adult bird at very close range on the island of Martha's Vineyard. It was so close and was watched with glasses for such a long time, both by myself and Mr. C. E. Brown of the Boston Society of Natural History, that there was not the slightest doubt in our minds as to its identity. We were spending several days on the island studying the birds and on one of our daily trips came upon this specimen very unexpectedly at a fresh meadow at the head of one of the ponds. When first seen he was sitting on a post not a hundred yards distant and we took him to be a marsh hawk, but on looking again before even raising our glasses, we saw that he was something very different. His white head and tail and more especially the black lesser wing coverts were very distinctive at that distance and immediately attracted our attention. The ashy blue back was what suggested an adult Marsh Hawk at first glance. From this distance we watched him for some time with our glasses and on a nearer approach he flew to another post, which he shortly abandoned to soar above the meadows at a height of a hundred or more feet. There were many Red-wing Blackbirds nesting in the bushes by the stream and they were so alarmed at his presence that they several times attacked him. We imagined he was looking for mice or perhaps frogs, as he apparently did not bother the birds. When he saw his prey below he would commence fluttering like a Sparrow Hawk, and then, on seeing his chance, he raised his wings above his back, so that they almost touched, whereupon he descended, gaining speed as he went. Instead of checking himself on nearing the ground, he seemed to dive headlong into the grass and bushes, remaining out of sight several seconds before reappearing. We were unable to make out if he had anything in his claws when he arose again. This process was repeated several times and was a remarkably interesting performance. Finally he lit on another post and I crawled towards him keeping close to the fence, so that I actually got within ten yards of him before he flew, getting a wonderful view. He arose from there very much startled at my presence, flew over the hills and disappeared. The following week, on our next trip, which we made in hopes of again locating him, he was seen once more at long range, but except for these two times we never caught another glimpse of him. I believe this Kite has never before been seen in New England, but of course it can only be regarded as a very rare straggler, scarcely deserving a place on our New England list. — S. Prescott Fay, Boston, Mass."[1]

[1] Auk, Vol. XXVII, 1910, pp. 453–454.

Fig. 42. — Nest and Eggs of Marsh Hawk

Courtesy of Eugene W. Schmidt

Page 100

Fig. 43. — Downy Young Marsh Hawks

Courtesy of Eugene W. Schmidt

Page 99

Círcus hudsónius (LINNÆUS). Marsh Hawk.

Other names: BOG HAWK; MOUSE HAWK; FROG HAWK; SNAKE HAWK.

Plates 37 and 38.

DESCRIPTION. — Bill small, set about with curved bristles which project above cere; face broad, with partial facial disk or ruff of stiff compact feathers, and with very large ear and ear-flap, thus somewhat resembling an owl; brow projecting over, as in other hawks; first four primaries graduated from 1st to 4th (the longest); these four have inner webs sinuated, or cut away toward end; wing, tail and legs long, giving the bird a much larger appearance than the light, small body warrants. *Adult male:* Head, neck, upper breast and upper plumage chiefly light bluish-gray, often with some brownish clouding; some rather faint mottling of darker gray, mostly on back and wings; back of head darker above than rest of head, and often streaked with rusty whitish; back a deeper brownish-gray than back of head and first five primaries (all except outer edges which are light gray), blackish toward tips; inner primaries, secondaries and tail have light tips; tail has a broad dark gray or blackish subterminal bar and five to seven narrower dark brownish-gray or dusky bars; *upper tail-coverts chiefly white;* lower plumage from breast to tail, and under surfaces of wings chiefly white, sparsely spotted (including larger under wing-coverts) with crosswise spots of light brown or rusty; axillars white with broad brown arrowheads along shafts; bill blackish, lighter toward base, cere greenish-yellow or yellow; iris yellow; legs and feet yellow; claws blackish. *Adult female:* Above, dusky umber-brown; facial disk buffy with dark central streaks on each feather; head and neck streaked; lesser wing-coverts spotted and feathers of rump edged with light or pale brown or rusty; upper tail coverts white; tail darkest in center, becoming quite pale on outer edges, and crossed by five to seven broad dusky bars; flight feathers varied with light and dark brown; ends of inner primaries and secondaries pale-edged; below dull buffy or buffy-whitish, growing gradually paler toward tail, and streaked narrowly with dark brown, the streaks becoming narrower toward tail; axillars dark brown, spotted buffy, under surface of wings marked and barred brown; "bill dark bluish horn, darker at tip; cere yellowish-green or yellow; iris light straw yellow; legs and feet light orange yellow" (B. H. Warren). *Young in first winter plumage:* Similar to juvenal. *Young in juvenal plumage:* Similar to that of adult female but darker brown; *white upper tail-coverts more or less tinged yellowish,* and facial disk dark brown, broadly edged rusty; below, rich rusty yellowish and streaked (if at all) only on neck, breast, sides and flanks; tail with but four dark bars; eyes dark. *Downy young:* Pale buffy or whitish above, whitish below; down grows longer and darker as bird grows older, becoming darker above but remaining whitish on belly.

MEASUREMENTS. — *Male:* Length 17.50 to 20.00 in.; spread 40.00 to 45.00; folded wing 12.50 to 15.00; tail 8.00 to 10.00; bill, without cere, .60 to .80; tarsus 2.75 to 3.25. *Female:* length 19.00 to 24.00; spread 43.50 to 54.00; wing 14.00 to 16.50; tail 9.50 to 11.00; bill .70 to .95; tarsus 3.00 to 3.50. Weight, female 1 lb. to 1 lb. 5 oz. (B. H. Warren); male 12 to 16 oz.

MOLTS. — Apparently short down of chick is replaced later by longer down, and that is succeeded by juvenal plumage, which seems to be unchanged during first winter; in ensuing year there seems to be considerable molting (April to November) and immature birds may be found in all stages between juvenal and adult plumage; in summer or autumn of following year, when about or over two years old, probably most of them become as adult. Some may require another year; adults have complete molt during milder part of year.

FIELD MARKS. — Larger than crow; wings and tail long; *upper tail-coverts always white;* beats about chiefly over marshes, meadows and other open lands, usually flapping along low down with some sailing; picks up most of its food from grass or ground and rarely alights on trees. Might be mistaken at a distance for a larger hawk with its immense spread of wing, but wings are narrow for their length and they slant upward from the shoulder; its flight is gull-like rather than hawk-like. *Adult male:* Lightest in color of New England Hawks. Rather light gray above with black wing-tips; nearly white below. *Female and Immature:* Rich brown above, lighter below, where wings have dark barring. In length of wing and tail somewhat resembles Rough-legged Hawk at a distance, but latter has the white patch mainly on upper part of *tail, not* on *tail-coverts.*

VOICE. — Various notes; alarm call of male, "a shrill screaming *cha-cha-cha-cha-cha-cha*" (Florence M. Bailey); female, "a prolonged shriek — *kee, kee, kee, kee, kee, kee, kee, kee*"; or *check-eck, check-eck, check-eck, check-eck, check-eck, check-eck* (Bailey); "a series of syllables like *kuh! kuh! kuh!* repeated very fast and quite a number of times without pause" (H. O. Green); female when disturbed at nest, a flicker-like call sounding like *pé-ter pé-ter pé-ter;* another call *stee-whit-a-whit-a-whit,* also *pee pee pee* repeated fifteen to twenty times and *swit, wat, wat,* the notes sometimes run together like a whinny. (C. W. Townsend); rather weak nasal whistle, also a sort of chuckle; at nest with eggs *quip-quip-quip-quip-quip;* male at times has a complaining, scolding note like *chu-chu-chu* or *choo-choo-choo,* quite unlike the usual short, weak but sharp whistle of the bird — this when nesting-area is invaded. The male's voice is deeper, fuller and heavier than the female's higher-keyed note (J. A. Farley).

BREEDING. — Usually in meadow, marsh or low pasture, less often in high, dry, open lands, often for many years on same site (J. A. Allen). *Nest:* On ground (usually a dry spot) among grasses, bushes or other low vegetation, and commonly not far from water; in most cases a slight affair, little hollowed, but if on wet ground may be raised on a platform of sticks; in such cases a rather elaborate nest may be made, high and deeply hollowed; built and lined with dry grass, stubble, weed stalks and similar material. *Eggs:* 3 to 6, sometimes 7 or 8; 1.25 to 1.53 by 1.75 to 2.00 in. oval or ovate; very variable in shape; bluish-white or greenish-white, rarely marked at all, but occasionally faintly and sparsely spotted with pale reddish or purplish-brown or lilac. Illustrated in Bendire's "Life Histories of North American Birds" Vol. I, Plate V, Figs. 8 to 10. *Dates:* April 29, Texas; April 30 to June 8, southern New England; June 12, New Hampshire; June 4, Maine. *Incubation:* Period 21 to 28 days (various authors); difficult to determine, as several days may elapse between periods of oviposition, and young in same nest may hatch on dates some days apart; by both parents. One brood yearly.

RANGE. — North America, and south to northern South America. Breeds from northeastern Siberia, northwestern Alaska, northwestern Mackenzie, northern Manitoba, northern Ontario, central Quebec, and Newfoundland south to Gulf coast and the Mexican border; in winter from southern British Columbia, western Montana, western South Dakota, southern Minnesota (very rarely), southern Wisconsin, southern Michigan, Ohio, southern New York, southern Vermont and southern New Hampshire south to Bahamas, Cuba and Colombia; casual in Hawaii; accidental in Barbadoes.

DISTRIBUTION IN NEW ENGLAND. — Rather common migrant and summer resident in open lands; rare or local in heavily wooded mountainous regions; more common on coastal plain and in river valleys than on higher lands; formerly much more common; in winter rare in coastal regions of Connecticut, Rhode Island and Massachusetts, very rare in interior Massachusetts, casual in southern Vermont and southern New Hampshire.

SEASON IN MASSACHUSETTS. — (February 17) March 20 to November 10 (November 22; winter).

HAUNTS AND HABITS. The slender graceful Marsh Hawk is a bird of tireless flight. It is one of the "ignoble" hawks — a lowly mouse hunter; a "harrier" of the marsh, hunting mainly close to the ground. It seldom alights in a large tree, where I have seen it but once, although it rests occasionally on very small trees, shrubs, hay-cocks, or fence posts. As Mr. J. A. Farley says: — It alights as "light as a feather; seems as if the slightest puff or zephyr beneath its body would send the bird afloat again like a bit of thistle-down." It feeds usually upon the ground, nests there and probably often roosts there. A male Marsh Hawk, shot just after daybreak of a very frosty morning (November 5, 1925) at South Andover, Maine, by Mr. J. D. Smith of the Boston Society of Natural

History, had its back and tail-feathers covered with *frost*. This may indicate that the bird had passed the night on the ground or in the bushes of that very frosty meadow. This hawk is not by any means confined to the marsh in its peregrinations, as it may be seen hunting on the dryest kind of sandy lands or on upland pastures, and in some parts of the western prairie country it nests on high ridges. Its nest has been found by Mr. John F. Carleton among the dry sand dunes of East Sandwich, bordering on Cape Cod Bay. It is seen rarely in the woods, except about woodland lakes or rivers or small ponds near the borders of the forest. Its flight and its appearance in the air about the shores of Lake Umbagog are graphically described by Brewster as follows:

"Even when its shores are almost everywhere submerged in May, and early June, they are not infrequently included within the regular daily beats of adult male Marsh Hawks in full-nuptial plumage, looking almost as white as Gulls, and indeed not always to be distinguished from them, when seen at a distance skimming low over blue water, or against a dark background of evergreen foliage. Flying ever in the buoyant, unhurried manner so characteristic of their race, now renewing waning impetus by a few deliberate wing-strokes, next gliding for several rods on wings set with the tips held well upwards, much as those of a gliding Turkey Vulture are held, tilting their bodies more or less perceptibly from side to side and rarely pursuing a perfectly straight course for more than a few yards at a time, they may skirt the shore for miles, following all its windings closely, and keeping just outside the outer ranks of living trees, but taking no especial pains to thus avoid outstanding dead ones. For the most part such flight is apt to impress one as unheeding if not perfunctory, but all the while the bird is doubtless keenly scanning every stump and floating log within its range of vision, while every now and then it will hover low over rafts of driftwood collected in sheltered coves, to scrutinize them with obviously eager interest. . . . A Marsh Hawk engaged in low and for the most part straight-onward, gliding flights is not unlikely to remind one, as has been said, of a Turkey Buzzard similarly employed, because of the decided upward angle, nearly, if not quite, 45°, at which its wings are held, and of the lateral tilting of its body. But when, as often happens, it soars in circles, perhaps hundreds of feet above the earth, its wings are set almost level, like those of a soaring Buteo which it otherwise resembles in general carriage, but from which it may easily be distinguished, even at distances too great to make out its characteristic colour and markings, by its slenderer body, and longer tail. At the Lake I have repeatedly seen Marsh Hawks mount in this manner, with rarely a wing-beat, until they were almost lost to sight overhead, and apparently above the crests of the higher mountains." [1]

The Marsh Hawk lives so great a part of the daylight hours in the air that it is rarely seen elsewhere, unless one comes upon it while on the ground in the act of devouring its prey.

With the warm days of April many Marsh Hawks, leaving their southern winter homes, appear in New England. Some already are mated when they arrive here and

---

[1] Brewster, William: The birds of the Lake Umbagog Region of Maine, 1925, Part 2, pp. 311 and 314.

they may mate for life, as pairs have been observed in winter hunting together. Both sexes probably mate in their second year, as mated pairs, both in brown plumage have been seen at the nest.

The courtship of the Marsh Hawk is carried on largely in its favorite element. In warm spring days a pair may be seen soaring to a great height, when one will suddenly plunge far downward and turn a complete forward or sidelong somersault in the air. Sometimes one falling thus from a height will turn over and over again in the manner of a tumbler pigeon. As it bounds up and down in the air, it seems to move more like a rubber ball than a bird. This tireless behavior usually occurs over the marsh or meadow that they have chosen for a home. When two of these birds are mated or mating they keep together much of the time, either on the ground or in the air. When the female alights the male follows her and walks or flies around her. On the ground he bows to her and swells with amorous ardor. Sometimes the male flies alone across the marsh rising and falling alternately and with each fall turning a complete somersault, as if to show his larger mate what a clever and wonderful bird he really is. Again he "carries on" in the same way while flying in her company. He is a good father, as he assists at times in nest building and also in incubation and in caring for the young, but his principal function after the young have hatched is that of providing food for the family. Hunting tirelessly over marsh far and near or along marshy borders of some lake or stream, he beats over the ground here and there until he perceives the movement of some mouse, frog or other suitable prey in the grass, when, rising a little in the air and poising for an instant with rapidly vibrating wings, he falls upon his victim; or, if in his flight he catches sight of some fleeing timorous prey beneath him, he turns like a flash and snatches it up, or, having overrun it, he, in his eagerness to check his flight, may even turn a complete somersault in striking his victim; then rising high, he flies swiftly homeward. As he nears the neighborhood of his domicile he hails his mate with shrill cries, and she, replying, leaves her precious charge and rises to meet him. When directly over her, he drops his prey and she, turning partly over in the air, catches it with her claws as it falls, or if not near enough darts after it and dexterously snatches it ere it reaches the ground, then drops to her nest, while he either follows her or turns again to his hunting.

The Marsh Hawk seems usually to be anything but a bold and warlike bird; a fussy old hen will sometimes succeed in frightening one away from her chicks; a group of Least Terns will drive one away from their nesting grounds, and blackbirds occasionally chase one, but there are some courageous individuals among these hawks, as in nesting time on their breeding grounds they have been known to charge a human intruder or a dog. In the breeding season some become very pugnacious. Dr. Henry J. Perry tells me that recently at Carlisle, Massachusetts, he saw a Marsh Hawk attacking a Red-shouldered Hawk, and that on the 26th, at Chatham, he saw a pair assail a Red-tailed Hawk; also that in 1924 he saw a pair give battle to a Red-tailed Hawk, a Black Vulture and several Crows. Marsh Hawks have even been known to harry eagles. Maynard asserts that he has seen the Marsh Hawk repeatedly rob the Duck Hawk of ducks that it had killed.   He says that he saw one attack a Duck Hawk that was feeding on a scaup and appropriate its prey, while the "noble" falcon protested ineffectually.[1]   Probably, however, the usual procedure in similar contests is described by Mr. William Gordon Means in a letter addressed to me, dated February 11, 1926.   Mr. Means writes: "When out shooting ducks on the Mississippi Delta, I noticed what appeared to be a male Duck Hawk sitting on a muskrat house about half a mile from the blind.   The shooting that I was doing did not seem to disturb him at all and during the lulls in the shooting I would watch him through my glasses, preening his feathers and sunning himself.   Presently I shot a duck which, evidently, I hit through the heart as it set its wings and toppled over dead, about a quarter of a mile off in the alligator grass.   It was in plain sight from the blind, although in a rather inaccessible spot and I did not send my guide to get it, fortunately.   In a few minutes I noticed a large female Marsh Hawk come down and begin feeding on my duck.   She had not been there long before the little falcon jumped up and went over to where she was feeding.   He promptly knocked her off the duck and began depluming it and eating his morning meal.   This performance took about half an hour. After he had eaten his fill he went over to another muskrat house where he sat contentedly, with a full crop, gazing idly in the sun.   The Turkey Buzzards then appeared and cleaned up such portions of my duck as the Falcon had not taken.   During his meal the other hawk came back once or twice and made rather faint-hearted attempts to regain her quarry, but the little fellow was too much for her every time and I think she knew it from the way she acted."   The Marsh Hawk has been known, however, to kill a Green Heron and even to drive away a Bald Eagle.

In late August or early September the autumnal migration of the Marsh Hawk begins, and some birds continue to move southward until late in November; probably those that are seen in December are among the few that winter in the coastal region of southern New England.   The principal migration here seems to move along the coastal plain. Many Marsh Hawks coming south through the region below Boston follow down the west side of Buzzards Bay and then turn westward across Narragansett Bay and along the coasts of Rhode Island and Connecticut.   Others cross Vineyard Sound to Marthas Vineyard where they also breed plentifully, and, as "Chicken Hawks," are considered great poultry pests by the poultry raisers of that island.

A very full exposition of the Marsh Hawk's food has been given by Dr. A. K. Fisher of the Biological Survey.   Ornithologists are indebted to him for the only exhaustive and complete investigation of the food of the rapacious birds of the United States.[2]   He tabulates in this report the stomach contents of 124 Marsh Hawks from many parts of the United States, taken in 11 months of the year and finds that 7 contained poultry or game birds; 34, other birds; 57, mice; 22, other mammals — chiefly squirrels, gophers, and rats; 7, reptiles; 2, frogs; 14, insects; 1, undetermined material and 8 were empty.

---

[1] Maynard, C. J.: Birds of Eastern North America, 1896, p. 257.

[2] The Hawks and Owls of the United States, Bulletin No. 3, U. S. Department of Agriculture, Division of Ornithology and Mammalogy, 1893.

Dr. B. H. Warren informs me that he found eggs of Clapper Rails in two Marsh Hawks taken on Wallops Island, Virginia. This hawk is fond of locusts and grasshoppers. Remains of 69 locusts were found in one stomach among those examined by experts of the Biological Survey, and Professor Samuel Aughey found 249 Rocky Mountain Locusts in 5 Marsh Hawks' stomachs.[1]   Ordinarily the Marsh Hawk kills few birds, mostly small ground-frequenting species such as the sparrows of the marsh and meadow.   Occasionally a Bob-white is taken; also rails and their young come into its bill of fare; now and then a young skunk or a young rabbit is eaten.   This bird frequently eats dead or wounded ducks.   I once saw one feasting on a domestic pigeon in a salt-marsh, and a friend writes to me that he found one eating a Green Heron, still warm.   Marsh Hawks along the Atlantic coast seem to take more birds than those in the interior, and on the littoral they often become a nuisance by catching young chickens.   A number of Marsh Hawks collected on Marthas Vineyard had been eating small birds.   I have never known a full grown fowl to be attacked, and Mr. Charles W. Nash, the well-known economic ornithologist of Ontario, says he has never known one there to attack any domestic fowl.   Mr. H. K. Coale, however, tells of an individual that killed seven "Hungarian" Partridges within two weeks.[2]   At need the Marsh Hawk will feed on any small dead animal, including fish, and will not disdain carrion.   In feeding, this hawk apparently swallows the smaller mice, fur and all, but it plucks most of the feathers from small birds before tearing off the flesh.

ECONOMIC STATUS.   Evidently the Marsh Hawk is a useful species over most of its range, but along the Atlantic coast it is more harmful than in many other regions.   Even there, however, it probably is worthy of full protection by all except poultry raisers, as, were this hawk exterminated, the injury done by the mice, rats and squirrels that it now consumes and their progeny, would soon far exceed that attributable now to the Hawk.

In the rice fields of the south it is extremely useful as it frightens the "rice birds" and keeps them moving and thus interrupts their depredations, while in the game preserves it destroys cotton rats which rank among the greatest enemies of the Bob-white. (See Introduction, pages xliv–xlv.)

Accípiter vélox (WILSON).   Sharp-shinned Hawk.

Other names: PIGEON HAWK, CHICKEN HAWK, SMALL STUB-WINGED BULLET-HAWK.

Plates 37, 38 and 39.

DESCRIPTION. — Tail and wings ample, but wings rather short and rounded at tip, tail rather long, square-tipped or nearly so, very rarely slightly rounded, legs and toes rather long and slim, middle toe very long. *Adult male:* Above rather dark bluish-gray, top of head darker, but *not black;* tail crossed by four or more obscure blackish bars, usually five on outer tail feathers, four on others, the basal bar under the tail-coverts, the subterminal broadest, tip of tail whitish (barring above and below corresponding); primaries marked with blackish bars, and whitening towards bases, especially on under side;

[1] First Annual Report of the United States Entomological Commission, 1878, Appendix II, p. 43.
[2] Auk, Vol. XLII, 1925, p. 269.

PLATE 39

PLATE 39

SHARP-SHINNED HAWK
Page 104

COOPER'S HAWK
Page 112

YOUNG MALE IN
FIRST WINTER PLUMAGE

ADULT FEMALE

YOUNG FEMALE IN
FIRST WINTER PLUMAGE

ADULT MALE

GOSHAWK
Page 116

YOUNG MALE IN
FIRST WINTER PLUMAGE

ADULT FEMALE

All about one-fourth scale.

secondaries also barred; ear coverts light rufous, streaked darker, sides of head otherwise whitish, little marked; scapulars with concealed white spots; below, barred and cross-spotted with vinaceous rufous on a white ground, often nearly immaculate white on throat and under tail-coverts, but chin and throat usually with blackish shaft-streaks; wing-linings and axillars slightly more buffy than other under plumage, spotted and barred brown or dusky; under surface of wing finely and narrowly barred; bill bluish horn color at base, tip blackish, cere yellow or greenish yellow; iris yellow to red; legs and feet yellow, sometimes with a greenish tinge, claws black. *Adult female:* similar to male, but less bluish above and lighter below. *Young in first winter plumage:* Like juvenal. *Young in juvenal plumage:* Dusky umberbrown above, with paler rusty-brown edgings to most of the feathers, and some white spots (mostly concealed), which are largest on scapulars; tail darkly barred; below white or buffy-white, streaked with dark brown or reddish-brown, except on tail-coverts, which are little marked, and on sides, flanks and leg-feathering, which are spotted crosswise with brown; (some apparently juvenal birds have sides and flanks barred); axillars and under wing-coverts pale brownish or pale buffy, barred and spotted brown; under surfaces of flight-feathers and tail-feathers pale silvery-whitish or grayish, barred with dark brown or dusky; bill pale bluish horn color, tipped black, cere whitish; iris grayish-yellow, yellow or straw; legs and feet yellow or yellowish, claws blackish. *Downy young:* yellowish, white or creamy-white.

MEASUREMENTS. — *Male:* length 10.00 to 12.00 in.; spread 20.00 to 23.00; folded wing 6.00 to 7.10; tail 5.00 to 7.00; tarsus 1.80 to 2.05; bill, without cere, .40 to .50. *Female:* length 12.00 to 14.00; spread about 24.00 to 27.00; wing 7.00 to 8.80; tail 6.00 to 8.20; bill .40 to .53; tarsus 1.80 to 2.25. Female usually larger than male, often much larger. Weight, male 3½ oz.; female 7½ to 8¼ oz. (Audubon).

MOLTS. — First short yellowish down is replaced by longer down, which may have a gray tinge on back; juvenal plumage, assumed by the time the young bird is fully fledged, apparently is worn through first winter, often fading materially by March; in spring a molt begins (April to August or September) after which bird assumes virtually adult plumage; highest plumage may require another year or more; adults acquire winter plumage by a complete molt (July to October).

FIELD MARKS. — Rather longer and slimmer than either Sparrow Hawk or Pigeon Hawk, the two small falcons with which it is sometimes confounded; size near Nighthawk but commonly somewhat larger, tail longer, wings shorter and wider, more rounded; its flight an alternation of quick wing-beats and sailing, intermittently, soaring at times, usually in small circles. *Adults:* Dark bluish-gray above; whitish, barred reddish-brown, below; under surface of wings and tail as seen in flight white, barred narrowly and darkly. Largest specimens are about the size of smallest Cooper's Hawk which it so much resembles in colors although having a *square* tail instead of the *rounded* tail of Cooper's. *Young:* Browner above, body streaked brown below; female with reddish streaks, male with darker streaks.

VOICE. — Common note sounds rather like *cac, cac, cac* (W. L. Ralph); a repeated *quee* (J. A. Farley); but much less loud and strong than the "*cuck*" of Cooper's; male's voice is weaker than female's. "Two distinct alarm notes when nest is approached — the usual cackling call in the earlier stages of the nesting season and a second series of squealing notes, not unlike those of Ruffed Grouse after young are hatched, alternating from one call to the other when the young are well grown."

BREEDING. — Commonly in woods, but frequently in small groves and very rarely in trees in the open; white pine groves or wood lots very often chosen. *Nest:* Usually in a tree from ten to 80 feet up, sometimes near top of coniferous tree, such as white pine, pitch pine, hemlock, white cedar and spruce, but deciduous trees, as oaks, elms, birches and lindens, sometimes chosen; rarely in hollow tree or some cavity in a cliff; nest on branches and against trunk; large for the size of bird, about size of crow's nest (in some cases an old crow or squirrel nest rebuilt), and six to seven inches deep, composed of small sticks, and lined chiefly with small twigs and sometimes pieces or strips of bark; rarely moss, grass or leaves; very few feathers may be seen; in eastern Massachusetts often an *all-stick* nest, with lining of bits of bark; not often very noticeable and sometimes high enough in top of tree to be well concealed.

It is hard to imagine a cleaner structure for a hawk's nest than a new, well-woven, all-sticks and twigs "Sharp-shin's" nest. *Eggs:* Usually four or five, rarely six to eight; very variable in size and shape; 1.18 to 1.60 by 1.06 to 1.24 in.; oval to short ovate; bluish-white or greenish-white, spotted and blotched with various browns and lavender or lilac; markings very irregular and varyingly distributed; eggs are usually beautiful objects; illustrated in Bendire's "Life Histories of North American Birds," Vol. I, Plate V, Figs. 11 to 17. *Dates:* April 29 (rarely) southern Ontario; May 3 to June 10, Massachusetts; late May or early June, northern New England. *Incubation:* Period about 21 to 24 days; by both parents. One brood yearly.

RANGE. — North and Middle America. Breeds throughout most of United States and Canada from northwestern Alaska, northwestern Mackenzie, central Manitoba, northern Ontario, central Quebec, southern Labrador and Newfoundland south to Florida, the Gulf coast, Texas and Arizona; in winter from southwestern Alaska, southern British Columbia, western Montana, southern Nebraska, southern Minnesota (accidental), Illinois, Indiana, Ohio, southern Ontario, New York, southern Vermont, southern New Hampshire and (rarely) southern Maine, and New Brunswick (casually) south to Guatemala and (casually) to Panama; accidental in Bahamas; recorded (perhaps erroneously) in Cuba.

DISTRIBUTION IN NEW ENGLAND. — *Maine:* Not uncommon migrant; less common summer resident; rare winter resident in southern parts. *New Hampshire:* Rather common migrant, less common summer resident, rare winter resident in southern counties. *Vermont:* Uncommon to common migrant and summer resident and rare winter resident in lower lands of southern part. *Massachusetts:* Common to abundant migrant and rather uncommon to rare summer and winter resident; less common breeder than in the past. *Rhode Island:* Rather uncommon migrant except along southern coast; rare summer and winter resident. *Connecticut:* Common to abundant migrant; less common summer and winter resident.

SEASON IN MASSACHUSETTS. — Resident. Most common in spring and fall; migrations March to May and late August to November; occasional or rare in winter in the lowlands.

HAUNTS AND HABITS. The Sharp-shinned Hawk is the American counterpart of the European Sparrow-hawk. It is so bold, swift, impetuous and daring that it does not hesitate at times to strike much larger birds. It has been known to attack the northern Pileated Woodpecker, the Wood Duck, the Black-crowned Night Heron and full-grown domestic fowls. In reference to its assault on a Black-crowned Night Heron, Mr. C. J. Maynard says that the little hawk struck the larger bird to the ground; then left it there, perhaps frightened away by the astonishing squawks of its victim.[1] Sometimes this hawk seems to attack poultry purely for sport.[2] One day I watched a lone crow harrying one of these hawks that was peacefully flying across a pasture. The hawk kept on its way until the crow attempted to assault it, when the smaller bird turned on its sable tormenter and punished it so severely that the crow was fortunate to escape with its life. During the breeding season the spirited little "Sharp-shin" has been known to chase an Osprey that trespassed on the former's breeding grounds.

The Sharp-shinned Hawk is remarkably swift, graceful and skilful in flight. It swings and circles through the forest aisles and even among thick branches with the greatest ease. Its usual cross-country flight consists of periods of steady flapping, with short intervals of sailing, but sometimes, especially during its migrations when hundreds may

---

[1] Birds of Eastern North America, 1896, p. 278.
[2] Cameron, E. S.: Auk, Vol. XXIV, 1907, p. 260.

be seen passing at very considerable heights, much soaring is indulged in.   The spring flight to and through New England usually occurs chiefly in April and early May.

The courting activities and the building of the nest also occupy part of this period. As is the case with other hawks the male often fights fiercely with any rival that makes advances toward his mate.   Mr. R. I. Brasher describes such a battle in the air as a marvelous exhibition of flying.[1]

The birds having made choice of a nesting site are likely, if unmolested, to return to the same neighborhood year after year.   Usually a new nest is built yearly.   The nest is not hard to find, as often it is not over 20 or 30 feet high, and the hawks advertise it by scolding when any one appears in the immediate neighborhood.   Often the little male will dart boldly at an intruder on the ground either before or after the nest-tree has been climbed.   Frequently the female will stay on the nest until the tree is tapped, or even partly climbed.   Sometimes her long tail may be seen sticking over the edge of the nest. She almost never flies because of some one merely walking beneath the tree.   The eggs are laid usually on alternate days.   Five little downy young "Sharp-shins" in a nest are a beautiful sight.   They fill the nest full to overflowing with their palpitating, snowy, fluffy mass, with five pairs of bright black eyes punctuating the "fluff."   The young remain in or near the nest for about four weeks, and during this time there is a constant and ever increasing demand for food suitable for hawklets.   Therefore it is at this season that the depredations of this species are most noticeable.   Now both parents are engaged much of the time in hunting for food to fill the yawning cavities always presented to them by their hungry offspring.[2]   As the young birds approach maturity probably each requires at least three or four small birds every day, or their equivalent, to supply sufficient aliment to insure rapid growth and development ;   and while the parents are bold and skilful hunters, they do not seem to be so uniformly successful in their forays as many ornithologists seem to believe them to be.   If so, they would not find it necessary to brave so often the perils of the poultry yard in quest of little chicks.   We are told that this hawk is "feathered lightning" and that it can closely follow every turn of its victims, but the creatures on which it chiefly preys are so wary and agile as to be able often to escape the swift rush of the hawk, and by sudden dodging and twisting to gain a refuge in some dense and thorny thicket or pile of brush where the larger pursuer cannot enter ;   nevertheless the hawk sometimes follows one into a thicket, and not always in vain.   In some cases where the hawk dashes into a flock it seems to be bewildered by the numbers of its potential victims, and fails to secure a bird.   Sometimes the little raptore is so hard pressed for food that it is reduced to hunting mice, ground squirrels or insects, or even to stealing young birds from their nests.   Many times have I seen this hawk harrying the small birds, but only five times have I actually seen it strike down its prey.   One day at Concord, William Brewster was standing by the corner of one of his barns, near the opening of the

---

[1] American Magazine, Vol. CI, 1926, p. 162.

[2] Mr. J. A. Farley examined a nest from which the young had flown and found the interlocking twigs to be littered with thrush's legs.

barn cellar watching a Phœbe which had a nest in the cellar, and was fly-catching from a low limb near by. A Sharp-shinned Hawk made a sudden rush at the Phœbe. The little bird avoided the stroke and then shot downward directly at Mr. Brewster, passed under his elbow, around his body and vanished into the cellar, while the hawk, completely baffled, quickly withdrew. One day on the Concord meadows a Red-winged Blackbird, which had been accustomed to chase the rather slow-flying Marsh Hawk started after a Sharp-shinned Hawk that was crossing the meadow. Fatal error! The hawk immediately turned, but the blackbird evaded him and, realizing its mistake, attempted to gain the woods which, by turning and twisting, it finally reached ahead of its swifter but less agile pursuer. I was unable to see the end of that chase, but it was the longest and most persistent pursuit that I have known a hawk of this species to undertake. The hawk may have been angered by the attack of the blackbird, and that may have accounted for the determined chase. Its usual method is to flap and sail at a rather low altitude and to strike its prey by a quick drop or turn or a sudden dash at some incautious small bird, caught in the open and perhaps paralyzed by fear for an instant at the sudden approach of its redoubtable enemy.

Such hunting often is successful in thinly forested land where trees or shrubbery mask the approach, or even in open undulating land where the hawk flies low and where its coming is screened by a ridge or a patch of brush. In such a case on the coast of British Columbia, the hawk missed his victim. I was watching from my canoe a flock of small sandpipers, feeding on the strand, when suddenly the hawk shot like an arrow into their midst; he had thrust his feet forward to strike, when every little bird sprang away as with one accord; even a poor cripple with one leg useless was as quick as his companions, and so rapid were their concerted evolutions that the marauder never touched one, and soon gave up the pursuit. Often the hawk will take a commanding position in a tree where it can overlook the haunts of its prospective victims and, partly concealed behind the leaves, wait and watch for its prey. In this way, by watching its chances, it secures little chicks by a sudden rush in spite of the vigilance of the hen-mother.

Mr. Ned Dearborn writes as follows of the boldness and swiftness of the Sharp-shinned Hawk: "Its audacity when hungry is astonishing. I have seen one pounce on a chicken, right in the village, and wait till it had very deliberately fixed its claws in the chicken's back, eyeing at the same time a man, just across the street, with the greatest insolence imaginable. I once saw one of these hawks dash among a flock of goldfinches that were feeding in a weedy run. They took flight precipitately in all directions, but he singled out one and gave chase. No matter how that goldfinch turned, the hawk was always headed for his mark and constantly nearing it. It seemed as if every tack of the little bird was anticipated by its relentless pursuer. I suppose less than a minute after the hawk's appearance he had the goldfinch in his clutches. The final scene was enacted within thirty feet of my face, yet such was the lightning-like quickness of the hawk's grasp, that I could not perceive it. I saw the birds about eight inches apart; I heard the cruel sound of claws in contact with the goldfinch's pinions; I saw the triumphant murderer holding his luckless victim, one of its little wings still spread, but the act of capture was like a trick of sleight of hand. The hawk's motion was not arrested in the least at the capture. He kept on straight ahead for a short distance, till his momentum was reduced, then turned about and descended to a wall, where he began at once to enjoy the fruit of his labors." [1]

Many of this hawk's victims are taken by stealth. Mr. J. A. Farley says that as he watched a female of this species, she had a catlike grace; both her poising and movements were very cat-like, especially as she heard the near-by note of a small bird.

Now and then a pack of Blue Jays will gather about one of these hawks, while he is perched, and revile him. At first their numbers and noise may confuse and baffle him, but if he is at all hungry let them beware, for then the hawk makes a sudden dash, bearing one of his assailants to the ground. The victim fights valiantly, but its cowardly companions retreat in disorder, leaving their comrade to its fate, which is soon settled by the impetuous little hawk. Two such occurrences have come under my notice, but in one case my dog sprang at the hawk and both birds flew, the hawk closely pursuing the jay. When this hawk attacks a Robin, the smaller bird seems helpless with terror, and screams as if in mortal agony. All the small songsters recognize that cry, which I have never heard from the Robin on any other occasion, but they can only protest, while the hawk, unmindful of their cries, despatches its victim. Apparently this hawk rarely attempts a second rush at a bird that escapes its first dash, but it has been known to try time and again without success. When not hungry it apparently does not kill for sport and many times it has been seen flying near small birds without making any attempt to molest them; again it may strike as if in play or practice without harming the object of its rush. It has been seen frequently to strike at flickers leaving them untouched when it might easily have killed them. The peculiar actions of one seen at Concord, September 5, 1907 may have indicated that it was merely playing or it might have been catching insects. It launched itself from a tree on which it had been sitting and, turning completely over in the air, feet uppermost, clutched something from the under side of a branch. This was repeated twice.

The Sharp-shinned Hawk not infrequently crosses wide waters and it has been seen at sea, though usually while migrating near the sea it follows the shore. Mr. Richard B. Harding tells me that on August 9, 1923 a wearied bird of this species attempted to alight on a yacht some five miles off Cape Porpoise, Maine, but, unable to reach the craft, fell into the sea. The vessel was put about in an attempt to pick up the hawk, but the bird succeeded in rising and escaping. Before it had gone a quarter of a mile, however, the weary creature was driven into the water by some terns which attacked it from above.

The southward migration of this species probably begins in August, but we see few actually in migration before September. Then they pass in great numbers, and some are still passing in October or later. I shall never forget my first sight of this fall migra-

---

[1] The Birds of Durham and Vicinity, 1903, p. 43.

tion. We had been "haying" in blue joint grass on the river meadow, and one hot day in early September I was lying on top of a load of hay, which the horses were hauling a mile to the barn, when, gazing upward into the blue, I became aware that in the far heights the sky was alive with birds. There were hundreds, sailing and drifting southward at different heights, and all that were near enough to be identified were Sharp-shinned Hawks. Several such flights have been observed since that day, and they always leave an impression of awe at the numbers and movements of the concourse.

In autumn great numbers of Sharp-shinned Hawks follow the flights of small birds across Lake Erie, starting from Point Pelee, Ontario, at the west end of the Lake. Taverner and Swales give some idea of the number of these hawks during the migration as follows:

"After the coming of the first in the fall their numbers steadily increased until from six to a dozen can be noted in a day, which in most localities would be accounted common. Then there came a day, September 11, 1905, and September 15, 1906, when the morning's tramp found Sharp-shins everywhere. As we walked through the woods their dark forms darted away between the tree trunks at every few steps. Just over the tree tops, a steady stream of them was beating up and down the length of the Point, while in the air they could often be discerned at every height until the highest looked like a mote floating in the light. As concrete illustrations of the number present: — In 1905 we stood in a little open glade and at various times of the day counted from twenty-five to thirty in sight at one time, and Saunders writes: 'When I saw the flight in 1882 it was probably even greater than in 1905. There were more Sharp-shins than one would suppose were in Ontario, and one day my brother and I stood thirty paces apart facing each other, with double-barrel, breech-loaders, and for a short time the hawks passed so thick that we had to let some go by unmolested because we could not load fast enough to fire at each as it came.' A farmer told us of sitting in his front yard one afternoon and shooting fifty-six without leaving his chair. . . . This great abundance lasted, in 1905, three days, and the next year four, when they gradually began to thin out, though to the latest of our stay (the 22d, in 1906), they still remained more than common, and at least fifty could be observed in a day. All this time there was a steady stream flying across the lake towards the Ohio shore. Near the extreme end of the Point is a wooden observatory tower built by the U. S. Lake Survey for the purpose of making observations on the changes of the shore contour. It is about fifty feet high, and stands with its base in the red cedar thicket whilst the platform rises well above all surrounding foliage. On this vantage point Saunders and Taverner took their stand the 18th, and with watch in hand counted the Sharp-shins that passed, nearly all within gunshot. From 11:24 to 11:54, 281 passed us, 207 making for the end of the Point and 74 returning, making 133 that started across the lake within half an hour. As far as we could make out without remaining on the spot the whole time this rate was kept up all day and every day of the greatest abundance of the species. The 13th was the last day of the great flight in 1905, but Swales, driving into Leamington, five miles from the base, found them as common the whole way between as they were on the Point itself. As he drove along every field had its quota of hawks and at times every fence post supported one. Even in the business section of Leamington he saw a number." [1]

Similar great flights of this hawk take place at Cape May, New Jersey, where the birds gather to await a favorable opportunity to cross Delaware Bay in their southward migration. Dr. Witmer Stone, editor of the Auk, says that in one week in 1920, no less than 1,400 were known to have been killed by gunners who make a specialty of shooting them to eat. [2]

With fair winds these birds often fly very high in migration and drift onward, but with contrary winds they fly low, with much flapping and little sailing.

The individuals that winter in New England are sorely pressed at times by want. Then they seem to have no fear of consequences, and strike their prey wherever it may be found. Frequently at this season they have dashed through windows in the attempt to reach caged birds, and they pursue their prey to the very doors of the houses; I have seen birds thus struck down beneath my very windows. They hunt in all weather, even in the face of a driving storm. Dr. P. L. Hatch states that while riding across the prairies of Minnesota during a furious winter gale with the thermometer 46 ° below zero one of these hawks passed close to the ground with inconceivable velocity, seizing in its course and bearing away an unfortunate Snow Bunting.

Having killed a small bird this hawk usually plucks off and discards about all the feathers, except a little down and some of the wing feathers, then tears off the head and feet and swallows them, after which it proceeds to devour the rest. It seems to be a common habit with many hawks and owls to swallow their prey whole if very small, but if not, to remove the head and legs or feet and eat them first, but this is not an invariable rule.

The food of the Sharp-shinned Hawk normally consists very largely of small birds. All observers agree on this, and not uncommonly it slays birds as large as the Bob-white. Dr. Fisher gives the following summary of the results of examining the contents of 159 stomachs: 6 contained poultry or game birds; 99, other birds; 6, mice; 5, insects; and 52 were empty. The birds taken were mostly songsters, from the size of Robins and other thrushes down to warblers and wrens. This is a very large proportion of bird-remains, but Mr. Joseph Peters writes that a Sharp-shinned Hawk shot in Truro, Massachusetts, because it had been accused of catching chickens, had in its stomach 52 grasshoppers, besides remains of many other insects and one mouse. This hawk has been seen to eat numbers of the destructive Gipsy Moth.

ECONOMIC STATUS. The Sharp-shinned Hawk is rated by Dr. A. K. Fisher, Dr. B. H. Warren and other ornithologists as injurious to man's interest. It is not a bird for the farmer to tolerate about his chicken coops nor is it desirable about a bird preserve. Nevertheless in the eternal scheme of the universe, its existence serves to check the undue increase of small birds and to prevent the propagation of unfitness and disease among them.

---

[1] Taverner, P. A., and Swales, B. H.: Wilson Bulletin, Vol. XIX, 1907, pp. 92–93.   [2] Auk, Vol. XXXIX, 1922, p. 567.

Accipiter coóperi (Bonaparte).　Cooper's Hawk.

Other names: CHICKEN HAWK; QUAIL HAWK; BLUE DARTER; BIG STUB-WINGED BULLET-HAWK.

Plates 38 and 39.

DESCRIPTION. — Similar to Sharp-shinned Hawk, but larger, a trifle stouter; legs and toes proportionately stouter, tarsi more rounded than those of Sharp-shinned Hawk, and *tail somewhat rounded.* *Adult male:* Similar in color to adult male Sharp-shinned Hawk, but top of head black or blackish, rufous sides of head often washed bluish-gray, sides of breast tinged same and tip of tail more decidedly white; iris yellow; cere greenish; bill and claws bluish-black; legs and feet greenish-yellow. *Adult female:* Colors duller than in male, top of head more brownish-black and upper plumage less bluish; sides of breast without bluish-gray tinge; as in male, white scapular spots not many nor large. *Young in first winter plumage:* Similar to same stage of Sharp-shinned Hawk, but rather more narrowly striped beneath and less of cross-spotting on sides and flanks. *Young in juvenal plumage:* Similar to first winter plumage, but feathers with broader reddish edges; more or less concealed white spots above; tawny head contrasts strongly with general dark brown of upper plumage; a white line over eye. *Downy young:* Whitish or yellowish-white in first stage.

MEASUREMENTS. — *Male:* Length 14.00 to 18.00 in.; spread about 27.00 to 30.00; folded wing 8.85 to 10.00; tail 7.00 to 8.30; bill, without cere, .62 to .69; tarsus 2.30 to 2.65. *Female:* Length 16.50 to 20.00; spread 29.00 to 36.00; folded wing 10.10 to 11.00; tail 8.00 to 10.50; bill .65 to .75; tarsus 2.50 to 2.85. Female usually much larger than male.

MOLTS. — Similar to those of Sharp-shinned Hawk.

FIELD MARKS. — Same as Sharp-shinned Hawk (page 105) but larger, size nearer that of Crow; a very large female "Sharp-shin" may be nearly as large as a male "Cooper's"; *tip of tail not square* as in "Sharp-shin" *but rounded;* a large female "Cooper's" might be mistaken for a "Red-shoulder" if her differently-shaped "stubby" wings and her long, rudder-like tail did not betray her. (See Plate 38, Nos. 6 and 9.)

VOICE. — *Cac cac cac* or *cuck cuck cuck* often repeated; even young birds, two-thirds grown, utter very faint *"cucks";* loud scream by female when frightened from nest, also a note something like *trick, tick,* frequently repeated (C. Bendire).

BREEDING. — In woodlands, groves and forests; not always in coniferous trees but white pine a favorite. *Nest:* In the east usually in a tall tree but in the western open country sometimes in low timber along creek bottoms or even on the ground; if in a pine tree, in a fork of trunk or against trunk, at the base of several branches; if in an oak, in a fork of a branch; height usually 30 to 65 feet, or even higher; sometimes as large as the large nest of Red-shouldered Hawk, but a much cleaner structure, being composed of smaller sticks, often lined with bark and sometimes a little moss, grass or leaves; may measure 18 inches to 2 feet externally and be hollowed little or much; an old nest is sometimes used and a large superstructure raised thereon; in Massachusetts usually a new nest of dried sticks with bark lining. This species loses comparatively few feathers at the nest — as a rule. *Eggs:* 2 to 6, often 4 or 5; 1.80 to 2.10 by 1.50 to 1.62 in.; variable in shape, usually rounded oval, often approaching spherical; bluish-white or greenish-white, sometimes nearly or quite unspotted, but often faintly spotted with yellowish-brown or lilac or both, sometimes in a ring round the large end; illustrated in Bendire's "Life Histories of North American Birds," Vol. I, Plate V, Figs. 18–20. *Dates:* May 12–30, New Hampshire; April 22, Vermont; April 25 to June 11, Massachusetts; April 25 to June 18, Connecticut. *Incubation:* Period about 21 to 24 days; "27 days" (F. H. Carpenter); by both sexes. One brood yearly.

RANGE. — North America, north to about the southern border of Hudsonian Zone and south through Central America. Breeds from southern Alaska (Sitka), central British Columbia, central Alberta, northern Manitoba, southern Ontario, southern Quebec and Prince Edward Island south to southern border of United States, from Florida to California and south into Mexico; in winter from northern Oregon,

Colorado, Nebraska, southern Michigan (rarely), southern Ontario (unusual in Toronto region), southern Illinois, Indiana, Ohio, southern New York, Massachusetts and southern Maine south to Costa Rica.

DISTRIBUTION IN NEW ENGLAND. — *Maine:* Common migrant and summer resident, and rare winter visitor or resident in southern part. *New Hampshire:* Uncommon to common migrant and summer resident, mostly at lower elevations. *Vermont:* Uncommon to common migrant and summer resident, casual in winter. *Massachusetts:* Fairly common migrant; less common summer resident; rare winter resident. *Rhode Island:* Common migrant; less common summer resident; rare winter resident. *Connecticut:* Common migrant, less common summer resident, occasional winter resident.

SEASON IN MASSACHUSETTS. — March 15 to November 30 (winter).

HAUNTS AND HABITS. Cooper's Hawk is a forest rover. It is cradled in the wind-swept woods, and fledged amid the creaking and groaning of great trees. Alert, swift and dauntless it roams the green wood with falcon-like freedom, carrying terror to the hearts of weaker creatures and leaving behind it a trail of destruction and death.

When the "Cooper's" loud "cucks" ring through the sunny, leafy woods of June, the hush of death pervades everything. All erstwhile cheerful thrushes and warblers become still and silent. The "Cooper's" fierce "cucks" are the most merciless sounds of our summer woods. There is indeed death in the air. This bird hunts more or less upon the wing, usually flying low near the ground or at a very moderate height above the trees, darting suddenly upon any victim taken by surprise. It gets up great speed almost immediately, and it alights on a perch with the quickness and readiness of a flycatcher. It will follow a bird into a thicket, often plunging through by sheer velocity, and so driving its victim out into the open and capturing it by its superior powers of flight, or by so terrorizing it that it becomes almost helpless from fright. Mr. J. A. Farley reports just such a case from Meriden, N. H., where on a very early fall morning a Cooper's Hawk dashed headlong through a wayside bush and emerged triumphant on the other side with an unfortunate Song Sparrow in its claws. The Hawk went down into the dewy grass to enjoy its feast, but flew at the approach of the observer, still carrying the Sparrow in his claws. More commonly, however, this hawk secretes itself in a tree near some clearing, lake or stream, from which by sudden forays it surprises and captures its unsuspecting prey. Sometimes, with true cat-like grace, it will leap from limb to limb. Its long tail is loosely hung and it flirts easily and nervously. It will alight in a tree near a poultry-yard and watch its chance until, unobserved, it can glide rapidly along near the ground, or else drop straight down and bear away a chicken. Often the "Cooper's" will carry away a pullet almost as heavy as itself, scarcely clearing the grass. If scared by a shout (for the human voice is likely to terrify any wild creature) it may drop the pullet, which will run back to the farm-house for safety, scarcely the worse for its experience save for the superficial bloody marks of the hawk's claws in its back. Again the "Cooper's" will kill a full-grown pullet or a hen too heavy to carry off. In this case, it returns to feed on its kill and may then be caught easily in a steel trap. When opposed by the gallant cock, it has been known to grapple with him and leave him lying dead on the ground.

This fierce Hawk is often most persistent in its attempts to get a chicken.   Mr. Farley writes: "This Sunday morning, May 2, 1909, soon after 9 (apparently his usual hour), the Cooper's Hawk (or another just as bad) which is getting so many chickens from poultry-raisers here on Chiltonville Hill, Plymouth (we have lost 25), appeared, coming for the coops.   Mr. Graves fired at him, but the hawk, not stopped by the report, circled within a few rods and came in again.   But the second barrel sent him away, apparently hit.   During this entire episode there were five people standing close to the coop.   A few mornings ago also, as Mr. Graves was pounding away making another coop, the hawk caught and carried off a chicken within a few yards of him.   A Cooper's Hawk two years ago in East Bridgewater behaved similarly.   Four times this daring bird (with people standing near) tried to get a chicken out of a hen-yard that adjoined the mixed woods where it had its nest.   The people 'shooed' the hawk away three times, but at the fourth attempt, despite their cries, it carried off a pullet."

Dr. L. C. Jones tells me that he trapped a Cooper's Hawk by setting a trap beside a Guinea hen that the hawk had killed.   This settled the identity of the hawk and proved that the bugbear of hawks, the Guinea hen, had no terrors for this bird.   Notwithstanding its speed and prowess, however, and the advantage given it by coming upon its victims unawares, the smaller birds often evade its rush and escape into some friendly thicket impenetrable to a bird so large as a hawk.   Some of the larger birds when struck by the hawk turn and fight valiantly for their lives.   Mr. Aaron C. Bagg tells of a friend who found a large number of crows mobbing a Cooper's Hawk, which was trying to kill one of them which it had partly disabled.   The Crow, however, had grasped the hawk about the base of the tail and held it off.   As the men came up, the hawk essayed to fly, but the Crow held on with a death grip, and both birds were captured.   All attempts to nurse the Crow back to health failed; it would not eat, and finally died, while the undaunted hawk seemed to have suffered no injury from the mob of Crows, had an excellent appetite and thrived on raw meat.

Cooper's Hawk usually arrives in New England from the south in March, and its flights through our territory continue from late March to late April or early May.   In the latter part of the last century Cooper's Hawk was a very common bird.   In the bird-nesting days of my boyhood from 1868 to 1875, it was one of the most common hawks, and many nests were found.   My old friend, the late Edward A. Samuels, wrote (about 1868) as follows: "Throughout New England where it was formerly a comparatively rare species, it is now one of the most abundant of our birds of prey." [1]   In the twentieth century the species has been decreasing and it is no longer the common breeder of my boyhood.   It is so persecuted now that we may expect progressive decrease of the species in the future.   In the old days there were many nests of this bird in both coniferous and deciduous trees, some high up near the top of the pines or hemlocks, others out on the high limbs of tall oaks, hickories, or chestnuts, often necessitating high climbing for the adventurous youth who sought their eggs.   Usually they build a new nest each year, some-

---

[1] Birds of New England, 1870, p. 27.

where in the neighborhood of last year's nest, for hawks like to return to the same nesting ground year after year; rarely the deserted nest of a Crow is occupied. As is the case with some other hawks, incubation may begin as soon as the first egg is deposited, or soon after, and there may be young of several sizes in the same nest. They remain there from 21 days to about 25. During the last few days they exercise their wings in preparation for flight. When the nest is approached by a human intruder, the parent birds usually keep out of gun-shot and confine their protests to complaining "cucks"; and although occasionally a bold bird will dart down toward the intruder, I have never known one to strike a man. Cooper's Hawk is a wild creature. As a *species*, the bird is shy, although like all hawks, birds at the nest differ in this respect. Individuals vary, and the same individual will act differently at different times. Some fly from the nest before it is even sighted, while others fly straight away when the tree is hit and never appear again. Like their cousins, the little "Sharp-shins," they often sit on the nest until the tree is reached and struck. And again some do not. They often linger and cry near by but are too shy to approach.

Dr. A. K. Fisher states in his "Hawks and Owls of the United States" that Mr. C. D. Walcott was attacked by one of these hawks in August while collecting fossils. He repelled the bird with his geological hammer. It continued to attack him, however, and he finally killed it with the hammer. This hawk must have been insane.

I know of no case where a hawk has attempted to drown his prey, therefore the following tales may have some other explanation. Mr. Thornton Fay, of Westboro, tells me that his brother, while recently riding along a country road, saw a rather small hawk standing on something in shallow water near the margin of a pond. The peculiar actions of the bird aroused the observer's curiosity. The hawk was frightened away, leaving a nearly drowned Robin in the shallow water. The impression left in the mind of the observer was that the hawk was trying to drown the Robin.

Mr. H. H. Waterman, of Auburn, Maine, wrote me on May 15, 1921, that while riding he noticed two birds about fifty feet from the road in a field, apparently fighting. The larger bird was a Cooper's Hawk and the smaller one a flicker. Soon the hawk arose from the ground, bearing the flicker in its claws, and, flying low, came straight toward the road until it reached a roadside ditch containing about a foot of water. Here the hawk settled and plunged the flicker under water, and held it there for about three minutes, meanwhile supporting itself by flapping its wings. Then when the advancing team came very close, the hawk arose from the water, alighted a little farther on, and then, seeming for the first time to notice Mr. Waterman, took flight and flew away, leaving the flicker breathing its last. In either of these cases the hawk should have had no difficulty in killing the smaller bird without recourse to the "water cure."

While the young are in the nest, considerable numbers of game birds, other birds and young poultry are slain for their subsistence. As soon as the young are strong on the wing, the family leaves the summer home and all roam at will, wherever food is plentiful, until the young birds have learned to hunt for themselves. In September and

October when the great southbound migration of small land birds is well under way, the Cooper's Hawks follow, often moving in Company with other hawks in daylight migration, hunting more or less as they go.

The food of Cooper's Hawk consists more largely of game-birds and poultry than that of any other common hawk. The Goshawk and the Duck Hawk are even more destructive, but most Goshawks live and breed in northern forests where little poultry is available, and the Duck Hawk is comparatively rare. The thievery of Cooper's Hawk is so adroit that often the bird is not seen or suspected, while the soaring hawks, such as the Red-shouldered or the Red-tailed Hawk, have to pay the penalty, because they are so conspicuous and may be seen occasionally soaring over the hen-yard. I know a farmer who lost 40 chickens and young fowls in a season through the depredations of a pair of Cooper's Hawks that nested in the woods near his farm. He vowed vengeance on a pair of Red-shouldered Hawks, also nesting there, because they were the only hawks that were visible. They never touched a chicken, but were commonly seen soaring overhead. After the Cooper's Hawks were taken, by setting a steel trap in their nest, no more chickens or fowls were lost, and the "Red-shoulders" were left in peace to catch the mice about the farm. Cooper's Hawk is so powerful and active and so swift of flight that it can destroy animals of superior size and weight. It kills rabbits, grouse, ducks, squirrels and small birds, but when game is scarce, it will content itself with snakes and other reptiles or even mice, grasshoppers and crickets.

Dr. B. H. Warren examined the stomach contents of 34 Cooper's Hawks, of which 16 contained remains of poultry; 10, small birds; 2, Bob-whites; 1, bullfrogs; 3, mice and insects; and 2, remains of small mammals. Dr. A. K. Fisher summarizes the contents of 133 stomachs of this species as follows: "34 contained poultry or game birds; 52, other birds; 11, mammals; 1, frog; 3, lizards; 2, insects and 39 were empty."[1]

ECONOMIC STATUS. From an economic standpoint this Hawk stands near the foot of the list. It is not a bird to be protected by the farmer, poultry-man or game-keeper.

Ástur atricapíllus atricapillus (WILSON). Goshawk.

Other names: BLUE HAWK; PARTRIDGE HAWK.

Plates 38 and 39.

DESCRIPTION. — Similar to Accipiters, but larger and more robust; tarsus feathered about halfway down in front and on sides; tip of tail rounded. *Adults (sexes alike or very similar)*: Above, dark bluish-gray or bluish-slate, with black feather shafts; top of head conspicuously blackish or slate-black, each feather white beneath surface; a white or pale gray stripe, finely streaked with blackish, from base of cere back over eye to back of head, growing wider after passing eye, and wide blackish stripe or patch below it (behind and in part under eye) spreads over ear-region; tail slightly darker and less bluish than back, with three or four broad blackish bars (sometimes obsolete) one near the pale gray or whitish tip; below pale gray or whitish, often with many dusky shaft-streaks, and irregularly or narrowly barred gray or slaty-grayish, except on throat, chin and jaws, where black shaft-lines are the principal marks;

---

[1] The Hawks and Owls of the United States in their Relation to Agriculture, 1893, p. 43.

Photograph by J. Nelson Spaeth

Fig. 44. — Young Goshawks, Petersham, Mass.

The first taken in Massachusetts.   Quill feathers of juvenal wings and tail showing;
the background has been retouched

Page 117

Photograph by Daniel Donald McDavid

Fig. 45. — Downy Young Red-shouldered Hawks in Nest

Courtesy of Eugene W. Schmidt

Page 129

under tail-coverts white or whitish, marked little if at all; axillars and wing-linings like breast but more coarsely or sparsely marked; under surface of flight-feathers grayish-white or whitish, marbled with gray and barred slaty; bill dark bluish horn color, darker at tip, cere yellow or greenish (cere slate, N. S. Goss); iris orange red, brown or reddish brown; legs and feet chrome yellow, or greenish-yellow, claws black or dusky. *Immature in second winter plumage:* Much as adults, but lower plumage more coarsely marked; breast feathers have broad rather brownish shaft-streaks and some broad bars; some juvenal feathers sometimes retained on rump and lesser wing-coverts. *Young in first winter and following summer plumage:* Similar to juvenal. *Young in juvenal plumage:* Above "dusky grayish-brown," more or less spotted and feather-edged with buff, rusty or whitish; tail lighter than back, white-tipped and crossed by four or five wide bars of dark brown or dusky; tips of greater wing-coverts form narrow light bar across wing; primaries and secondaries barred darkly; under plumage rufous-buff to whitish, with drop-like, dark, brown streaks, narrowing on chin, throat, leg-feathering and under-tail coverts. *Downy young:* At first white with some grayish tinge on back, and on front face; later more gray above.

MEASUREMENTS. — *Male:* Length 20.00 to 22.00 in.; spread 40.00 to 44.50; folded wing 12.00 to 13.00; tail 9.00 to 10.50; bill, without cere, .68 to .90; tarsus 2.70 to 3.10; *Female:* Length 22.00 to 26.50; spread 44.00 to 47.00; wing 13.00 to 14.50; tail 10.00 to 13.00; bill .70 to 1.00; tarsus 2.70 to 3.17. Weight, male from 1 lb. 12 oz. to 3 lbs.; "2 lbs. 15 oz." (L. A. Fuertes); immature male 2 lbs. 6 oz. (B. H. Warren); adult female 4 lbs. (W. R. Spofford). Female usually larger than male. Immature birds sometimes larger than adults.

MOLTS. — Downy young probably have two sets of down, the first short, sparse and white, the second, which comes on as bird grows, longer and more woolly; second down is succeeded by juvenal plumage, assumed when bird is fledged (July and August); apparently no further change of plumage until autumn of second year, when bird after postnuptial molt (September to November) assumes plumage much as adult, being then about 1½ years old, though not fully matured until autumn of third season. Adults apparently have one complete molt in spring, summer and autumn, but material examined insufficient to give limital dates; in one case there seemed to be some molting of wings in spring.

FIELD MARKS. — *Adult:* A large, long-tailed gray hawk, light gray below with a barred tail, and a little lighter bluish-gray above than any other common New England hawk except male Marsh Hawk which is much lighter; a black cap and a white line over eye; flight much like that of Cooper's Hawk. *Young:* Very differently colored from adult; striped below and much like a large young Cooper's Hawk; difficult to identify unless in hand.

VOICE. — Decidedly accipitrine but not much louder than the "cucks" of Cooper's Hawk; wholly different, however, like *kwee-kwee-kwee*, shrill and sharp, with a touch of harshness, impossible to describe; "like the sound of a Cadillac brake" (Edith Parker); a young Goshawk uttered once notes (high and quite loud) in rapid succession like *qui-qui-qui-qui-qui* (J. A. Farley); usually silent except when breeding.

BREEDING. — Principally in great forests. *Nest:* In coniferous or deciduous tree, in top of tree or part way up; near trunk or well out in fork of large limb; very bulky; composed of sticks (often fresh) and lined with hemlock or pine twigs, sometimes a little grass or weed stalks, birch or coniferous bark. *Eggs:* 2 to 5, usually 3 or 4; 2.24 to 2.32 by 1.73 to 1.92 in.; ovate or elliptical ovate; distinguishable from those of Cooper's Hawk only by larger size; shell rough, whitish or bluish-white, sometimes faintly spotted with pale reddish-brown or yellowish-brown; illustrated in Bendire's "Life Histories of North American Birds," Vol. I, Plate VI, Fig. 1. *Dates:* May 5, New Brunswick; April 25 to May, Maine; April 23 to May 1, Vermont; April 1, Massachusetts. *Incubation:* Period probably about 28 days (Bendire). One brood yearly.

RANGE. — Boreal and temperate North America. Breeds northward probably to near limit of trees, from northwestern Alaska, northwestern Mackenzie, northern Manitoba, southeastern Ontario, northern Ungava (Quebec) and Newfoundland south to northern Michigan, northern New York, northern New England and Massachusetts (casually), and south in mountains to Pennsylvania, Maryland (one record) and Arizona; in winter from Alaska and southern Canadian Provinces south to Texas, Oklahoma, Missouri, Kentucky, Illinois, Indiana, northern Ohio, West Virginia and Virginia; accidental in British Isles.

DISTRIBUTION IN NEW ENGLAND. — *Maine:* Common to rare winter resident, varying much in numbers; less common to casual summer resident. *New Hampshire:* Irregularly common winter resident; rare summer resident. *Vermont:* Irregular winter resident; rare summer resident. *Massachusetts:* Irregularly common winter resident; very rare summer resident. Breeding records: Pair seen in summer of 1868, in Weston, but nest not found;[1] Townsend, a dozen or more years ago (about 1910 Ed.) two eggs, and female shot;[2] Petersham, May 22, 1922, two young taken from nest by J. Nelson Spaeth of the Harvard Forest;[2] three eggs and very large nest, April 28, 1923, taken by Prof. R. T. Fisher, Herbert Parker, P. W. Reed and J. A. Farley, now in the Thayer Museum at South Lancaster;[3] three eggs and nest taken April 18, 1924, by P. W. Reed and J. A. Farley, in collection of J. A. Farley.[4] *Rhode Island:* Irregular winter resident, seldom common. *Connecticut:* rather rare and irregular winter resident occasionally common, casual or accidental in summer. *Breeding record:* Winchester, nest and two eggs (female taken) collected by a Mr. Williams "about 15 years ago."[5]

SEASON IN MASSACHUSETTS. — September 28 to April 22 (summer).

HAUNTS AND HABITS. Among all the fierce raptores that inhabit the continent of North America, there is no hawk handsomer, braver, fiercer, or more powerful than the Goshawk. Its attack is swift, furious and deadly. In the death grapple it clings ferociously to its victim, careless of its own safety until the unfortunate creature succumbs to its steely grip. Its stroke is terrible. It is delivered with such force as sometimes to tear out most of one side of its victim, and its wing-power is so great that it can carry off rabbits and full-grown fowls. The Goshawk is a bird of the great northern coniferous forests, but in winter when pressed by hunger it hunts over all kinds of territory.

Every year in November or December some Goshawks enter southern New England from the north, and about once in 7 to 10 years, coincidentally with a scarcity of the so-called snow-shoe rabbits (varying hares) and ptarmigans in the fur countries, Goshawks appear here in large numbers.

In an interesting and valuable article in the Auk, Mr. Ruthven Deane recorded the facts relative to the famous Goshawk invasion of 1906–07, giving records of 275 birds from the northern part of the continent as far west as Minneapolis and Manitoba. He said that there had not been such a flight of "these bold robbers of our game and looters of the poultry yard" since the fall and winter of 1896–97, when they were especially abundant in New England.[6] In the great migration of 1896–97, in Toronto, young birds were almost entirely absent.[7] There were large flights of Goshawks in the autumns of 1915 and 1916 at Chicago.[8] In 1916 this abundance of Goshawks was widespread.

The limits of space preclude the publication of more records of these flights in this volume. The migrations of 1916–18 were quite fully reported in various publications and it was noticeable that grouse of all kinds within the range of the movement across

[1] Maynard, C. J.: Naturalist's Guide, 1883, p. 134.
[2] Farley, J. A.: Bird-Lore, Vol. XXIV, 1922, p. 278.
[3] Farley, J. A.: Auk, Vol. XL, 1923, p. 532.
[4] *Ibid.*, Vol. XLI, 1924, p. 478.
[5] Job, H. K.: The Sport of Bird Study, 1908, p. 297.
[6] Auk, Vol. XXIV, 1907, pp. 182–186.
[7] Fleming, James H.: *Ibid.*, p. 72.
[8] Auk, Vol. XXXVI, 1919, p. 517.

the country were much depleted.   We are now (November 1926) witnessing what seems to be one of the largest southward movements of Goshawks on record, which probably will be followed by a scarcity of Ruffed Grouse in New England.   Hundreds of Goshawks are reported as actually taken; the numbers observed, however, must be discounted somewhat as the same birds have been seen by several people.   A great flight of Goshawks into the United States in fall or winter is followed invariably by a scarcity of Ruffed Grouse.   Apparently "rabbits" so-called and ptarmigan are the principal food of Goshawks in their northern homes.   When some sudden epidemic destroys most of the abundant rabbits the Goshawks must feed on ptarmigan until they have greatly depleted the supply, when they wander south, fierce and hungry.   Sometimes these great flights consist chiefly of adult birds.   Perhaps when food becomes suddenly scarce the hawks rear practically no young.   During the summer they can subsist on birds, squirrels and mice, but when the birds go south and snow covers the runways of the mice, lacking rabbits and ptarmigan, the Hawks and Owls must eat each other or starve, unless they migrate. When they arrive in the United States they feed largely on grouse, and often attack poultry.   The scarcity of grouse which follows great invasions of these hawks is due in a measure to northern owls which also come in from the north whenever the numbers of rabbits there are greatly depleted.

Many Goshawks are as shy as any other hawk.   Some of them, however, coming from regions where they rarely see a human being, are quite unsuspicious, and many such are shot.   Forced by hunger to migrate to this region, they become careless of their own safety when in pursuit of their prey.   Their persistence at such times is well exemplified by the following experience related to me by my friend, the late Edward L. Parker of Concord.   Mr. Parker had planted along a wire fence near his stable a tangle of shrubbery and vines to furnish food for birds and protection from their enemies.   One morning the stable-man saw a large gray bird plunging at the thicket and beating against it.   He soon perceived that a female pheasant had sought refuge under the dense shrubbery and that the hawk could not get at her.   Presently the hawk succeeded in pushing under the thicket, but could not reach the pheasant, so it came out, flew back a short distance and, turning, hurled itself with great force against the yielding mass of small vines that covered the bushes.   Meanwhile the pheasant had moved but little.   The hawk then went over the thicket and dashed against the other side with such a shock that the frightened pheasant flew out and started for the woods.   The hawk swiftly gained on her and had almost reached her when she rose to clear a high wire fence which enclosed the paddock.   As the pheasant passed over the fence the hawk, which evidently did not see the wire until too late to avoid it, struck it with a bang, rebounding, evidently injured by the shock.   However, it did not relinquish its pursuit of the pheasant but followed her with wobbling flight as she passed into the woods.   Under the fence which the hawk struck there were a few feathers from its breast, one of which sent to me served to identify the bird.

Dr. C. Hart Merriam writes as follows of an adventure with an enraged Goshawk:

"On the morning of October 3, 1882, I saw a Redpoll Warbler in an unusually dark plumage, and wishing to procure it for a specimen, went to my office and loaded a small .22 cal. rifle with a light charge of dust shot. On leaving the building I heard a hen cry out in distress from behind a pile of stones in the bushes near by. Guided by the sound I soon reached the spot, and found a Goshawk perched upon an old hen not more than ten feet distant. Aiming at his breast I fired, but with no other effect apparently than of arousing his indignation and wrath, for he immediately rose and dove at my head with great fury. I struck him on the wing with the barrel of the rifle and loosened one of his tail-feathers, but did not succeed in knocking him down. The bold hawk left me and gave chase to her. She rushed into the bushes, which were so thick that the hawk could not fly between them. Not to be baffled by this move, he closed his wings and followed her up on the ground with a succession of long and rapid hops, and quickly overtook her and pounced upon her back. The hen was a large and strong one and ran carrying the hawk for nearly a hundred feet before tumbling over. I soon reached the scene and struck at the hawk with the empty gun. He dodged the blow by dropping on his back and then flew up into a tree overhead, but was gone before I could get a cartridge. The poor hen was so frightened that she hid under a catnip plant near the door of my office, and remained there until driven away five hours later." [1]

The following incident regarding an individual of the western race is related by **Major Bendire**. "I was returning from a short hunt one afternoon in September, 1882, my breech-loader charged with dust shot. At the outskirts of the garrison, near the cavalry stable, was an old brush corral, much frequented by the fowls kept in the neighborhood. While walking past this fence I suddenly heard a great outcry and saw quite a commotion among a number of chickens in the place, which were squeaking and scattering in all directions at a lively rate. At the same instant a large Goshawk, an adult female, dashed through the inclosure, failing to get a chicken this time, however, I fired at her at short range, and, as it subsequently proved, peppered her well with dust shot as she went by, which possibly disconcerted her aim a little. Never dreaming for an instant that the bird would return after such a reception, I nevertheless inserted a heavier cartridge in my gun, and had scarcely done so when she came back to make a second and last attempt at a too venturesome chicken. This time I brought her down with a broken wing, and her flight was so suddenly arrested that she rolled over several times after striking on the ground. I never saw more vindictive fury expressed in a bird's eyes than was shown by hers. She tried to attack me, and would have done so had she not been so badly wounded. The will and courage to do so were there, but her strength failed her. On skinning her I found a number of dust shot imbedded under the skin, showing that she had been hit the first time I fired. This, though, was not sufficient to cause her to leave without her intended victim, notwithstanding the fact that she saw me plainly enough the second, if not the first time." [2]

<hr />

[1] Forest and Stream, Vol. IX, 1882, p. 225.
[2] Bendire, Charles: Life Histories of North American Birds, Vol. I, 1892, p. 201.

Many instances could be related showing the audacity of the Goshawk. One day in the great British Columbian forest I had a good opportunity to collect a number of Long-crested Jays as a flock passed me high overhead among the tall trees. I had shot three or four when I noticed that not one had reached the ground. Shooting another I watched it fall, when a Western Goshawk swept out from among the trees into the very smoke from my gun and snatched it in the air.

Dr. William Wood of East Windsor Hill, Connecticut, told of a Goshawk that followed a hen into a kitchen and seized her on the kitchen floor in the very presence of an old man and his daughter. The father beat off the hawk with a cane, while the daughter closed the door and finally killed the bold bird.[1] Mr. J. A. Farley relates a similar tale from Lambert Lake, Maine. A Goshawk caught a half-grown hen. The hen, escaping, ran under a woman's skirts. The hawk followed right up to the skirt but was killed. They had to kill the hen too, for its crop was torn open as a result of the hawk's fierce grip.

The ability of the Goshawk to carry weight is well illustrated by the following experience related to me by Mr. Ralph Holman. He was hunting in the woods when his attention was attracted to a disturbance in a near-by thicket where two large birds were struggling. He soon saw that one was a hawk, and immediately killed it with the charge from his right barrel. The other bird, startled by the shot, attempted to fly away, only to be brought down with his left. He then went over and picked up a large Goshawk and a Guinea Hen. Farmers frequently raise Guinea Hens to scare away hawks from their chickens. Evidently the Guinea has no terrors for a Goshawk. Mr. Holman investigated and found that the nearest place where Guinea Hens were kept was three-fourths of a mile from the place where he shot the hawk.

Several cases are on record where Goshawks have attacked persons who have attempted to rob their nests. Mr. L. M. Turner tells of a female Goshawk that was so vicious when a native attempted to climb to her nest that it was necessary to shoot her. The male then attacked the intruder, snatched his cap from his head and "tore his cotton shirt into shreds." [2] Under such circumstances the bird should be commended.

Another case illustrating the ferocity of the Western Goshawk (a subspecies) is recorded by Earle R. Forrest who says that when half-way up to her nest, he was struck so hard by the old bird that for a moment he was dazed. She repeatedly darted at him, but, seeing him prepared with a dead limb which he had broken off for a club, she sheered off. Her first blow made a deep gash extending from just above the left eye across temple and ear.[3]

Still another case is recounted by Rev. G. Eifrig of Ottawa, who tells of an Ontario farmer who went to inspect a pasture that adjoined extensive woods. He was attacked viciously again and again by a Goshawk that probably had her nest in the woods near by.[4]

---

[1] Merriam, C. Hart: A Review of the Birds of Connecticut, 1877, p. 80.
[2] Contributions to the Natural History of Alaska, 1886, p. 157.
[3] Oölogist, Vol. XXXII, 1915, p. 84.
[4] Auk, Vol. XXIV, 1907, p. 437.

When hungry the Goshawk does not hesitate to attack and kill other birds of prey, but sometimes it meets its match. Mr. S. S. Stansell relates the following: " While traveling about forty miles northwest of Edmonton I found where one of these birds and the Hawk Owl (*Surnia ulula caparoch*) had engaged in deadly combat. On getting out of the sleigh and examining more closely, I found the snow trodden down and bloody, while feathers were lying in every direction. The Hawk Owl was dead in the claws of the Goshawk and the completely severed head of the Goshawk lay a few inches away from its body. Examination showed that the claws of the Goshawk had reached and penetrated the heart of the Hawk Owl." [1] It seems hardly possible that a Hawk Owl could have beheaded the Goshawk. A larger creature may have taken a hand in the fight. The Rev. G. Eifrig tells of a somewhat similar duel at High Falls, Wright County, Quebec. "There, one morning last February, Mr. Hugo Paeseler, a farmer, on going out into the woods adjoining his farm, noticed a space of about ten to fifteen feet square, where the snow had recently been much disturbed, deeply plowed up from some great commotion. That a fierce fight had been going on but a short while before was evident from the liberal quantities of blood sprinkled on the snow and the masses of feathers, single and in whole bunches, lying about and adhering to bushes and trees. On looking around for the principals of the fight, he found about ten feet away in one direction a Goshawk, lying on the snow with wings extended and frozen stiff. About ten feet away from the scene of hostilities, in the opposite direction, he found an owl, more damaged than the hawk, but still warm. It had alighted after the fight on a small spruce and fallen off, as the snow showed, and with its last strength crawled into a small log, lying with its hollow part conveniently near. The farmer took both along home, skinned and 'stuffed' — here that term is appropriate — the hawk, and also the head of the owl, which was all he could make use of in her case. When the writer saw them at the farm house, they turned out to be the Barred Owl and the American Goshawk. It must surely have been a battle royal if one could only have witnessed it." [2] Mr. J. A. Farley tells of a similar happening. A gang of men were startled one winter's day a few years ago in Medfield woods by the sight of what seemed like a huge bird "with four wings" whirring past. The "bird" dropped into the snow not far away. It turned out to be a Goshawk and a Barred Owl locked in deadly clasp. Both were dead when picked up.

In striking a bird on the wing the Goshawk does not dive from a height as a falcon often does, but overtakes its quarry by swift and powerful flight, coming, perhaps, down a slight incline from its post in some tree-top, and when near its prey sets its wings, throws its powerful feet forward almost beyond its head, and strikes its victim under the wing, driving in its powerful talons.

The following note from Mr. W. E. Cram exhibits an interesting habit of this hawk. — "February 18. Followed the track of a Hawk, apparently a Goshawk, twenty or thirty rods through the birch woods west of the cove. From the appearance of the tracks the bird must have walked much after the manner of a Crow, though dragging its claws

[1] Oölogist: Vol. XXIX, No. 1, Jan. 15, 1912, p. 232.   [2] Auk, Vol. XXIV, 1907, p. 438.

PLATE 40

PLATE 40
RED–SHOULDERED HAWK
Page 128

YOUNG IN
FIRST WINTER PLUMAGE

ADULT

BROAD–WINGED HAWK
Page 135

RED–TAILED HAWK
Page 123

ADULT

IMMATURE

IMMATURE

ADULT

All about one-fourth scale.

Louis Agassiz Fuertes

more. Occasionally it hopped for a few feet. There was no sign of its having killed any game near there and having eaten so much as to be unable to fly at once, as is sometimes the case. At times it followed in the tracks of rabbits for some distance. I have often known them to do this, and am inclined to think that they occasionally hunt rabbits in this manner where the underbrush is too dense to allow them to fly through it easily. I have sometimes followed their tracks through the brush until I came upon the remains of freshly killed rabbits which they had been eating.[1] " It may be that the bird finds the rabbit asleep.

The late F. H. Mosher, a very keen observer, also noticed this rabbit-hunting proclivity of the Goshawk. He was inclined to believe, however, that the hawk caught the rabbit chiefly by flying, hitting the snow only occasionally and rebounding therefrom in great leaps.

The late C. E. Bailey, a most competent and reliable field naturalist, used to tell how on a hunt one winter's day in Winchendon, his home, he shot two white hares which he hung over a limb with their feet tied together to keep them safe from foxes or other prowlers. Returning in the afternoon for his hares, he found them nearly devoured by a Goshawk which had eaten so much that it could not fly, and had made quite a path in the snow as it marched back and forth, stretching itself the while. It was still marching when Mr. Bailey came up.

The Goshawk sometimes begins its feast by tearing off the head and legs and swallowing them. It decapitates a rabbit almost as if the head had been cut off with a knife. Birds are usually plucked. In some cases if the bird is large the breast is eaten first, sometimes the entrails are removed. The food of the Goshawk includes birds from the size of a Song Sparrow to that of a full grown domestic cock, and birds form a considerable part of its sustenance. It feeds also on squirrels (red squirrels in particular), rabbits, mice, weasels and insects. Dr. A. K. Fisher examined the contents of 133 stomachs; 34 contained poultry or game birds; 52, other birds; 11, mammals; 13, frogs; 3, lizards; 2, insects, and 39 were empty.[2] No more thorough investigation of its food habits has been made.

ECONOMIC STATUS. While the Goshawk is a fine bird and doubtless fills an important place in the economy of nature in the forest, it is not a bird to be encouraged by the game keeper, the sportsman or the farmer.

Búteo boreális borealis (GMELIN). Red-tailed Hawk.

Other names: RED-TAIL; HEN HAWK.

Plates 37, 38 and 40.

DESCRIPTION. — Large, heavy and robust; wings long and broad; tail even or little rounded; tarsus feathered half-way down in front. *Adults (sexes alike).* Above chiefly dusky grayish-brown, sometimes reddish-brown about head and neck, with more or less lighter variegation, gray, tawny or whitish; many

---

[1] Bird-Lore, Vol. I, 1899, p. 184. [2] Hawks and Owls of the United States, 1893, p. 43.

feathers have subterminal or central dark markings and light tips; top of head and back very dark, wings lighter; feathers of hind head and neck white beneath surface, this showing when feathers are disturbed; upper tail-coverts paling to yellowish or whitish with deep reddish-brown bars; tail rich chestnut above, with narrow subterminal black bar (sometimes broken), and white or whitish tip; (some specimens have also a few more incomplete dark bars on tail) large dark spot on each of posterior middle wing-coverts, and one (or a broad dark bar) near end of each greater covert and each secondary; greater coverts and all flight-feathers inconspicuously and narrowly barred darker; secondaries and inner primaries often whitish at tips, primaries blackish toward ends, their inner webs basally white or whitish; a dark brown or blackish mustache-like stripe runs from above angle of mouth down side of neck, marking off darker upper plumage, from white under plumage; lores and sides of forehead whitish; below, chiefly yellowish-white, buffy or whitish; sides of neck and upper breast largely dark reddish-brown with more or less streaks of same on throat and breast; leg feathering and under tail-coverts usually unmarked; a broad belt of longitudinal blackish marks, not always complete, crosses body in front of legs; a few blackish shaft-streaks on breast; some have more or less reddish-brown there; linings of wings yellowish-white with diamond-shaped spots of pale brownish-red; under surface of tail brownish-gray with bars faint or obsolete; bill bluish-horn color, blackish at tip, cere yellow or greenish-yellow; iris brown; legs and feet yellow, claws bluish-black. Cases of partial albinism occur occasionally, some are wholly white.

Young in first winter plumage: Like juvenal. *Young in juvenal plumage:* Similar to adult above, except tail, but somewhat darker, and leg feathering narrowly barred dusky; tail-coverts more or less white, with broad dark bars; tail grayish-brown, tinged brownish-red, the tinge becoming stronger near base, with 10 or more narrow black bars, tip whitish; generally lighter below than adults, especially on breast, which is less marked; *a large unmarked whitish or pale area on breast;* bill, cere and feet much as in adult, but iris light-grayish, straw or yellow; juvenal birds may rarely have red tails. *Downy young:* Chiefly white; eyes dark.

MEASUREMENTS. — *Male:* Length 19.00 to 22.00 in.; spread 46.00 to 50.00; folded wing 13.50 to 16.50; tail 7.00 to 10.00; bill, without cere, .90 to 1.08; tarsus 2.40 to 3.20. *Female:* Length 21.00 to 25.00; spread about 48.00 to 56.00; wing 14.50 to 17.75; tail 8.00 to 10.50; bill .90 to 1.15; tarsus 2.90 to 3.40. Weight 2½ to 4 lbs.; a small male, 2 lbs. 6½ oz. Female usually much larger than male.

MOLTS. — Juvenal plumage succeeding down assumed by complete molt when young bird is fledged (July or August) and apparently retained with little change through autumn and winter; molting goes on during spring and summer, and in autumn young bird becomes virtually as adult; in autumn of the next year after complete molt all apparently become fully adult; adults have one complete molt yearly during the milder months of the year, continuing at least in some cases into October.

FIELD MARKS. — Largest common hawk, except Osprey; in flight wings appear long, broad and ample, with turned-up tips; tail fairly long, broad and ample; on a gray sunless day (giving the hawk a dark appearance all over) this bird when on the wing at a distance often resembles a Turkey Vulture quite closely in shape, but is really much smaller with wings relatively shorter, and not tipped upward when soaring. *Adult:* Neither wings nor tail copiously barred (tail beneath not at all) black and white as usually the case in Red-shouldered Hawk, which is the most common soaring hawk in southern New England; *a large whitish area on breast;* seen from below in flight, wings chiefly whitish; a rather small, dark crescentic spot shows beyond bend of wing, some rather indistinct barring on back part of wing, and tips of all flight-feathers appear dark; tail of adults chestnut, or sorrel-red above, shining white beneath; sometimes red tail of adults may be distinguished in bright sunlight when seen from either above or below; soars much like an Eagle, but wings relatively shorter and wider; flight of this species and that of Broad-winged Hawk more buoyant than that of Red-shouldered Hawk. *Young:* Recognizable only by general resemblance to adult; tail not red but much barred, grayish and blackish (see *Field Marks* under Red-shouldered Hawk, page 129); unlike adults in lacking dark hind border on under side of wing and dark spot beyond bend, but ends of longer primaries blackish.

VOICE. — When soaring, and often when perched, a "long-drawn squealing whistle, somewhat resembling the syllable Kee-aahrr-r-r-r," and in the nesting woods it utters a sharp scream like *kerr* or *chirr* (E. H. Eaton); call note almost a pig-like squeal, rather weak for bird of its size; also likened to sound of escaping steam from small safety-valve; *chirr* or *pii-chirr* (Bendire).

BREEDING. — Usually about edges of forests, on either high or low ground, heavy timber preferred, very rarely in a tree in an open field, as the Red-shouldered Hawk sometimes does; but in settled regions may breed in small patches of woods quite near roads or houses and in neighborhood of many open fields; often in oak or other deciduous tree in extreme southern New England, but farther north a pine or other coniferous tree seems the favorite; in western Massachusetts oak or chestnut or other deciduous trees often are chosen, while in the eastern part of the State a pine is almost as regularly taken. *Nest:* From 20 to 70 or 80 feet up, usually high (often nearly at top and thus sometimes somewhat concealed by pine-needle bunches), in large tall tree, of sticks and twigs, sometimes unlined, more often lined with grasses, weeds, dead leaves, corn husks or moss; often deciduous or evergreen twig or twigs with green foliage attached; some nests nearly as small as Crows' nests, others nearly as large as Ospreys', often occupied for years. *Eggs:* 2 to 4, usually 2; 2.07 to 2.93 by 1.59 to 2.05 in.; very variable in shape, size, color and markings; elliptical, oval, ovate, short ovate, etc.; white, dull or pale creamy-white, or bluish-white; sometimes unspotted, but usually spotted and blotched with various shades of reddish-brown or yellowish-brown, varying in size, shape and intensity, some also with lavender and drab, often as under-markings, all variously distributed; illustrated in Bendire's "Life Histories of North American Birds," Vol. I, Plate VI, Figs. 5 and 6. *Dates:* Late March, southern Illinois; Apr. 5 to 30, Rhode Island; March 30 to April 30, Massachusetts; May 6 to 26, Maine. *Incubation:* Period 28 to 32 days (authors); by both sexes. One brood yearly.

RANGE. — Eastern North America north into Hudsonian Zone and west to the Great Plains. Breeds from northern Manitoba, northern Ontario, southern Quebec and Newfoundland south to central southern Texas, northeastern Oklahoma, Arkansas, Tennessee and northern Florida; in winter from southern Kansas, northeastern Iowa, southern Illinois, Indiana, Ohio, central New York, Vermont, New Hampshire and southern Maine south to northeastern Mexico and Gulf coast of United States; western forms of the species extend its range to the Pacific; and a southern form, separated by Bangs, ranges from Florida to Greater Antilles.

DISTRIBUTION IN NEW ENGLAND. — *Maine:* Uncommon to rare summer resident generally, more common in migration; rare winter resident in Cumberland and other southeastern counties. *New Hampshire:* Uncommon summer resident, wintering rarely from White Mountains southward. *Vermont:* Uncommon summer resident generally, but more common locally in northern half of the state and among hills of southern part; rare in winter. *Massachusetts:* Rather common locally, but rare and local summer resident generally; uncommon to rare winter resident. *Rhode Island:* Rare summer resident and uncommon winter resident. *Connecticut:* Common resident locally in hills of interior, rather rare in coastal region (more common usually in all the states in spring and fall migrations).

SEASON IN MASSACHUSETTS. — Permanent resident.

HAUNTS AND HABITS. The great Red-tailed Hawk was one of the common birds of my boyhood. Then they nested in numbers over all New England wherever big timber grew. In the '60s and '70s of the 19th century we found their nests about the cities, even within city limits, and their wide wings wheeling in the summer sky were a common sight. To-day I know of no place in Massachusetts where this hawk is common in the breeding season, except on Marthas Vineyard and in some parts of western and northern Massachusetts; probably it will not remain common on the Vineyard very long. Like all our hawks it is destined to give way before the advance of modern civilization, with its intensive operations of farming and game breeding.　The "Red-tail" is a fine, large, sturdy hawk and its soaring flight is almost as impressive as that of the eagle.　It does not migrate very far in winter, merely moving out of the bleak and inhospitable parts of its northern range and shifting but a few hundred miles south of the southern border of its breeding range.　Oftentimes a "Red-tail" wintering in our climate will resort year after year to the same place, appearing with clock-like regularity in the late fall.　In its spring migration it becomes most common in Massachusetts from about the second week in April until the last week in May.　The migrating birds sail and soar at various heights, some of them at such lofty altitudes as to seem mere specks in the sky.　Usually they are accompanied by Red-shouldered Hawks, and sometimes by Marsh Hawks and other species.

Some of the resident Red-tails begin making preparations to nest at a very early date, even as early as the last week in February in mild seasons, though eggs are rarely laid before the last days of March or early April.　The nest when first built is not very large, but when it is used (probably by the same pair) from year to year and yearly additions are made, it may become in time almost as large as that of the Osprey.　I have seen one or two such immense nests.　A climber to the nest of one of these hawks is not in danger of attack by the owners.　They usually content themselves with flying overhead, uttering cries of protest, though in some cases one or the other may swoop toward the intruder.　Often only the female appears.　The young grow slowly, and remain in or about the nest for a long time, but when once fledged they soon equal or exceed their parents in size.

I believe that this hawk rarely pounces upon its prey from on wing, though I have seen one, soaring, stoop toward the earth with a rush of wings, as if about to seize some animal from the ground.　It prefers to sit quietly erect and motionless on an elevated perch such as a dead limb of some tall tree in a pasture or field, or at the edge of the woods, occasionally turning its head, but so slowly that the motion is almost imperceptible; here it scans its surroundings, ready to pounce on any mouse or other small mammal that presents itself.　Crows seem to regard the "Red-tail" as a deadly enemy, and his presence as a personal affront.　They rarely lose the opportunity to attack one, especially during the breeding season.　Mr. A. W. Higgins writes to me that he saw three crows attempting to punish a Red-tailed Hawk on the wing.　Every time the crows struck at the hawk, it turned over in the air and presented its talons to their attack.

This hawk is not so active as an Accipiter or as one of the falcons, but is more deliberate in action.　Nevertheless, it is fast enough to pick a gray squirrel off a branch.　If the squirrel proves an adept at dodging, the hawk may seek the assistance of its mate, and then, by alternately rising and swooping, one of the hawks gets its prey while the squirrel is dodging around the limb to evade the other.

In September and October, with favorable winds, the more northern members of the race may be seen wending their way southward over New England.　Slowly they circle and drift at far heights, often up among the clouds.　Now and then the keen far-seeing eye of one will detect the movement of some timorous field mouse far below. Nearly closing its wings it rushes head foremost through the air, falling like a hissing meteor from the clouds until it nears a convenient tree-top, when with spread wings and tail it checks its flight and alights gracefully on some dead projecting limb, only to fall presently on the trembling victim.

Not infrequently, during their migration, two hawks will do battle in the air. Grappling they fall, tumbling over and over, until at last, their safety endangered by the close proximity of Mother Earth, they separate, check their course and mount again towards the clouds. Sometimes they fly so high that they are only to be seen through rifts in the drifting vapors of the sky. My friend, the late Dr. B. H. Warren, has well described the flight and the combat of this species.[1] Mr. William Gordon Means wrote to me of the tragic ending of a fight between an immature female " Red-tail " and a smaller hawk, which, judging from the description, might have been one of the Red-shouldered species. Sometime in October, 1925, according to his letter, a servant of Mr. Frederick H. Prince, of Wenham, while walking in the woods, caught the " Red-tail " with its claws embedded in the breast of the smaller bird so that it was unable to free itself from its victim.

Large flights of hawks still pass in spring and autumn, but we do not see now such great annual migrations as swept over New England in the days of my boyhood. Mr. Clarence Farrar, of Lewiston, Maine, tells me that one day in April about 1868 he saw countless flocks of hawks flying north northeast. The individuals of each flock ranged in size from that of the Pigeon Hawk to that of the largest species. The flight was first noted about 9 : 30 in the morning and lasted until well into the afternoon. He says that it did not seem possible that there were so many hawks in the entire country as he saw that day. Hundreds of hawks, if not thousands, are shot and trapped yearly. I remember that about 1876 Mr. Will Perham, of Tyngsboro, Massachusetts, wrote Mr. C. J. Maynard, offering to send him some live hawks. Mr. Maynard replied, naming a price, and said that he would take all the hawks his correspondent could get. Very soon he received as a start a shipment of 50 Red-tailed and Red-shouldered hawks. Mr. Maynard decided after all that he did not need any more immediately.

The food of the " Red-tail " consists very largely of mice. It kills rabbits, gophers and squirrels. It takes comparatively few birds. When rattlesnakes or other snakes abound, a considerable number of these reptiles are among its victims. Though the farmers know it as the " Hen Hawk," it is not so destructive to poultry as are the *Accipiters* or the Goshawk. Nevertheless, when mice are scarce and hens are easily and safely obtained, now and then an individual " Red-tail " will get the chicken-killing habit and become destructive. The late Dr. B. H. Warren examined visceral contents of 173 of these birds, and found in 128 of them remains of small mammals, principally field mice, nine of these also contained some remains of small birds. Fourteen had fed on chickens, 6 on Meadowlarks and Sparrows, 3 on Bob-whites, 3 on red squirrels, 3 on both mice and insects, 3 on

---

[1] Birds of Pennsylvania, 1890, pp. 127, 128.

snakes,* 2 on skunks, 2 on carrion, 1 on ham and another on what appeared to be beef. Repeatedly 4 or 5 mice were found in one hawk, and in a few instances 7.   Dr. A. K. Fisher examined the stomach contents of 562 of these hawks.   Fifty-four contained poultry; 51, other birds; 278, mice; 131, other mammals; 47, insects; 37, batrachians or reptilian forms; 8, crawfish; 13, offal, and 89 were empty.   Those that I have examined have contained only mice.

ECONOMIC STATUS.   Dr. Fisher sums up the case for and against the " Red-tail " by stating that "it has been demonstrated by careful stomach examinations that poultry and game birds do not constitute more than 10 per cent of the food of this hawk," and that all the other useful animals eaten by it will not increase the proportion to 15 per cent. This leaves a balance of at least 85 per cent in favor of the hawk.   It destroys so many noxious rodents and other destructive mammals that, as a rule, it should be allowed to live.   Nevertheless, the farmer must protect his fowls against the attacks of any individual with the chicken habit, while the gamekeeper rearing young game birds will take every opportunity to destroy a Red-tailed Hawk.

Buteo lineátus lineatus (GMELIN).   Red-shouldered Hawk

Other names: HEN HAWK; CHICKEN HAWK; WINTER HAWK.

Plates 38 and 40.

DESCRIPTION. — Slightly smaller than Red-tailed Hawk, not so heavily built, tarsi less feathered, feet more slender, and four outer primaries emarginate, *i.e.* part of inner web cut away abruptly toward tip; coloration variable, some dark, some pale.   *Adult male:* Above chiefly dark brown, variegated with reddish-brown and buffy or whitish; flight-feathers brownish-black or blackish, barred with lighter brown and white; tail above chiefly black or blackish, narrowly barred (about 5 bars) and tipped white; head and neck streaked dark brown or dusky, with a broad dark "moustache" mark running backward from the angle of mouth; throat and lores often whitish with black shaft-streaks and cheek paling somewhat; lesser wing-coverts bright reddish-brown, with dark brown or blackish shaft-streaks; other wing coverts variegated, with dark centers and pale or white margins and with more or less concealed white bars; rump blackish-brown; upper tail coverts

ENDS OF A HAWK'S PRI-MARIES (much reduced), showing rounded wing-tips, sinuate outer webs and emarginate inner webs

END OF A FALCON'S WING, showing the pointed shape

darker, tipped and barred white; below, rather light reddish-brown becoming paler toward tail; blackish shaft-streaks on breast, abdomen and sides; middle of breast with narrow bars of yellowish-white; leg feathering paler and more yellowish than breast, lightly and narrowly barred reddish-brown; wing-linings pale reddish-brown with deeper cross spots; under surface

* A female of this species shot in Wisconsin contained, among other food, a garter snake 21 inches long, and a water snake 15 inches long.   Heads of both snakes were missing, but otherwise the bodies were not mutilated.   Due to the crowded stomach, the garter snake was contained in the mouth and gullet of the bird, and several folds of the snake could be seen on opening the beak.   (Oölogist, Vol. XXX, 1913, p. 272.)

of tail whitish with barring sometimes distinct, sometimes not; bill bluish horn-color blackening toward tip, cere yellow, iris brown; legs and feet yellow (cere, legs and feet sometimes greenish-yellow or yellowish-green). *Adult female:* Similar to male, but reddish-brown more extended, and darker below. *Young in first winter plumage:* Like juvenal plumage. *Young in juvenal plumage:* Above, similar to adult, but more dusky and less rufous; head and neck marked much as in adult, but with vandyke brown, light gray and pale brownish replacing reddish-brown of adult; lesser wing-coverts showing much less reddish-brown; primaries and tail not so black as in adult, basal parts showing ochreous buff or yellowish-red; rest of primaries blackish-brown with light edges, and rest of tail grayish-brown; entire tail barred narrowly with 8 to 10 dusky or blackish bars, subterminal bar widest, tip whitish; below, entirely unlike adult, white or whitish, streaked with rows of long drop-shaped overlapping spots of vandyke brown. *Downy young:* White when hatched, often with a strong pink tinge, which later fades leaving young nearly pure white; some have a brownish tinge.

MEASUREMENTS. — *Male:* Length 18.00 to 23.00 in.; spread 32.50 to 44.00; folded wing 11.00 to 13.50; tail 7.50 to 9.70; bill, without cere, .75 to .90; tarsus 2.23 to 3.25. *Female:* Length 19.00 to 24.00; spread 39.12 to 50.00; folded wing 12.00 to 14.75; tail 7.50 to 10.00; bill .80 to .92; tarsus 2.45 to 3.20. Weight 2 to 3 lbs. Female often much larger than male.

MOLTS. — Juvenal plumage attained by postnatal molt when nearly full grown, and this or similar plumage retained through first winter and succeeding spring; complete molt then takes place during summer and autumn, and young bird probably in most cases assumes adult plumage when about one year and six months old. Adults have complete molt in summer and autumn, apparently beginning in some individuals in April or May and extending in some cases at least to October.

FIELD MARKS. — Nearly as large as Red-tailed Hawk. The *only necessary* field mark when bird is soaring (even at a height or distance which may require a glass) is the apparent translucent spot in the wing near its tip formed by the short black and white wing-barring. This is diagnostic and no other New England hawk has anything like it. When seen near-by in the woods, look for the bright ruddy *shoulders*. *Adults:* Ruddy lower plumage, lesser wing-coverts and wings barred distinctly black and white distinguish it from other New England hawks although the Broad-winged may appear ruddy beneath, but is smaller and shows but three rather *wide* black bars on tail, alternating with the white, where the larger bird shows *more* and *narrower* bars, white bars especially narrower; wings of the "Broad-wing" resemble much more (on a small scale) those of the "Red-tail" than those of the Red-shouldered Hawk; sometimes a "Red-shoulder," although having sufficiently red shoulders, will be otherwise rather pale, both in respect to breast and tail-barring; the "Broad-wing" and the "Red-tail" soar and sail much more buoyantly than the "Red-shoulder," but all three also progress by steady flapping; the "Red-tail's" tail is relatively longer than the "Red-shoulder's" and it is a "cleverer" bird on the wing. *Young:* Distinguished from young of "Red-tail" by dark streaks, uniformly distributed over lower surface of body, where young of "Red-tail" has an unmarked whitish area on breast and a wide abdominal band of dark streaks.

VOICE. — Most common note a rather prolonged *teé-ur teé-ur* or *keé-you keé-you*, the last syllable drawn out, with a falling inflection at the end — a cry imitated by the Blue Jay; also a cry *whee-ee-e*, one like *yeh-ack yeh-ack* and occasionally *ca-ac* (W. Ralph) or *cac-cac-cac* (O. W. Knight); as they "talk" to one another, little weak *peeps;* though the male is supposed to have a weaker voice than the female, sometimes an individual male will scream as loudly as a female (J. A. Farley).

BREEDING. — Usually in patches of woods, often wet, not far from open fields and swamps, frequently near houses or roads, in both deciduous and coniferous trees. In Massachusetts pines, oaks and chestnuts are favorites, but they nest in birch, maple, ash, beech, etc., and may even choose a tree (one of a few) in field or pasture; in eastern Massachusetts a white pine is oftenest chosen. *Nest:* Usually lower down than "Red-tail's" and in plain sight; usually on branches next the trunk or in crotch of tree (less often out from trunk in crotch of branch), from 35 to 60 feet up, built of sticks and twigs, lined with strips of bark, bits of lichen, desiccated oak and other leaves, and often (but not always) small green twigs of deciduous or coniferous trees, with leaves attached (as pine-needle bunches), and a few feathers.* Sometimes (but not often) there is an excess of brown oak leaves (the commonly accepted and usual sign of squirrel occupancy) in the nest which can be seen from the ground. *Eggs:* Usually 2 to 4, rarely 5, very rarely 6; 1.65 to 1.85 by 2.14 to 2.37 in.; variable, oval to ovate, some are short and much rounded at ends; dull white to pale bluish or yellowish, more or less heavily spotted, blotched and smeared with reddish-brown in various shades, buff, fawn and gray, usually more heavily spotted than those of "Red-tail," but very rarely unspotted; after rains eggs often become stained by wet nest-lining; illustrated in "Bendire's Life Histories of North American Birds," Vol. I, Plate VII, Figs. 1 to 5. *Dates:* April 3 to June 5, Massachusetts. *Incubation:* Period 25 to 28 days (authors); by both sexes. One brood yearly.

RANGE. — Eastern North America west to the edge of Great Plains. Breeds from Manitoba, Ontario, southern Quebec and Prince Edward Island south to southern Kansas, Northeastern Tennessee and North Carolina; in winter from central Iowa, Illinois, Indiana, southern Ohio, southern Ontario, central New York, southern Vermont and southern New Hampshire (casual farther north) south to Gulf coast and Texas; accidental in Scotland (one occurrence); other forms of this species extend its range west and south.

DISTRIBUTION IN NEW ENGLAND. — *Maine:* Rather common to uncommon and local summer resident generally. *New Hampshire:* Rather uncommon summer resident north to the White Mountain region; recorded every month in the year in southern part. *Vermont:* Uncommon summer resident in hills of northern counties, more common in valleys, especially in southern part, where a rare winter resident. *Massachusetts:* Common migrant and common summer resident in eastern counties where it largely replaces *borealis* and west to the Connecticut Valley; less common in the wooded hills of Berkshire County, and in winter. *Rhode Island:* Uncommon resident, more common locally in summer than in winter; common migrant; less common winter resident. *Connecticut:* Common migrant and not uncommon winter resident; less common summer resident.

SEASON IN MASSACHUSETTS. — Permanent resident; most common in migration, March and April, September and October.

HAUNTS AND HABITS.   There is no more pleasing spring sound than the lusty scream of the "Red-shoulder" as it rings through the bare leafless woods as they stand up straight and brown against the pale blue sky of April. The Red-shouldered Hawk probably is to-day the most generally common and conspicuous bird of its family in New England. When we speak of a hawk as common, we do not mean that it may be met with as often as a Robin or a Song Sparrow. The commonest hawk is rare compared with the Robin, though it may be common for a hawk. The Red-shouldered Hawk is conspicuous because of its habit of circling up into the sky with widely extended wings, a habit which it shares with the less common "Red-tail." In the last part of the nineteenth century when the latter commenced to decrease in numbers in southern New England, the present species began to increase, and soon largely took the place of its larger congener. In recent years its numbers seem to have fallen off somewhat in the same region. It seems moreover to prefer the more open and cultivated land, while the "Red-tail" is more at home within the borders of the forest and among heavily wooded hills. But since the larger and more stately bird has deserted many of its former woodland haunts, the smaller bird has regularly occupied them. The Red-shouldered Hawk will breed wherever it is allowed to settle in woodland or in small patches of large trees near open fields and

---

* In the summer of 1916, in Kansas, a nest with four eggs was found *on the ground.* Oölogist, Vol. XXXIV, 1917, p. 58.

meadows, where it finds its chief sustenance. Having once chosen an abiding place, it prefers to come back year after year to its old home, and often will use the same nest for years, rebuilding it somewhat and adding to it each year until its size and depth have increased considerably, and a good part of the structure is full of all sorts of old woods-dirt. Some of its nests would doubtless fill a bushel basket. Often in March it will begin to build a new domicile or repair an old one (chiefly with a broad encircling fringe of mossy twigs and branches and a freshened lining of the usual bark-strips, bits of oak leaves, lichens, etc.), both male and female working together, but rarely are eggs deposited in Massachusetts until well into April.*

Nests, whether renovated or new, found in hardwood trees are likely to be handsomer and neater than nests in pines, in the one case with their hardwood sticks and twigs, in the other with their pine twigs, etc.

June nests are in great contrast to those built or renovated in April, with their dead leaves, lichens, etc., deposited before the trees have leaved out. Hawks often break off fresh green twigs with leaves on them to put into the nest (frequently after incubation has begun or after eggs hatch), and now and then one is carelessly dropped. A nest found in an oak in June, in Georgetown, apparently new, was neither large nor deep and had a lining of green oak leaves which made "a cool, fresh, pretty mat or bed for the eggs." This nest lacked both dead leaves or lichens.

As hawks begin molting early in the year, some of the feathers shed by the sitting bird (which loses feathers as readily as a hen in a hen-yard) will cling to the nest, so that a person standing on the ground below can usually see some feathers about the edges of an occupied nest; another indication of occupation is the presence of freshly broken twigs at the nest or scattered on the ground below. These signs of promise may be seen about the occupied nests of most hawks, but they are not always present.

The larger the hawk the more feathers are lost, may be laid down as more or less of a rule. But some individuals are more likely to lose feathers than others. And in some cases where a nest is excessively "feathered," so as to make a downy mat or bed for the eggs, it is impossible to resist the impression that such "feathering" is not only decorative but indicates design.

Hawks are supposed to mate for life, but if one of a pair is killed during the nesting season, the other soon finds another mate.

During the mating and until the eggs are laid the mated pairs are quite vociferous, and they betray their nesting place by their cries. After their eggs are laid the birds seem more quiet and secretive. Now and then a "Red-shoulder" will fly so quietly from the nest that she might be mistaken for an owl. Sometimes the female will scream at an interloper while she is still sitting on her nest, but as a rule, she flies from it while the invader is still 50 to 75 yards away. The females differ regarding shyness; some are

---

* A Red-shouldered Hawk in Georgetown, Massachusetts, was robbed of her eggs which she had laid in a new, large nest in an oak; whereupon she laid another set of eggs in the *same* season in the *same* nest. This does not often occur in New England.

very shy and leave the nest quietly before the intruder even catches sight of it. After the breeding season they seem to be as silent as any hawk. Usually shy, they sometimes become bold when an intruder visits the nest, although one rarely sits on the nest after climbing has begun. Sometimes the female will alight on a branch over the intruder's head, screaming long and loudly. I have even seen one dive furiously at my head with a rather terrifying roar of rushing wings when I merely walked within sight of her nest containing young. Mr. J. A. Farley informs me that once when he with a companion had climbed to a nest, the female dashed in swiftly and passed between their heads, brushing their cheeks with her wing-tips.* When the young are nearly fledged, with the down still clinging to their feathers, they leave the nest by day and climb about among the branches with flapping wings, thus exercising the muscles that control the pinions which are soon to bear them away from their home forever. It is well known that hawks, as well as many other species, will not tolerate the nesting of a pair of the same species near their home, though they may dwell in peace in the same grove with other rapacious birds.

When the young are fledged and well able to hunt, the parents drive them out to shift for themselves. This species, like the " Red-tail," does not seem to be a very active hunter. It chases birds occasionally, but seems to be content mostly with sitting on some tree or pole where it can overlook a meadow, teeming with field mice, or the marshy border of some pond, where frogs and snakes abound. It was always a puzzle to me how these hawks could kill a snake so quickly as they do. As boys we believed that life remained in a dying snake until the setting of the sun, and we usually found some sign of life in the tail for a long time after the reptile was decapitated; but when a hawk flies away with a snake dangling from beak or talons, the creature hangs limp and lifeless; at least that has been my experience. A friend observed a hawk holding a snake in its bill and beating it upon a stone wall. This may account for a quick demise. Some of the hawks have learned to fly high with the snake and then let it fall on hard ground or rock to kill it at once.

When the leaves begin to turn and fall, many of these hawks leave the northern parts of their range and drift southward, at a considerable height, often in large scattered flocks and in company with other species. But some remain to eke out a precarious living along the larger streams or about the swamps, marshes, lakes or springs of southern New England. Mr. Wilbur Smith informed me that a Red-shouldered Hawk appeared in Birdcraft Sanctuary, Fairfield, Connecticut, on January 1, 1920, and was seen by the superintendent daily for two months thereafter. There were nine pheasants in the sanctuary and also a bantam hen with several chicks in a coop, open at the top, but neither chickens nor pheasants were molested by the hawk. About February first it entered a hen-yard, where it found a skinned deer's neck and a dead opossum, and it fed on the carrion every day for about two weeks, while the hens merely withdrew to the coop. Mr. Frank Novak, the superintendent, saw the rooster standing one day within four feet of

---

* A case of an audaciously daring hawk of this species which struck a climber at its nest, drawing blood, is reported. (Auk, Vol. XXX, 1913, p. 582.)

the hawk. During the worst kind of weather this bird did not molest a bird or a chicken, but it was repeatedly seen to catch rats and mice.

The food of this hawk consists very largely of small rodents, principally mice, batrachians and snakes. It catches few birds but now and then an individual gets the poultry-killing habit. Dr. B. H. Warren in the Birds of Pennsylvania, records the stomach contents of 57 of these hawks as follows: 43 stomachs contained field mice, a few other small mammals and insects; 9, frogs and insects; 2, small birds, remains of small mammals and beetles; and 1, hair, apparently of a skunk. Some individuals, at least, evince a taste for fish, and will even go into the water for them. Rarely one is shot while fishing in a trout pond, and taken with its lower plumage wet and with trout in its gullet. Dr. A. K. Fisher summarizes as follows in his Hawks and Owls of the United States: The examination of 220 stomachs of this species showed that 3 contained poultry; 12, other birds; 102, mice; 40, other mammals; 20, reptiles; 39, batrachians; 92, insects; 16, spiders; 7, crawfish; 1, earthworms; 2, offal; 3, fish; and 14 were empty.

ECONOMIC STATUS. Evidently this is one of the most useful hawks. It should never be killed unless in the act of destroying poultry or game. As a rule it kills few small birds or birds of any kind, and it destroys many snakes which are destructive to small birds and their eggs. Ordinarily it does not molest game birds, but if one gets troublesome on a game farm, the gamekeeper naturally will destroy it.

Buteo swaínsoni BONAPARTE. Swainson's Hawk.

DESCRIPTION. — Somewhat smaller than "Red-tail," usually lighter in weight; only three outer primaries notched (emarginate) or cut away on inner webs toward tips, otherwise much like "Red-tail" in shape but unlike it in color, which is very variable. *Adult male (normal plumage)*: Nearly uniform dark grayish-brown above, but very variable in shade, wearing or fading as season advances, often with paler brown or reddish-brown feather-edges; crown feathers whitish under the surface which shows when feathers are raised; tail grayish-brown or brownish-gray, crossed by many narrow, dusky bars which become gradually faint or obsolete near base; tip narrowly whitish or much paler; chin and throat normally white, and often forehead also, usually distinctly defined; upper breast usually reddish-brown or cinnamon, rarely mixed with (or interrupted by) whitish; from upper breast to tail white or whitish, usually barred or spotted more or less with brown; colors of axillars and wing-linings resemble those of abdomen; under side of tail pale grayish-brown or whitish, rather narrowly barred darker; bill slaty black, bluish toward base, cere light yellow; iris usually brown or hazel; legs and feet greenish-yellow to chrome yellow, claws black. *Adult Female (normal plumage)*: Similar to male, but patch on upper breast grayish-brown instead of reddish-brown or cinnamon; often much darker above or below than male; ground color of wing-linings and axillars similar to or paler than other under plumage and similarly marked, though sometimes very little marked. *Dark phase, both sexes*: Entire plumage sooty brown; under tail-coverts spotted or barred in some cases with rusty or paler. Some have upper plumage dark and lower plumage as in light phase. *Note*: Individuals may be found in all shades and variations between normal and dark phase. They may be recognized by the emargination of the three outer primaries. *Young in first winter plumage*: Like juvenal, but becoming paler with age. *Young in juvenal plumage*: Tail as in normal adult; elsewhere above, blackish-brown variegated with buffy or tawny, head, neck and lower plumage creamy buff or fawn color, head and neck streaked blackish; throat unstreaked or merely pencilled; other lower plumage usually more or less sprinkled with blackish spots which are numerous on upper breast, and enlarge into bars on flanks and into broad arrowheads on lower belly and leg-feathering; tail barred as in adult, but bars less conspicuous, and tip usually more broadly whitish; flight-feathers more or less marbled with white on basal parts of inner webs, which are faintly barred black; young also have a dark phase and are as variable as adults; iris gray, cere greenish-gray; feet grayish-yellow; bill and claws blue-black (Coues).* *Downy young:* White and fluffy, sometimes tinged creamy-pink or gray.

MEASUREMENTS. — *Male:* Length 18.75 to 20.63 in.; spread 47.25 to 51.00; folded wing 14.40 to 16.00; tail 7.50 to 9.00; bill, without cere, .80 to .95; tarsus 2.30 to 2.75. *Female:* Length 18.86 to 22.00; spread 47.00 to 57.00; folded wing 14.75 to 17.50; tail 8.25 to 10.00; bill .80 to 1.00; tarsus 2.50 to 2.90. Weight 1 lb. 10 oz. to 3 lbs. 8 oz. Female larger than male.

MOLTS. — Juvenal plumage is acquired by complete postnatal molt as bird develops. Apparently this plumage is worn through first winter. Probably molt begins in spring and continues through summer and part of autumn (at least from June to October). According to Cameron this species becomes as adult (molting annually) when about 4½ years old.[1] Adults have one complete molt during the milder part of year; specimens examined were in molt from July to October.

FIELD MARKS. — *Adult* (*light phase*): When seen in flight from below resembles "Red-tail," but is mainly white below with *very wide dark band* across upper breast, separating white throat from nearly white abdomen; wings slightly narrower and longer relatively than those of "Red-tail" with ends rounded; a white patch on each side of rump. (Species so variable that no uniformly reliable field marks can be given for dark phase or immature; most eastern specimens are of the dark or melanistic phase; mistakes in identification often made with bird in hand.)

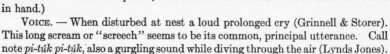

SWAINSON'S HAWK
Adult-Normal Phase

VOICE. — When disturbed at nest a loud prolonged cry (Grinnell & Storer). This long scream or "screech" seems to be its common, principal utterance. Call note *pi-túk pi-túk,* also a gurgling sound while diving through the air (Lynds Jones).

BREEDING. — Almost anywhere, largely in solitary trees in open country, or in wooded lands bordering on it, such as small groves or belts of timber along river bottoms. *Nest:* On ground, bush, tree, or cliff, mostly from a few to 60 ft. above ground, built of sticks and twigs, lined with leaves, weeds or grass. *Eggs:* Two to four, about 2.30 to 2.38 by 1.75 to 1.82 in.; usually short oval to rounded or short ovate; spotted and blotched with reddish-brown or umber, variously distributed, with occasional purplish gray or drab markings; some eggs nearly spotless, with fine dots and irregular lines, a very few heavily marked; illustrated in "Bendire's Life Histories of North American Birds," Vol. I, Plate VIII, Figs. 1 to 6. *Dates:* From April 10, southern California, until June or even early July, northern states. *Incubation:* Probably by both parents; period from 25 to 28 days (Burns). One brood yearly.

RANGE. — North and South America. Breeds from central northern Alaska, Yukon, northwestern Mackenzie and Manitoba, east rarely to Illinois and south to Chile; casual in Michigan, Ontario, Quebec and New York, Vermont, Maine and Massachusetts; in winter from Colorado, South Dakota and Iowa (casually) southward.

DISTRIBUTION IN NEW ENGLAND. — Casual or accidental visitor. *Records: Maine:* Gouldsboro, September 15, 1886, immature bird taken[2] by E. Gordon, and sent to William Brewster.

Glenburn, May 19, 1888, one taken and sent to Brewster collection;[3] Calais, about October 8, 1892,

* For an informing discussion of plumages of Swainson's Hawk, see Cameron, E. S.: Auk, Vol. XXX, 1913, pp. 386–394; and Vol. XXV, 1908, pp. 468–471.

[1] Cameron, E. S.: Auk, Vol. XXX, 1913, pp. 386–387.

[2] Brewster, William: Auk, Vol. IV, 1887, p. 160.

[3] Brewster, William: Auk, Vol. V, 1888, p. 424.

immature bird taken and in Boardman collection.[1] In addition to these definite records, Manly Hardy said that he had seen two (both melanistic) taken "here" (apparently in Penobscot County).[2] *Vermont:* Hartland, May 23, 1915, one very dark adult male taken, now in collection of Mrs. A. B. Morgan of Woodstock;[3] Lunenburg, W. E. Balch.[4] *Massachusetts:* Hamilton (not Salem), April 20, 1872, one killed by Nelson Butler, now in collection of Peabody Academy;[5] Wayland, about Sept. 12, 1876, young male taken;[6] Salem, Oct. 28, 1889, male shot by R. L. Newcomb, now in collection of Peabody Academy;[7] Essex, May 29, 1892, adult female killed;[8] Ipswich, October 28, 1917, bird seen by Dr. C. W. Townsend.[9]

In addition to the foregoing definite records, William Brewster notes that in 1893 he saw for two days (April 8 and 9) on the Concord (Mass.) meadows a small *Buteo* which apparently was wholly black in color and almost certainly a *swainsoni*.[10]

SEASON IN MASSACHUSETTS. — April 20 to November 7.

HAUNTS AND HABITS. Swainson's Hawk is a buzzard of the open country, although it usually nests in trees. Its home is always near wide, open lands, and it will even nest in low bushes or on the ground in its favorite regions. Its habits are somewhat similar to those of the Red-tailed or Red-shouldered Hawks, and young birds might be mistaken for either of these. It does not require extended notice here as it is a mere straggler in New England, though probably it occurs here more often than the records indicate.

It feeds mostly on small injurious creatures such as field mice and gophers, and on destructive insects, and rarely troubles birds, as small birds not infrequently nest in the same tree with it and some even build their nests among the sticks of which its nest is composed, while orioles suspend their domiciles from the twigs of the hawk's structure. It is very fond of frogs and sometimes eats cottontail rabbits, also snakes.

ECONOMIC STATUS. In Senate document 132, sixtieth Congress, first session, 1907, a message of the President of the United States, Theodore Roosevelt, containing a report of the Secretary of Agriculture on the work of the Biological Survey, it is stated that Swainson's Hawk saves the farmers of the western states $57,600 yearly by the destruction of grasshoppers alone during the grasshopper season. It is one of the most useful of our birds of prey, but is so rare in New England as to be of no economic importance here.

Buteo platýpterus (VIEILLOT). Broad-winged Hawk.

Plate 40.

DESCRIPTION. — Similar in shape to Red-tailed Hawk, but much smaller, shorter, never much more than 18.50 inches; bill very wide at base; head large, broad; only three outer primaries emarginated on inner webs; tail short, outer and middle feathers shortest. *Adults (sexes alike):* some individual

---

[1] Brewster, William: Auk, Vol. X, 1893, p. 82.
[2] Knight, Ora W.: Birds of Maine, 1908, p. 230.
[3] Auk, Vol. XL, 1923, p. 546.
[4] Perkins and Howe: Birds of Vermont, 1901, p. 18.
[5] Allen, J. A.: Bulletin Essex Institute, Vol. X, 1878, p. 22, and Brewster, William: Editor, Minot's Land Birds and Game Birds of New England, Appendix, 2d ed., 1895, p. 476.
[6] Brewster, William: Bulletin Nuttall Ornithological Club, Vol. III, 1878, pp. 39–40.
[7] Brewster, William: Editor Minot's Land Birds and Game Birds of New England, 2d ed., 1895, p. 476.
[8] Brewster, William: Auk, Vol. X, 1893, p. 82.
[9] Supplement to Birds of Essex County, Mass., 1920, p. 102.
[10] Minot's Land Birds and Game Birds of New England, Brewster, Editor, 1895, p. 476.

variation. Crown, back of head and nape dark brown, some reddish-brown edges posteriorly; sides of head paler, with ground color shown only in streaks around eye, and in dark "moustache" mark along lower jaw; above, chiefly dark umber-brown, with black shaft-lines on head, upper back and wing-coverts, feathers paling toward edges, more uniform and darker on back; upper tail-coverts barred or spotted white; *tail banded rather broadly and conspicuously with black and light gray, grayish-white or white*, the broadest black zone at end (subterminal), the others (2 commonly visible) narrowing successively toward base; tail tipped more or less with white; barring above corresponds generally with same below; outer webs and ends of primaries and secondaries blackish, most of inner webs white, more or less barred blackish; lower plumage mixed white and tawny brown, darker brown or dull chestnut, whitening toward tail; heavily marked on breast with broad bars or wide arrowheads of brown (sometimes coalescing so that a unicolored breast results), which are usually farther apart on sides and flanks, and narrower on leg-feathering; wing-linings dull yellowish-white with sparse and rather small spots of brownish-red and a few dark brown spots on primary coverts; axillars white with reddish-brown bars connected by shaft-streaks; bill largely blackish, lightening to bluish toward base, cere yellow; iris straw or dark yellow to dark brown; legs and feet yellow, claws black or blackish. *Second year plumage:* Upper tail-coverts and upper plumage generally much as in adult, dark brown or blackish, but barred very light gray or light brown; upper tail-coverts tipped and banded white; below whitish, tinged pale buff, and either streaked with rows of reddish-brown spots, or more or less barred reddish-brown on breast and leg-feathering; bill black, sometimes fading to lead color on base of upper mandible and most of lower, cere yellow; iris light umber, hazel or brown, pearl-gray, grayish, straw, straw-yellow, or yellow with brown stain on inner edge; legs and feet yellow, claws black. *Young in first winter plumage:* Like juvenal, but often lighter both above and below, the result of fading. *Young in juvenal plumage:* Above chiefly blackish-brown, variegated with raw umber, chestnut, buffy or dull whitish, *feather-edges narrowly rusty or reddish-brown;* upper tail-coverts white, tinged rusty on outer webs and more or less barred deep brown; tail rather light grayish-brown with 5 to 7 narrow dark brown bars and narrow white tip; primaries and secondaries fading on inner webs to white, with 6 to 9 bars of dark brown; chin and throat white or buffy-white, usually streaked more or less with dark brown; remaining lower plumage and sides of head yellowish or creamy-buff, streaked and striped with dark brown; markings below more properly rows of elongated spots, which are wanting, or nearly so, on center of breast, abdomen and under tail-coverts; tail pale, buffy-whitish below, narrowly barred darker; under primary coverts whitish, spotted brown; wing linings otherwise cream-buff, spotted near bend of wing; iris gray or very dark brown; legs and feet yellow. *Downy young:* Dull pale yellowish-white; iris blackish or gray.

MEASUREMENTS. — *Male:* Length 13.25 to 16.50 in.; spread 32.00 to 38.00; folded wing 9.75 to 11.00; tail 6.00 to 7.00; bill .58 to .80; tarsus 2.05 to 2.40. *Female:* Length 15.00 to 18.75 in.; spread 33.45 to 39.00; folded wing 10.14 to 11.55; tail 6.00 to 8.00; bill .58 to .80; tarsus 2.15 to 2.80. Weight, male 13 oz.; female 1 lb. 3½ oz. (F. L. Burns).

MOLTS. — Young birds retain juvenal plumage through first winter unchanged, except by wear and fading; then they molt (April to September), but require another year to attain perfect adult plumage; adults have one complete molt (May to September).

FIELD MARKS. — About Crow size, thus larger and heavier than the smaller hawks but much smaller than the Red-tailed or the Red-shouldered Hawk; about size of Cooper's Hawk, but the tail-barring above, and *broad*, dark, subterminal bar below with white bar adjoining will always distinguish it from that species; body and head broad; wings long, broad and rounded at tips and mostly silvery white below with black tips; in flight both flaps and soars, resembling very much its larger relative the "Red-tail"; the best field marks of adult are the few showy black and white tail bars above and below (usually 3 black and 2 white) and the "clubbed" wings (not always noted nevertheless) as the "Broad-wing" soars overhead. *Adults:* Largely reddish-brown on under surface of body where young are whitish with dark streaks.

VOICE. — A shrill *key, ky-ah, ky-ah-ke-ee kee-ee* (E. A. Samuels); a peculiar harsh, distressed cry, *ka ka ka ka* (F. L. Burns); a plaintive double note, slightly like (yet unlike) the note of the Wood Pewee long drawn out and diminishing in force toward the end, written down by Dr. C. W. Townsend as *te-whée*, or *tswa-ee* or *pss-wheé-e*. "A slight (but distinct) grate or catch at the end of this short complaining whistle, a relatively weak but extremely penetrating *pee-dee* or *chi-pwee* (uttered either while on wing or when perched), is usually heard and is diagnostic." (J. A. Farley.) It also utters some very short notes in different tone; male's voice is fainter than female's.

BREEDING. — Usually in tracts of woodland and among wooded hills. *Nest:* Commonly in tree, either coniferous or deciduous, sometimes on top of a branching stub, and from 20 to 35 feet from ground; often higher and occasionally lower; sometimes well built, like a small-sized "Red-shoulder's," with handsome well-hollowed and lined interior, and encircling fringe of mossy twigs, again crudely built (often on an old nest of a crow or other bird); of twigs, sticks, bark and sometimes mosses, and feathers of the bird itself; sprays of buds, blossoms or green leaves often are found in the nest (as with other hawks), and rarely a little grass or other small plants. *Eggs:* 2 to 4, usually 3; 1.72 to 2.04 by 1.43 to 1.80 in.; elliptical ovate to oval, short ovate most typical; color very variable, usually whitish or dirty white, sometimes with strong bluish, greenish or pinkish tinge, spotted and blotched with light tawny or reddish-brown; some eggs marked with various browns or with dark dots and fine lines, often with some drab, gray or lavender markings; spots often heaviest and most numerous about large end, but some heavily marked with chocolate and walnut brown about small end, sometimes almost unmarked; illustrated in Bendire's "Life Histories of North American Birds," Vol. I, Plate VII, Figs. 10 to 13. *Dates:* May 9 to June 2, Massachusetts; ranging from second week in April in southern states to early June, Maine, and mid June, Canada. *Incubation:* Period apparently 23 to 25 days (Burns); by both sexes. One brood yearly.

RANGE. — Eastern North America north to border of Hudsonian Zone. Breeds from central Alberta, southeastern Saskatchewan, southern Manitoba, northern Ontario, central Quebec, New Brunswick and Cape Breton Island south to central Texas, the Gulf coast and Florida; south in winter from southern Illinois, southern Indiana, southern Ohio, Connecticut and Rhode Island (rarely) to West Indies, and through Mexico and Central America, Venezuela, Ecuador and Peru.

DISTRIBUTION IN NEW ENGLAND. — *Maine:* Rather common summer resident. *New Hampshire:* Not uncommon migrant and summer resident in northern part, less common summer resident south of White Mountain region (one winter record). *Vermont:* Rather uncommon to rare breeder and uncommon migrant. *Massachusetts:* common migrant, less common summer resident, most common as a breeder in wooded sections of Plymouth, Worcester, Hampshire, Berkshire and Franklin counties, but likely to be found wherever there are woods enough. *Rhode Island:* Common migrant and uncommon resident. *Connecticut:* Common migrant, less common summer resident, and uncommon winter resident.

SEASON IN MASSACHUSETTS. — (March 31) April 10 to November 30 (winter records doubtful.)

HAUNTS AND HABITS. The Broad-winged Hawk is generally uncommon or rare in the breeding season in those parts of New England from which the forests have been cleared. It is most common in hilly, forested regions and even there it is more or less local in distribution, though it is more common in the woods than the published records indicate. Mention of the "Broad-wing" brings up a mental picture of the warm umbrageous woods of June, bright with the white of the flowering dogwood or ablaze with the pink azalea, with the little *Buteo*, with showy black and white tail, flying easily about and perching near, uttering the while its complaining *pe-dee*. It is a rather silent and sedentary woodland bird, except during the breeding season when intruders approach its nest, which it betrays by its "scolding." It is not often observed and identified save by those who, knowing it, go in search of it. As it rarely troubles poultry or pigeons about farmyards, its presence often is unsuspected in places where it breeds not uncommonly.   Formerly it was one of the most common hawks in Worcester County, Massachusetts, where in recent years its numbers seem to have diminished with the destruction of the older woods, while in Bristol and Plymouth counties, parts of which are still well wooded, it seems to have increased.   Altitudes such as we have in New England seem to make little difference to this hawk for it is found both in the valleys and on the mountain tops.   Its powers of flight are so great that it is able to rise at will from summer heat to winter cold in the upper air.   In warm summer weather it frequently soars to great heights with widely extended and almost motionless wings.   The turned-up wing-tips and the general free and buoyant flight (almost soaring) of the "Broad-wing" are strongly reminiscent of the "Red-tail."   In flight, at least, the "Broad-wing" is a miniature " Red-tail."   Possibly no hawk ascends higher in the heavens than this rather small, inconspicuous species.   Its broad, ample "clubbed" wings, which name the bird so aptly when they are well seen, often make this hawk seem larger than it really is.   The "Broad-wing" is a small hawk.   Such was not the impression of a well-known nature writer who, doubtless misled by the title "Broad-wing," once remarked that the large Buteo which he saw in the woods one day, must have been a Broad-winged Hawk because it was a *Buteo* of the largest size !

The most complete account of this bird is a Monograph by Mr. Frank L. Burns [1] in which he gives an interesting life history largely gleaned from the writings of others.   He includes in his account several tales showing the tameness of this hawk.   Among them is one from Audubon, who says that his brother-in-law climbed to a nest and took in his hands, nest, eggs, bird and all, merely covering the bird with his handkerchief.   Audubon asserts that he carried the bird home and that it sat quietly on a perch while he measured and drew it.   Mr. C. J. Maynard tells of another of which he went in pursuit, and says that he walked to within a few yards of it while it sat on a low limb.   Another was caught alive at Middletown Springs, Vermont, in the autumn of 1904, by a boy who crept along a fence and grasped it by the legs while it sat on the fence top.   Another in Illinois was knocked off a limb by a boy "with a ten foot stick."   These individuals, however, must have been exceptionally tame or stupid for, although the species is not usually as wild as other hawks and often may be approached to within easy gunshot, nevertheless such instances as those mentioned above probably are due to individual tameness or stupidity. The "Broad-wing," with its mild, gentle, characterless face and head is not a bird of distinguished appearance, for it perches often in a very homely and ungraceful attitude, round-shouldered and hump-backed, with head drooping and wings and legs placed very awkwardly on its perch.   How unlike the stately Goshawk or the alert "Coopers" ! Ordinarily the bird is inoffensive and seldom does battle even in defense of its nest.   Yet George A. Boardman says that a man whom he employed to collect specimens was attacked with great fury by one of these birds when he climbed to its nest.   Dr. Warren also quotes an instance where, when a boy was ascending to a nest, the bird attacked the

---

[1] Wilson Bulletin, Vol. XXIII, 1911, pp. 146–320.

boy furiously and fixed its claws in his arm. The hawk had to be killed.[1] Usually, however, when the nest is disturbed the birds merely circle about overhead or alight in near-by trees, uttering occasionally their plaintive complaining cries.

This species hunts either in the woods, flying above the tree-tops or coursing rather low over the open land. When it discovers its prey, it hovers sometimes until it sees a favorable opportunity to strike, when it swoops swiftly to the earth and rises with its prey in its talons. It will sit for long periods motionless on a perch watching for a movement of some small creature hidden in the leaves and grass and then pounce suddenly upon its prey, often leaping about among the leaves and other débris of the forest floor like a thing possessed, in its attempt to seize its victim. Having killed it, its captor either eats it on the ground or bears it away to the nest, or to some regular feeding place by a stream or pool.

Mr. A. B. Klugh of Guelph, Ontario, informed Mr. Burns that on September 11, 1903, he saw a flock of this species — the individuals sailing at various heights over a large "bush." Now and then one closed its wings, shot down at a "sharp incline" until close to the tree-tops and then swept upwards. In checking its descent it produced a "tremendous noise" almost resembling an explosion. The sound gave the observer the impression that he was about to be hit, and caused him to "duck his head."

Mr. J. M. Bromley writing to me in 1918 said that on one very hot morning in July he saw a pair of Broad-winged Hawks flying over the woods in close intersecting circles, sounding their high-pitched, plaintive whistle. Occasionally one fluttered its wings, making a chippering sound, and then continued sailing. Suddenly the smaller bird (probably the male) set its wings, shot straight downward for a few yards and then made a sudden upward turn; as it turned, its wings were spread wide, making a booming sound like that produced by the Nighthawk. This performance was repeated. It was similar to that noted by Mr. Klugh and as it occurred in mid-summer in Massachusetts, while the behavior observed by Mr. Klugh was in September in Ontario, probably the habit is a common one, not often noticed because of the retiring habits of the bird.

The "Broad-wing" normally nests rather near water in the unbroken forest, in a hollow among wooded hills, on a wooded hillside, near an old mill pond or beaver pond or along a running stream. In Worcester County, Massachusetts, it nested formerly in large chestnut trees. Now these trees have been killed by the blight. Frequently in the Maine woods it chooses the black birch or the yellow birch, but it nests not infrequently in pines and hemlocks as well as in many species of deciduous trees. Near settlements the nest in some cases may be found where one would least expect it, in small patches of woods or near wood roads or the edges of open fields. Usually it is fairly high, from 25 to 90 feet, but nests have been found from 3 to 10 feet from the ground. The parents complain when an intruder closely approaches the nest, but their cries may not be noticed, as on a windy day they may be mistaken for the creaking of the trees. As the nest is not usually occupied until May when the leaves have started to grow, it is not conspicu-

[1] Birds of Pennsylvania, 1890, p. 131.

ous, and so the birds avoid discovery. The young grow rapidly, but remain in or near the nest for at least four or five weeks while assuming juvenal plumage. Before they leave the nest for good, they frequently move about in or near it, flapping their wings and thus developing their flight muscles. Both parents feed the young, and green leaves or sprays of leaves are added daily to the nest; perhaps no other species of hawk is so much addicted to the use of green foliage. One or the other of the parents usually is at hand to guard and brood the young. In autumn the Broad-winged Hawk migrates in large numbers along the Atlantic coastal region and also down the Mississippi Valley. Possibly some of the birds which breed in northern New England come up the valley in spring, but probably most of those nesting here come by the coastal route. The species seems to be rare at all seasons along the seaboard of the Carolinas. Probably, therefore, the migration south of Virginia passes over the interior. The spring flight begins in March and April. Some continue to come in May, and in the Provinces they are seen moving even in June. The fall flight commences in late August or early September and continues into October. This flight, when both young and old come down, is the largest, and the great majority is composed of young birds. In fine weather, with favorable winds, they often fly very high, but strong northwest winds drift them towards the coast and necessitate low flight to escape the great force of the wind at high altitudes. Then they appear in large numbers with hawks of other species along the coastal regions of Connecticut, Long Island and northern New Jersey, and many are killed during these flights by gunners who lie in wait for them. Some use decoy owls to attract hawks. "Broad-wings" fly sometimes in flocks, but more often are much scattered. During favorable winds they soar or sail much, and drift with the wind.

The Broad-winged Hawk feeds largely on small mammals, reptiles, batrachians and insects, and ordinarily destroys very few birds. Most of the birds found in the stomachs examined were fledglings taken from the nest or when learning to fly. Chickens are taken rarely. Young rabbits, red squirrels and chipmunks occasionally are killed, and many mice, particularly wood mice, also a few moles and shrews. Snakes and frogs are freely eaten and some individuals eat many toads, but Mr. Burns says that an immature bird in captivity seemed to prefer other food. Lizards are taken in numbers and sometimes small fish where they are abundant.* It eats many of the large larvæ of night-flying moths and many other caterpillars, also many beetles, grasshoppers and crickets; among the crustaceans eaten are fiddler crabs and crawfish; if stomach examinations are made, at least one large green larva will almost always be found at the proper season for this creature. Dr. Fisher found in 65 stomachs of this species the following food materials: 2 contained small birds; 15, mice; 13, other mammals; 11, reptiles; 13, batrachians; 30, insects; 2, earthworms; 4, crawfish; and 7 were empty. Dr. Warren found similar food materials in the stomachs of the species examined by him, but no remains of birds.

---

* A female Broad-winged Hawk shot April 9, 1911, in Cuba, had 16 whole minnows in her gullet. (Auk, Vol. XXVIII, 1911, p. 485.)

ECONOMIC STATUS. Weighing all the evidence both for and against the bird, it must be classed as a useful species, as mice, small squirrels, reptiles and injurious insects form by far the greater part of its food.

Archibúteo lagópus sáncti-johánnis (GMELIN). Rough-legged Hawk.

Plates 38 and 41.

DESCRIPTION. — Bill rather small, wings very long and broad, four or five primaries emarginate; tail nearly even; *legs feathered to toes;* feet small as compared to the *Buteos,* with long claws. *Adults (normal phase)* : Head and neck whitish, streaked heavily with dusky; rest of upper plumage varied, white, grayish and dusky (very variable), lighter tints often predominating, usually with some rusty; upper tail-coverts partly white, and basal part of tail white — sometimes for more than half its length, and crossed on the white with a few narrow broken blackish bars, and rest of tail with alternate irregular (sometimes broken) light and dark bands, the light bands narrow, the dark bands narrow toward base of tail and growing wider gradually toward widest — a dark subterminal band, tip rather broadly grayish white; flight-feathers chiefly dusky brownish-gray, barred more or less distinctly with blackish toward ends; below, whitish and pale rusty, more or less marked and spotted (heavily on breast) with dusky, dark brown or blackish; confluent dark streaks form a wide band, more or less interrupted, across under body; long dark feathers of sides of breast cover sides and flanks; bill dark horn, somewhat lighter or bluish at base; cere yellow; iris brown to yellow; feet yellow, claws black. *Young in first winter plumage:* Like juvenal. *Young in juvenal plumage:* Much like normal adult, but end of tail unbarred, plain grayish-brown, its base whitish, marked somewhat as in adult; usually more buffy below than adult, with streaks forming a continued or almost unbroken wide band across the belly; primaries chiefly blackish, outer web of first five grayish; inner primaries often with lighter tips; inner webs partly white toward bases and on under sides. *Dark phase:* Adults and young ranging from slightly darker than normal to sooty black, except part of the bases of wing feathers, some bars or marblings on tail, and under sides of flight-feathers and the front of forehead, which are sometimes more or less white; base of tail sometimes white; iris pale brown; cere and feet yellow. *Downy young:* From nearly white to a variable pale brownish-gray; down extends on front and sides of tarsus to toes.

MEASUREMENTS. — *Male:* Length 19.50 to 22.00 in.; spread 48.50 to 52.25; folded wing 13.50 to 17.50; tail 8.35 to 10.00; bill .80 to 1.00; tarsus 2.25 to 2.75; *Female:* Length 21.45 to 23.50; spread 52.00 to 56.00; folded wing 14.50 to 18.00; tail 9.00 to 11.00; bill .90 to 1.02; tarsus 2.50 to 3.00 Weight 1 lb. 14½ oz. to 2 lb. 1¾ oz.

MOLTS. — Young bird puts on juvenal plumage as it develops toward adult size. This is retained through first winter with some wear and fading. In April or May complete molt begins and in some instances may last until November; following this as bird becomes 1to 1½ years old, it assumes plumage similar to adult, but may require another year to perfect it; adults have complete molt (May to November).

FIELD MARKS. — A large hawk, spread sometimes approaching five feet; wings shaped somewhat like those of a *Buteo* but relatively longer; tail also long like that of Marsh Hawk. A white patch above at base of tail. *Adults:* Generally dark grayish-brown above; white with much dark spotting, barring, etc., below; flies commonly low and might be mistaken for female Marsh Hawk; often alights on low trees (which Marsh Hawk seldom does), where it watches for mice; also at times circles upward, spirally, like an eagle, showing large black patch on forepart of white under-surface of wing, well out beyond wrist joint. Black phase appears almost wholly black, with under surface of wings largely white. *Immature and juvenal (most commonly seen):* Similar to ordinary light phase, but has a wide blackish belt across abdomen.

VOICE. — Common note imitated by the Eskimo name of the bird "*Kin-wi-yuk.*" Its loud screams have given it the name of "Squalling Hawk" among the people of Labrador.

BREEDING. — Chiefly on rugged sea-coast or high banks of rivers and lakes. *Nest:* Large, 2½ to 3 feet across. On ledge of rock, top of cliff, on high ground overlooking water or in tree. Those on trees built not far from top, composed of sticks and roots, well lined with dry grass, feathers and down. *Eggs:* 2 to 5; 2.00 to 2.43 by 1.63 to 1.90 in.; very variable in size and shape; often short oval; white, greenish-white, buffy-white or pale buffy, spotted and blotched more or less with various browns, from light yellowish-brown to very dark brown and drab or purple and lavender; some eggs slightly marked, but none entirely unspotted; illustrated in Bendire's "Life Histories of North American Birds," Vol. I, Plate VIII, Figs. 10 to 12. *Dates:* May 23, northern Ungava, to June 20, northern Mackenzie. *Incubation:* Period about four weeks (Bendire). One brood yearly.

RANGE. — North America, north of Mexico. Breeds chiefly in Hudsonian Zone from Aleutian Islands, northwestern Alaska, Arctic coast, Ungava (northern Quebec), and northeastern Labrador south to central British Columbia, northern Alberta, the lower St. Lawrence valley, north shore of the Gulf of St. Lawrence and Newfoundland;[1] south in winter from southern British Columbia; northern United States and southern Ontario to southern California, Texas, Oklahoma, Louisiana, and North Carolina; accidental on St. George, one of the Pribilof Islands.

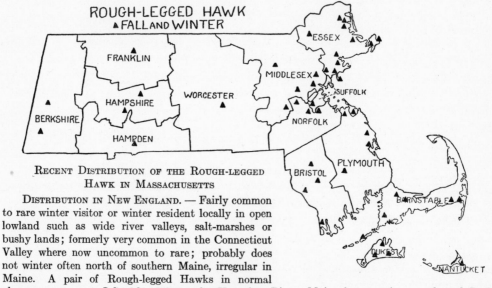

RECENT DISTRIBUTION OF THE ROUGH-LEGGED HAWK IN MASSACHUSETTS

DISTRIBUTION IN NEW ENGLAND. — Fairly common to rare winter visitor or winter resident locally in open lowland such as wide river valleys, salt-marshes or bushy lands; formerly very common in the Connecticut Valley where now uncommon to rare; probably does not winter often north of southern Maine, irregular in Maine. A pair of Rough-legged Hawks in normal plumage were seen July 2d, 1909, on the Kennebec River, Maine, between its mouth and Bath.[2]

SEASON IN MASSACHUSETTS. — October 25 to April 24 (May 8 and 14).

HAUNTS AND HABITS. The Rough-legged Hawk formerly was a common migrant and winter resident in suitable localities in southern New England. It was especially common in open meadows and (formerly) bushy plains along the Connecticut Valley, but hundreds were shot year after year by sportsmen and farmers, and for the last thirty years it has been growing rare there.

---

[1] One record of breeding in southeastern South Dakota. (G. S. Agersborg, Auk, Vol. II, 1885, p. 285.)

[2] Maynard, C. J.: Records of Walks and Talks with Nature, Vol. II, 1909, p. 116.

It was very common many years ago on the bushy lands and marshes about Boston. Some fine dark birds in the black phase were secured in those days. Mr. W. G. Smith, an old experienced gunner of Quincy, Massachusetts, used to shoot "Rough-legs" from a buggy. He drove his horse within range as the hawk sat in a tree.[1] This hawk is common still in many winters on the bushy plains of Marthas Vineyard, less so on similar regions on Cape Cod and in parts of the coastal plain of southern Connecticut. When cold weather comes in the Hudsonian Zone with its accompaniment of deep snow and thick ice, a vast army of Rough-legged Hawks moves southward toward the United States. When starting on migration they soar to a great height and then set their course. Probably they travel at such high altitudes that they are seldom noticed in migration, but by November they are distributed over their usual haunts in southern New England. They seem to be able to see well in the gathering dusk, as they hunt very early in the morning and after sunset when mice are active. As they fly low when hunting, and often over lowlands, such as meadows or marshes, it is not difficult to make out the location of the white patch on the upper part of the long tail.

There is a district in southeastern Massachusetts extending from the "great woods" of Plymouth and Carver southeasterly through Bourne and into Falmouth where fire has swept over the land so often that most of the soil has been burned away. Large tracts of this region are now covered chiefly with low chinquapin and shrub oaks, small shrubbery and bearberry interspersed with small pitch pines. The region is largely deserted by mankind except about the cranberry bogs in the swales, and in winter there is little human life even there. This country has been in times past a favorite winter resort for Rough-legged Hawks. To-day they seem to be more common on the bushy plains of the interior of Marthas Vineyard than anywhere else in Massachusetts. There from autumn until spring they may be seen slowly flapping along not far above the ground or sitting erect on the tops of small trees or posts watching for their favorite prey. Occasionally one soars to considerable heights with motionless wings and tail fully spread. My friend, Dr. C. W. Townsend, well describes the flight of this hawk as follows:

"The flight of the Rough-legged Hawk is graceful and indicative of skill and power. In soaring, the wings and tail are spread to their full extent; the first half-dozen primaries are spread out separately like fingers and curve upward at their tips. On motionless wings, if the wind be favorable, this bird may often be seen soaring high up over the land. In April and May, I have several times seen two of them, probably a pair, rising up higher and higher as they circled, and, arrived at a considerable elevation, striking out in flight for the northeast.

"When soaring they may be seen looking down, and I have several times seen them partially close their wings, lower their long feathered tarsi and drop like a plummet. On one occasion the bird secured a large mouse with which it flew to the marsh and perched on an ice cake. On another occasion a fine Rough-leg pounced successfully on a cotton-tail rabbit and bore it off.

---

[1] Smith, J. D.: *in litt.*

"In searching the ground for game of this sort they often fly slowly, alternately flapping and sailing, from fifty to a hundred yards up in the air. Occasionally they hang over one place by hovering, and often drop their legs preparatory to pouncing on the prey and draw them up behind when they change their minds. If the wind be favorable, they hang suspended in the air as motionless as a kite. The wind needed for this is an up-current over the brow of a steep hill or cliff. In this case gravitation acts like the kite-string, and by skilful disposition of the plane of the wings to the up-current, the bird remains motionless if the wind is steady. When the wind is irregular and flawy, the bird swings about more or less, just as a kite acts under similar circumstances. When the wind drops for a moment the bird hovers." [1]

It is now a well known fact that the food of the Rough-legged Hawk in the United States consists chiefly of field mice, while on its breeding ground its principal prey is the lemming. There are a few reports to the effect that this species has killed wounded ducks and I have seen a statement that remains of the western Meadowlark have been found in its stomach. There is one record of a specimen taken in November while flying from a hen-yard with a full grown fowl in its talons.[2] On the other hand it has been known to eat dead birds and mammals and even carrion — a harmless habit. Of forty-nine stomachs examined by Dr. A. K. Fisher, 40 held mice; 5, other mammals; 1, lizards; 1, insects and 4 were empty.

ECONOMIC STATUS. Probably the Rough-legged Hawk, viewed from the stand-point of the farmer, is one of the most useful birds in the country. Nevertheless it has been slain in large numbers by both farmers and sportsmen, either because it is large and slow, making a good target, or because they believe it to be harmful. I have concealed myself with loaded gun watching for hawks that had taken my poultry and have seen the " Rough-leg " circling overhead but paying no attention to the alarmed flock. Mr. E. O. Damon of Northampton, Massachusetts, who has shot hundreds of " Rough-legs " in the Connecticut Valley, says that he never found anything but mice in all the stomachs that he has examined. Field mice, if allowed to increase unduly, become very destructive pests. When numerous they attack many kinds of vegetation and even destroy the eggs of game birds.

Áquila chrysáëtos (LINNÆUS). Golden Eagle.

Plates 38 and 41.

DESCRIPTION. — Large, robust and powerful; feathers of head and neck loose and lanceolate; wings long, pointed, outer five primaries deeply emarginate on inner web; tail of medium length, rounded; tarsi *feathered all around down to toes;* basal web between middle and outer toes. *Adults (sexes alike or similar)* : Nearly uniform dark brown, with a purplish gloss, except where worn, faded feathers show; feathers of nape, hind neck (sometimes top of head) and tarsus tawny-yellowish or tawny-buff, sometimes much paler; flight-feathers nearly black, and tail often with a few irregular, obsolete lighter brown bars

---

[1] Townsend, C. W.: Supplement to The Birds of Essex County, Massachusetts, 1920, pp. 104–105.
[2] Wilson Bulletin, Vol. XIV, 1907, p. 27.

PLATE 41

PLATE 41

GOLDEN EAGLE
Page 144

BALD EAGLE
Page 150

ADULT

ADULT

IMMATURE

ROUGH–LEGGED HAWK
Page 141

IMMATURE
NORMAL OR LIGHT PHASE

DARK PHASE

All about one-sixth scale.

becoming ashy on two middle feathers; female sometimes has more or less light tawny on legs and under tail-coverts; extreme tip of tail sometimes pale or whitish; bill bluish-horn, or blackish; iris, dark brown; cere, edges of mouth and feet yellow or greenish-yellow; claws bluish-horn or blackish. *Juvenal and immature plumages:* Juvenal birds much darker (almost black) below than adults, with much of upper tail white; older immature birds similar to adults, but half or more of tail from base toward tip white, and often some white about bases of flight feathers and some upper tail-coverts; bill brownish-black to blue-black or bluish-horn; iris brown or hazel; feet like adults'. *Downy young:* Usually covered at first with short, white down with grayish tips; the later and longer down is whiter or more creamy white.

MEASUREMENTS. — *Male:* Length 30.00 to 35.00 in.; spread 75.00 to 84.00; folded wing 20.50 to 24.70; tail 12.00 to 15.00; bill, without cere, 1.40 to 1.55; tarsus 3.40 to 4.00. *Female:* Length 35.00 to 41.00; spread 82.00 to 92.00; folded wing 24.87 to 27.50; tail 13.75 to 16.00; bill 1.40 to 1.85; tarsus 3.50 to 4.30. Weight 7 lbs. to 14 lbs. 12 oz. Female larger than male.

MOLTS. — Juvenal plumage succeeds natal down, and is worn until molt into second-year plumage, which is not completed until the bird is from a year to 18 months old; this molt is complete, after which there is a complete molt yearly; white at base of wing feathers and base of tail varies until at the age of 4½ or 5 years bird apparently becomes as adult. Adults have one complete molt yearly, very gradual, and distributed through a great part of the year, at least from March to October.

FIELD MARKS. — Size of Bald Eagle or larger; difficult to distinguish at a distance from immature of latter; in flight seems like a big *Buteo*, circling upward often to great heights; has similar but longer wings with wide-spread primaries curving upward at tips; wings not uptilted in soaring like those of Turkey Vulture; usually shows whitish area on under side of each wing toward end. *Adults:* Chocolate to tawny with yellowish or golden-brown on back of head. *Immature (comprising about 95% of birds seen):* Often almost black or very dark brown, upper part of tail white or grayish-white, with very broad, dark brown band at end; head as adult.

VOICE. — A single loud sharp cry; occasionally a barking note, also a yelping cry (F. C. R. Jourdain). "The usual call note is a shrill *keé, keē, keé* uttered in a high tone. . . . alarm note *kiah-kiah*, repeated a number of times" (Bendire); *kich kich kee* (O. W. Knight)"; "a penetrating scream"; "short rattling screams," when fighting. (J. B. Dixon.)

BREEDING. — Usually in a mountainous country, on inaccessible crags, steep bluffs or the high banks of streams, rarely in forests, except on Pacific coast where forests seem to have the preference and where it nests high up in trees. *Nest:* On a shelf of rock or earth, on crag, cliff or bluff, or high bank of lake or stream; sometimes in tall tree on mountain side, but sometimes relatively low in tree in rather open country; a huge structure, a pile of sticks, etc., sometimes very well lined, often 3½ to 7 feet across and three to five feet high; if used for many years, becomes moist and in part decayed; has (like various birds of prey) two or more nesting sites. *Eggs:* 1 to 4, usually 2 or 3; 2.35 to 3.50 by 1.96 to 2.68 in.; short ovate; dirty white or whitish, rarely unspotted; usually marked very variably with shades of brown and claret; illustrated in Bendire's "Life Histories of North American Birds," Vol. I, Plate IX, Figs. 3 and 5. *Dates:* Last of February and into April, South California. *Incubation:* Period about one month (W. L. Finley); 27 days (Irene G. Wheelock). One brood yearly.

RANGE. — Northern part of Northern Hemisphere, south in the Old World to North Africa and the Himalaya Mountains. In America breeds from Alaska, northwestern Mackenzie and Ungava (northern Quebec) south to central Mexico, western Texas, Ontario and North Carolina; south in winter to Louisiana, Alabama and Florida (rarely southern Texas); breeds normally chiefly in mountainous parts of its range, but probably not now in United States east of the Mississippi, except possibly in Maine, eastern Tennessee and western North Carolina.

NOTE. Three Old World races have been recognized, and some authorities distinguish the American bird as A. c. canadensis.

DISTRIBUTION IN NEW ENGLAND. — Very rare visitor, chiefly in migration, but may appear at any season; formerly bred in mountainous regions of Maine, New Hampshire (White Mountains), Vermont and western Massachusetts.

SEASON IN MASSACHUSETTS. — May appear at any time but usually in autumn and winter.

HAUNTS AND HABITS.   Since man came up from barbarism the stately Golden Eagle has been considered the noblest of birds.   He it is that typifies royalty among the feathered tribes, and has caused the eagle to be named the king of birds.   In the olden days when falconry flourished in Europe the Golden Eagle was flown by kings.   He was the pet of royalty, and was looked upon as a bird of great distinction.   Comparing him with our national bird, the Bald Eagle, we find that he seems built of finer clay.   His beak is not so large and coarse as that of the White-headed Eagle; his feet are smaller, though the talons are very long, keen and powerful; his form seems to be more compact.   In the air he makes even a finer figure than the Bald Eagle; he soars grandly in wide circles, wheeling above the clouds, and his hunting is like that of the "noble" falcons.   He hunts chiefly mammals and birds which he captures by open approach, speed and skill.   At obscure heights he hangs suspended until an opportunity comes, when he closes his wings and shoots down upon his victim like an arrow from the bow, coming so swiftly as to take his prey by surprise, and striking it dead in an instant, while the Bald Eagle lives largely on dead fish and carrion or by robbing the Osprey.   The Golden Eagle builds her nest usually in the wild and savage wilderness and in its sublimest solitudes on giant mountain crags while the Bald Eagle builds her nest chiefly in trees in low country along the coast or near the larger streams or bodies of water where she can find her chief food.   From his aery the Golden Eagle soars to vast heights from which he can survey great regions.   As the poet says —

> "He clasps the crag with hooked hands,
> Close to the sun in lonely lands."

The "tumbling" in the air by the Golden Eagle is a remarkable performance common to both sexes in the breeding season and may be repeated again and again.[1]

Mr. F. C. Willard describes as follows the behavior of this bird in pursuit of its prey:

"Fast as the Bandtailed Pigeon (*Columba fasciata*) is, I have seen it flying its fastest to get away from a pursuing eagle.   While seated near the summit of the Huachucas watching some warblers, a sudden rush and roar of wings startled me and close by, on a level with my eye shot a Bandtailed Pigeon.   Its short, quick wing-beats fairly made it sizzle as it dodged along close to the ground, under and among the towering pines.   Almost within reach, followed a huge eagle, its motionless wings almost closed.   In spite of its great size it followed accurately the track of the fleeing pigeon, its swiftly moving bulk as it rocked from side to side, making a roar like an express train.   I am happy to say that a few seconds later a thick clump of fir trees enabled the pigeon to dodge its pursuer and it dashed down the mountain side into the safety of the deep canon below.

---

[1] Auk, Vol. XXV, 1908, p. 252; Bird-Lore, Vol. II, 1909, p. 252; and Oölogist, Vol. XXXIII, 1916, p. 6.

"Most of the eagle's hunting takes place on the treeless plains at the foot of the mountains. Here a scanty growth of bushes offers little cover to its principal quarry, the jack rabbit. In company with some friends one day, I watched a pair of these eagles hunting jack rabbits. They swooped down and drove the rabbit to cover under a mesquite bush. Then one alighted close by and began to walk toward the rabbit. He was so frightened he dashed from his shelter only to be snatched up by the other eagle which had been hovering close overhead." [1]

A study of ornithological literature and some attention to the traditions of the people furnish convincing evidence that the Golden Eagle formerly bred in the mountainous regions of New England, from which it has been extirpated by gun, trap and poison; so that now it is seen here only casually, unless possibly a few may breed even now on some of the more remote mountains of Maine. However, it never was common here, as few New England mountains are vast and lofty enough to suit its temperament. Heavily feathered to the very toes, it can endure the extreme cold of high latitudes and great altitudes; but when food becomes scarce it wanders far in search of it, and so reaches New England mainly in winter during a dearth of food in the north. Its migrations are, therefore, mostly wide wanderings in search of food.

Although I have handled a large number of specimens I have seen but one that was fully adult, as all the others had more or less white at the base of the tail. Evidently the old birds have learned to take good care of themselves and so seldom reach the museums. As a species it is wild, and difficult to approach, although on a western ranch the bird will become so used to droves and the attendant riders that it will take little notice of a horseman. Although a fearless bird the Golden Eagle has learned to beware of mankind. Any person may disturb its nest, if he can reach it, without the slightest fear of an attack from the birds. On all such occasions they keep far away in the upper air and manifest little if any concern.

The old tales of eagles carrying off children probably have little foundation in fact, but I have investigated one instance of an attack by an eagle on a child which seems to be authentic. I received a report from Mr. M. Semper, Mapes P. O. British Columbia, who saw the attack. Mr. Semper writes that he was at a neighbor's house sharpening a "mower sickle" when the neighbor's little girl, Ellen Gibbs, nine years of age, came running toward the house crying "mamma, there's a big chicken hawk." At that moment, said Mr. Semper, the bird sailed directly over his head in pursuit of the child. He dropped his "sickle," but before he could reach her the bird had sunk its claws into her arm. He kicked the eagle, partially disabling it, when the child's mother rushed up with an ax and decapitated it. The child's arm was much discolored and cut by the grip of the bird. It was a Golden Eagle.

Oberholser says that this species probably seldom, if ever, carries a weight of more than 10 or at the most 12 lbs. Cameron limits this weight to 8 lbs. at the very most.

---

[1] Oölogist, Vol. XXXIII, 1916, pp. 6–8.

Nelson tells of a pair of Golden Eagles disturbed by a friend of his while they were eating a hog. This man shot one almost at the muzzle of his gun, but the other continued the attack until disabled.[1] Such instances as these must be very unusual.

The food of the Golden Eagle consists chiefly of birds and small mammals. It does not hesitate to attack animals much heavier than itself. Wild turkeys, geese and other waterfowl, herons, small fawns (rarely good-sized deer), grouse, rabbits, squirrels, racoons, skunks, prairie dogs, marmots, young pigs, cats and foxes are destroyed by the powerful bird.[*] Sometimes the bird catches a Tartar as in the case of the porcupine.[2] When urged by hunger it has been known to kill young lambs, kids, calves, and poultry, but it feeds its young largely on wood rats, squirrels and mice. It is a cleanly bird, plucking or skinning its prey before eating, and keeps its plumage in excellent condition by bathing and preening, which, by the way, is customary with most birds of prey.

ECONOMIC STATUS. As a check on the multiplication of small rodents, the Golden Eagle is a valuable bird, but in a country where sheep are raised, it may do considerable damage to the flocks.

Haliæetus albicilla (LINNÆUS). Gray Sea Eagle.

Other name: WHITE-TAILED SEA EAGLE.

DESCRIPTION. — Tarsus not feathered to toes. *Adults (sexes alike)*: Much like Bald Eagle, *but head and neck usually light grayish-brown or brownish-gray* (some much darker), with pale or whitish tips (not abruptly lighter than body), and tail coverts not white, as in Bald Eagle, but dusky grayish-brown with paler feather edges like rest of body plumage; tail white; bill and feet yellow. *"Young:* Prevailing color above light umber-brown, cinnamon-brown or isabella-color, each feather with a median streak and terminal spot of blackish-brown; breast broadly striped with brownish-black on a brownish-white and isabella-colored ground; rest of lower parts nearly plain dull isabella-brown, each feather with a median streak and terminal spot of blackish, and thighs darker and more uniform" (Robert Ridgway); bill and cere black or blackish; iris dark brown. *Downy young:* Varying from gray to buffy, with some tufts of whitish down here and there; later a coarser, longer down, lighter in color above than below.

GRAY OR WHITE-TAILED SEA EAGLE.

MEASUREMENTS. — *Male:* Length 31.00 to 35.00 in.; folded wing 23.00 to 26.00; tail 11.50 to 12.00; bill, without cere, 2.00 to 2.20; tarsus 3.30 to 3.80. *Female:* Length 35.00 to 40.00 in.; folded wing 27.50 to 28.00; tail 14.00 to 16.00; bill 2.25 to 2.45; tarsus 3.50 to 3.65.

---

[1] Nelson, E. W.: Report upon Natural History Collections made in Alaska, 1887, p. 144.
[*] For vivid story of destruction of a fox see Journal Maine Ornithological Society, Vol. V, 1903, p. 41.
[2] Auk, Vol. XXXIX, 1922, p. 258.

FIELD MARKS. — Size of Bald Eagle. *Adult:* Resembles Bald Eagle, but *head gray, never white like tail. Young: Tail not white.* Resembles young Bald Eagle but ground-color much lighter, spotted blackish above and striped blackish below.

VOICE. — No details.

BREEDING. — Along sea-shore. *Nest:* On sea cliffs or cliffs near sea-shore or an island in some large lake; rarely in tall tree, casually on open level ground. *Eggs:* 1 or 2, rarely 3; about 2.25 to 3.10 by 2.13 to 2.30 in.; ovate to rounded ovate; dead white, often stained yellowish, indistinguishable from those of Bald Eagle, but averaging larger. *Dates:* First week of March to middle of April, Scotland (Seebohm). *Incubation:* By both sexes. One brood yearly.

RANGE. — Northern part of Eastern Hemisphere, breeding from Scotland (formerly), northern Europe and northern Asia to Spitzbergen and Novaya Zemlya; in migration south to Japan, China, northern India, southern Europe and northern Africa; resident in Iceland and southeastern Greenland; recorded from Cumberland Sound; casual on Aleutian Islands; accidental off the coast of Massachusetts.

DISTRIBUTION IN NEW ENGLAND. — One record: An immature bird taken alive November 14, 1914, near Nantucket lightship and recorded by L. S. Crandall.[1]

HAUNTS AND HABITS. The Gray or White-tailed Sea Eagle is a fine bird, having great powers of flight. Its appearance in New England is purely fortuitous. Its first arrival in the United States, so far as we are aware, was in the instance given above. It may never have landed on the soil of Massachusetts; but if so, probably it would have reached Nantucket, if the Dutch Steamer Arundo had not come along past Nantucket Light at an opportune moment to furnish a resting place for the weary bird, which was captured alive by the captain and taken to the New York Zoölogical Park. I have never seen the species alive, but in view of the fact that it has now been taken near our coast and as it breeds in Greenland and may appear here again, and for the further reason that it may easily be mistaken for an immature Bald Eagle and therefore may have been overlooked, before, and may be again, I have included its description in this volume. Where this lone and weary voyager came from, whether from Greenland, Iceland, or some of the coasts of continental Europe, we never shall know, but very probably it crossed the water from some one of these regions. Seebohm writes as follows of this bird:

"The haunts of this noble-looking bird are the brown hills of the Hebrides and the adjacent isles, and the wild mountain-country of the mainland in the West. On the bold and rocky headlands of this wild, rugged coast, whose hoary peaks are washed by the treacherous waters of the Minch, the Sea-Eagle finds a congenial home. The scenery of Skye is typical of this eagle's favorite haunt. On that bleak and desolate isle it occurs in probably larger numbers than in any other place in Great Britain. . . .

"In Pomerania, especially between Stettin and the Baltic, the Sea-Eagle is a common resident, breeding in the forests. It builds an enormous nest, sometimes six to eight feet in diameter, near the top of a pine or on the horizontal branch of an oak or beech, preferring forests near inland seas and large lakes. Instances have been known of its breeding in the same 'Horst' for twenty years in succession. Every year some addition is made to the nest, until it becomes five or six feet high. Occasionally a pair of Sea-

---

[1] Auk, Vol. XXXII, 1915, p. 368.

Eagles have two 'Horsts,' which are used alternately.   They are shy birds and leave the nest at the least alarm, but do not easily forsake their old home.   If the eggs are taken early in the season they will frequently lay again in the same nest." [1]

Haliæetus leucocéphalus leucocephalus (Linnæus).   Bald Eagle.

Other names: BALD-HEADED EAGLE; WHITE-HEADED EAGLE; GRAY EAGLE (YOUNG).

Plates 37, 38 and 41.

DESCRIPTION. — Rather smaller than Golden Eagle, but bill longer and more powerful; five outer primaries deeply emarginate on inner webs; tarsus feathered only to within an inch or more of base of toes; no web between outer and middle toes.   *Adults (sexes alike):* Head, neck, upper tail-coverts and tail pure white; rest of plumage dusky grayish-brown, varying to blackish, often with faded, worn feathers, especially in wings, and sometimes with many pale feather-edges; primaries blackish; bill, cere and feet corn yellow; iris pale yellow, cream or grayish-white, in one specimen clear vermilion.   *Immature:* Very variable, but generally mixed grayish-brown and blackish, often intermixed with white or whitish areas, patches or spots on back, abdomen, head, wings or tail; in second winter, much lighter with much white or whitish showing above and below, very variable in second and third years, later, pure white appears on head and tail.   *Juvenal plumage:* Chiefly dark brown or blackish, but feathers of lower plumage with white bases more or less exposed, resulting in a blotched appearance of breast and abdomen; bill and cere black or blackish; iris brown or dark brown.   *Downy young:* Whitish or light straw at first, later sooty gray.

MEASUREMENTS. — *Male:* Length 30.00 to 34.00 in.; spread 72.00 to 85.00; folded wing 20.00 to 23.50; tail 11.00 to 12.00; bill, without cere, 1.75 to 2.50; tarsus 2.65 to 3.40.   *Female:* Length 35.00 to 37.00; spread 79.00 to 90.00; folded wing 22.00 to 26.00; tail 11.60 to 12.75; bill 1.75 to 2.45; tarsus 3.50 to 3.65; Female larger than male.   Weight $7\frac{1}{4}$ to $11\frac{1}{2}$ lbs.   Immature birds often larger than adults.

MOLTS. — Young apparently retain juvenal plumage through first winter, and afterward have one complete molt annually, molting very slowly and partially until plumage is complete.   Molting birds are found in spring, summer and autumn and apparently even in winter; for the first two years, plumage remains quite dark, in third year white appears in variable quantities on breast, back and wings, often so mixed with ground color as to give bird a gray appearance; young appear to come to full maturity when from 3 to 4 years of age; Dr. Wm. T. Hornaday, whose opportunities for studying this eagle in captivity have been unexcelled, says that it does not acquire white head and tail until 4th year.[2]   Mr. Lee S. Crandall of the New York Zoölogical Society tells me that when a bird is three years old and in 4th year at 4th autumnal molt, white head and tail are assumed.   Some birds may require another year to eliminate all the dark feathers on head and tail.   Audubon gives instances where birds in captivity came into full plumage when 5 and 6 years old.   Adults molt completely once each year, by sections, the molt requiring a long period.

FIELD MARKS. — Size in flight apparently about that of Great Blue Heron; flies ordinarily over or near water at no great height, flapping heavily, or soars like Red-tailed Hawk with tail partly spread, swinging in wide circles with some intermittent flapping.   *Adult:* Unmistakable; a dusky brown bird with pure white head, neck and tail (adult Black-backed Gull has white head and tail, but also white breast).   *Immature:* Very dark with little or no white on head and usually little if any elsewhere; some show some small light or whitish patches or blotches below, above, or on upper tail; difficult to distinguish in field from Golden Eagle.   *Juvenal:* Darker than older birds, but usually more or less blotched and streaked below with blackish and whitish.

---

[1] Seebohm, Henry: A History of British Birds with Colored Illustrations of Their Eggs, Vol. I, 1883, pp. 88 and 90.
[2] Hornaday, Wm. T.: The American Natural History, 1904, p. 228.

VOICE. — A high-pitched, cackling scream. *Male:* A loud, clear "*cac-cac-cac*," quite different from that of female; call of latter more harsh and often broken (W. L. Ralph); *Young:* A low whistling cry.

BREEDING. — Generally in forested regions near sea, large streams or large bodies of water. *Nest:* Usually very high in top of large tree, rarely on mountain cliffs or ground (on an island); composed of sticks chiefly, flat-topped; used year after year, repaired and built up until very large, 5 to 8 feet across and often as high or higher. *Eggs:* 1 to 4, usually 2; 2.75 to 3.00 by 2.16 to 2.50 in.; rounded ovate to ovate, white but usually stained yellowish; illustrated in Bendire's "Life Histories of North American Birds," Vol. I, Plate IX, Fig. 7. *Dates:* From November 1, Florida, to February 11, Pennsylvania, and April 4 to 21, Maine. *Incubation:* Period (reported) 28 to 42 days (various authorities). One brood yearly.

RANGE. — Temperate and subtropical North America, chiefly in United States, south to southern Lower California, central Mexico and southern Florida. Breeds throughout most of its range; once taken in Sweden — the only authentic occurrence in Europe.

DISTRIBUTION IN NEW ENGLAND. — *Maine:* Uncommon resident and migrant; winters chiefly coastwise. *New Hampshire:* Uncommon visitor and rather rare summer resident, chiefly in northern part; rare in winter coastwise. *Vermont:* Occasional summer resident about Lake Champlain and probably other lakes. *Massachusetts:* Formerly resident, but not known to breed now; * uncommon visitor; except on or near Cape Cod where more common, chiefly coastwise at all seasons. *Rhode Island:* Occasional at all seasons; not known to breed. *Connecticut:* Occasional at all seasons; bred formerly but not now known to breed.

SEASON IN MASSACHUSETTS. — Most common locally in spring but recorded in every month.

HAUNTS AND HABITS. I well recall the day when, as an impressionable lad, I first saw the Bald Eagle wheeling majestically up the sky until it rose to a height almost beyond the utmost compass of my straining vision, and there — a mere speck in the blue — it sailed away until it vanished in the vast spaces of the upper air. The great bird had been fishing about Podunk Pond in West Brookfield and, startled at the sound of my gun, had passed away from that mundane scene apparently as lightly as a drifting cloud. Since then I have seen many eagles on the shores of the Atlantic and Pacific oceans and witnessed many of their aerial evolutions, but never since have I experienced the feeling of awe with which I watched this living embodiment of the emblem of American freedom ascending grandly into the autumnal sky. My emotions on that occasion were somewhat similar to those experienced when I first viewed in the near distance the great dome of the capitol at Washington, for around both bird and building cluster many memories and traditions of a great country and a mighty people. Our eagle may deserve some of the epithets that have been heaped upon him; he may be a robber, a skulker and a carrion feeder; nevertheless he is a powerful and noble bird and a master of the air.

I know of no authentic record of an attempt by this eagle to carry away an infant, except possibly that given by Alexander Wilson, which many regard as a fact. In that case the eagle is said to have grasped at the child which was sitting on the ground near its mother, but the claws of the bird penetrated only the cloth of the child's frock which gave way, and a part of it only was carried off by the eagle.

The Bald Eagle is a brave bird, but tales of its attacks on human beings must be received with caution. An adult eagle usually has had enough sad experiences with man-

---

* Dr. J. A. Allen, said in 1864: "Sometimes breeds on Mt. Tom."

kind to teach it circumspection.   Sometimes immature birds seem to be full of curiosity regarding man and his ways, but attempts on the part of an eagle even to approach human habitations are likely to be promptly met with a charge of shot or a rifle ball, and the birds that escape with their lives soon become very shy.   In the final quarter of the last century eagles were very common breeders along Indian River and the Banana River, Florida. A young man formerly in my employ collected more than 90 sets of their eggs in that region, but no eagle ever attacked him, although now and then one may have threatened an assault.   Like the Golden Eagle the Bald Eagle almost always rises high in the air when disturbed at its nest.

I have known of but one instance where this species has attacked a man.   A farmer once brought me an eagle which had killed a full-grown cock in the hen-yard.   Hearing a commotion among the fowls the farmer looked out and saw a great bird among them. He seized a stick from the woodpile and ran to defend his poultry.   As he came up, the eagle, according to his account, left its prey, flew at him and was met with a heavy blow from the stick which stretched it helpless on the ground.   I dissected the bird which evidently had been disabled by a blow on the head.

The Bald Eagle is by nature a fish eater, and fish form his principal food.   He takes them alive or dead and when opportunity offers he seizes those already caught by the Osprey.   When some mortality occurs among fish, causing them to die by thousands, eagles often assemble in numbers to the feast.

The keen eye of the eagle is proverbial.   Eaton tells us in his " Birds of New York " how, as he watched an eagle soaring at a great height over a lake, the bird started diagonally downward in a dive toward a floating fish which it picked up three miles from the spot over which the bird had been soaring, and brought it ashore.   The bird was so far away from the observer when it picked up the fish that he could not see it in the bird's talons with a six-power glass.

Afar in the sky or on a branch of some tall tree near the water the eagle's eye follows the fishing Osprey and marks every plunge.   When the Osprey rises with a fish the eagle shows his speed and power.   With flashing eye and quickening wing, he speeds toward the laboring Fish-hawk, which exerts itself to the utmost to escape, but usually in vain. A strong, swift Osprey with a small fish sometimes escapes, but a heavy fish is too great a handicap.   Reaching the Osprey, the speeding eagle passes under his victim ; the Osprey, turning and twisting in the air, rises to escape, but the eagle having driven the lesser bird high enough for his purpose, threatens it with beak and claws.   Striking at the Fish-hawk, and sometimes almost enveloping the poor bird with his great beating wings, he drives it here and there, trying to frighten it so that it will drop the fish.   Usually intimidation accomplishes his object, but if not, the eagle strikes the Osprey with force enough to send it reeling through the air.   At last it relaxes its hold on its prey.   As the fish falls, the eagle with a few swift strokes catches it with one foot, or if the Osprey has dropped it at a moment when the eagle is not in a position to snatch it immediately, he poises an instant, then shooting downward with partly closed and hissing pinions, he overtakes his booty in its rapid descent and bears it away to a dead branch of some tall tree to eat it at his leisure. At least this is the picture drawn by those who claim to have seen the action.

I have never seen the eagle actually seize the fish in its fall. In my experience the great bird is quite likely to allow the fish to drop. Twice I have seen one shoot down from a far height with breath-taking speed only to check his flight near the surface with vibrating wings and wide-spread tail, while the fish just below him disappeared with a splash in the water. At any rate the eagle does not depend on the Osprey, but watches for dead fish, and if he finds none, and no Osprey is at hand, he catches them himself or pursues some other quarry. His usual method is to flap or soar at no great height above the water, occasionally hovering; and at the proper moment he glides diagonally downward with set wings, grasps the fish without plunging under water and carries it to the shore; or he sits perched on some tall tree near the water and when a good opportunity presents itself, sails down on set wings and picks up his victim. He is said to plunge straight down at times, but I have never seen an eagle in the act. Rarely he strikes a fish too large to raise from the surface but he holds to it tenaciously as long as possible until eventually he either tows it ashore or is himself dragged under water and forced to relinquish his hold and come to the surface for air. I have not known of the drowning of an eagle by a large fish — an accident which now and then occurs to an Osprey.

An eagle having caught its fish is rarely molested by its fellows, but once I watched a battle between an immense immature eagle and an old "white-head," much of which took place in the air above me. The larger and younger bird had a fish which the "white-head" apparently had marked for its own. Their evolutions in the air were wonderful to witness. They whirled over and over, striking and clawing, but in the end the younger bird retained the fish.

The history of the Bald Eagle in New England is that of all our larger birds. Formerly breeding commonly in the primeval forest, the species has been greatly reduced in numbers, and in southern New England the breeding birds have been extirpated. Probably from fifty to one hundred pairs of Bald Eagles still nest and rear their young in the forests of Maine and along its coast. But in the Kennebec Valley the nests are much less numerous than they were years ago. A few pairs nest in New Hampshire from about the region of Lake Winnepesaukee northward, and a pair or more may still breed in the region about Lake Champlain. Elsewhere we do not know of an actual breeding location in New England. There are records to the effect that the species formerly nested on Mt. Tom, in the Connecticut Valley, in northern Massachusetts and on Cape Cod; also in the mountains of western Connecticut. The region in southern Massachusetts which now harbors more eagles than any other tract of similar size lies in the townships of Carver, Wareham, Plymouth, Bourne, Falmouth and Mashpee. Dr. L. C. Jones, who lives in Falmouth, tells me that seeing a fox seize one of his hens, he left the house with his rifle in pursuit of the marauder. The culprit took to its heels, dropping the hen, and did not return. The next day a Bald Eagle circled the pond near which the carcass of the hen lay, alighted in a tree, sat there for about ten minutes, then sailed down to the ground and walked over to the remains, which he devoured.   On July 14, 1924, one of the doctor's neighbors heard, early in the morning, a scratching noise on the roof of his house. Thinking it might be caused by a cat or a squirrel he did not rise to investigate.   The next day he heard it again and, becoming curious, went outdoors.   What was his surprise to see a white-headed, white-tailed eagle walking about on the ridgepole and apparently enjoying the scenery.

From Halfway Pond, the source of the Agawam River, to Popponesset on Cape Cod, the eagles follow the alewives when they begin in April to run up the streams.   An old resident of Wareham told me that in his early days he had seen as many as 30 eagles in one day following up the Agawam River.   At my farm at Wareham on the banks of the Agawam there was in 1900 a tall dead pine that we called the "eagle tree," on which eagles often perched while scanning the river for alewives.   A few years later the tree fell, and after that the great birds used another about half a mile up the river which has now gone the way of all trees.   I have often approached quite near a young eagle perched in one or the other of these trees.   There are eagles about many of the lakes of Cape Cod. I have seen two or three at a time about a pond in Hatchville and six at one time about a small pond between Waquoit Bay and Popponesset.   This is now a wild country, which has been largely left to the deer, wild-fowl, herons, hawks, owls, and eagles, but the eagles are slowly decreasing, and the country along this coast eventually will be cut up into building lots for summer cottages.   It is only a question of time when the eagles will disappear unless a wild life reservation can be established in this region.

An eagle, if taken young enough often makes a fine pet, with its capers, pranks, and dignified poses, and an occasional outburst of anger.   There have been some famous pet eagles, from "Old Abe" of Civil War days to "A Prince of the House of Eagles." [1]

The late Ex-Mayor C. B. Pratt of Worcester, Massachusetts, whose fondness for pets of all sorts was notorious, kept in a large flying cage a Bald Eagle which was said to have been taken from a nest on Lake Washacum in Sterling, Worcester County, in the days when that region was heavily and extensively wooded.   More or less meat, food for the eagle, lay about on the ground under the eagle's tree.   This often attracted stray cats. The eagle had a peculiar method of killing the cats.   When it noted one of the beasts within its wire enclosure it descended by stealthy hops from branch to branch of its leafless tree.   Finally it dropped, with a heavy "flop" on the cat's back, seizing the animal by the spine and the neck with its great claws in such a way that the victim was immediately disabled and soon killed.

Mr. F. B. Currier who has spent some time watching eagles in winter near the mouth of the Merrimac River says that the moment an eagle comes along, all the Black-backed Gulls, Herring Gulls and Crows leave the ice in a hurry.   The gulls often leave an eel or two on the ice rather than encumber and hinder their flight, and the eagle seizes the eels, tears them to pieces and devours them.   When the eagle is engaged in eating an eel or a

---

[1] Bird-Lore, Vol. XXIV, 1922, pp. 330–335.

duck, the Crows often gather near him. If they get too near for comfort, the great bird lifts his wings quickly and the Crows take the hint at once. If he keeps on with his meal, they return. They do not seem to fear the eagle while he is feeding, but the moment he is in the air all the gulls and Crows within a quarter of a mile take the alarm. Occasionally someone finds an eagle lying dead, starved, frozen, shot, or poisoned. On November 5, 1921, Mr. Adrian P. Whiting of Plymouth while deer hunting observed a tall white pine which had been blasted by a tremendous bolt of lightning. While passing the tree he saw the remains of a great bird lying on the ground, which proved to be those of a Bald Eagle. An examination of the bird convinced Mr. Whiting that it had been killed when the lightning struck the tree.

In my experience the Bald Eagle, while here, rarely kills birds and is more sinned against than sinning. Crows often mob them and Red-tailed Hawks not infrequently hector them in the breeding season. My kind friend, the late William Brewster, told of an immature eagle perched on a stub on the shore of Lake Umbagog which was so harassed by a Crow, which alighted on its back and began pecking at its head, that it launched into the air, sailed down a steep incline and plunged headlong into the lake. The Crow kept its hold until the eagle had reached the water.[1] Usually, in my experience, the eagle seems to pay little attention to his tormentors, which, although they may be threatening and vociferous in their attacks, do not venture within striking distance.

The eagle ordinarily seems a heavy bird in flight and very deliberate as it flaps along with its rather long neck extended and its feet stretched out behind under its tail, but it is capable of great speed at need, and instances are known where it has overtaken and struck down swift-flying water fowl.[*] Sometimes its speed is extraordinary. It can overtake and master the swan, the Canada Goose and the Brant, and it has been seen to strike down a flying Pintail. In the north I have not seen the Bald Eagle attack any bird, but in the south it often chases ducks, which may elude it by diving, although a persistent eagle may finally tire out and capture an unwounded duck. Wounded ducks and Coots are captured frequently, while unwounded Coots are taken with ease.

Mr. C. F. Batchelder relates how an eagle on the St. John's River, Florida, caught a Coot. So long as the flock kept together they all escaped. The flock finally separating, the eagle followed a single bird until he got it, once following it under water and finally emerging after a few seconds with the Coot. Mr. J. A. Farley who watched an eagle catch a Coot on the Banana River, Florida, describes its action as follows. The eagle descended low over the flock of Coots which rushed together into a great ball, "making the water boil." When the eagle, with dangling talons, was only a few feet above the flock of Coots, all the latter dived. The eagle remained hovering leisurely over the spot. Soon the coots all came to the surface to get a breath of air, when the eagle again deliberately lowered himself close down to the birds, when they again dived. The next time they came up more quickly, and soon the eagle was able to take an exhausted Coot with

---

[1] Birds of the Umbagog Region, Part 2, 1925, p. 346.

[*] William Brewster in Bulletin Nuttall Ornithological Club, Vol. V, 1880, pp. 57–58.

the greatest ease.   The eagle's nest with young was near by, and the great bird flew straight to it with his living prey whose feet could be seen pitifully "paddling" air as it was clutched in its captor's claws.

This eagle kills mammals from the size of a rat to that of a fox.   Mrs. Elizabeth Caswell was surprised one day to see an eagle flying directly at her house.   Before it reached the building, however, it swooped down and picked up what seemed to be a very large rat.   Mr. Harry McGraw wrote to me that on December 18, 1921, he was with a party of the Alpine Club in a wild section near Loop Run in Blair County, Pennsylvania, when an immature Bald Eagle flew toward them and then turned away.   A hundred yards up the ravine the party came on a pool of blood, and near it the body of a red fox still warm, with the entrails torn out.   The fox had a few eagle feathers in his mouth and many marks of the eagle's talons on his body.

Dr. A. K. Fisher reports on the contents of twenty-one stomachs of this eagle.   One had eaten two prairie dogs; 7, mice; 7, rats; 9, fish; 2, carrion; and 5 were empty. This eagle has been known to attack pigs, lambs, calves and domesticated geese.   Its ability to carry away its kill is shown by the fact that one was seen to reach the shore of the Neuces River, North Carolina, bearing a young lamb, having crossed the river near its mouth where it is about five miles wide.[1]

Mr. A. A. Cross, of Huntington, Massachusetts, informed me on January 26, 1918, that two eagles were then feeding on the carcass of a horse, and that a trapper who approached them saw one of them attempt to carry off the detached head of the animal. The eagle actually lifted the head from the ground but, of course, could not carry it.[*]

ECONOMIC STATUS.   In New England the Bald Eagle is virtually harmless.   It plays the part of scavenger about the shores of many bodies of water.   Only once have I known it to disturb poultry, and never have I heard of an unwounded bird killed by it in this region. It should be rigorously protected at all times by law and public sentiment to save it, if possible, from extirpation.   In some parts of the country it destroys water-fowl and poultry or young calves, pigs and lambs.   Where that occurs of course it becomes injurious.

Haliæetus leucocephalus alascánus.   C. H. TOWNSEND.   Northern Bald Eagle.

DESCRIPTION.—Largest bird of prey found in New England. Like Bald Eagle at every stage but larger.
MEASUREMENTS. — Length 34.50 to 43.00 in.;   spread 82.00 to 98.50; folded wing 24.00 to 28.00; tail 12.00 to 16.00; bill up to 2.60; tarsus 3.50 to 4.40.   Weight 12 to 15 lbs.   Female larger than male.
MOLTS. — Similar to those of Bald Eagle.
FIELD MARKS. — Field Marks, Voice and Breeding same as Bald Eagle, but eggs averaging larger about 2.97 to 3.09 by 2.22 to 2.37 in.
RANGE. — Boreal zones chiefly, from Commander Islands, northwestern Alaska, northwestern Mackenzie, northern Keewatin and Ungava (northern Quebec) south to borders of United States; in winter south on the Pacific coast at least to Washington, Montana, Great Lakes region and on Atlantic coast at least to Connecticut.

---

[1] The Hawks and Owls of the United States, 1893, p. 99.

[*] For an intimate study of the home life of the White-headed Eagle the reader is referred to articles by Prof. Francis H. Herrick in the Auk for 1924, pp. 89–105, 213–231, 389–422, and 517–541.

DISTRIBUTION IN NEW ENGLAND. — Possibly the majority of wintering New England Bald Eagles may be referred to this subspecies, but many certainly cannot be, as I have measured some very small ones. There are few authentic records of this race in New England. *Massachusetts:* In the winter of 1896–97, before the race was recognized, an eagle was brought into the shop of Mr. C. J. Maynard in Newtonville to be mounted. It was taken on the coast of Massachusetts. Although not fat, it spread 8 feet and weighed fully 12 pounds, the largest eagle I have ever seen in the flesh. No further data were preserved. *Connecticut:* Willimantic, a young female taken October 27, 1909, by G. H. Champlin and recorded by L. B. Bishop.[1] Branford, a young male found dead, March 14, 1915; recorded by L. B. Bishop.[2]

SEASON IN MASSACHUSETTS. — Autumn, winter and early spring.

HAUNTS AND HABITS. As the Northern Bald Eagle is virtually identical with the Bald Eagle, except for its larger size, and as it has been recognized only recently as a distinct race, we have no very definite information regarding its breeding range, which possibly may include northern Maine. Probably the larger eagles that winter along the Maine coast are referable to this race. When the waters of the north are frozen and the wild-fowl have left for the south, doubtless many of these eagles go to the coast for food and thus work southward along the shores of New England. I have seen in winter a number of eagles in Frenchman's Bay where both seals and eagles were seen on floating ice, as much at home as within the Arctic Circle. I have seen many Northern Bald Eagles also in British Columbia, where in the salmon season they commonly feed on dead or dying salmon that they find on the beaches or along the streams. They are common in Alaska where they are regarded as injurious, chiefly, I believe, because they eat salmon and kill foxes. They also destroy wild-fowl and grouse,[3] and a price is fixed on their heads by the territorial government.* Under the bounty law thousands of eagles are killed every year. The habits of this eagle apparently are the same as those of the Bald Eagle, the other subspecies, with some allowance for differences in latitude and environment.

ECONOMIC STATUS. The economic place of this race is not known, as no thorough study of its food habits has been made.

FAMILY **FALCONIDÆ**. FALCONS, CARACARAS, ETC.

Number of species in North America 12 ; in Massachusetts 5.

This family is represented in New England only by the

SUBFAMILY **FALCONINÆ**. FALCONS.

Number of species in North America 10 ; in Massachusetts 5.

The Falcons are among the most remarkable and picturesque of the birds of prey, as they are the most celebrated. The Old World members of this group were commonly used in the chase for centuries, because of their bravery, skill and speed, which permitted

---

[1] Auk, Vol. XXVII, 1910, p. 462. [2] Auk, Vol. XXXVIII, 1921, pp. 585–586.

[3] Brooks, Allan: Auk, Vol. XXXIX, 1922, pp. 556–559; and Oölogist, Vol. XXXIII, 1916, pp. 156, 158.

* On April 22, 1920 in a letter from C. D. Garfield, Secretary of the Alaska Fish & Game Club to Dr. T. Gilbert Pearson of the National Association of Audubon Societies, it was stated that the Territorial record showed that bounty had been paid upon a total of 8356 eagles since the passage and taking effect of the act.

them to attack and kill, for their masters, birds and mammals much larger than themselves. In the *Falconinæ* the bill is provided with a tooth near the end of the cutting edge of the upper mandible, and the end of the under mandible has a notch near the tip. The wings are long, strong and pointed with only one or two outer primaries emarginate on inner webs. The tail is rather short and its feathers slightly tapering. Falcons are of medium to small size, but very sturdy, robust and vigorous, with extremely strong feet and powerful talons; more than fifty species are recognized, widely distributed over the world.

ECONOMIC STATUS. Falcons are regarded generally as destructive birds because of their attacks on poultry and game-birds, but some of the smaller species are believed to be more useful than injurious.

Fálco islándus BRÜNNICH. White Gyrfalcon.

Plates 38 and 42.

DESCRIPTION. — Large, heavy and powerful; feet very stout and strong; tarsus feathered more than half way down, with a bare strip behind, covered by over-lapping feathers, part below feathers not scaled but reticulate; wings long and rather pointed, 2nd primary longest, 1st rather shorter than 3rd, and only one with inner web notched and cut away (emarginate) toward end. *Adults* (*sexes alike*): General color white; top of head and hind neck sometimes pure white, but more often narrowly streaked dusky; rest of upper plumage barred or cross-spotted more or less with dusky slate or dark slaty brownish-gray; under plumage often without well-defined markings, more often with small, elongated, dusky spots on each side of body; under tail-coverts unspotted white; bill, cere and feet bluish-white; iris very dark. A dark, slaty phase is marked and barred above with white and is white below with dark grayish-brown spots or streaks; bill, pale bluish-gray or slaty, blackening at tip; cere and feet yellow. *Young:* Usually like adult in color but dark markings less slaty or dark brown, and disposed in streaks, stripes or elongated spots, not in bars; cere and feet bluish-white to grayish; both light and dark nestlings have been seen together in nests of this species.

MEASUREMENTS. — *Male:* Length 21.00 to 22.50 in.; spread about 48.00 or 49.00; folded wing 14.50 to 16.50; tail 8.50 to 10.00; bill .88 to .98; tarsus 1.80 to 2.52. *Female:* Length 23.00 to 24.00; spread about 49.00 to 51.50; folded wing 16.00 to 17.21; tail 9.00 to 11.00; bill .55 to 1.08; tarsus 1.95 to 2.85. Female larger than male.

NOTE. In the third edition of the Check-list of the American Ornithologists' Union, this alleged species and one other, of which there are supposed to be three subspecies, are recognized. Probably there is but one species; there is much variation. Probably the birds known as White Gyrfalcon, Gray Gyrfalcon and Gyrfalcon are referable to one race, the Black Gyrfalcon may be a distinct race or a melanistic phase.

MOLTS. — Holboell is said to have found young birds molting all through the winter, but there is no appreciable change in their colors or markings then and the first winter plumage cannot be distinguished from juvenal; in the next summer and autumn and second winter immature birds undergo what seems to be a complete postnuptial molt, after which apparently most immature birds are as adult; adults have one complete molt annually (June to January).

FIELD MARKS. — A large white hawk, size of Goshawk and as white as or whiter than most Snowy Owls; distinguished from Snowy Owl by shape of head and pointed wings. The only hawk normally white. The dark phase cannot be distinguished in the field from other gyrfalcons. Flies with rapid wing beats followed by a "short sail."

PLATE 42

PLATE 42

GYRFALCONS *

BLACK GYRFALCON
Page 162

WHITE GYRFALCON
Page 158

GYRFALCON
Page 161

IMMATURE

ADULT

All about one-fourth scale

* Probably all these forms will be recognized eventually as members of one species.   There is great individual variation.

VOICE. — Rattling, piercing screams, *gyak* and *ke-a ke-a ke-a* repeated more and more rapidly until the syllables merge into a rattling scream; the cry of these falcons, which is often heard when two or more are together, is reported by Hagerup as "a not loud, quivering, lengthened tune, much resembling that of *Falco tinnunculus*." [1]

BREEDING. — About rocky cliffs on or near sea-coasts "at a height of 50 to 1000 feet" (E. Ekblaw), probably always on a rocky shelf or vertical cliff. *Nest:* No real nest in the far north but as the aery is occupied year after year, an accumulation of pellets, etc. is built up. In more southern parts of range, nest said to be built of sticks lined with dried grass, moss, hair and feathers. If so, probably it is the deserted nest of some other bird. *Eggs:* 2 to 4, normally 4; 2.14 to 2.45 by 1.67 to 1.81 in.; ovate to rounded ovate; creamy white to reddish-brown or cinnamon, sometimes pinkish, usually thickly marked with dark or light reddish-brown; indistinguishable from those of other Gyrfalcons; illustrated in Bendire's "Life Histories of North American Birds," Vol. I, Plate IX, Figs. 6, 8 and 9. *Dates:* May 27 to June 7, northern Greenland. *Incubation:* Period about 29 days (Manniche); chiefly by female. One brood yearly.

RANGE. — Arctic regions chiefly. Breeds in Greenland (north at least to 82° 30'), Arctic North America, and Arctic Asia east to Commander Islands, probably south to near tree limit on Arctic coasts and to Ungava and northern Labrador; south in winter casually to British Columbia, Montana, Ontario, southern Quebec, Nova Scotia, Maine and probably New York; also to Faroes, British Isles, north France and Germany, and not so rarely to Iceland.

DISTRIBUTION IN NEW ENGLAND. — Accidental visitor to Maine. *Maine:* South Winn, a specimen (young bird, probably male) shot about October 8, 1893 by a Mr. Wyman; recorded by William Brewster, and in his collection; [2] now in collection of Museum of Comparative Zoölogy.

NOTE. C. J. Maynard records that he saw a white hawk in Errol, New Hampshire, on November 4, 1898, which he believes was of this species, but as albino hawks occur this can hardly be accepted as a record for the state; [3] Ralph Forbes of Milton, Massachusetts, says that on December 15, 1919, he saw a white hawk over the Neponset Marshes.

HAUNTS AND HABITS. The White Gyrfalcon is, like the Snowy Owl, a bird of Arctic regions, chiefly, beyond the tree limit. This is the greatest and most powerful of all the northern falcons. In the days when falconry was in vogue, it furnished sport for kings. Commander Donald B. MacMillan, the Arctic explorer, says of it, "This bird stands as the dominant king of northern bird-land, fearless, aggressive, and the swiftest of all. In lonely and inaccessible places it builds its nest, scorning the friendship of bird or man. Although the Gyrfalcon lived within two miles of our house, we rarely saw it. A rapid white dash and the bird was gone." [4] The voracity of this powerful falcon is shown according to Commander MacMillan by an enormous pile of bones of the Dovekie accumulated near its nesting-place. In preparing a Dovekie for its use the Gyrfalcon bites off head and wings, plucks out the feathers, and swallows the body whole. When digestion has disposed of the soft parts, the bones are disgorged. The only specimens that I have seen alive were three young birds, fully fledged, that were brought in 1925 from an aery in northern Greenland by Commander MacMillan. From his vessel he saw the aery of the falcon and three well grown young high up on a sea cliff, and he sent an Eskimo to climb the cliff and secure the birds. The man finally reached them, got them down and,

[1] Chamberlain, Montague: Auk, Vol. VI, 1889, p. 293.
[2] Auk, Vol. XII, 1895, p. 180.
[3] Naturalists Guide, 1883, p. 134.
[4] Four Years in the White North, 1918, p. 103.

placing them in the bow of his skin boat, paddled back to the ship.   In the meantime one had fallen overboard and been picked up.   There was no room for them below decks on the crowded, heavily-laden vessel, which was then homeward bound, so a cage was made for them on deck.   The voyage home was very rough and the young birds were drenched time and again by the boarding seas, but while they complained and shivered in misery, they were so tough and hardy that they lived and prospered.   On their arrival at Boston they were consigned to the Zoölogical Garden at Franklin Park, where they were kept in a large cage out of doors with concrete floor and a dead tree for a perch.   As there are no trees in northern Greenland, they never seemed to regard the tree as a resting-place and did not use it, but sat constantly on the cold concrete or rocks.   Two of them finally succumbed to the summer heat, but one survived until recently when it, too, died.   The Gyrfalcon's flight is lofty and swift.   It progresses by quick flappings, interspersed occasionally with a short sail.   It takes its prey either by a swift stoop from a height or by a chase, overtaking its victim by dint of speed, lung power, and endurance.   It can catch in this way many swift water-birds.   It is said to strike down in flight such large birds as Eider Ducks and Snow Geese.   Its food is quite varied but consists largely of lemmings, Arctic hares, guillemots, ducks, Dovekies, shore birds, Snow Buntings, and Kittiwakes.

ECONOMIC STATUS.   Not determined.

Falco rusticolus rusticolus LINNÆUS.   Gray Gyrfalcon.

Plate 42.

DESCRIPTION. — Like White Gyrfalcon in form but darker gray above and somewhat smaller; in typical specimens head and neck lighter than back.   *Adults:* Fore parts of upper plumage more or less distinctly barred with grayish and white, very pale gray or buffy-white and bluish-gray; gray above; sides of head marked like that of Duck Hawk, with heavy dark moustache stripe; similar light and dark bands on tail, usually strongly contrasted, the dark bands there often slate-gray; flanks and leg-feathers barred or spotted with slaty, but never very heavily; otherwise white below; iris dark brown; bill, cere and feet chiefly pale gray (probably yellow in fully mature birds), bill darkening at tip.   A darker phase has under tail-coverts always more or less marked dusky or with small slaty spots, and little if any white on upper plumage and sides; flanks and leg-feathers barred or cross-spotted dusky.   *Young* (*light phase*): Dark streaks of lower plumage usually much narrower than white spaces, upper plumage usually spotted with pale buffy or whitish, and most of the feathers with pale margins; outer webs of primaries more or less spotted whitish toward bases.   *Young* (*dark phase*): Like adult but without cross-barring on upper plumage, and marks on lower plumage longitudinal.

, MEASUREMENTS. — *Male:* Length 20.00 to 21.00 in. ; spread about 44.00 ; folded wing 13.40 to 15.00 ; tail 8.00 to 9.30 ; bill, without cere, .88 to .98 ; tarsus 2.10 to 2.65.   *Female:* Length 22.00 to 24.50 in. ; spread about 50.00 ; folded wing 15.25 to 16.50 ; tail 9.10 to 10.50 ; bill .95 to 1.10 ; tarsus 2.30 to 2.60.

FIELD MARKS. — Size about that of Goshawk.   Typical birds resemble an adult Duck Hawk, but are larger and grayer, not so strongly marked on head; streaked rather than barred below, on sides and under tail-coverts.   So much individual variation in gyrfalcons that field marks are of little value.

VOICE. — Voice similar to those of other gyrfalcons; cry often heard when two or more falcons are in company, reported by Mr. Hagerup as "a not loud, quivering, lengthened tune much resembling that of *Falco tinnunculus.*" [1]

----

[1] Chamberlain, Montague: Auk, Vol. VI, 1889, p. 293.

BREEDING. — Similar to that of other gyrfalcons. *Nest:* Not always on cliffs but said to be at times in trees.

RANGE. — Arctic Regions. Breeds in Arctic America from Alaska east to southern Greenland; in winter casual south to British Columbia,* Washington, Montana, South Dakota, Kansas, Minnesota, Wisconsin, Ohio, Ontario, New York and Maine.

DISTRIBUTION IN NEW ENGLAND. — Accidental winter visitor. Records: *Maine:* Cape Elizabeth (near Portland), October 13, 1877, specimen taken;[1] now in Stanton collection at Bates College; recorded as *Hierofalco gyrfalco islandicus.*

NOTE. F. W. Putnam lists a "Jer-Falcon" as *F. islandicus* (Proceedings Essex Institute, Vol. I, 1848–1856, p. 226) which on the authority of S. Jillson was "killed at Seekonk Plains [Massachusetts] about 1840"; the Gyrfalcon then known as *F. islandicus* has since been known as *F. rusticolus* under the arrangement first proposed by Dr. Stejneger (Auk, Vol. II, 1885, pp. 187, 188) and later adopted in the A. O. U. Check-List (Brewster, William: Auk, Vol. XII, 1895, p. 180). Nothing is now known of this specimen. Rev. W. B. O. Peabody in his Report on the Ornithology of Massachusetts, 1839, p. 260, says that the "Jer-Falcon, *Falco islandicus*, is only in the depth of winter ever seen as far south as Massachusetts;" but we have Nuttall's high authority for saying that a "pair is occasionally seen within our borders." Nuttall, however, treated all four forms of gyrfalcon as one.

HAUNTS AND HABITS. Little seems to be known of the haunts and habits of this alleged race. I have never seen a gyrfalcon alive except in a cage and all I know of them is derived from reading, from conversation with those who have met them in the field and from examining numbers of dried skins. I have seen no two alike. There seems to be remarkable individual variation in coloration. I follow here the classification and nomenclature adopted by the A. O. U., and published in the third edition of the Check-List (1910), in the hope that systematists of large experience may be able finally to determine the correct status of the gyrfalcons. Under the circumstances, I see no reason to differentiate between the habits of one alleged race or species and those of another. The present example, which seems to range farther south than the White Gyrfalcon commonly does, may nest at times in trees. Gyrfalcons reside during the entire year in southern Greenland [61°, 12′ lat. : 48°, 10′ long.] and breed there, but are met with near the settlements more frequently in winter than in summer; in the latter season they are quite rare. Mr. Hagerup has considered that the white form (*F. islandus*) predominates in winter and the gray form (*F. rusticolus*) in summer.[2]

Falco rusticolus gyrfálco LINNÆUS. Gyrfalcon.

Plate 42.

DESCRIPTION. — Like Gray Gyrfalcon, sometimes almost indistinguishable, but *head and neck darker than back* in typical specimens. *Adults:* Top of head gray or brownish-gray, mottled with black; elsewhere above bluish-gray with broad grayish-black bands; lower back, rump, upper tail-coverts and tail much clearer bluish-gray, with narrower cross-bars of grayish-black; lighter bars on tail minutely freckled with blackish, and all tail-bars about the same width (as in other Gyrfalcons); forehead and

---

* "A regular winter visitant west of the Cascades." Brooks, Allan: Auk, Vol. XVII, 1900, p. 105.
[1] Brown, N. C.: Proceedings Portland Society of Natural History, Vol. II, 1882, p. 21; also Knight, Birds of Maine, 1908, p. 241, and Norton, A. H.: *in litt.*
[2] Chamberlain, Montague: Auk, Vol. VI, 1889, p. 292.

lores whitish; sides of head (from behind eye) and nape varied with whitish; whitish cheeks and sides of head streaked blackish, and a rather narrow blackish "moustache" stripe; flight-feathers mostly dark grayish-brown mottled and speckled gray externally, but inner secondaries and tertials like back; below white or buffy-white; sides of neck and breast streaked blackish; elsewhere rather scantily spotted grayish-black, except flanks and under tail-coverts, which are barred same; wing linings white, spotted black, and axillars barred same; bill very pale grayish or blue, growing gradually blackish toward tip; iris brown; legs and feet light gray. *Young:* Brown with sooty spots and mottlings on edges of scapulars, tertials, inner secondaries and upper tail-coverts; tail darker brown, with broken sooty bands; wing-coverts and flight-feathers dotted externally with sooty and barred buff on undersides; below white, with dark brown patches along shafts of each feather, these narrower on throat.

MEASUREMENTS. — *Male:* Length 20.00 to 23.00 in.; spread about 50.00; folded wing 13.35 to 14.50; tail 8.00 to 8.75; bill, without cere, .86 to .93; tarsus 2.15 to 2.50. *Female:* Length about 24.00; spread about 55.00; wing 15.80 to 17.00; tail 9.00 to 10.50; bill 1.00 to 1.10; tarsus 2.25 to 2.65. Weight about 5 lbs. to 5 lbs. 4 oz.

FIELD MARKS. — Field Marks, Voice and Breeding, similar to those of Gray Gyrfalcon.

RANGE. — Arctic regions. Breeds on Ellesmere Island and in northern Greenland, east to Franz Josef Land and south to northern Alaska and northern Mackenzie; south in winter to British Columbia, Wisconsin, New York and New England.

DISTRIBUTION IN NEW ENGLAND. — Very rare winter visitor. Records: *Maine:* Katahdin Iron Works, December, 1876,[1] male taken and now in Museum of Brown University, Providence, R. I.; recorded as *Falco gyrfalco* var. *sacer*; North Deering (now part of Portland), bird taken Dec. 11, 1906;[2] Jacques Island, March 7, 1907, female taken and reported by H. H. Brock;[3] Specimen labeled "Maine," no locality or date given, in collection of Prof. A. L. Lane of Waterville;[4] Brunswick (Merrymeeting Bay), October 22, 1925, bird shot by Will Darton and now in possession of J. F. Fanning of Portland. Observed for several days at Merrymeeting Bay, identified by Arthur H. Norton.[5] *Massachusetts:* Northampton, February, 1880, bird taken by E. O. Damon,[6] now in mounted collection, Science Museum, Springfield; Melrose, January 1, 1891, bird taken and originally recorded as "Black Gyrfalcon" and as shot "near Lynn."[7] *Rhode Island:* Providence, winter of 1864–65, bird taken near that city by Newton Dexter and now in mounted collection of Boston Society of Natural History, originally recorded as *Falco sacer*.[8]

Falco rusticolus obsolétus GMELIN.   Black Gyrfalcon.

Plate 42.

DESCRIPTION. — *Adults (sexes alike or similar):* A dark phase of the Gyrfalcon, dusky, or more or less leaden brownish-black, with the usual markings apparent but obsolete and often nearly obliterated, and most of the feathers edged narrowly paler; the pale feather-edges become broader and quite white below. Some, however, are very dark below; under tail-coverts said to be always spotted with whitish. *Young:* Similar but having a streaked appearance, and there are white spots on flanks and leg-feathering; bill, iris, legs and feet said to be darker than in Gyrfalcon.

[1] Purdie, H. A.: Bulletin Nuttall Ornithological Club, Vol. IV, 1879, p. 188.
[2] Norton, A. H.: Journal of the Maine Ornithological Society, Vol. IX, 1907, p. 18.
[3] Knight, O. W.: Birds of Maine, 1908, p. 242.
[4] Journal of the Maine Ornithological Society, Vol. I, 1899, p. 1.
[5] Norton, Arthur H.: *in litt.*, and Maine Naturalist, Vol. VI, 1926, pp. 21–22.
[6] Vennor, H. G.: Forest and Stream, Vol. XIV, 1880, p. 204.
[7] Tufts, A. M.: Ornithologist and Oölogist, Vol. XVI, 1891, p. 61.
[8] Allen, J. A.: American Naturalist, Vol. III, 1869, p. 513.

MEASUREMENTS. — *Male:* Folded wing 14.00 to 14.60 in.; tail about 8.50; bill, without cere, .90 to 1.00; tarsus 2.12 to 2.70. *Female:* Length about 22.50; spread about 51.00; folded wing 15.75 to 17.50; tail 9.60 to 11.00; bill .98 to 1.05; tarsus 2.00 to 2.70.

FIELD MARKS. — Difficult to distinguish from either of the two last but darker. Voice and breeding as in other Gyrfalcons.

RANGE. — Not definitely known. 2 specimens taken in Manitoba, now in Manitoba Museum. Breeds in Ungava (northern Quebec) and Newfoundland-Labrador; south in winter to Ontario, New York, New England and Nova Scotia.

DISTRIBUTION IN NEW ENGLAND. — Rare winter visitor. Records: *Maine:* Near Spruce Head (South Thomaston) about Thanksgiving time (November), 1886, female taken, recorded by William Brewster as "at Rockland," [1] now in collection of Boston Society of Natural History; Cape Elizabeth (Spurwink-"Mitchell's") "about the middle of September," 1887, specimen shot by E. P. Carman of Bridgton; [2] Eagle Island (Penobscot Bay), Knox County, about March 22, 1888, female taken, sent to Brewster collection and recorded by Brewster, [3] now in collection of Museum of Comparative Zoölogy; Oxford County one shot in 1892 or 1893, collection of Harry Lane; [4] East Waterford, one shot "recently" by a Mr. Doughty, specimen preserved; [5] Bangor, December 21, 1898, female shot by Adrian De Costa, in collection of Harry Merrill, and recorded by him; [6] Alton, October 20, 1905, a very dark bird taken,[7] and now in mounted collection of Boston Society of Natural History.

Manly Hardy of Brewer, Maine, writing to Dr. Brewer, says that he "saw one today (Dec. 10, 1900) and saw another two years ago." NOTE. The Calais records given by Dr. T. M. Brewer, are erroneous, as the birds were seen in New Brunswick (O. W. Knight).[8] *New Hampshire:* Milford, January, 1891, bird shot 12 miles from the village, preserved and recorded by James P. Melzer.[9] *Massachusetts:* Ipswich, November 7, 1874, male taken by J. J. Gould, in Essex County collection, Peabody Academy, Salem, Mass.; [10] Boston, latter part of October, 1876, adult male taken on Breed's Island; [11] now in collection of Field Columbian Museum, Chicago; Stowe, 1881, adult male taken, now in Museum of Comparative Zoölogy; [12] Ipswich, March 11, 1893, female taken and recorded by N. Vickary; [13] Ipswich, about 1898, bird shot in spring by G. L. Woodbury, owned by Dr. F. H. Stockwell of Ipswich; [14] Essex, Dec. 10, 1921, female shot, now in collection of Boston Society of Natural History; [15] Newton, a handsome immature Gyrfalcon (variety?) shot about October 27, 1925, as it was flying off with a duck which it had caught. Possibly this bird may be referred to *obsoletus.* It is now in the possession of Mr. E. J. Ramhofer, of Clinton Street, Cambridge. *Rhode Island:* District of Narragansett, October 11, 1883, young bird taken at Point Judith, by E. S. Hopkins, now in mounted collection of Boston Society of Natural History, recorded in Auk as *sacer* (Jencks, F. T.: Auk, Vol. I, 1884, p. 94 and Random Notes Natural History, Vol. I, 1884, p. 6), formerly recorded as *F. r. gyrfalco;* [16] Newport, November 22, 1891, female taken on Conanicut Island (near Jamestown), in museum of Natural History Society of Newport,

---

[1] Auk, Vol. IV, 1887, p. 75.

[2] Norton, Arthur H.: Journal Maine Ornithological Society, Vol. IX, 1907, p. 19.

[3] Brewster, William: Editor, Minot's Land and Game Birds of New England, 2d edition, 1895, p. 480.

[4] Knight, O. W.: Birds of Maine, 1908, p. 243.

[5] Adams, Stephen J.: Three Kingdoms, March, 1898.

[6] Auk, Vol. XVI, 1899, p. 182.

[7] Allen, G. M.: Auk, Vol. XXV, 1908, p. 234.

[8] Proceedings, Boston Society of Natural History, Vol. XIX, 1878, p. 306.

[9] Ornithologist and Oölogist, Vol. XVI, 1891, p. 79 (wrongly given as "Vermont").

[10] Purdie, Henry A.: Bulletin Nuttall Ornithological Club, Vol. IV, 1879, p. 189.

[11] Cory, C. B.: Bulletin Nuttall Ornithological Club, Vol. II, 1877, p. 27.

[12] Brewster, William: Bulletin, Nuttall Ornithological Club, Vol. VIII, 1883, p. 184.

[13] Ornithologist and Oölogist, Vol. XVIII, 1893, p. 51.

[14] Townsend, C. W.: Birds of Essex County, Massachusetts, 1905, p. 212.

[15] Fuller, Arthur B.: Auk, Vol. XXXIX, 1922, p. 425.

[16] Brewster, William: Editor, Minot's Land and Game Birds of New England, appendix, p. 479.

recorded by A. O'D. Taylor; [1] Tiverton, December 26, 1896, adult female taken by Arthur Scudder, collection of A. C. Bent, recorded by him; [2] Newport, October 28, 1896, bird taken, collection of C. H. Smith and now in museum at Roger Williams Park, Providence.[3] *Connecticut:* Durham, Jan. 27, 1907, female shot by A. Banks, and now in Sage collection.[4]

Falco peregrínus ánatum BONAPARTE.   Duck Hawk.

Other names: AMERICAN PEREGRINE FALCON; LEDGE HAWK.

Plates 38, 43, and 44.

DESCRIPTION. — A medium-sized dark falcon, upper mandible strongly "toothed," lower mandible notched; wings long, stiff and sharp-pointed; 2nd primary longest; 1st abruptly emarginate on inner web; tail long and ample; slightly rounded; tarsus feathered but little, toes very long and strong, middle toe longer than tarsus. *Adults (sexes similar):* Extreme forehead whitish; top and sides of head to and below eyes very dark slate, this continuing and growing black along jaw; general color above dark bluish-ash (lighter and more bluish on tail-coverts and base of tail), barred and spotted with dark slate, the spots smaller and more elongated on rump and upper tail-coverts; most of the feathers with paler edges; tail crossed by 6 or more narrow black bars and a broad, black, subterminal bar, tip white; chin and throat whitish, sometimes slightly buffy; rest of under plumage and ear region yellowish or buffy, often becoming pinkish-buff, regularly barred from upper breast downward and on under sides of wings and tail with blackish-brown, quite pronounced on sides, flanks and under tail-coverts; markings on leg-feathering tending to broad arrow-heads; under plumage also sometimes "very finely peppered with gray"; iris dark brown; bill, horn-blue, becoming light greenish at base; cere, gape and feet yellow or greenish-yellow; claws blackish. *Young in first winter plumage:* Like juvenal. *Young in juvenal plumage:* Similar to adults in markings of upper plumage, except that tail is *dark* crossed by narrow *light* bars where tail of adult is *light* crossed by *dark* bars; (some have dark unbarred tail and some have light spots on inner webs); ground-color of upper plumage entirely unlike that of adult, being dark brown with light brown edges and tips; below chiefly pale buffy to deep buff or pinkish-buff, with dark brown streaks from throat downward; narrow bars of same on under tail-coverts; under sides of flight-feathers, axillars and wing linings variable, but darkly barred; iris very dark brown; bill pale bluish on basal half, the rest blackish; cere and naked eyelid pale livid bluish or plumbeous; feet pale wax-yellow or chrome-yellow (Allan Brooks). *Downy young:* Creamy white; later this down is succeeded by longer grayish-white down.

MEASUREMENTS. — *Male:* Length 15.00 to 18.00 in.; spread about 38.50 to 43.00; folded wing 11.30 to 13.50; tail 6.00 to 7.25; bill .75 to .88; tarsus 1.60 to 2.00. *Female:* Length 18.00 to 20.00; spread about 43.00 to 46.00; folded wing 13.00 to 14.75; tail 7.00 to 9.25; bill .85 to 1.00; tarsus 1.70 to 2.25. Female larger than male.

MOLTS. — As young bird approaches flight stage, juvenal plumage is assumed by complete postnatal molt; apparently this is worn unchanged through or nearly through first winter, after which by gradual molt a plumage similar to adults is acquired; adults apparently have either one complete postnuptial molt or two partial molts; molting specimens are found during a large part of the year.

FIELD MARKS. — Size about that of Cooper's Hawk; a dark bird of swift flight on rapidly beating sharp-pointed wings and rather long, rounded (almost pointed) tail; flight resembles that of a pigeon; distinguished from other hawks when near at hand by its conspicuous black cap and its black "moustache" on a light background; does not soar very much in circles, but sails easily and plunges from a

[1] Auk, Vol. IX, 1892, pp. 300, 301.

[2] Auk, Vol. XV, 1898, p. 54.

[3] Howe, R. H., Jr., and Sturtevant, E.: Birds of Rhode Island, 1899, p. 59.

[4] Sage, John H.: Auk, Vol. XXVI, 1909, p. 429.

FIG. 46. — EGGS OF DUCK HAWK
Page 165

FIG. 47. — DOWNY YOUNG DUCK HAWKS IN AERY
Courtesy of F. Gilbert Hinsdale
Page 164

PLATE 43

PLATE 43

DUCK HAWK *
Page 164

Adult

* This plate is a gift to the Commonwealth of Massachusetts through the courtesy of Mr. and Mrs. Aaron C. Bagg.

Louis Agassiz Fuertes.

height on its prey or overtakes it by rapid flight. "Male bird could be distinguished by smaller size, more prominent barring of the tail, and browner face markings" (A. A. Allen).

VOICE. — A harsh shrill chattering or cackling and a fierce screaming *werch-werch-werch kay yak, kay yak* or *kea kea;* "the female squawking is hoarser than that of the male" (W. C. Clarke). "A hissing menace like that of the Owls, an exceedingly loud and piercing scream of anger, and a reiterated shrieking, almost exactly like that of the Kestrel, but stronger and in a deeper key" (Ernest E. T. Seton).

BREEDING. — Usually on high rocky mountains overlooking a stream or a body of water; sometimes on high river bluff. *Nest:* None. The shelf of a high ledge, cliff, bluff or crag, some hole in a cliff or bluff, or a cavity in broken top of some great tree; eggs deposited on bare ledge or earth (usually covered with dead or decaying vegetation) or on crumbling wood of tree cavity; said by Audubon to construct a nest of sticks, moss, etc., on the cliffs of Labrador and Newfoundland; found once in old nest of Bald Eagle. *Eggs:* 2 to 6; 2.00 to 2.25 by 1.50 to 1.90 in.; rounded oval to short rounded ovate; deep creamy ground color often nearly or entirely obscured by confluent markings of rich chocolate brown; some specimens appear entirely reddish-brown, either little or very sparingly marked, others variegated with reddish-brown, chocolate and very dark brown; illustrated in Bendire's "Life Histories of North American Birds," Vol. I, Plate X, Figs. 5 to 7. *Dates:* April 7, Pennsylvania; March 21 to May 23, Massachusetts; May 2 to June 30, Vermont; April 30, Colorado; June 5 to July, Keewatin. *Incubation:* Period 28 days (Burns), by both sexes. One brood yearly.

RANGE. — North and South America. Breeds locally (except Pacific coast from Alaska to Oregon), from Norton Sound, Alaska, northern Mackenzie, Boothia Peninsula, Baffin Island, and coast of west central Greenland south to central Lower California, central Mexico, Arizona, central western Texas, Kansas, Missouri, and Arkansas (formerly), southern Illinois, Indiana, Pennsylvania, and Connecticut and in mountains to eastern Tennessee and probably South Carolina (replaced in the Northwest coast region by geographic race *Falco peregrinus pealei;* south in winter from southern British Columbia, Colorado, southeastern Nebraska, southern Illinois, Indiana, Pennsylvania, New Jersey, Long Island (New York) and Massachusetts to West Indies and Panama; occurs also in most of South America; accidental in England.

DISTRIBUTION IN NEW ENGLAND. — *Maine:* Migrant (sometimes in flights along coast, especially in fall) and rare local summer resident;* breeds in Washington and Oxford counties and probably in Hancock County, in the mountains of northern Penobscot County and probably in other mountains of northern Maine. *New Hampshire:* Rather rare migrant and uncommon, local, summer resident; breeding still (or recently) in the Presidential Range, near Lake Umbagog, near Plymouth, Alexandria and Newfound Lake, at Intervale and other places, and possibly still at Mount Monadnock. *Vermont:* Rare migrant and local summer resident; breeds in mountains; at least 20 breeding pairs known (Karl Pember). *Massachusetts:* Rather rare migrant, generally more common coastwise; rare local summer resident in western counties; occasionally winters; breeds on mountains in Connecticut Valley and others to the westward — now, or in recent years, on a cliff near Mt. Everett near boundary between Sheffield and Mount Washington, Monument Mountain in Great Barrington and other localities in Berkshire County; Mount Tekoa in Russell; on the Mt. Tom and Mt. Holyoke ranges, Sugar Loaf Mountain in South Deerfield and Rattlesnake Mountain in Pelham. *Rhode Island:* Rare migrant, chiefly coastwise; "very common both spring and fall, 46 in fall of 1917" (Miss E. Dickens), Block Island. *Connecticut:* Uncommon migrant, chiefly coastwise and very rare and local summer resident in the hill country; has bred on Talcott Mountain near Hartford, on Mount Carmel in North Haven, and at Castle Craig in Meriden.

SEASON IN MASSACHUSETTS. — Resident in western counties in some seasons but rare in winter; migrant, chiefly coastwise, August 17 to October 20, April 4 to 24; rare winter resident in Boston, roosting on tall buildings.

---

* Capt. Spinney writes that there was a large flight of Duck Hawks during the fall of 1903 at Seguin. He never saw so many before. (Journal Maine Ornithological Society, Vol. VI, 1904, p. 70.)

HAUNTS AND HABITS. The Duck Hawk is the American representative of the Peregrine Falcon, a noble bird, a "falcon gentil," that was used for hawking by the knights and ladies of the days of chivalry. Its American representative is, virtually, identical with the European bird in spirit, habits, form, size and coloration, with the exception of lighter and less marked lower fore parts. In size and color it approaches the European bird so closely that in some cases it is difficult or impossible to distinguish one from the

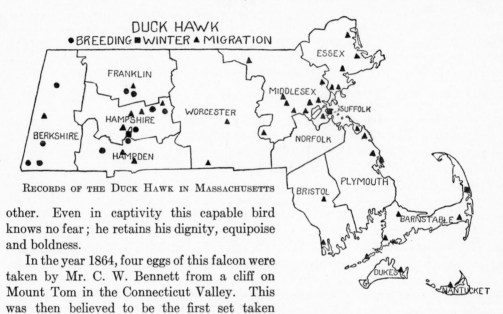

RECORDS OF THE DUCK HAWK IN MASSACHUSETTS

other. Even in captivity this capable bird knows no fear; he retains his dignity, equipoise and boldness.

In the year 1864, four eggs of this falcon were taken by Mr. C. W. Bennett from a cliff on Mount Tom in the Connecticut Valley. This was then believed to be the first set taken within the limits of the United States. Since that time the bird has been found breeding in many places in this country. This, of course, indicates no increase. Undoubtedly the falcons have bred for centuries on these same crags. It would not be surprising if, eventually, records of nesting on many more New England cliffs should be obtained. Mr. K. A. Pember, State Ornithologist of Vermont, knows of many haunts of this bird in that state and has collected many eggs of the species. The breeding places in New England now known number less than 40, but there are many cliffs in northern New England suitable for nesting, which have never been explored.

Every person who ranges the woods knows that jays are accustomed to assemble and hector certain hawks and owls. There is one hawk, however, that the jays let severely alone and that is the Duck Hawk. This swift and powerful falcon is the jay's worst enemy. From its mountain heights this hawk surveys the shining waters and the valleys spread below. Its piercing eye selects its prey in full flight, and it falls on its victim like a thunderbolt from the sky. It is the master of the air within its wide domain.

Two men who were trimming apple trees at South Deerfield in the valley of the Connecticut River saw a Blue Jay flying across a field and making for the woods. Suddenly a Duck Hawk shot down from the mountain cliffs high above them, the air hissing from its half-closed wings. The jay's usual jaunty assurance vanished in a breath. He stayed not to insult the enemy, but in mortal terror dived precipitately into a pile of apple-tree trimmings. Quick as he was, the hawk was swifter. As the jay reached the brush heap, the clutching falcon relieved him of his tail, snatching it out as the hawk's headlong, downward course was changed barely in time to escape collision with the heaped-up limbs. The two farmers were curious to know whether the jay had escaped unharmed, so they walked over to the brush heap and beat upon it. At first the jay in his fear of the hawk would not leave his place of refuge, but by trampling on the pile they started him at last, and the tailless scamp flew swiftly and silently to the woods, as if " Old Nick " were after him.

The favorite retreats of this hawk are cliffs or crags overlooking some broad river valley with a stream meandering far below. It often watches from a dead tree on the steep mountain side, but more often patrols the valley at a considerable height or swings upward in wide circles until it reaches such an altitude that it is unseen or forgotten by its prospective victims. Its flight is one of the most wonderful exhibitions of speed and command of the air shown by any bird. At times when heading into the wind it will slide off sidewise covering a mile thus in a matter of seconds. It can so regulate its flight at will as seemingly to bound upward for one hundred or two hundred feet like a flash and apparently with the greatest ease. It can overtake and capture any of our birds in flight except possibly the Chimney Swift, and the only hope its victims have to elude it is by dodging its rushes, until they can dive into some tangle of vines and shrubbery. Fierce and audacious in pursuit of its victims, it does not hesitate to rush with incredible rapidity into the very farm-yards in pursuit of poultry or pigeons, and to strike down its terrified quarry in the near presence of its arch enemy, man. Dr. Hatch tells of an incident, in connection with a shooting match at a gun club of which he was a member, which illustrates the fearlessness of this bird when engaged in pursuing its prey. This occurred in the days when live pigeons were used for trap-shooting. The firing was rapid, when a pigeon got away and circled about over a corn-field back of the stand. It had flown almost beyond reasonable gun range unscathed by the shot from a dozen guns, when suddenly a Duck Hawk appeared from somewhere in pursuit of the unfortunate bird, and, undismayed by the increasing roar of guns, drove it directly over the heads of the shooters, where both hawk and pigeon quickly met their fate.[1]

In March and April many Duck Hawks come in from the south. Their line of migration follows chiefly the coast, but in Massachusetts some of them are on their breeding-grounds in March, and a few have been seen in winter about their nesting places. Eggs are laid late in March or early in April. The mated pair often hangs about its breeding cliff to guard the nesting place from interlopers or squatters of their own kind long before

[1] Hatch, P. L.: Notes on the Birds of Minnesota, 1892, p. 200.

the eggs are laid. When choosing an aery the falcon usually finds a high shelf on some cliff for her future home. It must be high enough to command an extended view. It must be free from danger from falling rocks, and it must be inaccessible to quadrupeds and unwinged bipeds. Danger from rocks falling from the cliff is lessened either by choosing a shelf near the top or by occupying a recess or small cave under firm overhanging rock. Commonly the eggs are laid on a projecting cliff which gives a wide view, but this is not always the case. If the cliff is very high, the aery may be situated in some recess half-way up. Occasionally it is so near the summit as to be readily accessible from above, but probably this is exceptional. Often when the birds are watched, they will not go to it or will use great caution in approaching it. Mr. W. F. Lisk tells me that he watched a female go to her nest. She alighted on a ledge at some distance from it and moved over to it so slowly that her motion was barely perceptible. She occupied half an hour in getting to her eggs, watching the observer meanwhile. Usually the young are ready for flight before June 1. In the meantime one may fall over the edge of its rocky shelf to its death on the broken talus far below. While the young are developing, the parents continually bring them small birds that they kill while ranging far and wide over the valley below. In about four weeks the natal down is nearly all replaced by the brown of juvenal plumage. The whole family lingers near the aery till snow flies, but only one pair nests there the next spring. When the fledglings have become skillful in flight, both young and adults in practice or in play often strike at birds which apparently they have no intention of capturing. Dr. T. Gilbert Pearson writes as follows of an incident illustrating this which he witnessed at Cumberland Island, Georgia: "On May 4, while driving along the beach a few miles from Dungeness a Duck Hawk appeared coming from the direction of Fernandina up the bay. It was at the time flying perhaps a hundred feet above the water. Nearing the beach it suddenly dived at an Oyster-catcher we had been watching on the shore. The big shore bird took refuge in flight, but the hawk almost immediately overtook it, but when within a few feet it swerved upward and towered. It quickly dived for another harmless attack, then pursued its way along the beach parallel with our course. At my suggestion Mr. Carnegie released the engine and the indicator showed a speed of forty miles an hour before we had attained a rate equal to that of the Duck Hawk. The bird, however, appeared to be moving with indolent ease and without haste."[1] Brewster relates three somewhat similar instances as follows: "1894, September 23. — While bathing in our boat-cove at Pine Point early this morning I heard a Kingfisher rattling excitedly, and looking out over the Lake caught sight of it some two hundred yards away, flying towards me at a height of fifteen or twenty feet above the water. About thirty yards behind it was a male Duck Hawk coming very swiftly, on rapidly-vibrating wings. Within the next hundred yards or so he overtook the Kingfisher, but when seemingly within his grasp it eluded him by suddenly plunging down into the water with a great splash not, however, completely immersing itself. Nor did it remain there more than a few seconds before mounting into the air to continue its flight. The Falcon meanwhile

---

[1] The Wilson Bulletin, June, 1922, p. 87.

had been carried twenty yards or more beyond the spot by his exceeding and apparently uncontrollable momentum, but he wheeled back just as the Kingfisher rose on wing, and again overtook it with the greatest ease. This time it kept straight on and I fully expected the Falcon to seize it, but instead, he rose slightly above it, and darting forward close over its back, turned as if to meet it face to face. The Kingfisher had to double then, but being now well within the cove was able to still head shorewards, although obliged to change its course. Once more the Falcon dashed after it, but only for a short distance before abandoning further pursuit, to fly back low over me, when I had a clear view of him, and saw plainly that he was a young bird. Will Sargent, the guide, who also witnessed this interesting chase from first to last, shares with me the impression that the Falcon could have caught the Kingfisher had he really cared to do so, and hence must have been pursuing it more in sport than earnest. No other conclusion seems possible with respect to similar behaviour on the part of another Duck Hawk which I once saw follow and overtake a Lesser Scaup flying over Indian River, Florida. After glancing close past and well in advance of her, with amazing velocity, he wheeled and hovered directly in her path, yet refrained from using, or even displaying, his sharp talons when she passed within easy reach of them. Nor did he trouble her further in any way. . . . 1896, August 27. — As I was sailing down the Androscoggin in a cruising canoe a large female Duck Hawk, probably the same noted on the 20th of the month, flew swiftly across the River and thence over Moose Point where two Great Blue Herons, evidently alarmed at her approach, rose with loud outcry to soar skyward in spiral courses. They did not succeed, however, in thus eluding the Falcon, for by what was virtually a single, uninterrupted aerial bound, truly wondrous to behold, she mounted above, and then shot down close past them. This was repeated several times in quick succession. It must have been done merely for the fun of frightening the Herons, for no attempt was made to injure them."[1]

The late Eugene P. Bicknell wrote to me that on November 12, 1922, he "saw a Duck Hawk manœuvre and capture a Monarch Butterfly on the wing. The Butterfly either slipped from its claws or was flung down in disgust as very thin game, or from the dashing action of the bird. Anyway it escaped death, for after falling swiftly a few feet it recovered itself and resumed its flight." This seems like play, as the Duck Hawk would get hardly nourishment enough from a butterfly to repair the tissue wasted in its pursuit. This bird needs red meat. When a Duck Hawk "stoops" from a great height upon its prey, its plunge is so lightning-like that the bird seems to have been evolved out of a clear sky, and the sound of its rush is like that made by a rocket. The sudden arrow-like fall of this bird from far heights is one of the most impressive sights in bird life. However, it does not always strike thus, but frequently perches on some tall tree at the water's edge and launches out at water-fowl flying by. Mr. C. J. Maynard asserts that in such cases the eye can hardly follow its movements, and it overtakes and strikes swift-flying ducks in this manner with the greatest ease.

---

[1] Brewster, William; The Birds of the Lake Umbagog Region of Maine, Part 2, 1925, pp. 350–352.

When I was hunting one day on the Banana River, in Florida, with the late C. E. Bailey, a flock of Blue-winged Teals came flying over the water. The rapid flight of these Teals is well known to sportsmen. Suddenly, from somewhere, a Duck Hawk shot through that flock like a meteor, struck down three birds, one after another, and passed swiftly on, leaving the little ducks lying dead on the water. For some reason diving ducks, when resting on the surface, seem to have no fear of this falcon — perhaps because it rarely strikes anything on or in the water, but prefers to take its prey on the wing in sportsmanlike fashion; nevertheless individuals have been known to dive into the water, osprey-like, or to strike wooden duck decoys riding on the surface.

The courage and intrepidity of this falcon are so great that it sometimes attacks very large birds. Commander Donald MacMillan says that he once saw one drop like a comet out of the blue sky and knock down a Blue Goose with such force as to partially disable it. He was positive that in this case the falcon threw her wings far back and struck the goose with her breast. Others have reported similar observations. This hawk usually does not trouble other birds of prey unless they approach its aery. Then let them beware!

Mr. Aaron C. Bagg in a manuscript paper on the Duck Hawks of Mount Tom, which he has kindly placed at my disposal, says that "Mr. John Fairbanks once witnessed an attack on a Red-shouldered Hawk that ventured too near the Mount Tom aery. He saw the Duck Hawk descend in a plunge and, with his beak, strike the *Buteo* squarely on the head, crumpling it up forthwith and felling it to the ground." Mr. Fairbanks went to the place and found the skull of the hawk split wide open. Mr. Lisk tells me that he saw one of the falcons of Rattlesnake Mountain strike a Red-shouldered Hawk, which fell down into the forest below. Audubon tells of a Snowy Owl which snatched a young Duck Hawk from its rocky perch, but was followed by the avenging parent, which quickly struck the larger bird dead. The power of the falcon's death-stroke is almost unbelievable. Large birds, ordinarily very tenacious of life, are killed as if struck by lightning. My friend, the late William S. Perry, of Worcester, Massachusetts, told this story to illustrate the power of the Duck Hawk's stroke. He was shooting one day on the banks of the Connecticut River when a large Merganser flew past, high over the water. A Duck Hawk suddenly darted down from the sky, struck the bird such a powerful blow as to throw it diagonally to the shore, and sped away so quickly that my friend's shot failed to reach it. He picked up the dead Merganser and found that most of its side had been torn out by the force of the blow or the clutch of those powerful claws. Those who know the hardiness of Mergansers and their tenacity of life will appreciate the power of that stroke. Water-fowl of considerable size are the usual prey of the Duck Hawk, and while some of them are swift fliers, they cannot turn quickly enough to evade the falcon's rush. The smaller shore birds are more successful in eluding its pursuit, but it captures some of them. When its young are small it shows great aerial skill in catching small birds on the wing, some of which are adepts at dodging, as for example the Phœbe and the Barn Swallow. Swifts are believed to be the swiftest of all birds, and it has been generally asserted that the Duck Hawk is unable to overtake them. I have never found the feathers of a swift near a Duck Hawk's aery, but a farmer in the Connecticut Valley states that he saw this falcon capture a Chimney Swift. Many swifts, he says, were coursing above the fields, when the falcon made several dashes at them, but missed. At last as one turned to evade the rush, the hawk swung over on its back, and reaching up one foot as it shot by, caught the swift in its powerful grasp.

On May 20, 1917, I climbed a mountain above an aery, and then worked down to it from the top of a precipice 500 feet above the river. The single young one — the only one left from the clutch of three eggs — was more than half-grown and covered with white down. There was nothing that could be called a nest on this rock-shelf, but the nesting place was surrounded by small bushes growing from the scanty mold that had accumulated there. Here the young bird sat and viewed the world from the shadow of the overhanging rock. He was surrounded by feathers of many Blue Jays and some feathers of other small birds which had been brought by his parents. He called intermittently to his sharp-winged, powerful, screaming mother, sailing high overhead. Soon the male joined her, and both swooped down at me with menacing cries. One of the birds suddenly shot straight down like a feathered arrow-head from a height of about 100 feet directly over my head, and passed me with a startling rush of wings, bounding upward to its original height without any perceptible motion of its pinions, which were held less than half open. What tremendous power and spirit these birds evince! Later both of them hung in air against a gale that rushed furiously over that mountain top, and hardly a motion of a flight-feather could be detected. What held them, as if by sheer force of will, against such a wind far above that rocky summit?

Probably no bird in the air can escape the Duck Hawk by direct flight. Even the Carrier Pigeon is overtaken. When the pigeon sees the falcon, he rises upward to a tremendous height, but eventually the hawk gets above him, and then, shooting down, strikes him to the earth.

On the rocky mountain side, at the foot of the cliff, on the talus where the rock has weathered away and earth has been formed through the ages, the forest growth stands. All along the foot of this cliff are scattered feathers of birds which the falcons have killed. Those of Pheasants, Pigeons, Nighthawks, Blue Jays, Bluebirds, Orioles, Flickers, Phœbes, Kingbirds, Robins, Meadowlarks, and the wings of other small birds show the destructiveness of these hawks.

On June 10th I visited the aery again. Lowering clouds in sheets of white mist, drifted above the mountain top, now hiding the valley below, now unveiling the lovely landscape. The woods were wonderfully beautiful; the leaves were fully developed, and the miracle of spring and summer was consummated. The young falcon, a few weeks earlier a little downy white chick, was now a hawklet, nearly full-grown, with wings and tail ready for flight and only a few down-filaments of his chick plumage remaining. On June 11th he launched out over the gulf on strong and perfect pinions, riding in a moment the unstable, shifting element that man, after centuries of failure, has only just begun to conquer.

The Duck Hawk feeds for the most part on birds, including usually those from the size of a Snow Bunting to that of the largest ducks and grouse.   Domestic fowls are occasional victims, and pigeons are a favorite prey in settled regions.   In Boston, New York and Philadelphia, Duck Hawks occasionally resort in winter to some tall building where they can overlook the city and prey on the street pigeons which abound there.   The Custom House Tower in Boston is a favorite roost for a Duck Hawk, which divides its attention between the pigeons and the ducks in the harbor.   Very small birds such as the smaller sparrows and warblers seldom are troubled by this species, except perhaps when its young are small and are fed almost entirely on small birds.   Among the feathers found about the nests of this species those of Pheasants and Ruffed Grouse appear occasionally, but I have observed very few remains of mammals.

The Duck Hawk amuses itself at times by catching on the wing large insects such as beetles and dragon-flies.   Otherwise its food seems to consist almost entirely of birds.

ECONOMIC STATUS.   The Duck Hawk is anathema to the poultryman and the game-keeper.   Its only redeeming trait seems to lie in the destruction of many jays and some crows and hawks.   It is fortunate perhaps that the species is rare in New England.   It is well worth preserving, however, as an example of rapacious power.

Falco columbárius columbarius LINNÆUS.   Pigeon Hawk.
Plates 38 and 44.

DESCRIPTION. — Much smaller than any of the foregoing falcons, nearer size of Sharp-shinned Hawk, but much more robust, legs and tail shorter, wings long and pointed; 2nd primary usually slightly longer than 3rd; 1st and emarginate near end of inner webs, 2nd and 3rd have outer webs sinuate; tail some-what rounded at tip.   *Adult male :* above, bluish-gray to bluish-ash or bluish-slate with fine black shaft-lines; primaries blackish, the edges or tips lighter, and many cross spots of white on inner webs; outer webs sometimes showing light spots which give the effect of barring; tail banded variably with black, subterminal band widest, tip white; below whitish or buffy, unmarked or nearly so on chin and throat, tinged tawny elsewhere and streaked dark umber-brown; these markings variable, but usually heavy on breast, lighter behind and sometimes changing to spots or bars on flanks which in some are tinted bluish; a light stripe over eye; sides of head light, but streaked darker, the light, streaked area extending down sides of neck and around on back of neck, thus interrupting uniformity of upper coloration; moustachial streak down side of jaw narrow and not prominent; most of bill slaty-blue, blackening at tip; base of bill and cere greenish-yellow; iris dark brown; legs and feet yellow, claws bluish-black.   *Adult female:* Similar in markings to adult male, but deep umber-brown above, nearly uniform or only interrupted by lighter, streaked neck-band; spots on wing-feathers rather tawny; tail like back, but usually crossed by three or four yellowish or whitish bars and tipped white; tip of bill black shading into dark brown and into greenish-yellow at base of lower mandible; cere yellow or greenish-yellow; iris dark brown; legs and feet lemon yellow (B. H. Warren).   *Young in first winter and juvenal plumages:* Similar to female.   *Downy young:* Yellowish (Audubon).

MEASUREMENTS. — *Male:* Length 10.00 to 10.50 in.; spread about 23.50 to 26.00; folded wing 7.00 to 7.85; tail 4.65 to 5.25; bill .48 to .50; tarsus 1.30 to 1.40.   *Female:* Length 12.00 to 13.50 in.; spread about 24.00 to 26.50; folded wing 8.30 to 8.60; tail 5.30 to 5.50; bill .55 to .60; tarsus 1.55 to 1.60.   Female larger than male.   Weight, male 5 to 6 oz.; female nearly 8 oz. (B. H. Warren).

PLATE 44

PLATE 44

DUCK HAWK
Page 164

Immature Male

PIGEON HAWK
Page 172

Adult Male

Immature Female

SPARROW HAWK
Page 178

Adult Female

Adult Male

All about one-third scale

Louis Agassiz Fuertes

MOLTS. — Juvenal plumage acquired after natal down by complete molt. No noticeable change during winter, but in May young birds begin molt of back and scapulars; after this molt (which is complete) immature bird becomes virtually as adult in first winter plumage; may require another year to acquire highest plumage.

FIELD MARKS. — Size so near that of Sparrow Hawk that difference cannot be determined in field, except by lighter brown back and distinguishing marks of latter; (see field marks under Sparrow Hawk, page 178); in poor light and with brief glimpse a Nighthawk in flight might be mistaken for it; but in good light, Nighthawk's white wing spots identify it at once; Pigeon Hawk is a heavy, stocky bird with the long sharp-pointed wings of a falcon; resembles a pigeon in flight, with rapid wing-beats; sails more or less with extended wings; long, pointed wings and dark breast distinguish it from Sharp-shinned Hawk, with longer tail and shorter rounded wings. *Adult male:* Bluish above; whitish, darkly streaked, below. *Female and young:* Dusky brownish above, streaked below; distinguished from Sharp-shinned Hawk by stockier form and "rowing" flight of the long, pointed wings. "Sharp-shin" is slimmer and often larger.

VOICE. — Usually silent, but vociferous when nesting, if disturbed, uttering piercing, quavering cries. "A rapidly repeated *wheet, wheet, wheet,* varied to a *ki ki ki,* harsher in the female than in the male." (C. W. Townsend); when disturbed at nest an angry *cac, cac, cac, cac, cac,* varied by a shrill piercing *ki-e-e-e-e* (O. W. Knight); while on the wing a rapidly delivered *kla-kla-kla-kla-kla-kla* like a familiar note of the Sparrow Hawk (Brewster).

BREEDING. — In northern forests. *Nest:* Commonly in coniferous tree from six feet up on a thick branch to near the top of tall pine; sometimes in a deserted crow's nest or in a hollow tree, on ledge of rocky cliff or on face of bank or bluff; very rarely on ground, built usually of sticks, and lined with grass or moss and strips of bark and sometimes some hair; bulky, as large as a crow's, but when on ledge only a few dead leaves or bits of decaying rock. *Eggs:* 4 to 7, often 5; 1.48 to 1.80 by 1.14 to 1.30 in.; rounded, short ovate, sometimes almost elliptical; varying from nearly pure white to deep purplish-brown, and probably always spotted and blotched with reddish-brown of various shades; closely resemble, except in size, those of Duck Hawk; illustrated in Bendire's "Life Histories of North American Birds," Vol. I, Plate X, Figs. 4, 8. *Dates:* April 20, Oregon; April 28, Iowa; May 13, Idaho; July 5, Montana; June 6, Great Slave Lake; June 9, Magdalen Islands. *Incubation:* Period probably about 21 days (Bendire); probably by both sexes. One brood yearly.

RANGE. — North America, Middle America and northern South America. Breeds from northwestern Alaska and northwestern Mackenzie south, except in Pacific coast region, in mountains to California; and from Ontario, northern Ungava (Quebec) and Newfoundland south to Minnesota, Iowa and Wisconsin (casually), northern Michigan, southern Ontario, northern New York, Vermont (rarely) and Maine; south in winter from southern British Columbia, southern Colorado, Nebraska, Missouri, Ohio, Pennsylvania, Connecticut, Rhode Island, Massachusetts and Maine (occasional), through Middle and Southern states to West Indies, and through Mexico and Central America to Ecuador and Venezuela; there are nesting records in Jamaica, in Cuba and one in Delaware.

DISTRIBUTION IN NEW ENGLAND. — *Maine:* Migrant, and rare summer resident; no definite breeding record, but pairs remain for summer in various parts of the state, and young birds unable to fly have been observed.[1] Rare in winter near southern coast. Capt. Herbert L. Spinney, former President of the Maine Ornithological Society, states that the Pigeon Hawk usually migrates at Seguin in the fall, by the hundreds.[2] *New Hampshire:* Common migrant, may breed in northern mountains.[*] *Vermont:* Irregular migrant, apparently more rare in spring than in autumn, doubtful summer records. *Massachusetts:* Fairly common migrant, especially in fall, most common coastwise; rare in winter; no au-

---

[1] Knight, O. W.: Birds of Maine, 1908, p. 245.
[2] Journal, Maine Ornithological Society, Vol. VIII, 1906, p. 101.
[*] In May, 1926 a nest with 3 eggs of this species was reported at Manchester.

thentic breeding record. *Rhode Island:* Common migrant, especially in fall, most common coastwise; rare winter resident. *Connecticut:* Fairly common migrant, spring and fall, most common coastwise; occasional in winter.

SEASON IN MASSACHUSETTS. — April 10 to May 16; September 7 to November 24 (winter).

HAUNTS AND HABITS. The handsome, speedy, little Pigeon Hawk is a small falcon resembling the Duck Hawk in power and speed, but, being much smaller and of less weight, it cannot attain such momentum as is exhibited in the swift dashes of the latter. It has received its name either because it was accustomed to prey on wild pigeons (as in fact it was) or because of its resemblance to a pigeon in form and flight. This hawk is seen here chiefly in the fall migrations, when from September to November it follows southward the flights of smaller birds. Oftentimes it appears quite tame. A few have been recorded in winter, but winter records should be received with caution, as the Sharp-shinned Hawk frequently is mistaken for the Pigeon Hawk. Although the latter is naturally a forest bird and breeds in the woods, it hunts while in southern New England mainly in open lands or about the shores of the larger streams or bodies of water and along the sea coast. It likes to take a stand on post, pole or tree where, having an unobstructed view, it can survey at leisure the wild life of the locality, and from which it can launch forth in swift pursuit of some passing bird, or plunge into some near-by thicket after some timid warbler or sparrow. I never saw one descend almost perpendicularly from a great height upon its prey, as the Duck Hawk often does, and I have not seen one actually strike its prey. Its usual method is to chase the prospective victim, which in most cases it can overtake with apparent ease; but in my experience it is frequently baffled by the sudden doublings of the pursued, until it gives up the chase or the hunted bird escapes by suddenly diving into water or dense shrubbery. I have seen a Pigeon Hawk chase a small flock of Common Terns without even touching one, and once in Florida I watched one pursuing for a long time a flock of Sandpipers, but it was unable to catch one as long as the chase was maintained within my field of vision. The hawk seemed to be able to overtake them and to follow their flash-like turns quite closely, but could not lay its claws on a single bird; snipes and sandpipers continually escape, and probably the hawk cannot often take a vigorous shore bird in full possession of its faculties, but a weak, sickly or wounded bird would stand little chance before it.*

My good friend, the late Wm. Brewster, said that in an experience of 50 years, he had seen a Pigeon Hawk capture its prey only twice. It is quite possible that the bird may be merely playing with its victims at times, as the following beautifully written descriptions from Brewster's pen seem to indicate: "1895, September 10. — The shrill outcry of a little Falcon, coming from the further shore of our cove at Pine Point as I was bathing there early this morning, sounded exactly like that of a Sparrow Hawk, but its author proved to be a Pigeon Hawk. He was either playing or fighting with a Crow, the former I thought, for although the behavior of both birds was rough and aggressive,

---

* The Pigeon Hawk's failure to catch flickers is described in Journal Maine Ornithological Society, Vol. VI, 1904, p. 74.

it seemed to represent mutual participation in a sportive game curiously regulated and much enjoyed. Thus the successive lungings and chasings were not either one-sided or haphazard, but so conducted that each bird alternately took the part of pursuer and pursued, and when enacting the latter rôle gave way at once, or after the merest pretence of resistance, to flee as if for its life, dodging and twisting; yet it was prompt enough to rejoin the other bird at the end of such a bout, when the two would rest awhile on the same stub, perching only a few feet apart and facing one another, perhaps not without some mutual distrust. During these aërial evolutions the Hawk screamed and the Crow uttered a rolling croak, almost incessantly. They separated and flew off in different directions when my presence was finally discovered . . . 1895. September 24. — About seven o'clock this morning a Pigeon Hawk drove a flock of ten or a dozen Blue Jays into the birch grove near our camp on Pine Point and during the next ten minutes circled or hovered low over or near them. As long as they remained perched he made no attempt to attack them, although the foliage was everywhere too thin to afford them much shelter. Nor did they stay in it long at a time, being too restless and venturesome. Whenever one rose on wing above the trees and tried to steal away, as happened every half-minute or less, the Hawk instantly gave chase, vibrating his pinions ceaselessly, rapidly, and tremulously, as those of the Duck Hawk are moved on similar occasions, and flying with such exceeding velocity that my eyes could scarce follow him. His lavish expenditure of speed and energy in pursuit of the slow-winged Jays seemed almost as absurdly needless as that of a race horse might be were he employed to run down a cow or a goat. Of course I expected to see the Hawk capture his prey at the end of every swoop, especially when, with evident eager hope of such result, he checked his impetus more abruptly than birds of his kind are often able to do and thrust forward his widespread talons; but the Jay always dodged them at the last available moment by dropping suddenly into a tree-top. After keeping straight on for a short distance the little Falcon would then circle and rise to make ready for renewed assault. He never hovered directly over the Jays when they were in the trees, but invariably kept well off to one or another side of the flock, as if to offer them what might seem a tempting chance to escape, although it may have been done for the purpose of enabling him to avoid steep descent when making his dashing swoops. These were ordinarily from twenty to forty yards in length, and trending so slightly downward that the total drop was no more than six or eight feet for the entire distance which was often covered by the Hawk before the Jay had flown one quarter as far. Altogether his admirably swift and graceful forays furnished one of the most beautiful and interesting spectacles of the kind that I have ever witnessed, despite their unvarying ill-success. Although appearing to make them in dead earnest he may, perhaps, have been merely amusing himself. Such, apparently, was the impression of the Jays; at least they did not take him seriously enough to seem very much afraid of him." [1]

There is one bird, however, that this hawk rarely misses. It will follow every twist and turn of the English Sparrow and soon overtakes its victim. Then its talons flash out

---

[1] Brewster, William: The Birds of the Lake Umbagog Region of Maine, Part 2, 1925, pp. 358–359.

and the chase is ended. Blackbirds, Meadowlarks and sparrows in flight over the water or over the salt marsh are easy victims and occasionally a swallow is caught. Sometimes the hawk in pursuit of a bird will rise abruptly in the air above it and then plunge diagonally downward upon it with the speed of an arrow. Such tactics must be successful in some cases, but when the fleeing quarry eludes the rush, the impetus of the hawk's plunge carries him by, and thus the victim gains ground.

The food of the Pigeon Hawk consists chiefly of small birds, small mammals and insects. In autumn it hangs about flocks of slow-flying birds, such as blackbirds, and has been seen to dive through a flock of them and come out with "one in each fist." It picks up many sickly or crippled birds, and captures birds from the size of a warbler to that of a flicker or a small dove. Dr. Fisher reports on the contents of 66 stomachs of Pigeon Hawks as follows: 2 contained poultry; 41, small birds; 2, mice; 16, insects; and 5 were empty. Among the bird contents was one Chimney Swift which shows that this hawk is skillful and fast enough to catch now and then one of the swiftest fliers among birds. Often when insects are plentiful or other food is scarce, this hawk eats many pests. Mr. Brewster found large numbers of grasshoppers in the viscera of one bird.[1] Mr. H. H. Bailey found in the stomach of another taken in Florida three scorpions, a large "dor-bug," remains of grasshoppers and several large beetles.[2]

ECONOMIC STATUS. Apparently this hawk does little harm to game or poultry but is destructive to small birds. The mice and insects and "English" Sparrows that it takes should be set down to its credit. On the whole, as it is not generally a very common bird in New England and is here chiefly as a migrant, it is of little economic importance in the region.

Cérchneis tinnúnculus (LINNÆUS). **Kestrel.**

DESCRIPTION. — Resembling American Sparrow Hawk somewhat in shape, color of back and markings, but much larger. *Adult male:* Above largely slaty-bluish on head, rump, upper tail-coverts and

HEAD OF KESTREL
Adult Male

tail, which has a broad black subterminal band and white tip; head with dusky shaft-lines; back, scapulars, tertials and wing-coverts reddish-brown or pale chestnut-red, spotted black; primaries and secondaries chiefly dark grayish-brown, barred white and reddish-brown on inner webs; forehead, lores, a stripe over eye, chin and throat creamy, ear coverts ashy-gray, and blue gray moustachial stripes; below variable, but usually pale buff with brownish-black shaft-streaks which broaden on lower breast and flanks, sometimes becoming broad arrow-heads on flanks and belly; under tail-coverts and leg-feathering marked little or not at all; axillars and wing linings white, spotted or barred dusky; bill bluish-horn, paler horn at base; cere and bare skin around eye yellow; legs and feet yellow, claws blackish. *Adult female:* Reddish-brown or reddish-chestnut above, streaked black on crown and nape, and barred black on back, scapulars and secondaries; below, as adult male, but leg-feathers more heavily streaked or barred. *Young in juvenal plumage:* Similar to female. *Downy young:* Nearly pure white at first, pale gray later.

---

[1] The Birds of the Lake Umbagog Region of Maine, Part 2, 1925, p. 361. [2] Birds of Florida, 1925, p. 72.

MEASUREMENTS. — *Male:* Length 12.50 to 14.50 in.; spread about 27.00; folded wing 9.00 to 9.62; tail 5.71 to 6.52; bill .47 to .54; tarsus 1.30 to 1.36. *Female:* Length about 14.50 to 15.50 in.; spread 28.00 to 30.00; folded wing 9.04 to 9.75.

MOLTS. — Apparently juvenal plumage is worn through first winter and spring; in summer, molt begins and may be continued until another spring, with young male in a mixed nondescript plumage most of the time; molting goes on more or less of the time until the bird is between two and three years old, when in June or July the plumage seems to become as adult; some adults may be found molting nearly every month in the year.

FIELD MARKS. — *Male:* Resembling Sparrow Hawk in color and markings of back, but larger, and head, *rump and tail slaty or bluish-gray;* has subterminal black band on tail. *Female:* Similar but duller.

VOICE. — Cry, a sharp scream *kee-kee-kee.*

BREEDING. — Usually about cliffs or ruins or in woods. *Nest:* Some old and flattened nest of crow, rook, hawk or squirrel, or a scratched-out hollow on shelf of some cliff or in hollow tree, or some recess in a building, rarely on ground. *Eggs:* Usually 4 or 5, rarely 7 to 9; averaging about 1.54 by 1.28 in.; white, washed or blotched dark reddish-brown, this sometimes covering entire egg; some have yellowish-brown or violet markings; illustrated in Morris' "Natural History of the Nests and Eggs of British Birds," 1896, Vol. I, Plate XVII. *Dates:* About middle of April to middle of May, England. *Incubation:* Period 27–28 days. One brood yearly.

RANGE. — Northern part of Eastern Hemisphere. Breeds over most of its range, south in winter to East Africa and parts of India, accidental in Greenland and Massachusetts; subspecies represent the species on Cape Verde, Canary and Madeira Islands and in northeastern and eastern Africa, Japan and mountains of India and China.

DISTRIBUTION IN NEW ENGLAND. — Accidental visitor; one record. *Massachusetts:* Hull, female taken at Strawberry Hill, Nantasket Beach, September 29, 1887 by F. H. Brackett.[1] NOTE. This date appears to be correct, Dr. G. M. Allen gives it wrongly as "1889" *not* "1887" in the "Aves," Part II, Fauna of New England. The same error is made by Howe and Allen in their "Birds of Massachusetts" although in the foot-note the record and the correction thereto (correct as to date) of Cory is given — a comedy of errors, for in the first report (Jan. Auk) the locality of the capture is given as "Nantucket" which is corrected in the April Auk to "Nantasket Beach;" but Howe and Allen give the name of the shooter, "F. H. Brackett," which Mr. Cory fails to do.

HAUNTS AND HABITS. This species hunts like the Sparrow Hawk much in the open country and has similar habits of perching and flight. It is called the "windhover" by the country people of England, because of its habit of hovering over its prey exactly as does the American Sparrow Hawk. Its food consists largely of mice, rats, moles, a few small birds and many insects; occasionally it takes young game birds; moles, shrews, lizards, frogs and earthworms are taken at times. As it has been recorded once in Massachusetts, it may occur here again and should be looked for.

ECONOMIC STATUS. Dr. W. E. Collinge, the chief British authority on the economic value of birds, estimates that the beneficial elements in its food constitute 64.5 per cent while it is only 6 per cent injurious.

---

[1] Cory, C. B.: Auk, Vol. V, 1888, pp. 110 and 205.

Cerchneis sparvéria sparveria (Linnæus). Sparrow Hawk.

Plates 38 and 44.

DESCRIPTION. — Smallest American Hawk. Emargination and sinuation of primaries as in Pigeon Hawk; 2nd and 3rd longest. *Adult male:* Top of head ashy-blue with chestnut patch on crown (sometimes wanting); a conspicuous black patch running from before eye down to and along jaw, bounding side of throat, another similar patch on hind border of ear coverts, and three others forming a broken band around nape (some of these sometimes wanting); back chestnut or reddish-cinnamon (like crown-patch) and barred black, sometimes very sparingly; back of neck unbarred; tail chestnut with broad black subterminal band and white, buffy or tawny tip; outer feathers chiefly white, barred black; wing-coverts and secondaries ashy-blue, former with more or less black spots (sometimes wanting), a large black spot on secondaries, primaries black on outer webs and all primaries and nearly all secondaries with black and white bars on inner webs, tips of most flight-feathers margined white; forehead (more or less), lores and sides of head whitish where unmarked with black; chin and throat white; below white or whitish, usually tinged with buff or tawny anteriorly and sometimes over whole lower body, and often spotted more or less with black; wing linings and axillars white, with black and dusky spots; bill pale bluish-horn or slaty-bluish darkening at tip; iris medium brown to very dark brown or hazel; cere, bare skin around eye yellow, sometimes bordering on orange; legs and feet yellow or orange, often greenish-yellow. *Adult female:* Similar to male but duller; top of head and back of neck usually with fine black shaft-streaks; wing-coverts and alula usually cinnamon *copiously barred black;* back and tail cinnamon with many narrow black bars and no white; below (except chin, throat and hinder plumage), streaked with dark brown; wing linings and axillars whitish, spotted with brown. *Young in juvenal plumage:* Both male and female closely resemble parents of their respective sexes, but, in general, color of back deeper and bars broader and even blacker; feathers of body plumage more loose and fluffy than in adults; tail and wings usually shorter; legs, feet and cere paler yellow; young males usually more streaked below where adult males are spotted.*

MEASUREMENTS. — *Male:* Length 8.75 to 10.60 in.; spread 20.00 to 22.00; folded wing 6.55 to 8.05; tail 4.20 to 5.50; bill, without cere, .40 to .50; tarsus 1.25 to 1.55. *Female:* Length 9.00 to 12.00; spread 23.00 to 24.50; folded wing 6.90 to 8.15; tail 4.50 to 6.00; bill .45 to .55; tarsus 1.35 to 1.45. Female usually but not always larger than male. Weight about 4 oz. (E. H. Eaton).

MOLTS. — Young birds acquire a plumage resembling adults before nestling down is entirely shed; they appear to be as adult after postnuptial molt the second season when about a year and a half old; adults apparently acquire winter plumage by complete molt (June to October).

FIELD MARKS. — Near size and shape of Pigeon Hawk, but smaller; often mistaken for it, but much lighter (reddish-brown back) and with three upright black marks on side of head; female Sparrow Hawk has *bright reddish-brown tail with many narrow black bars;* female and immature Pigeon Hawks are dusky brownish above *with several incomplete lighter bars on tail;* frequently hovers over the grass; jets its tail once or twice upon alighting; Pigeon Hawk and Sharp-shinned Hawk also do this but less commonly; in flight the long pointed wings, which make the tail appear rather short, distinguish it from the "Sharp-shin" with its long tail and shorter, rounded wing-tips; the Sparrow Hawk, when flying and sometimes when perched, looks like a great swallow.

VOICE. — Familiar call *killy-killy-killy-killy-killy-killy;* "a shrill clamorous *kee-kee,* male's voice is higher keyed than that of female, cry oft repeated," also a call *"clac-lac-lac-lac-lac-lac"* (William Brewster); *ki-wee, ki-wee, ki-wee* repeated several times (O. W. Knight); has a mild *quee-quee-quee,* but bird screams loudly when nest or young are disturbed (J. A. Farley).

---

*For a full discussion and description of the details of the varying plumages of the Sparrow Hawk, see Mearns in "A Study of the Sparrow Hawks of America," Auk, Vol. IX, 1892, pp. 252–270.

BREEDING. — In woodland, orchard, village or on city street. *Nest:* Usually in hollow tree, sometimes in rock cavity, hole in bank, compartment in bird house or some nook or cranny in a building; without nesting material except such as some former occupant may have left there; said sometimes to make nest of grass in the west or to occupy deserted nest of crow. *Eggs:* 4 to 7, usually 5; laid on chips in tree cavity or rarely in old open nest of some other bird; 1.20 to 1.48 by 1.04 to 1.35 in.; approaching spherical or spheroidal form; from white to reddish-white, creamy-buff or (rarely) reddish-cinnamon, spotted, blotched and marbled more or less, with various browns or cinnamon, and rarely with a few lavender shell markings; very variable; illustrated in Bendire's "Life Histories of North American Birds," Vol. I, Plate X, Figs. 11 to 16. *Dates:* April 5 to May 15, middle and southern states; April 26 to May 20, Connecticut; April 27 to May 26, Massachusetts; May 25 to June 14, Maine; some pairs have eggs much earlier than others. *Incubation:* Period given by some authors as about 21 days, and by others as 29 to 30 days, latter probably nearly correct; both sexes incubate. One brood yearly.

RANGE. — North America (except extreme northern parts), chiefly east of Rocky Mountains and south to Central America. Breeds from Yukon, northwestern Mackenzie, Manitoba, southern Ontario, southern Quebec and Newfoundland, west to Colorado, and south to western Oregon, central Alberta and eastern Texas (except most of southern part), and other Gulf states (except Florida and southern parts of other Gulf states where its place is taken by a smaller subspecies); in California and the more arid western regions west of the Rocky Mountains is replaced by the Desert Sparrow Hawk; in winter from southern British Columbia (very rarely), Kansas, Iowa (rarely), southern Michigan, central Illinois, Indiana, Ohio, southern Ontario, central New York, southern Vermont, Massachusetts, southern Maine (occasionally) and Nova Scotia (casually) south through eastern Mexico to Costa Rica.

DISTRIBUTION IN NEW ENGLAND. — *Maine:* Common migrant and summer resident; rare winter resident in southern coastal region. *New Hampshire:* Common migrant; less common or rare summer resident north to White Mountain region; rare in winter in southern part. *Vermont:* Uncommon to common migrant and summer resident; rare in winter in central and southern parts. *Massachusetts:* Rather uncommon to common migrant and summer resident; uncommon to rare winter resident, chiefly near coast and in Connecticut Valley. *Rhode Island:* Common migrant; rare winter and summer resident. *Connecticut:* Resident; more common in summer in the northern half of state.

SEASON IN MASSACHUSETTS. — Permanent resident.

HAUNTS AND HABITS. The pretty little Sparrow Hawk seems to have become more common of late in eastern Massachusetts than it formerly was. It adapts itself to civilization,* and has learned to utilize for nesting purposes bird-houses and nesting-boxes and nooks and crannies in churches, factories and other buildings. Not long ago a pair had a nest near the building of the Boston Society of Natural History, and one summer day the young appeared on the lawn beside the museum. In recent years Sparrow Hawks have been seen frequently sitting erect on trees in the Boston Public Garden or flying about the Garden in an irregular, erratic manner; and a pair has bred close by the State House on Beacon Hill. In 1922, so Mr. George F. Morse, Jr., informs me, a pair reared a brood in a hole under the eaves of a house on Walk Hill Street, Mattapan, a populous part of Boston. Sparrow Hawks have nested in recent years in a tannery in Peabody and in a factory at Holyoke, Massachusetts. I have seen two pairs nesting in Martin houses, one in Concord, Massachusetts, the other in Groton.

* The Sparrow Hawk has been seen to take advantage of forest fires in driving out its prey — insects, small reptiles and rodents — and to dash fearlessly within a few feet of the flames and perch in smoke so thick that it was lost to view. As many as 20 individuals were noted at one time at a fire (Auk, Vol. XXXIV, 1917, p. 209).

Sparrow Hawks usually begin mating in Massachusetts some time in April.   It is quite possible that they mate for life as some other hawks are supposed to do.   The female seems to take the initiative in mating, when they play about in the air in a peculiar way which is well described by Brewster as seen by him in May at Lake Umbagog on the border of Maine and New Hampshire.   His description of this mating play is succeeded by another note on play of another kind; both of these passages follow: "1881, May 17. — A pair of Sparrow Hawks are haunting the shores of the flooded river-meadows near the Lake House with the evident intention of breeding somewhere there.   To-day I saw them sitting not far apart on the tops of neighbouring dead balsams.   Every now and then one, always the male, I thought, would mount high in air to fly very rapidly, in a wide circle over and around where the other was perched, bending the tips of his wings downward and quivering them incessantly, at the same time uttering a shrill clamorous *kee-kee* cry, oft repeated.   Sometimes both would start off together, to chase one another far and near, describing all manner of beautiful curves and occasionally sweeping down almost to the surface of the water.   On re-alighting they invariably chose the very top-most twigs, often very slender ones, and settled on these with no less abruptness than precision, yet with admirable grace, scarce checking their speed until the perch was well-nigh reached and just then deftly folding their shapely wings: "1888, September 12. — In a broad expanse of hilly burnt ground bordering on the Dead Cambridge above the Sluice we saw a Sparrow Hawk amusing himself at the expense of two Flickers.   Calling *clac-lac-clac-lac-clac-lac* he would first hover over them for a few seconds, and then dart down close past them, to rise and hover again.   Whenever they took flight he accompanied them, describing graceful curves and circles above and around them.   That all this was done without malice on his part seemed obvious, and the Flickers evidently so interpreted it, for they showed no fear of him and more than once flew into a tree where he had just settled, alighting within a few feet of him." [1]   (See in this connection "Habits of the Flicker" (Howitt), Auk, Vol. XLII, 1925, p. 134.)

Such behavior is common among Sparrow Hawks, as they are playful and frolicsome creatures.   Oftentimes birds pay no alarmed attention to the hawk and equally the hawks do not seem to regard the birds, but if pressed by hunger they do not hesitate to attack birds fully as large as themselves, and then a flicker or a Blue Jay may be the first victim, and very rarely it has been seen to strike a "quail."   Prof. W. W. Cooke records a case where a Sparrow Hawk was seen chasing a shrike.[2]   It is a common habit of this hawk, while hunting, to hang suspended in the air by its hovering wings while watching for an opportunity to pounce on some insect or mouse in the grass.   Mr. Aretas A. Saunders says that while he watched one hovering close by, it squealed several times like a mouse, and he wonders if it was trying to entice a mouse from its concealment. Both parents join in the care of the eggs and young, and they are liberal providers and fierce defenders.   They have been known to attack the Crow and both Red-shouldered

---

[1] Brewster, William: The Birds of the Lake Umbagog Region of Maine, Part 2, 1925, p. 363.
[2] Auk, Vol. XXXI, 1914, p. 480.

and Red-tailed Hawks in defense of their young. Occasionally, however, one "catches a tartar." This was the case with one observed by Mr. S. G. Emilio in an attack on a Pigeon Hawk. After several swoops by the Sparrow Hawk, which its enemy deftly avoided, the latter turned on its assailant and pursued it for its life, but the Sparrow Hawk, by an unexpected exhibition of speed, escaped.

My esteemed friend, Aaron C. Bagg of Holyoke, the accredited ornithologist of the Connecticut Valley, now that Robert O. Morris has passed, relates an incident which indicates both strong parental attachment and intelligence on the part of one of these birds. "Recently," he says, "one of the young Sparrow Hawks from a nest behind a water-spout near the roof of our factory fell to the ground and great was the hue and cry soon after. The mother bird came to the rescue and catching him up in her talons carried the helpless fledgling to the roof — some fifty feet or more."

The principal part of the food taken to the young consists of mice and insects, but if for any reason such food is hard to obtain, small birds are substituted. The young remain in the nest about three weeks, but are fed by the parents for some time after they are able to fly. When the young are strong on the wing and have become expert in feeding themselves, in late August or early September, the great majority of our Sparrow Hawks begin to move southward; probably most of the birds of this species seen here in winter are migrants from farther north. They are noticeable in the region about Boston during every winter month. Dr. Lucretius H. Ross of Bennington, Vermont, wrote to me that four were taken there during January and February, 1923. Sparrow Hawks wintering about the cities are obliged to feed principally on "English" Sparrows and Starlings, as at that season they can find few of the insects of which they are so fond. Dr. H. Porter Hall of Leominster, Massachusetts, saw a Sparrow Hawk strike a bird in the air which he thought was a Starling; other Starlings gathered and followed the aggressive little falcon and attacked it. In the ensuing struggle the hawk was turned over or threw himself on his back, but he finally flew off with the bird in his talons. In migration as well as in their summer home Sparrow Hawks roam over all kinds of country; they pass over unbroken forests, over the summits of our highest mountains and cross large lakes and arms of the sea, but they seem to hunt more in open country than in the woods. Grasshoppers form their chief food, when obtainable. Where grasshoppers are abundant, Sparrow Hawks appear to feed almost wholly on these insects, and rarely trouble birds.

Professor Aughey examined the stomach contents of ten of these birds from 1865 to 1873, a time when the Rocky Mountain locust, one of the greatest insect pests known, was abundant in Nebraska; in the stomachs he found 55 locusts and 311 other insects; other food found in these stomachs was mice and other small mammals, batrachians and two birds.[1] Dr. A. K. Fisher tabulates the results of examining 320 Sparrow Hawk stomachs. One contained remains of a Bob-white; 53, other birds (mostly sparrows); 89, mice; 12, other mammals; 12, reptiles or batrachians; 215, insects; 29, spiders and 29 were empty. The usual food was largely grasshoppers, crickets, caterpillars and

---

[1] First Annual Report of U. S. Entomological Commission, 1878, Appendix II, p. 45.

beetles.[1]   Mr. H. H. Bailey says that in Florida he has never known this hawk to strike a bird and that in more than twenty stomachs examined he has found only insects.[2] Once I saw one catch a Myrtle Warbler in Florida.   Occasionally about a game farm one will pick up a few very small pheasants, but they rarely take chickens.

ECONOMIC STATUS.   Ornithologists seem to be agreed that the Sparrow Hawk is a useful bird and should be protected.

FAMILY **PANDIONIDÆ**.   OSPREYS.

Number of species in North America 1 ; in Massachusetts 1.

The Ospreys are specialized hawks.   They have a peculiar close, firm plumage ; head densely feathered to bill which is toothless and heavily hooked ; wings very long ; tail ample ; both furnished with very stiff hard feathers ; legs long, very strong, but without the usual, long leg-feathering of other hawks, and clothed in short close feathers ; tarsi nearly bare ; feet large, very strong, covered with rough, reticulate processes, and talons very long and powerful.   Their oily, tough plumage is especially fitted for plunging into water, and their feet are specialized for fishing, having a reversible outer toe like the owls, so that in striking their prey the talons are paired, the pairs opposing each other. There is a bony canal at the back of the tarso-metatarsus leading the common extensor tendon of the toes through the bone near what would be called the heel in man, and thereby adding strength and rigidity to the grip of the talons, as in most of the owls. There is but one species, nearly cosmopolitan, with three or four subspecies.

ECONOMIC STATUS.   Most of the fish taken by Ospreys are believed to be of little commercial value, and the birds are a picturesque feature of shores and waterways.

Pandion haliaëtus carolinénsis (GMELIN).   Osprey.

Other name: FISH-HAWK.

Plates 37 and 38.

DESCRIPTION. — Wings very long ; 2nd and 3rd primaries longest ; tail short ; legs and claws long and powerful ; tarsi feathered part way down in front, elsewhere naked and reticulated.   *Adults* (*sexes alike*) : Above chiefly dark, vandyke brown, primaries almost black ; all flight-feathers barred with white on part of inner web ; tail with dusky bars and narrow white tip, inner webs of all but middle pair of tail-feathers regularly barred white ; head, neck and all lower plumage chiefly white ; top of head more or less streaked blackish, and a wide blackish stripe from eye down sides of neck, merging into brown of upper back ; breast more or less spotted or streaked with dark brown, heaviest spots here usually found on female ; under primary coverts banded with dark gray ; wing linings largely brown toward bend ; axillars white, sometimes marked dark brown ; iris yellow to brown ; bill black, bluish at base or on much of lower mandible ; cere, legs and feet pale bluish or bluish-white ; claws blackish.   *Young in first winter plumage:* Same as juvenal, but white tips of upper body plumage more or less worn off.   *Young in juvenal plumage:* Similar to adult but not so much pure white on head and more or less buffy below ; many

---

[1] Hawks and Owls of the United States, 1893, p. 127.   [2] Birds of Florida, 1925, pp. 72–73.

feather-edges and tips of upper plumage white; tail more regularly and profusely barred. *Downy young:* Whitish when hatched and some tufts of whitish down show on birds partly grown; such birds rather dark brownish-gray with dusky, rusty and whitish markings, a broad white stripe down entire length of hind neck and back.

MEASUREMENTS. — Length 21.00 to 24.50 in.; spread 54.00 to 72.00; folded wing 17.00 to 20.50; tail 7.00 to 10.50; bill 1.25 to 1.60; tarsus 1.95 to 2.40. Female usually larger than male, but sexes more equal in size than in most other hawks, and female sometimes the smaller; but both sexes very variable in size. *Weight:* Female 3 lbs. 3 oz. to 4 lbs. 10 oz. (B. H. Warren); male 2 lbs. 13 oz. to 3 lbs. 4 oz.

MOLTS. — Juvenal plumage usually perfect by August, and worn in some cases through first season, changed only by fading and wear; molt begins in late autumn, winter or spring, as the case may be; tail and sometimes wings molted in spring; molt of body plumage very gradual, but young bird apparently becomes as adult in autumn, when about one and a half years old; may require another year for full development; individual adults seem to be molting in every month of the year, indicating one gradual complete molt, varying somewhat in time with different individuals.

FIELD MARKS. — Size nearly as large as a small eagle; unmistakable, very dark brown above, often with considerable white on upper head, but back of neck never white like that of Bald Eagle; mostly white below with very long, bent, "crooked" wings; often seen over water; flaps rather slowly and sometimes sails and soars; often hovers high over water and then plunges down and in; as it flies away, its flapping flight, with flexible wings, resembles very much similar flight of Great Blue Heron.

VOICE. — A shrill, plaintive, rapidly repeated whistle.

BREEDING. — Usually near sea, large river or some large body of water. *Nest:* Commonly near top of tall tree (often dead), more rarely on rock, surrounded by water, and still more rarely on cliff or on ground of some island; occasionally on roof or chimney of an unoccupied building or a derrick-mast in a quarry, the crossbar of a telegraph pole, or on an artificial support furnished by man — in short, almost anywhere in a protected colony; composed of sticks, twigs, driftwood, corn-stalks, and stalks of weeds and all sorts of material, often lined with grass or seaweed and a few feathers; usually larger than the nest of any other hawk (repaired from year to year); often large enough to fill a tipcart, but rarely (on some island) a mere circle of sticks with the eggs resting on bare sand. *Eggs:* 2 to 4, commonly 3, 5 very rarely indeed.* 2.25 to 2.75 by 1.60 to 2.00 in. Very variable in size, shape and markings; short, rounded elliptical or elongate ovate; commonly white or buffy white, but varying to buffy-fawn and reddish-brown, usually heavily spotted and blotched with shades of deep brown variously distributed; illustrated in Bendire's "Life Histories of North American Birds," Vol. I, Plate X, Fig. 17 and Plate XI, Figs. 5 to 9. *Dates:* From late January to March, southern Florida; early February to late May, Alachua Co., Florida; April 12 to June 7, New Jersey; May 2 to early July, New England. *Incubation:* Period about 28 days; probably principally (generally as a rule) by female. One brood yearly. In the Okanagan District of British Columbia, Canada Geese nest more or less in trees, and in one case a pair of Geese and a pair of Ospreys were found to have eggs in the same nest.

RANGE. — North America, south to northern South America. Breeds from northwestern Alaska, northwestern Mackenzie, northern Manitoba, southern Ungava (Quebec), east coast of Labrador and Newfoundland south to Lower California, western Mexico, the Gulf coast and southern Florida; in winter south from southern California, the Gulf states and Florida through Mexico, Central America and the West Indies; recorded south to Peru and Paraguay.

DISTRIBUTION IN NEW ENGLAND. — *Maine:* Common migrant and common to rare summer resident locally, coastwise and near various bodies of water. *New Hampshire:* Rather common migrant, more common coastwise, and rare local summer resident. *Vermont:* Rather common migrant and rare local summer resident. *Massachusetts:* Common migrant coastwise; less common in interior, and common to rare and local summer resident in Plymouth, Barnstable and Bristol Counties; casual summer

---

*R. H. Howe reports the unprecedented number of 7 young in a nest at Bristol, R. I. See Auk, Vol. XII, 1895, p. 389.

resident elsewhere.   *Rhode Island:*   Common migrant and common to rare local summer resident.
Connecticut: Common migrant and uncommon to rare local summer resident; chiefly coastwise and in
Connecticut Valley.

SEASON IN MASSACHUSETTS. — (March 7 to 16) April 2 to May 31; (summer) July 31 to November
28 (December 15).

HAUNTS AND HABITS.   The Osprey is one of the few large birds that is still a familiar
sight to the inhabitants of New England, but it has decreased greatly in recent times.
There is every reason to believe that it was once a common breeding bird along the whole
coast of New England and locally in the interior.   It breeds commonly now only

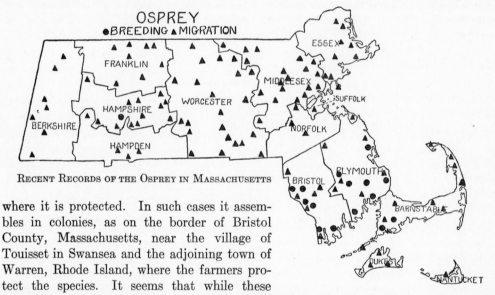

RECENT RECORDS OF THE OSPREY IN MASSACHUSETTS

where it is protected.   In such cases it assembles in colonies, as on the border of Bristol
County, Massachusetts, near the village of
Touisset in Swansea and the adjoining town of
Warren, Rhode Island, where the farmers protect the species.   It seems that while these
birds are incubating their eggs and rearing their young, they will not allow other
hawks in the vicinity of their nests, and, as the young chickens are allowed to run at large
at that season, the Ospreys protect the chickens from the forays of other hawks.   For this
reason the farmer desires to have a pair of Fish-hawks nesting as near the farm-yard as
possible.   Here and there someone has erected a tall pole in the dooryard with a cart-
wheel fixed horizontally across its top.   This makes a convenient and safe location of
which the Osprey is not slow to take advantage.   When I first visited this colony in 1900,
there were apparently about 75 nests scattered over the two townships though some of
them may have been within the boundaries of Bristol, Rhode Island; probably the colony has decreased since that time.   The region lies along the shores of Narraganset Bay
and its estuaries which then were an ideal fishing ground for the birds.   The country
near the coast being quite open and cultivated, did not offer many suitable nesting sites
for the Fish-hawks.   Most of the conveniently located, large, isolated trees were already

occupied, and some of the birds were forced to use telegraph poles or even chimneys as supports for their domiciles. On one of the roads a pole with several cross arms supporting many wires was chosen as a nesting site by a pair of these birds. The linemen tore down the nest but the birds persisted in rebuilding until one day the superintendent happened along and told the men to take the wires off the pole, set up another pole back in the field and string the wires to that. This was done and the birds triumphantly occupied the nest on the first pole.

A good friend of mine bought a farm in Touisset. The house had been unoccupied for some time, and when the family moved in they found a great nest on the top of the kitchen chimney with a pair of Ospreys in full and complete possession of the premises. Before starting a fire in the range it became necessary to remove that nest, which was accomplished by strenuous labor, as a great mass of material had been accumulated on the chimney top. Immediately the birds began to rebuild the nest. They brought large sticks and placed them across the chimney, and to hold them down they brought clods and stones. Destruction of their domicile did not discourage them in the least. At last in self-defense my friend was obliged to shoot the female. The male did not mourn long but flew away and in a few hours was back again with another mate ("just like a man," the good wife said), and the pair, having first reconnoitered the place, decided to recommence building. When they had finished, they had filled up that chimney from bottom to top with sticks, stones and rubbish, so that it became necessary to either destroy those birds or give up the house to them. When they were finally gotten rid of, it was found necessary to take out a large section from one side of the chimney in order to clear out the rubbish which choked the flue.

A few Ospreys arrive in interior southern New England in March,* but most of them return to their inland breeding grounds here early in April, and some begin to repair their old nests, for the Osprey is accustomed to utilize the same nesting-site year after year. In building on to the old nest and repairing it a great mass of material is gotten together, in time, so that the nest becomes nearly as large as that of an eagle. Some of them are enormous, and when fixed in the top of some tall dead tree one may be seen for miles. I have observed similar great nests on the Maine coast on tall rocks jutting up from the water in a bay or estuary. On Gardiner's Island, New York, where the birds are protected, many of them build their nests on the level ground, while along the coast of some Southern states nests may be found resting upon the tops of sand-dunes on sea islands.

When a nest is visited, the Ospreys usually fly about overhead uttering their complaining whistle, but sometimes they attack an intruder. There are many such cases recorded. Dr. Brewer tells of an instance in Maine where one of these birds struck a boy with such force that its talons penetrated a cloth cap, laid bare the scalp, and very nearly hurled him to the ground; and Mr. W. W. Worthington asserts in Bendire's "Life Histories of North American Birds" that one of these birds struck in the back a friend of his who

---

*An observer on the coast in the Swansea neighborhood says that the Ospreys arrive there year after year on the morning of March 24. (Bird-Lore, Vol. XVI, 1914, p. 276.)

was ascending to a nest and "nearly knocked him off the tree." There are other cases recorded where the brave birds with their strong curved claws have done the prying mortal serious harm.

Mr. Henry H. Richards, who observed a colony of Ospreys in Maine says that the young were fed indiscriminately or promiscuously without regard to family ties. Four or five different birds fed the young in one nest, and the question of which nest should receive the next fish seemed to be determined by the vociferousness of its occupants.[1] The Osprey's well-known method of fishing is to flap along over the water at a height of from 30 to 100 feet, scanning the depths below. When it sees a desirable fish near the surface, it hovers for an instant and then closing its wings shoots downward, plunging into the water with great force and often disappearing from sight. The force of the bird's plunge is so great that it must strike the surface head first, as any deviation from its course on entering the water might result in injury. Dr. A. K. Fisher remarks that he saw one of these birds actually break a wing when it struck the water. Rising to the surface it rests a mere instant, flaps into the air and starts for its nest or some tree where it intends to devour its victim. In flying away with the fish it always turns it head foremost. The robbery of this bird by the Bald Eagle is described on page 152. At least one case is recorded where the Osprey has been seen to retaliate. It was on Lake Androscoggin in Maine. An eagle had forced an Osprey to drop his fish when the smaller bird swooped down from 80 feet above the robber and attempted to strike the latter's broad back. The eagle cleverly warded off the blow with one great wing and tossed the Osprey aside, apparently without effort. After several repetitions, the Osprey gave up the unequal fight and flew away, while the eagle picked up the fish from the water.[2] Where a large colony of Fish-hawks is located, the eagles will find little chance to rob them as they will band together to resist the larger bird and even drive it from the field. The Osprey appears to be an affectionate bird; while the young are in the nest one or the other parent usually is within call, always ready to defend its offspring. When the young are fledged and able to fly well, they begin to practice catching fish for themselves. They require no teaching, as individuals that have been brought up by hand and have never seen their parents catch fish, will begin fishing for themselves as soon as they have fully mastered the intricate problem of flight. At first they have very little success. I have seen a young bird plunge into a river seven times in succession without securing a fish, but the bird did not appear to be in the least discouraged, for it continued to follow the river and scan its waters in search of a victim. The adults also now and then fail, and a wetting is all they get.* They frequently drop part way only to check their fall with spread wings and tail when the fish has gone too deep. I have evidence from eye-witnesses to the effect that a Fish-hawk has struck a fish too heavy for it to lift from the water, and has been drowned by its powerful victim. This might readily happen with a fish like a sturgeon

---

[1] Journal of the Maine Ornithological Society, Vol. XII, 1910, p. 51.

[2] Burr, Freeman F.: Auk, Vol. XXIX, 1912, p. 393.

*The Osprey has been seen to drop a strong struggling fish on to the ground, apparently to kill it, and then descend to its now quiet victim and fly off with it again. (Ornithologist and Oölogist, Vol. VI, 1881, p. 69.)

or any fish with a skin so tough that the hawk's talons driven with all the force of muscle and weight behind them could not be retracted. I have seen the bird when it had quite a struggle to lift its prey from the water, and have no doubt that in some cases it has been unable to do so and has been carried under water and drowned. Mr. Lester W. Smith affirms that he saw an Osprey carry a fish which seemed to be of a girth as large as that of the bird and its tail extended fully a foot beyond the tail of the latter. Several reports have come from the Canadian wilderness to the effect that a hawk and a big Salmon or a Sturgeon have been found locked together in death drifting on the surface of a river.

When the frosts of autumn chill the coast waters and many fishes begin to move southward, the Ospreys follow, but before they go many of them repair their nests with strong, freshly-broken sticks as if to prepare them to withstand the storms of winter. They may continue their migration into the night, as Captain H. L. Spinney reports that one struck the lantern of Seguin Island light (one of the most powerful lights) at the mouth of the Kennebec, on October 2, 1899, at 7 P.M.[1] The concussion dazed the bird and smeared the glass with its blood, yet in a few minutes it flew off into the darkness.

The food of the Osprey consists principally of fish. Now and then perhaps a frog or some other small aquatic animal is taken, and more rarely a water-snake. The fish captured are principally surface fish of little value, such as carp, suckers, pike, alewives, menhaden and sunfish — fish which normally swim near the surface. Sometimes catfish are taken, including the hornpout of New England. Blackbirds or Kingbirds occasionally chase an Osprey. Apparently they believe it to be an enemy.

In this connection it should be noted that several small birds are known to build nests and rear young in the very interstices of Ospreys' nests, where they naturally receive from the owners the same protection from hawks that is afforded the farmer's chickens.

ECONOMIC STATUS. All the evidence available points to the conclusion that the Osprey is harmless to poultry, birds and game, and that most of the fish that it takes are species of little value to mankind. Fishermen usually welcome it as a guide to good fishing. All things considered, this great, handsome, picturesque and interesting bird must be regarded as a subject for perpetual protection.

SUBORDER STRIGES. OWLS.

Number of species in North America 20; in Massachusetts 12.

This suborder includes all night-flying birds of prey. Owls are placed next to hawks in order of classification because of a certain similarity in structure of their bills, wings and claws, and because they are birds of prey, but they show an even closer affinity to the goatsuckers. The head is large and broad, but shortened lengthwise with a more or less complete ruff or disk of peculiarly constructed feathers surrounding the face. The eyes are very large and look more directly forward than those of hawks. The eyeball is

---

[1] Journal of Maine Ornithological Society, Vol. V, 1903, p. 57.

surrounded by a bony framework, and so fixed in the socket as to be nearly immovable, so that to look to one side Owls are forced to turn the head. The openings of the ears are very large and often are provided with a movable flap. The bill is shaped much as in *Accipitres*, but beset at the sides of the base by close-set, bristly feathers. The legs are more or less completely feathered, and the toes also in many species. Because of the peculiar texture of their plumage which is provided with many soft filaments, their flight is noiseless. Their peculiar vision, their extremely acute hearing and their silent flight fit them to hunt at night and to take their prey by surprise, but probably all species can see well in daylight, and some hunt commonly by day or night. Owls swallow their prey whole or in large pieces, and after the soft parts have been digested the hair, feathers, bones, scales and other indigestible parts are ejected from the mouth in the form of pellets or cylindrical masses. Owls are cosmopolitan, and about 200 species are recognized the world over. The eggs of owls are always white and immaculate.

ECONOMIC STATUS. Dr. A. K. Fisher of the Bureau of Biological Survey, United States Department of Agriculture, who has made the most exhaustive investigation of the food of American hawks and owls that was ever undertaken, and who has tabulated the stomach contents of 2700 stomachs of these birds, says — "It may be stated with confidence . . . that owls are the most beneficial of all birds, inflicting very little damage upon the poulterer and conferring vast benefits upon the farmer." This is because of the fact that they feed very largely upon nocturnal rodents and insects which are very destructive to trees and other plants and which the diurnal birds have comparatively little opportunity to destroy. Mr. E. H. Eaton gives the common owls of New York the following rating:

FOOD OF NEW YORK OWLS[1]

STOMACHS EXAMINED CONTAINING VARIOUS KINDS OF FOOD

SPECIES EXAMINED	POULTRY OR GAME	OTHER BIRDS	REPTILES (Snakes, Etc.)	BATRACHIANS (Frogs, Etc.)	MICE	OTHER MAMMALS	INSECTS	CRAYFISH AND SPIDERS	EMPTY
Beneficial									
Barn Owl . . .	3	13			56	54	14		22
Long-eared Owl .	1	14			82	5	1		15
Saw-whet Owl . .	0	4			79		5		14
Short-eared Owl .	0	11			77	7	7		14
Screech Owl . .	1/3	15	1	2 (fish 1)	36	5	40	4 (sp. 3)	17
Barred Owl . . .	5	12	1	4 (fish 2)	42	17	13	9 (sp. 2)	18
Snowy Owl . . .	5	25			48	5			33
Injurious									
Great Horned Owl	25	7		(fish 3)	11	53	8		14

[1] Eaton, E. H.: Birds of New York, 1914, Vol. 2, p. 62.

PLATE 45

PLATE 45

LONG–EARED OWL

Page 194

BARN OWL

Page 189

Adult

Adult

SHORT–EARED OWL

Page 197

Adult

All about one-third scale.

Louis Agassiz Fuertes

Family **ALUCONIDÆ.** Barn Owls.

Number of species in North America 1; in Massachusetts 1.

The Barn Owls are readily separable from all other owls because of anatomical and osteological peculiarities, but they also differ in external characters. The face instead of approaching a circular form is almost heart shaped; the fore part of the skull and the bill are somewhat elongated. The eyes are comparatively small, the legs long and the claws very long.

Economic Status. Barn Owls probably are the most useful of the owls, and should have complete and perpetual protection.

Týto álba pratíncola (Bonaparte). **Barn Owl.**

Other name: MONKEY-FACED OWL.

Plate 45.

Description. — Head very large, without ear-like tufts; eyes not very large; facial disks elongated and exaggerated; wings very long reaching beyond tail; tail short and even at end or slightly emarginated; legs long, lightly feathered almost to toes, which are bristly and nearly bare, feathers reversed on tarsi; claws very long and sharp. *Adults (sexes often alike but coloring variable)*: Above tawny, brownish or yellowish, overlaid or clouded more or less by a grayish tint, dotted, mottled or vermiculated with dusky, and spotted with blackish and pale grayish or white; wings and tail also barred dusky; below, from pure white to tawny (including linings of wings and axillars) usually paler than above, and more or less dotted and speckled dusky or blackish; facial disk white to tawny (sometimes very dark), darkening to dark brown near eyes and edged by dark brown border; bill, iris and claws black. *Young in first winter plumage:* Like adults. *Young in juvenal plumage:* There seems to be no distinctive juvenal plumage, as the plumage that succeeds the down is like that of adult, a second growth of long creamy down may be said to take the place of juvenal plumage. *Downy young:* Mostly covered with short white or yellowish down with bare patches on sides of neck and sparsely covered on belly.

Measurements. — Length 15.00 to 21.00 in.; spread 43.25 to 47.00; folded wing 11.50 to 14.00; tail 5.50 to 7.00; bill to base of skull, 1.55 to 1.78; tarsus 2.40 to 3.75. Female usually larger than male but sometimes smaller. *Weight:* Female, 1 lb. 2 oz. to 1 lb. 8 oz. Male, 1 lb. 4 oz. (B. H. Warren).

Molts. — First winter plumage immediately succeeds second down; apparently no molt occurs then until ensuing summer, when young bird probably begins complete molt and in time assumes adult winter plumage. Adults seem to have a complete molt (July to winter) and apparently no spring molt, but material examined insufficient to confirm this. One bird showed some pinfeathers on rump Dec. 10.

Field Marks. — Size nearly that of Crow but wings longer. If seen sitting, may be recognized by its pale colors, long legs and long, white, nearly heart-shaped face. If seen in flight, may be told by buffy upper plumage, light or white under plumage and long wings; flies very lightly, often reeling from side to side.

Voice. — A weird scream; a nasal "snore"; "a loud prolonged rasping *sksck*" . . . . "a series of notes *click, click, click, click, click*, resembling in character the notes of a Katydid, but delivered with diminishing emphasis and shortening intervals during the end of the series" (Grinnell and Storer); "a growling rattle" (J. W. Lippincott); "a feeble querulous note sounding like *quaek-quaek* or *aek-aek*, sounding somewhat like the cry of a Nighthawk frequently repeated, only not so loud" (Bendire). Young, — a shrill, screeching rattle (Edgar Bedell); "note similar to clucking of a squirrel, probably a call-note" and "a most piercing hissing cry as if from fright" (J. Harris Reed).

BREEDING. — Almost anywhere — nesting in hollow trees, holes in banks, or even burrows underground, barns, deserted buildings, towers, cupolas and steeples. *Nest:* None, except when eggs are deposited in deserted nest of Crow or other bird; or in barn when rude nest of rubbish may be made; eggs laid on chips and rubbish on bottom of tree-cavity or on a mass of pellets composed mostly of fur and bones, ejected by young birds of former seasons. *Eggs:* 5 to 8, sometimes 9 to 11; 1.56 to 1.97 by 1.05 to 1.50 in.; variable in shape but commonly ovate, more pointed than most owl's eggs; chalky-white sometimes tinged yellowish; less compact in texture than eggs of other Owls; illustrated in Bendire's "Life Histories of North American Birds," Vol. I, Plate XII, Fig. 1. *Dates:* July to May, Florida; last week in March to April 15, Virginia; April 16, District of Columbia; April 24, Delaware County, Pennsylvania. Barn Owls have been found nesting in autumn in South Carolina [1] and New Jersey; [2] there is a winter record of breeding at Washington D. C.[3] *Incubation:* Period 21 to 24 days (authors), sometimes may be longer; probably mostly by female, though male often found with her or at the nest, and the sexes sometimes change places; incubation begins soon after laying of first egg; eggs laid on alternate days. One brood yearly, sometimes two, in the south.

RANGE. — Extreme southern Canada, most of United States, Mexico and Central America. Resident and breeds mostly in upper and lower Austral Zones from western Washington (where resident), southern Oregon, Colorado, Nebraska, Illinois, southern Wisconsin, southern Michigan, Indiana, Ohio, New York and Connecticut (casual occurrences farther north) south through the United States and Mexico to Central America; breeds in Bahamas; has been recorded in British Columbia, Minnesota, southern Ontario, Massachusetts and Vermont.

DISTRIBUTION IN NEW ENGLAND. — Accidental in Vermont; rare visitor from the south in southern New England; breeds rarely in Connecticut. Records: *Vermont:* Lyndon, male taken June 4, 1894; [4] Danby, 1902; [5] Bennington, October 29, 1909, bird taken, Dr. Lucretius H. Ross; [6] Boltonville, bird taken in 1920 (Wendell P. Smith); Glover, bird reported in May, 1923, by Allen King; also a bird was shot "about 25 years ago at Manchester, Vermont, and identified by Geo. H. Ross of Rutland." [7] *Massachusetts:* In addition to various old records given in Howe & Allen's Birds of Massachusetts, there are the following dating from 1900: Danvers, October 18, 1900, female taken by Willis Hackett, which went to Peabody Academy, Salem; [8] Weston, Nov. 14, 1906, bird taken by Charles Merriam and now in Thayer Museum at Lancaster.[9] Nahant, Nov. 18, 1909, sight record.[10] Lexington, June 10, 1915, female taken by Chas. Fowle; [11] Wenham, October 21, 1915, bird caught in trap, by Dr. John C. Phillips.[12] Longmeadow, Oct. 31, 1915, male taken and now in Science Museum, Springfield; [13] Barnstable, January 7, 1918, male picked up dead in poultry yard and given to H. A. Torrey; [14] Edgartown, October, 1918, bird caught in trap in Edgartown Great Pond by Allan Kenniston; [15] Springfield, about Dec. 1, 1919, bird taken at Forest Park; [16] Middleboro (Rock), July 1, 1920, bird seen by A. W. Higgins with field mouse in its claws; [17] Westborough, mounted bird, taken in Autumn about 1920 by Howard C.

[1] Wayne, Arthur T.: Auk, Vol. XXV, 1908, pp. 21–24: and Chamberlain, Rhett: *Ibid.*, Vol. XXVIII, 1911, p. 112.
[2] Potter, Julian K. and Gillespie, John A.: Auk, Vol. XLIII, 1926, p. 95.
[3] Bendire, Chas. E.: Auk, Vol. XII, 1895, p. 181.
[4] Tyler, M. G.: Auk, Vol. XI, 1894, p. 253.
[5] Allen, Glover M.: Fauna of New England, The Aves, p. 108.
[6] Vermont Bird Club, Bulletin Nos. 4 and 5, 1910, p. 23.
[7] Ross, George H.: *in litt.*
[8] Townsend, C. W.: Birds of Essex County, 1905, p. 215.
[9] Thayer, John E.: Auk, Vol. XXIV, 1907, p. 214.
[10] Richards, Albert K.: *in litt.*
[11] Brooks, W. Sprague: Auk, Vol. XXXIII, 1916, p. 328.
[12] Auk, Vol. XXXIII, 1916, p. 77.
[13] Morris, Robert O.: Auk, Vol. XXXIII, 1916, p. 201.
[14] Torrey, H. A.: *in litt.*
[15] Keniston, Allan: *in litt.*
[16] Morris, Robert O.: Auk, Vol. XXXVII, 1920, p. 467.   [17] Higgins, A. W.: *in litt.*

Chamberlain; identified by E. H. F.; now in possession of Mr. Chamberlain at Westborough. *Rhode Island:* Warwick, November 1886, bird taken at Sand Pond by John Ryder;[1] Cumberland, (date not given); one shot by J. Baxter; male taken in December, 1891, went to collection at Brown University; Charlestown, January 23, 1896, bird taken by J. H. Tower.[2] Messrs. Angell and Cash, taxidermists, received the following specimens in 1924: Woonsocket, October 14, and Block Island, October 28; Bristol, November 3, 1924, bird taken (Harry Hathaway). Fred Jencks received one at Bristol the same day (probably the same bird).

BREEDING IN CONNECTICUT. — The Barn Owl is a rare breeder in Connecticut. In addition to a number of records of the occurrence of the bird, given by Sage, Bishop and Bliss in their Birds of Connecticut and others received independently by me, there are the following breeding records, the first two also being given in the Birds of Connecticut: — Winsted, 1892, nest with six young found in an old factory by H. Kinney;[3] in 1893 a pair nested in same nest, seven eggs being taken by a Mr. Williams;[4] Cromwell, 1920, nest with four young found by Phil Sutton. South Windsor, 1921–1922–1923, pair nested in Walnut tree, broken off about twenty feet from ground and hollow down about nine feet; this nest had five young, June 6, 1924;[5] nest with young first found June 6, 1921, by Mr. C. W. Vibert, (prior to 1921 the pair had nested in a near-by barn).

SEASON IN MASSACHUSETTS. — May to December.

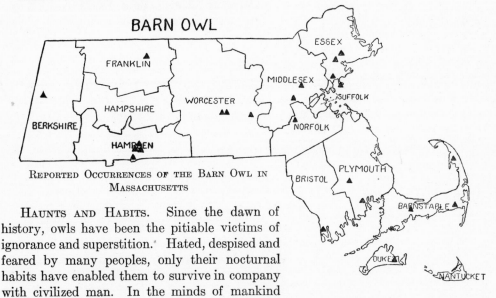

BARN OWL

REPORTED OCCURRENCES OF THE BARN OWL IN MASSACHUSETTS

HAUNTS AND HABITS. Since the dawn of history, owls have been the pitiable victims of ignorance and superstition. Hated, despised and feared by many peoples, only their nocturnal habits have enabled them to survive in company with civilized man. In the minds of mankind they have been leagued with witches and malignant evil spirits, or even have been believed to personify the Evil One. They have been regarded as precursors of sorrow and death, and some savage tribes have been so fixed in the belief that a man will die if an owl alights on the roof of his dwelling that, it is said, some Indians having

[1] Southwick, J. M.: Proceedings of Newport Natural History Society, 1888, p. 7; and Random Notes, Vol. III, 1886, p. 91.
[2] Howe, R. H, and Sturtevant, E.: Birds of Rhode Island, 1899, p. 61.
[3] Job, H. K.: The Sport of Bird Study, 1908, p. 298.
[4] Sage, J. H., Bishop, L. B., and Bliss, M. A.: Birds of Connecticut, p. 85.
[5] Vibert, C. W.: *in litt.* Reported also by Frank Bruen.

actually seen the owl on the roof-tree have pined away and died. Among all these eerie birds the Barn Owl has been the victim of the greatest share of obloquy and persecution, owing to its sinister appearance, its weird night cries, its habit of haunting dismal swamps and dank quagmires, where an incautious step may precipitate the investigator into malodorous filth or sucking quicksands, and its tendency to frequent the neighborhood of man's dwellings, especially unoccupied buildings and ghostly ruins. Doubtless the Barn Owl is responsible for some of the stories of haunted houses, which have been current through the centuries. When divested by science of its atmosphere of malign mystery, however, this owl is seen to be not only harmless but a benefactor to mankind and a very interesting fowl that will well repay close study. Unfortunately this Austral bird is seldom seen in New England. So rare indeed is it and so little known that when flushed by the hunter it is likely to be mistaken for a hawk, and so reach the termination of its useful career immediately. The name Barn Owl has reference to its habit of nesting and hiding in barns which, where both owls and barns are numerous, is a common habit, though not in New England, for I fear it would not meet with a welcome from our farmers; and here I believe it very rarely has been known to make its nest in a building. Usually it betakes itself to some hollow tree in a swamp where its retreat seldom is discovered. The Barn Owl is not really a shy and retiring bird. It has that reputation, perhaps because it seldom is seen abroad in daylight, unless disturbed by some intruder, when it flies off in an uncertain, irregular manner, as if it were unable to see well, and betakes itself to some quiet, dark retreat, where, undisturbed, it can doze away the daylight hours. Where these owls are common they frequent certain roosting places, and the ground beneath is littered with their pellets and excrement. A number of them may roost in the holes and hollows of some gigantic dead tree, and several have been found during the daytime in a partially covered old well or at the bottom of an old mine-shaft. Some roost in the shade of dense foliage; others on the ground under the shelter of tall, dense reeds or grasses.

Barn Owls frequent almost any kind of territory where mice and other little mammals may be found. In the long days of summer, when their rather numerous young require feeding often, they leave the nesting place very early in the evening, even considerably before sunset, and at this season or when driven by hunger they hunt sometimes on cloudy days. The female while incubating is steadily supplied with food by the male, but occasionally she leaves the nest, and he takes her place thereon, and probably in some cases he assumes some part of the duties of incubation, as both male and female have been seen sitting side by side on the eggs. As with some other raptorial birds, several days elapse between the laying of each of the five or more eggs in the clutch, and the young generally are of several sizes. The nestlings seem to resemble young vultures more than owls, as they are clothed like the vultures with white or yellowish down and have similar long heads and beaks. When nearly fledged the young (and the parents also) when the nest is approached, are accustomed to lower their heads and sway them from side to side, hissing like a snake, and thus presenting a gruesome

FIG. 48. — YOUNG BARN OWLS

Page 192

FIG. 49. — YOUNG BARRED OWLS

Page 203

and rather fearsome front to the enemy who comes upon them suddenly in the gloom of their retreat.

The young (see Fig. 48) are queer and weird-looking creatures and plucky, too. Some will leap savagely at an outstretched hand and scratch with their needle-pointed claws. If captured and they cannot find anything else to fight, they will often fight among themselves.[1]

The Barn Owl is not a migratory bird in the ordinary sense of the word, but it wanders in winter south of its breeding places, and in summer or fall individuals straggle northward from their summer homes. There may have been a gradual extension of the species northward in the last 50 years, as the number of records in the north has increased very materially since 1880, but this may be due to the increased number of observers.

Everything indicates that the food of the Barn Owl in the east consists almost entirely of mice and rats, with some other small mammals and a very few birds. In the west it destroys quantities of those destructive pests, gophers and ground squirrels or spermophiles; in the south the cotton rat is one of its chief victims. It is especially fitted to capture such creatures because of its power of night-sight, its remarkably large and sensitive ears which indicate wonderfully acute hearing, and its superlatively soft plumage, even more light and downy than that of other owls, which enables it to glide silently through the air upon its prey. A mouse is killed by crushing the base of the skull with the beak, and usually food is carried to the nest in the mouth rather than in the talons, the feet trailing backward in flight under the tail.

In looking through the literature regarding the food of this owl I have not been able to find an instance of the destruction by it of a single hen, chicken or game-bird; and only one pigeon appears in these tabulations. It nests occasionally in a place where pigeons breed, and the two species seem to live amicably together. All those who have had an opportunity to examine the breeding places of this owl find hundreds or thousands of pellets ejected by it, containing chiefly the bones and fur of mice, rats and other small mammals, particularly field mice, and little else, although it destroys a goodly number of insects. Professor Aughey, who examined the stomach contents of three Barn Owls in Nebraska found in them 39 locusts, 117 other insects and parts of 2 mice. Dr. A. K. Fisher summarizes the contents of 39 stomachs; 1 contained a pigeon; 3, small birds; 17, mice; 17, other small mammals, gophers, rats, etc.; 4, insects and 7 were empty. Lord Lilford, the eminent British ornithologist, remarks that a half-grown Barn Owl swallowed 9 mice, one after the other, although the tail of the last one stuck out of the greedy bird's mouth, and he estimates that a family of 7 young owls would require daily or nightly more than 150 rats, mice and such small vermin to satisfy their appetites.[2]

Economic Status. The Barn Owl is one of the most useful of birds and should be protected at all times.

---

[1] Bird-Lore, Vol. XVIII, 1916, pp. 92–96.
[2] Tegetmeier, W. B.: London Field, Vol. LXXV, 1890, p. 906.

FAMILY **STRIGIDÆ.** HORNED OWLS, ETC.

Number of species in North America 19; in Massachusetts 11.

This family includes all the owls except the Barn Owls, from which they differ conspicuously. The bill and fore part of the skull are shorter and the face is more circular or at least not triangular or heart shaped as in Barn Owls. The facial disks are developed very fully in some species, in others very imperfectly. There is a bony canal in the tarso-metatarsus for the passage of the common extensor tendon of the toes. The outer toe is reversible as in Ospreys. The outer ear parts are variously developed. Some species have twin crests on the head giving an appearance slightly resembling the ears of mammals. The eyes usually are large and prominent, although not in all species. *Strigidæ* are even more cosmopolitan than *Aluconidæ*, as representatives of the family are found in nearly all parts of the world, including the Arctic regions.

ECONOMIC STATUS. Most owls of this family are regarded as useful birds. Only one North American species, the Great Horned Owl, is condemned by the investigators. See page 188.

Ásio wilsoniánus (LESSON). **Long-eared Owl.**

Plate 45.

DESCRIPTION. — Ear-like tufts on head, long, rather narrow, conspicuous; only 1st primary emarginate near tip and only on inner web; wings long; tail rather long; legs and feet feathered to claws. *Adults (sexes alike):* Above very dusky or brownish-black, intermixed somewhat with buffy or tawny (which colors basal parts of feathers) and finely speckled or mottled with grayish-white; tail chiefly dusky with gray, marbled bars, but tawny toward base; outer primaries mainly blackish-brown, barred and mottled gray and growing tawny toward their bases; inner primaries and secondaries gradually grayer; below, whitish or tawny, marked on breast with dusky marbling, and on other lower plumage with dusky shaft-streaks, throwing off on both sides several narrow, dusky cross-bars on each feather; legs and feet, under tail-coverts and wing linings unspotted tawny, except a large dark spot or area on under primary coverts; legs and feet very rarely barred dusky, more or less; facial disk tawny, blackening about eyes and with narrow blackish border; bristles about base of bill, varying from whitish to blackish; bill and claws blackish; iris yellow. *Young in first winter plumage:* Like adults but a little more rufous. *Young in juvenal plumage:* Feathers of body and most of wing-coverts very loosely constructed and downy; flight-feathers and tail as adults; ear-tufts shorter and more downy than in adult; most of body-feathers brown, barred and tipped whitish; facial disk darker than in adult. *Downy young:* White.

MEASUREMENTS. — Length 13.00 to 16.00 in.; spread 36.00 to 42.00; folded wing 11.00 to 13.30; tail 5.50 to 6.50; bill from base of skull .70 to 1.10; tarsus 1.20 to 1.90; variable in size, but female averages a little larger than male. Weight 11¼ oz. (B. H. Warren).

MOLTS. — Juvenal body-feathers begin to molt in summer; first winter plumage much like that of adult is assumed during autumn; wing and tail quills are retained and young bird apparently becomes like adult, after complete molt the second autumn; adults appear to have one complete molt (August or September to December); some may molt a few body feathers in late winter or early spring.

FIELD MARKS. — Size approaching that of Crow; intermediate between Screech Owl and Barred Owl; if seen sitting, its rather dark colors, rusty-brown face and long "ears," rising from near the middle of head, distinguish it; in flight, which is light, wavering and uncertain, ears are not visible, nor all its markings and it may then be distinguished from Short-eared Owl by darker gray coloration (the latter is more buffy); usually seen in or near woods in breeding season, while the other is rarely if ever seen there, but in migration the Long-eared Owl may be found almost anywhere.

VOICE. — A cry "resembling the preliminary notes of a caterwauling contest" . . . "like the snarl of an angry feline" (W. L. Dawson); "a peculiar whining cry much like a very young puppy" (O. W. Knight); "a soft *wu-hunk, wu-hunk* slowly repeated several times and a low twittering, whistling note like *dicky, dicky, dicky, dicky*" (Bendire); a subdued *oo-oo* often uttered for hours at mating time, male mutters a subdued mournful cry *hoo-maa-ma-voo* when fluttering about the nest or "squeals like a half-grown rat in a trap" (J. W. Preston); "a softly whistled *whee-you*, the two syllables slurred together" (G. Clyde Fisher); "it constantly uttered low notes which suggested at times the barking of a small puppy, at times the notes *ud-hunk*." (C. W. Townsend).

BREEDING. — Generally in forest or woodland, preferring dark coniferous forests in the north. *Nest:* Usually in a coniferous tree, from 10 to 30 feet up (sometimes much higher); rarely in an isolated tree or bush; more rarely on cliff or in hole in ledge; still more rarely on ground or in hollow tree; commonly a deserted nest of crow, heron or some other bird, but occasionally builds own nest of sticks and twigs. *Eggs:* 3 to 7; 1.35 to 1.75 by 1.11 to 1.50 in.; oval or elliptical, sometimes nearly spherical; white and smooth; illustrated in Bendire's "Life Histories of North American Birds," Vol. I, Plate XII, Fig. 2. *Dates:* March 12, southern California; March 25 to April 10, Virginia; late March and April in middle states; March 15 to May 14, Massachusetts; nest with six young, about one week old, already hatched in Burlington, March 26, 1925 (A. H. Wood, Jr.). *Incubation:* Begins with first egg (eggs appear to be laid on alternate days); period variously estimated at 21 to 30 days; young remain in nest about 25 days. One brood yearly.

RANGE. — North America, north probably to about tree limit. Breeds from coast of southern Alaska, central British Columbia, southern Mackenzie, central Manitoba, Ontario, southern Quebec and Newfoundland south to southern California, Arizona, New Mexico, northern Texas, Oklahoma, Arkansas, central Tennessee and Virginia (probably North Carolina); in winter from southern Canada to central Mexico, Florida, Georgia and the Gulf states.

DISTRIBUTION IN NEW ENGLAND. — Rather common resident in the less settled regions of three northern states, often more common migrant in spring and fall; less common resident in Massachusetts and Connecticut and rare resident in Rhode Island but not uncommon in the three southern states in migration.

SEASON IN MASSACHUSETTS. — Permanent resident, most common in March and April, and October and November.

HAUNTS AND HABITS. The pretty little Long-eared Owl resembles in color the Great Horned Owl, but is much more delicately formed and its "horns" are much nearer together. Formerly it was a common bird throughout most of the forested region within its breeding range, and it is more common still than most of us realize. It once nested rather commonly within the present limits of the city of Boston and a nest has been found there within recent years. It is so nearly nocturnal that it is seen rarely except when disturbed at its nest, or surprised in some retreat in the daytime. It seems to inhabit dense coniferous woods by preference, where it hides during daylight amid the dark foliage, though at night it often hunts in the open. It is rarely seen hunting in daylight, except on very dark dull days, or just before dusk. During migration, however, it may be found anywhere, and if in a treeless country will take advantage of such hiding-places in the daytime as a thick bush or the loft of an old barn.

Mr. Allan Keniston once found one roosting in a barn on the Heath Hen reservation on Marthas Vineyard. As I happened to be there at the time, Mr. Keniston called me, and closing the door I succeeded (after several futile attempts) in catching the bird. Its flight about the barn loft was light, graceful and noiseless, much like that of the Short-eared Owl; the only sound it made was a sharp snapping of the bill such as is common to all our owls. We placed a band upon the right leg of the bird and liberated it.

The wings and tail of the Long-eared Owl are so long that in flight the bird looks larger than it really is. Its body is slight and slim, and its feathered feet are small. In winter, numbers of these birds are accustomed to hunt for field mice along river bottoms in open country where there are few coniferous trees, and to assemble to roost at night in some clump of ornamental evergreens planted to decorate the grounds of some residence. When in danger of being observed in such a retreat, they draw the feathers close to the body and stand erect so as to resemble the stub of a broken branch. If wounded or cornered and brought to bay, the bird seems to swell to about three or four times its real size, as its wings are partially extended as shields, while the feathers all over its body stand erect. Standing thus with flashing eyes, its ferocious appearance is intended to terrify its enemies. If actually attacked and unable to escape, it may throw itself on its back and present both beak and talons to the enemy.

We know little about the habits of this bird as it is abroad at night, when observation is difficult; but if one can approach its haunts on a moonlit night, and, standing perfectly still, imitate the squeaking of a mouse, he may be startled to see an owl suddenly hover within a few feet of his head.

Although nesting in trees this owl, when driven from its nest by a climbing human intruder, sometimes flutters to the ground where, uttering piercing cries and dragging her wings as if broken, she circles around and around, acting very like that ground-nesting species, the Ruffed Grouse.[1]

There seems to be a general belief that owls do not migrate, but with this species as well as with some others that range far to the north, there is a regular southward movement from the most northern part of the range, a general migration which is evident also for a greater or less distance to the southward of their usual breeding range. Therefore, in spring and autumn Long-eared Owls are more numerous in New England than at any other season. Mr. H. H. Bailey says that large numbers come into Florida from farther north to spend the winter there, the time of their arrival depending much upon weather conditions in the north, but that many arrive by December and depart northward in March.

The food of the Long-eared Owl consists almost entirely of field mice and other small mammals with many insects and a few birds.* Dr. B. H. Warren examined the stomachs

---

[1] Journal Maine Ornithological Society, Vol. IX, 1907, p. 110; and Auk, Vol. XLI, 1924, p. 479.

* Dr. C. W. Townsend reports very differently in regard to a pair of Long-eared Owls whose nest he found in the Ipswich sand dunes. The contents of pellets, etc., which he gathered at the nest, showed that the owls had eaten some thirteen different species of birds and twenty-three individuals; also seven species of mammals and twenty-five individuals. Dr. E. W. Nelson of the Biological Survey in commenting on these findings says: "This is an interesting lot of pellets, as it is very unusual to

of 23 of this species and found that 22 of them contained only mice, the other had remains of a small bird.[1]   Dr. Fisher reporting on 107 stomachs says that 1 contained a Bob-white; 15, small birds; 84, mice; 5, other small mammals; 1, insects and 4 were empty.[2]   This owl has been known to kill a Ruffed Grouse, but it takes many beetles, particularly wood-boring beetles, which are destructive to fruit and forest trees.   An examination of 225 pellets of this owl by Dr. Alexander Wetmore at Washington shows a total of 187 small mammals (mostly mice) and 5 small birds.[3]

ECONOMIC STATUS.   Wherever numbers of this species roost together, as they do commonly in many parts of the country, thousands of pellets may be found upon the ground under the trees, containing the bones and fur of small mammals, mostly mice, which the birds have eaten.   I have been unable to find a record indicating that they ever trouble poultry, and most of the few small birds that they eat are seed-eating or forest species, not of great value to agriculture.   The Long-eared Owl is a bird to be fostered, and protected.

Asio flámmeus (PONTOPPIDAN).   Short-eared Owl.

Other names: MARSH OWL; BOG OWL.

Plate 45.

DESCRIPTION. — *Ear-tufts small and very short;* ear-opening very large; wings long, rounded at tips, about twice as long as the long tail, which is slightly rounded, of 12 broad rounded feathers; legs and feet feathered to claws.   *Adults (sexes alike or similar)*: Ground color tawny to buffy-white, varying individually, usually lightest in spring and summer, streaked, spotted and mottled above (and streaked below) dark brown; wings regularly spotted and barred and tail rather regularly barred with the darker color; below, ground color grows paler from breast to tail; axillars and wing linings usually whitish with one large blackish spot near base of primaries; face whitish, often buffy or tawny above eyes (streaked there dark brown in some individuals), growing black around eyes, face edged with dark line; iris yellow; bill brownish-black to bluish-black or dark horn-color; claws bluish-dusky or dark horn, naked soles yellow.   *Young in first winter plumage:* Like adults or somewhat darker and more buffy.   *Young in juvenal plumage:* Above, darker than adults, lighter below; dark sooty brown above with broad buffy feather-tips; below, plain, dull buffy, lighter or darker individually, tinged grayer anteriorly; face plain blackish or brownish-black, surrounded by light border; iris very light straw-yellow; bill and claws dark horn color.   *Downy young:* Above pale buffy-yellow to buffy-whitish; below white with slight buffy tinge, usually some dark brown lines or patches showing on each side of body from base of wing backward.

MEASUREMENTS. — Length 12.50 to 17.00 in.; spread 38.00 to 44.00; folded wing 11.00 to 13.50; tail 5.50 to 6.60; bill .90 to 1.20; tarsus 1.50 to 1.90.   Female usually but not always larger than male, much individual variation in size.   Weight, female 13 oz. (B. H. Warren); male 1 lb. 1½ oz. (Audubon).

---

find the Long-eared Owl feeding upon birds to such an extent.   In a large number of pellets examined from winter roosts of these birds, we have found the bird remains making up considerably less than 10 per cent of the total animal contents.   The owls in question must have had exceptional opportunities to secure birds, and the breeding season may also have had some effect in producing this habit."

[1] Birds of Pennsylvania, 1890, p. 147.

[2] Fisher, A. K.: Hawks and Owls of the United States, 1893, p. 145.

[3] Bailey, B. H.: Iowa Geological Survey Bulletin No. 6, 1918, p. 185.

MOLTS. — Complete molt of natal down followed by juvenal plumage; postjuvenal molt begins very early, and by October or November first winter plumage (as adult) is complete. Adults have complete postnuptial molt (August to November), and, apparently, a partial body molt in spring.

FIELD MARKS. — Size, a little smaller than Crow; lighter, more yellowish than Long-eared Owl and wings longer, but broad, and chiefly white on under sides with a large blackish mark near base of primaries; wings and tail dark above, spotted and barred dark brown and whitish; keeps in open country, flies much in daytime with light, easy, irregular flight, flapping steadily most of the time with no neck showing; short "ears" rarely can be seen; eyes completely encircled by black; rests and roosts chiefly on ground.

VOICE. — Mating call, *toot toot toot toot toot*, etc., repeated rapidly 15 to 20 times; higher in pitch than hoot of Horned Owl; *whaq*, with a nasal intonation (Harlow); cries when nest is disturbed, barking notes when flying around or over the disturber, purring growl suggesting *mayów keyóu* or *ka-a-yóu;* a prolonged, high-pitched, squealing cry; calls to the young, a rapid series of *cuks* increasing in pitch and frequency; a series of squeaks (A. D. Dubois); "three short barks" (Mabel Densmore); when disturbed and pursued a hollow sonorous whistle (E. W. Nelson).

BREEDING. — On open moors, prairies, fields, marshes or sand dunes, usually in open, grassy, bushy lands or grain fields. *Nest:* Merely a slight hollow or trampled place in grass or reeds or in or under shrubbery; rarely in a burrow; sometimes a number of sticks collected; lined with scanty dried vegetation and some owl feathers. *Eggs:* 4 to 7, rarely up to 9; 1.37 to 1.65 by 1.22 to 1.30 in.; often elliptical, "varying from oval to elliptical ovate" (Bendire); white or faintly creamy; smooth shelled; illustrated in Bendire's "Life Histories of North American Birds," Vol. I, Plate XII, Fig. 3. *Dates:* May 9 to June 28, New Jersey; April 20, Michigan; April 28, Rhode Island; June 10, Massachusetts; May seems the favorite month in Oregon and June in northern Canada. *Incubation:* Period not certainly known, believed to be about three weeks; apparently by female. One brood yearly, may have two rarely, as in Europe.

RANGE. — North and South America, from the Arctic coast and Greenland to Tierra del Fuego and most of Europe and Asia. Breeds more or less locally throughout its range; not known to breed in southeastern United States south of New Jersey, Pennsylvania, northern Ohio, northern Indiana, northern Illinois, Missouri, Oklahoma and Colorado; in winter south throughout most of the United States to southern Texas and southern Florida; accidental in Cuba; a subspecies is resident in Hawaii.

DISTRIBUTION IN NEW ENGLAND. — *Maine:* Uncommon local resident; more common migrant coastwise. *New Hampshire:* Uncommon to rare local migrant; more common coastwise. *Vermont:* Uncommon migrant; casual local resident. *Massachusetts:* Uncommon to common migrant locally, mainly coastwise or in river valleys; locally common in winter in Nantucket; rather rare local summer resident generally. *Rhode Island:* Uncommon migrant, and rare summer resident. *Connecticut:* Uncommon to common migrant, rare summer resident and rare local winter resident.

SEASON IN MASSACHUSETTS. — Most common March 11 to May 4 and September 24 to November 30; seen every winter month, resident and breeding on Nantucket and Marthas Vineyard.

HAUNTS AND HABITS. The Short-eared Owl is a bird of the open. Over prairie, marsh, meadow, savannah and even over the sea its tireless dappled wings bear it on and on in soundless wavering flight. In air it exemplifies the poetry of motion. Its pinions press softly on the resistant element and waft the bird gently about over its favorite moors as lightly as a night-moth. In the wide savannahs of Florida, bathed in the effulgent moonlight of that subtropical land, it has fluttered noiselessly about my head, its curiosity excited by the strange intruder on its ancient hunting ground. On the rolling hills of Nantucket and on the bushy plains of Marthas Vineyard, I have watched with delight its daylight hunting, or have had three or four at a time floating erratically about me in the dusk of early evening.   In some regions it is called the Marsh or Bog Owl because of its apparent predilection for marsh hunting, and it quarters over marshes as assiduously as a Marsh Hawk; but like the latter it is by no means confined to marshes, for it hunts and even rears its young on high dry plains and desert dunes.   Its only requirements are open lands and an abundance of mice — its favorite prey.   It nests on the dry plains of Marthas Vineyard in the Heath Hen country, and on sandy islands in the sea, where there is no fresh water; and it is fond of cruising along sandy beaches and hunting insects over the water, sometimes pursuing them at some distance from land, as does the Laughing Gull.   In hunting it may fly only a few feet above the ground, its

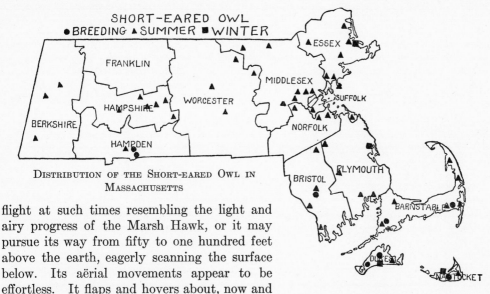

DISTRIBUTION OF THE SHORT-EARED OWL IN MASSACHUSETTS

flight at such times resembling the light and airy progress of the Marsh Hawk, or it may pursue its way from fifty to one hundred feet above the earth, eagerly scanning the surface below.   Its aërial movements appear to be effortless.   It flaps and hovers about, now and then sailing lightly along.   When it sees a favorable opportunity, it may hover for a moment or may drop directly on its prey and remain there to devour it; or if flying low it may snatch the unlucky victim from the ground, and pass on without even checking its speed, so swift and skillful is its stroke.   If three or four are cruising about together and one stops to kill and eat a mouse, the others are likely to alight also, either on the ground or on near-by bushes as if curious to see what their neighbor is doing.   If in hunting, one hears or sees a mouse that escapes to its hole or some other concealment, it may alight on a stump, bush or post where it sits in imitation of a snag, watching, meanwhile, like a cat at a mouse hole for the appearance of its victim; or it may even sit down at a mouse hole in the attitude depicted in the cut.   At Gray's Harbor, Washington, it sat much on the edges of deep sloughs as it waited for a species of rat,[1] and Mr. Sidney

---

[1] Lawrence, R. H.: Auk, Vol. IX, 1892, p. 355.

Chase of Nantucket watched one kill a field mouse "which," said Mr. Chase, "he made sure of by finally breaking the whole length of the backbone [with his beak] and then put it under a tuft of grass, apparently for future use."

In winter when snow is deep on the ground, this owl is likely to betake itself to some thick evergreen tree to roost, and it seeks shelter in stumps of such trees during storms. Commonly, however, it alights on the ground, where it probably always nests. It is not altogether confined to a treeless country nor even to lowlands, as it has been known to breed not only among shrubs but also among scattering trees and even on mountains. It hunts silently for the most part, and much of its vociferousness occurs during the mating season and while breeding, especially when its young are approached or disturbed by an intruder. If one is suddenly startled from the ground during its daylight slumber, it flaps uncertainly away near the surface for some distance, and then drops quickly down and hides in the grass or undergrowth.

THE SHORT-EARED OWL AS AN ANIMATED MOUSE-TRAP. After El Hornero

This owl migrates both regularly and irregularly; regularly in autumn it moves out of the northern part of its range toward the south; irregularly it remains for two or three years where it finds abundant food; at least it is believed that the same individuals remain without migration. Eventually the verity of this belief may be established by banding the birds. Few of the species winter in New England, but in spring the number increases, usually in the latter part of March or in April, as the migrants move northward. I have visited no breeding-places in Massachusetts, outside of the Islands of Marthas Vineyard and Nantucket, but there are others. The bird is somewhat gregarious where food is plentiful, as it nests sometimes in small colonies, and also occurs in small flocks in migration.

While courting or mating the male chases the female about, uttering his tooting call. Mr. A. D. Dubois gives in the Auk a very interesting series of observations on what he designates as the "song-flight" of this species.[1] Doubtless this is a manifestation of the mating period. The bird was flying at a great height with flapping wings and some soaring. The "song" was made up of 16 to 20 toots, given at a rate of three to the second. The most interesting part of its behavior consisted of an occasional short, slanting dive, terminated by an "upward swoop" and accompanied by a peculiar fluttering noise. When the bird began its dive, its wings were brought together beneath its body, the bird stretching them backward and striking them together with short clapping strokes. This produced a sound, which, heard from that great altitude, sounded like "the flutter of a small flag in a very strong wind." As Mr. Dubois well says, the bird really seemed to be "applauding his own aërial performance." Those familiar with this sound may hear

---

[1] Auk, Vol. XLI, 1924, pp. 262–263. (See also another interesting article by Mr. Dubois on "The Short-eared Owl as a Foster-mother," Auk, Vol. XL, 1923, pp. 383–393.)

it often on the bird's breeding ground, anywhere from March to August, usually after dark, but rarely this flapping may be both seen and heard in the daytime.

I have seen the Short-eared Owl hunting on bright sunny days, and commonly it is abroad in daylight during dull cloudy weather. Mr. Edward A. Preble, during his investigation of the Athabaska-Mackenzie region, noticed on April 30, 1901, that while owls of this species were flying in pairs, the males frequently swooped down toward their mates from a considerable height, "holding their wings high above the back and uttering peculiar quavering cries."

The eggs of this bird are deposited at intervals, usually of about two days, but sometimes longer periods intervene, and as incubation begins about the time that the first egg is laid, the young hatch at different times and there are various sizes in the same nest, as is the case with some other birds of prey. When the young have learned to fly, the family keeps together for a long time, and the parents continue to feed the young, which gradually learn to hunt for themselves. In September, the southward pilgrimage begins.

Mr. Brewster records as follows two instances where this owl struck at much larger birds, apparently in play, since it could hardly hope to injure them seriously. "1889, September 23. — When Henry M. Spelman returned to camp from Moose Point this evening, he had an interesting story to tell concerning a Short-eared Owl. It was first seen by him not long after sunset, flying about low over the marsh, apparently in quest of prey. On coming to a pond where a flock of Black Ducks were feeding, it swooped at them many times, uttering loud, nasal cries somewhat like those of a Great Blue Heron and repeated every few seconds for upward of a minute. Although it probably had no intention of harming any of the Ducks, they seemed afraid of it, quacking and splashing loudly every time it stooped at them. . . . . 1895, September 22. — Shortly after sunset this evening a Great Blue Heron alighted on the south side of Moose Point and soon began making a loud outcry there. Presently it rose and soared in circles to a height of two hundred or more feet, followed, or rather preceded, by a Short-eared Owl, who bullied it for several minutes with amazing audacity. He kept always a little above it except when swooping down, as happened every few seconds, to strike it forcibly on the back, but whether with beak or talons I could not make out. The big, clumsy Heron seemed unable to either repel or dodge these assaults. During their continuance it did nothing but circle, croaking incessantly and, when struck by the Owl, squalling so lustily that it might have been heard half a mile away. Quite evidently it was badly frightened. The Owl, without doubt, was merely amusing himself." [1]

The chief food of the Short-eared Owl consists of small mammals, principally mice, with many large insects and some small birds. During a great plague of field mice or voles which occurred in northern England and southern Scotland in 1890–92, the suppression of the plague was due largely to Kestrels and Short-eared Owls; not less than 400 pairs of these Owls appeared in the stricken area. There the owls, which normally produce from four to eight young and one brood a year, laid in some cases as many as

---

[1] Brewster, William: The Birds of the Lake Umbagog Region in Maine, Part 2, 1925, pp. 371–372.

thirteen eggs to a brood and produced two broods a year. The voles destroyed practically every green thing before them, and but for the work of these birds, the whole region might have been devastated.[1] Of 101 stomachs of Short-eared Owls, reported upon by Dr. A. K. Fisher, 11 contained small birds; 77, mice; 7, other mammals (such as moles, shrews, 1 rabbit and a gopher); 7, insects and 14 were empty. Dr. B. H. Warren found field mice in 11 stomachs, and beetles also in two. The remains of from 1 to 6 mice have been found in the stomach of an owl of this species. Professor F. E. L. Beal found only mice in the stomachs of 2, killed in a grove, swarming with small birds.

However, small birds are taken occasionally. Mr. Charles W. Nash tells of a marsh in Ontario where, when Short-eared Owls are migrating, he finds many remains of small birds killed by them. As he has found birds as well as mice in the stomachs of these owls, and as the destruction of small birds ceases after the owls have gone, we must consider his evidence. Occasionally a collection of wing-feathers and tail-feathers of small birds will be found about the nest of a pair of these owls, and Mr. Brewster has noted them feeding on terns at Muskeget. Mr. J. A. Munro also has noted in the migrations near Toronto that this species was apparently feeding almost entirely on birds. They preyed on the hosts of migrants that rested after crossing Lake Ontario. A dry meadow was swarming with voles, but with one exception, the castings contained bones and feathers of small birds.[2] The principal insects found in the stomachs of this species are beetles and grasshoppers or locusts. One taken by Professor Aughey had 30 Rocky Mountain locusts in its stomach.

ECONOMIC STATUS. As the Short-eared Owl feeds mainly upon mice and other small mammals, most of which are injurious to man's interests, as there seem to be very few records of attacks on poultry, and the only game found in the stomachs examined were a few remains of young rabbits, it must be regarded as a useful species. Usually it prefers mice and other small rodents, when obtainable, to all other food; it kills but few bats and probably does not ordinarily kill an important per cent of small birds. The chief value of the bird lies in the fact that when field mice become remarkably abundant, it feeds chiefly on them, and so becomes extremely beneficial when most needed.

Strix vária varia BARTON. Barred Owl.

Other names: BARN OWL (MAINE); HOOT OWL; BLACK-EYED OWL.

Plate 46.

DESCRIPTION. — Head very large, round, without ear-tufts; wings not so long relatively as in any of the three preceding species; tail rounded; legs and feet feathered to near end of toes. *Adults* (*sexes alike*): Above umber, sepia-brown or grayish-brown, barred on head, neck, greater wing-coverts, flight-feathers and tail (all of which are tipped white) and spotted elsewhere with buffy, pale brown or whitish; neck and upper breast barred all round, upper throat lightest and little barred; breast and other lower plumage whitish, sparsely marked with heavy dark brown streaks, these much narrower on under tail-coverts; face light gray (a mixture of black and white specks) whitening about bill where there are black

---

[1] Pycraft, W. P.: A History of Birds, 1910, p. 113.   [2] Auk, Vol. XXXV, 1918, p. 223.

PLATE 46

PLATE 46

GREAT GRAY OWL
Page 207

BARRED OWL
Page 202

Adult

Adult

GREAT HORNED OWL
Page 219

SNOWY OWL
Page 231

Adult

Adult Female

All about one-sixth scale.

shaft-streaks, with concentric narrow bars of dark brown on outer part of each disk; legs and feet buffy-whitish, with some dusky, obsolete cross-speckling; axillars and under wing-coverts buffy-whitish, little marked except under primary-coverts, which have a large dark brownish-gray spot occupying end of each feather, and matching in color under surfaces of flight-feathers, which are barred whitish; bill yellow or yellowish; cere greenish; iris brownish-black or bluish-black, always nearly black; bare ends of toes and soles yellowish, soles sometimes deep yellow, claws dark horn. *Young in first winter plumage:* Like adults, but some may be suffused with a reddish-brown tint both above and below, which shows particularly on white markings of upper plumage. *Young in juvenal plumage:* Head, neck and lower plumage broadly barred with lightish brown, pale buffy and whitish; back, scapulars and wing-coverts similar, but bars still broader, brown darker and end of each feather white, which appears in spots; wing and tail-feathers, when grown as adults. *Downy young:* Yellowish when hatched.

MEASUREMENTS. — Length 17.00 to 24.00 in.; spread 40.00 to 50.00; folded wing 12.50 to 14.50; tail 7.00 to 10.00; bill 1.25 to 1.50; tarsus 1.90 to 2.50; weight 1 lb. 4 oz. to 2 lbs. (E. H. Eaton). Female averages larger than male.

MOLTS. — Juvenal birds have molted into first winter plumage in October, and apparently wear this until the next summer or autumn, when, after complete molt, they appear as adult; adults molt completely at some time between April and October, but not sufficient molting birds examined to determine just when.

FIELD MARKS. — Appears larger than Crow or Red-shouldered Hawk; head large and round, no ear-tufts; grayish-brown above, barred or spotted with buffy or whitish; whitish below, barred darkly across breast and striped same on belly; *large black eyes;* bill yellowish.

VOICE. — Commonly a hoot; *hoo hoó hŏ-hoó, hoo-hoo-hŏ-hóoo-aw,* or *hoo ho hoo-hooo* repeated twice; the first call is often translated "who cooks for you? who cooks for you all?" and it requires but little imagination to perceive their similarity to the spoken words; resonant *who, ho, ho, hò,- who, ho-ho-hòo-ah* and an unusual hoot, *hoo-hoo-hoo, hoo-hoo, hoo-hoò,* a variety of harsh screams; also a thin high-pitched scream or whine, and many other odd sounds when mating, such as hoarse mocking laughter, prolonged outbursts of cackling, laughing and whooping sounds delivered very rapidly and interspersed with (as well as ending with) the familiar *ho-hòo-ah* (Brewster).

BREEDING. — In woodland (not invariably retired) and most abundantly in dense forests or deep wooded swamps among tall timber (often pine). *Nest:* Preferably in a hollow tree (not always in a high hole) or the deserted nest of hawk, squirrel or crow; rarely builds its own nest; eggs usually deposited without attempt to line nest; very rarely nests in a building. *Eggs:* 2 to 4 (latter number rare); 1.97 to 2.08 by 1.49 to 1.75 in.; oval or short rounded oval; white, slightly rough and not very glossy; illustrated in Bendire's "Life Histories of North American Birds," Vol. I, Plate XII, Fig. 4. *Dates:* Late February to May 10 (usually soon after March 15), New England. *Incubation:* Period 21 to 28 days (Bendire); probably chiefly by female. One brood yearly.

RANGE. — Middle and eastern North America, chiefly in Canadian, Transition and Upper Austral zones from northern Manitoba, northern Ontario, southern Quebec and Newfoundland, west to south central Montana, eastern Wyoming and eastern Colorado and south to northern Oklahoma, northern Arkansas, Kentucky, Tennessee, northern Georgia and western North Carolina; casual in northern Louisiana. Breeds over most of its range; noted in the Bahamas.

DISTRIBUTION IN NEW ENGLAND. — *Maine, New Hampshire* and *Vermont:* Rather common resident in forested regions up to 2500 or 3000 feet. *Massachusetts:* Uncommon to rare summer resident; common irregularly in fall and winter. *Rhode Island and Connecticut:* Uncommon to rare resident in wooded districts (in Connecticut more common near coast); common irregularly in autumn and winter.

SEASON IN MASSACHUSETTS. — Permanent resident; most common irregularly from November to March.

HAUNTS AND HABITS.　How strongly strange and striking images are imprinted on the impressionable mind of youth, to remain ineffaceable through the passing years. Thus it is that my first sight of a Barred Owl recurs in my memory to this day.　I can see that bird now.　Reverberant hooting in the big woods had called me from the roadway to follow the sound for half a mile, when suddenly — there sat the great owl before me, on a horizontal limb, keeping the ready attitude of apprehension, his head turned squarely around so that his dark, solemn eyes stared fixedly at me.　They bade me pause, but the moment I stopped, the owl whipped its head about and springing forward gave its broad pinions to the air.

The Barred Owl is the most common large owl of New England.　Here it is chiefly a bird of the woodland; hunting mostly at night and retiring to some dark retreat by day; but it is by no means confined to the woods.　In the west it may be seen on days when the sky is overcast or toward evening, flying low over the prairie grass in search of food, and in New England it sometimes courses over meadows in the dusk of evening with its wings almost touching the grass tops.　In settled regions it likes to nest in wooded swamps where people do not often go, but in heavily wooded districts it seems to live and hoot most on the ridges, while the Great Horned Owl occupies the swamps.　Both species become very fond of a certain locality and may continue in it even though the nest is often robbed and the place becomes more or less public.　It winters over most of its range, but seems to desert its most northern breeding grounds in winter, where a southward migration has been reported often.　In seasons of deep snow, when mice can keep under cover, and especially when northern hares are scarce, great flights of Barred Owls come from the north into New England.　At such times when in search of food this species may be found almost anywhere; many come into towns and cities where they find mice, rats, sparrows, doves and starlings, on all of which they prey.　In March, 1922, a Barred Owl roosted daily for a long time on the trees about the City Hall or in King's Chapel and the Granary Burying Grounds in Boston, where it attracted the attention of the passing crowds; and there was another on Beacon Hill.　One remained for several days in the trees in the Public Garden, and the species was reported here and there about the suburbs.

Often this owl is not very shy and may evince unusual curiosity.　The Barred Owl when young makes an interesting pet.　A young bird of this species kept in captivity "assumed when asleep" a most extraordinary attitude, "as it squats down upon its perch and allows its head and neck to hang way down below it, for a distance of at least 10 inches or more." [1]　Mr. Farley speaks of a young Barred Owl which seemed half human as it looked out of its dark eyes at people.

At one of my lonely wilderness camps in the month of March a pair of Barred Owls came to the trees over my campfire and made night hideous with their grotesque love-making, banishing sleep during the evening hours.　Their courting antics, as imperfectly seen by moonlight and firelight, were ludicrous in the extreme.　Perched in

---

[1] Shufeldt, R. W.: American Forestry, Vol. XXV, 1919, p. 941.

rather low branches over the fire they nodded and bowed with half-spread wings, and wobbled and twisted their heads from side to side, meanwhile uttering the most weird and uncouth sounds imaginable.   Many of them were given with the full power of their lungs, without any regard to the sleepers, while others were soft and cooing and more expressive of the tender emotions; sounds resembling maniacal laughter and others like mere chuckles were interspersed here and there between loud *wha whas* and *hoo-hoó-aws*.   Mr. J. W. Preston (quoted by Bendire) speaks of notes uttered "in a subdued muttering and complaining strain," parts of which sounded like "old fool, old fool, don't do it, don't do it."   These owls call less often after the mating season, but one may hear them occasionally, at times, toward evening or just before daylight in midsummer. The ordinary hooting is considerably higher in pitch than that of the Great Horned Owl.

It is difficult to study the habits of our larger, more cautious, forest-haunting owls. Their nocturnal rambles are almost unobserved by man, and during daylight it is hard to find them.   When one hears strange sounds issuing from the forest at night, he may attribute them to the wrong source.   For example, Mr. Brewster tells as follows of an experience at Lake Umbagog where it was impossible to be certain of the author of startling night cries : — "1896, September 8. — Those of us who slept under canvas last night at the camp on Pine Point were suddenly awakened, about midnight, by outrageous squalling, snarling, and growling, coming from somewhere close to the tents and exactly like that of tomcats engaged in nocturnal strife, but much louder.   This outcry was exceedingly startling because of its nearness, and of the perfect stillness of the night.

"It was immediately followed, without the slightest intervening pause and apparently from the same place, by normal hooting of a Barred Owl.   My impression was that all the sounds came from the same spot and from one and the same bird, in which case their author must have been an Owl belonging to the species just named.   Will Sargent (the guide) thought, however, that two birds took part in them and that all except the hooting ones were made by the so-called "Screech Owl" of the region which, for reasons already explained (p. 368), I believe to be the Long-eared Owl.   The caterwauling was very different from any utterance that I have ever traced to the Long-eared Owl and equally unlike the medley of laughing, cackling, and hooting cries which the Barred Owl often gives in early spring, but closely similar to an outburst of cat-like yelling which, several years ago, suddenly disturbed not only the serenity of a calm autumn evening, but also the peace of mind of some sportsmen whom I happened to be visiting at the time at their camp on Moll's Rock.   For these men insisted on attributing the cries to a Cougar, said to be then roaming the forests about the Lake, although the veteran guide, Luman Sargent, asserted positively, after listening to them attentively for a moment, that they came from a Barred Owl, as no doubt was the case, although they were unaccompanied by hooting on that occasion.   1897, September 11. — Just as we were about to leave a shooting stand in the Outlet marshes this evening a prolonged and cat-like scream rang out from among the stubs near Moll's Carry.   Although coming from a distance of nearly half a mile, this outcry was so loud, so piercing and so expressive of ferocity as to be very thrilling.   It ended, however, with a hoarse *hòo-ah* which could issue from no throat other than that of a Barred Owl, thus once more confirming my impression as to the authorship of the 'caterwauling.'   Why I have never heard it in the South where Barred Owls are so very numerous, or more than thrice at Lake Umbagog where they are not uncommon, is difficult to understand.   To-night it was much shorter and less varied than when given at Pine Point last year, but equally like the squalling of an angry cat only many times louder and without any growling termination which, however, may have accompanied it, yet failed to reach our ears because of the distance.   That most of it might have been heard more than a mile away I do not doubt." [1]

As I never have heard anything like caterwauling from a Barred Owl and as such vocalization is a well-known habit of the Long-eared Owl, and as I have found remains of the Long-eared Owl in two stomachs of the Barred Owl, I might have been inclined to attribute the above disturbance to both species, and the occasion to an attack of the former upon the latter, during which both gave vocal utterance to their outraged feelings ; but Mr. Brewster heard these sounds, while I did not, and in any case I should hesitate to express an opinion of sounds unheard by me.

At sunrise the Barred Owl usually retires to some shady nook, such as a north hillside, shaded by dark hemlock, or the hollow of some old tree, where it remains inert during most of the day.   When suddenly aroused from sleep in such a retreat it may appear rather stupid, but it can see perfectly in the daytime.   Its large, dark eyes even though partly closed will detect a hawk high in the sky, beyond the reach of ordinary human vision.   In winter it prefers a shelter from cold winds when it can find one.   Mrs. Elizabeth Caswell wrote to me on March 2, 1918, that in each of two summer cottages at Northfield Farms, Mass., she found a Barred Owl that had come down the chimney, and being unable to find the way out had starved to death.

Although its dark eyes give it a mild look, the Barred Owl is no sluggard nor coward. Witness its fight to the death with a fierce Goshawk, both birds being killed.   (*See* page 122.)

The Barred Owl feeds chiefly on mice and other rodents, destroying quantities of small mammals, among which are some of the farmer's most destructive pests.   Dr. Fisher reports on the examination of 109 stomachs of this species that 1 contained a pigeon ; 2, portions of fowls ; 1, remains of Ruffed Grouse ; 7, small owls ; 5, small birds ; 46, mice ; 18, other mammals ; 4, frogs ; 1, a lizard ; 2, fish ; 14, insects ; 2, spiders ; 9, crawfish ; and 20 were empty.   This owl may be forced at times to eat carrion.   Dr. Anne E. Perkins wrote to me on March 23, 1925, from Helmuth, New York, that pellets from a Barred Owl were picked up containing pig bristles and a piece of broken bone.

ECONOMIC STATUS.   The above indicates that this species is beneficial rather than injurious.   It catches chickens where the fowls are allowed to roost in trees, and in winter when driven by hunger, it may kill a few grouse, but its services in the way of destroying mice and insects probably outweigh its injurious habits.

---

[1] Brewster, William : The Birds of the Lake Umbagog Region of Maine, Part 2, 1925, pp. 375–376.

Scotiáptex nebulósa nebulosa (J. R. Forster). Great Gray Owl.

Plate 46.

DESCRIPTION. — Size apparently very great, but this appearance due largely to very long, lax and profuse plumage; head apparently very large; body really small in proportion to apparent size; face larger than that of any other American owl; bill and feet small, and eyes rather small for so large an owl; wings ample with six primaries cut away on inner web; tail rather long and rounded; feet copiously and completely feathered to claws. *Adults (sexes alike):* Above, largely dusky grayish-brown, marked and mottled with light gray or grayish-white, with partially concealed tawny spots on back of head and neck, barred with gray on greater wing-coverts, flight-feathers and tail; dark brown or blackish patch below bill on white throat; elsewhere below, grayish-white, streaked dusky and mottled grayish on neck and breast, streaks narrowing on belly, sides and flanks, which are narrowly barred dusky; under tail-coverts similarly barred; legs and feet also grayish-white, very finely streaked and barred dusky; face grayish, shading into white about bill, and marked except on the white with very narrow concentric dusky bars; a dusky or blackish space about inner corner of eye; bill light yellow; iris lemon-yellow or straw; claws black. *Young in first winter plumage:* Like adult; young bird taken September 8 was like adult but much smaller and some juvenal plumage still remaining on breast was dusky grayish-brown, barred narrowly light grayish, its texture loose and downy. *Young in juvenal plumage:* Similar in color tone to adult, but feathers of body and back of head with light tips, giving plumage an irregularly barred appearance. *Downy young:* Chiefly buffy-white; back of neck, back and wings more buffy.

MEASUREMENTS. — Length 23.50 to 33.00 in.; spread 48.50 to 60.00; folded wing 14.25 to 19.00; tail 11.00 to 15.00; bill 1.25 to 1.75; tarsus 2.00 to 3.00. Weight 1 lb. 15 oz. to 2 lbs. 14½ oz. (Albert Lane).

MOLTS. — Juvenal birds begin molting in June or July and apparently take on a plumage like that of adults by September or October; no molting adults available for examination.

FIELD MARKS. — In appearance our largest owl; a great, dark, gray bird without ear-tufts and with large round head, very large face and *yellow or straw eyes; not barred* across breast like Barred Owl *but dappled or striped there;* in flight, flaps slowly its broad, rounded wings.

VOICE. — A tremulous cry, not unlike that of Screech Owl (T. M. Brewer); "Several deep-pitched whoo's at irregular intervals" (Grinnell and Storer).

BREEDING. — In forested regions. *Nest:* In either coniferous or deciduous forest tree, from 20 feet high to top; built of sticks, twigs, weeds and mosses, thinly lined with down and feathers. *Eggs:* 3 to 5; (rarely 5); 2.00 to 2.30 by 1.69 to 1.80 in. (smaller than those of Great Horned Owl); rounded ovate to nearly oval, white and smooth; illustrated in Bendire's "Life Histories of North American Birds," Vol. I, Plate XII, Fig. 5. *Dates:* From April to June, Alaska and northern Canada. *Incubation:* Probably by female; period unknown. One brood yearly.

RANGE. — Boreal North America to tree limit. Breeds in Hudsonian and upper Canadian zones, from tree-limit in Alaska and northwestern Mackenzie south to southern Alberta, Manitoba and northern Ontario, and in mountains probably south to west central California; south in winter to California, Colorado, Nebraska, northern Iowa, northern Illinois, Indiana, northern Ohio, Pennsylvania, New Jersey, Long Island, Connecticut and Rhode Island.

DISTRIBUTION IN NEW ENGLAND. — Rare winter visitor, rather irregular and local; very rare straggler in Rhode Island and Connecticut.

SEASON IN MASSACHUSETTS. — November 10 to March 4.

HAUNTS AND HABITS. *Scotiaptex nebulosa*, the name which the systematists have given the Great Gray Owl, certainly is descriptive of the bird. Freely translated it runs thus — "The gray eagle-owl of darkness." In the far north where the summer sun hangs in the sky nearly all night, this bird, adapting itself to circumstances, hunts by daylight, but in the more southern parts of its range it prefers dusk or darkness for its hunting. When perched on a limb of some isolated leafless tree, it appears a monstrous fowl, but when taken in the hand its great apparent size is seen to be due largely to feathers. Its head and face seem immense, but its feet are small and it is indeed a light-weight, some weighing less than large Barred Owls.* Its long wings and tail increase its apparent size. Its covering of thick down and long fluffy feathers (particularly on breast) which make it seem so large and powerful, are grown as a protection from the cold. It is provided with such a thick non-conducting coat from beak to claws that it is obliged to move southward in winter only by scarcity of food, and it never goes so far south as does that typical Arctic bird, the Snowy Owl. Normally it is a forest bird, living in the wooded wilderness of northern Canada or in the timber on the slopes of immense mountain ranges of the far west. In winter, however, it moves southward irregularly, and then appears, in most seasons rarely, in New England. Occasionally adverse winter conditions in its usual haunts force it to move southward in unusual numbers. When the northern forests fail to produce cones for winter food of small arboreal birds; when deep snows cover the runways of mice, and grasses and weeds that feed ground-birds and when bush rabbits and ptarmigan are scarce in the northern wilderness; then we may expect an unusual invasion of Great Gray Owls. Such a combination of circumstances probably does not occur often, but in the winter of 1842–43, according to Dr. Samuel Abbott, seven of these birds were taken in Massachusetts,[1] and probably many more were seen and went unrecorded. In the winter of 1890–91 such numbers of this species were killed in eastern Maine that Mr. Crosby, taxidermist of Bangor, received 27 specimens. Some birds from this flight reached eastern Massachusetts, where a few were taken.[2] For some reason the published records of this species in New England are not very many, but I have seen in various collections a number of specimens without definite data which were taken in this region.† The bird is reported here and there in northern New England nearly every winter, but is noted seldom in any of the three southern New England states. Although it is a forest bird, it may be found almost anywhere in winter outside the cities and very rarely even within city limits, but it prefers deep woods, and as it is here chiefly in winter and moves about mainly at night, it is rarely seen. The Great Gray Owl frequents the woods, and often watches for its prey from a tall tree. It does not always sit erect in the conventional owl position, but like other owls it often sits with its body inclined forward at an angle of 45 degrees or more, especially if watching some object on the ground below. The food of this bird is known to consist largely of mice, rabbits and small birds, but we have little information about either the bird or its food.

ECONOMIC STATUS. See page 188.

---

* "The most bird for the least substance we ever examined." Fred T. Jencks in Bulletin Nuttall Ornithological Club, Vol. VIII, 1883, p. 183.

[1] Proceedings of the Boston Society of Natural History, Vol. I, 1843, p. 99.

[2] Brewster, William: Editor, Minot's Land and Game Birds of New England, 1895, pp. 344–345.

† C. H. Horton, Esq. of St. Johnsbury, Vermont, has in his mounted collection a number of Great Gray Owls which were taken in northern Vermont. About all the larger collections in Massachusetts have one or more.

Crýptoglaux funérea richardsoni (BONAPARTE). Richardson's Owl.

Plate 47.

DESCRIPTION. — A small owl *without ear-tufts*, fully as large as Screech Owl, larger than Acadian Owl; ear-openings very large; head, bill and eyes large; wings long and ample; tail short; feet feathered to claws. *Adults (sexes alike)*: Above, generally chocolate-brown, but variable, spotted white; top of head thickly marked with roundish and elongated white spots, hind neck with large variously shaped white spots; on back and scapulars the spots are very large, more or less sparsely distributed and partially concealed; on flight-feathers and tail-feathers they are large on both outer and inner webs, extending crosswise and giving the appearance of bars on closed wing; outer wing-coverts and some of greater coverts with large roundish spots; below silver-white, striped lengthwise with chocolate-brown; face white (black spot before eye) surrounded by a dark brown border, whitish brows run back over all to top of head; facial disk often washed more or less with brown; legs and feet buffy or white, often clouded or spotted with brown; bill light yellowish-horn on ridge and tip, grayish toward base; iris lemon-yellow or straw. *Young in first winter plumage:* As adult. *Young in juvenal plumage:* Flight-feathers and tail only as adult; elsewhere above, plain dark sooty-brown, with white spots like adult on wing and tail only; ear region and part of facial disk back of eye sooty-black; brows, space before eye, and corners of mouth white with some black shafts; below largely vandyke-brown, mixed (sometimes varied) with white, passing into dull buffy on hinder plumage.

MEASUREMENTS. — Length 8.22 to 12.00 in.; spread 19.00 to 24.00; folded wing 6.50 to 7.75; tail 4.10 to 4.70; bill .60 to .84; tarsus .83 to 1.12. Female averages larger than male.

MOLTS. — Juvenal plumage molted in first autumn, except flight-feathers, primary coverts and tail-feathers, after which young bird becomes as adult; adults have a complete molt annually (June to November).

FIELD MARKS. — Size of Screech Owl, but wings and tail longer; darker brown than red Screech Owl and *without ear-tufts;* usually very tame or stupid in daylight; the light bill distinguishes it from Saw-whet Owl, with black bill.

VOICE. — A "low liquid note that resembles the sound produced by water dropping from a height" (C. Hart Merriam); "a liquid note like dripping water" (N. A. Comeau); in the breeding season "a musical soft whistle" (O. W. Knight); "crying almost like a human being," once a peculiar grating cry (E. W. Nelson).

BREEDING. — In northern coniferous forests. *Nest:* Not known to build any; usually nests in holes in trees, sometimes in deserted nests of other birds. *Eggs:* 4 to 6, probably sometimes more; 1.25 to 1.28 by 1.05 to 1.08 in.; rounded ovate, approaching spherical; white and smooth; illustrated in Bendire's "Life Histories of North American Birds," Vol. I, Plate XII, Fig. 6. *Dates:* Eggs laid in May and June. *Incubation:* No details.

RANGE. — Northern North America. Breeds chiefly in upper Canadian and Hudsonian zones from tree limit in northwestern Alaska and in Yukon and Mackenzie east to Labrador and south to northern British Columbia, northern Alberta, southern Manitoba, Quebec, Magdalen Islands, and New Brunswick; has been seen in summer in Vermont and on Grand Manan; * in winter south to eastern Oregon, northwestern Idaho, Colorado, South Dakota and southeastern Nebraska (casually), Minnesota, Wisconsin, northern Illinois, Michigan, southern Ontario, southern Quebec, Pennsylvania, New York and southern New England; has been taken on Pribilof Islands; casual in Bermudas (?).

DISTRIBUTION IN NEW ENGLAND. — *Maine:* Winter visitor; irregularly common to abundant in forests of northern and eastern counties; more rare and irregular in southern and western parts. *New Hampshire and Vermont:* Rare winter visitor, occasionally more common, especially in northern forested sections. *Massachusetts:* Rare (as a rule) and very irregular winter visitor but occasionally not very

---

* Specimen seen July 18, 1923, near summit of Gen. Stark Mt. between Lincoln and Warren in northern Vermont. (Eaton, Warren F., and Curry, Haskell B., Auk, Vol. XLI, 1924, p. 155.)

uncommon. *Rhode Island:* Very rare and irregular winter visitor. *Records:* Five given by Howe and Sturtevant in the Birds of Rhode Island and another taken "probably" in Seekonk, Massachusetts. *Connecticut:* Very rare and irregular winter visitor. *Records:* Two given by Sage, Bishop and Bliss in the Birds of Connecticut; South Windsor, one killed in January, 1923, by an owl or hawk; feathers found by C. W. Vibert and identified by E. H. F.

SEASON IN MASSACHUSETTS. — November 26 to March.

HAUNTS AND HABITS. Richardson's Owl is a forest night-bird. It lives in dense coniferous forests, where it hides during the daytime, and therefore is seldom seen, and for this reason it is regarded as an exceedingly rare bird in New England. In forests within the Arctic Circle during the long days of summer it is obliged to hunt by day to feed its young, and therefore, being conspicuous, is seen to be common. As it is not supposed to breed regularly below the upper Canadian Zone, and is not known to nest anywhere within the boundaries of the United States, we may expect to see it only in late fall and winter, and rarely then, but owing to its retiring habits it has been considered far more rare in New England than it actually is. Probably it may be found in the woods of northern Maine in most winters in fluctuating numbers, but as ornithologists are far fewer in these winter woods than owls, it is seldom recorded. Now and then there comes a season when deep snow covers the northern country and conceals the mice. When a coincidental lack of food drives the northern arboreal birds southward, then the little owls must follow them or die of starvation, for they are too small to capture northern hares or grouse. Such a combination of circumstances occurred in the winter of 1922–23, when woodsmen in the Maine woods found little owls scattered through the woods, either alive or dead on the snow. Mr. T. A. James, at that time curator of the State Museum at Augusta, Maine, wrote to me on February 22nd, 1922, as follows: "I am receiving a great many Richardson's Owls, which appear to be starved. Most of them are picked up dead about farm buildings, and are in a very emaciated condition. At present I have six specimens that I have not had time to dissect and examine. I doubt very much if I find food in any of their stomachs." Later he sent me some specimens that proved to be in a similar condition. Letters from taxidermists or their friends in New Brunswick, Quebec, Maine, New Hampshire and Vermont showed that they were receiving far more of these birds than in ordinary winters, some having as many as 30 on their books. Miss Lucia B. Cutter of East Jaffrey in southern New Hampshire informed me that Mr. Wellington, the taxidermist there, had 26 up to March 13, all from southern New Hampshire and northern Massachusetts. Barr, Wight and Co., Bangor, Maine, had received about 30 up to March 3. In the meantime numerous reports of the species in Massachusetts, as well as five of the owls themselves, were received at my office. The starving birds left the woods in search of food and entered not only farm buildings but buildings in villages and cities, and many were captured in such situations. The bewildered, weakened birds wandered on until some of them reached the shores of Cape Cod and the valleys of Connecticut. Their exhaustion or their dullness in the daytime enabled some of those who saw them to take them in their hands. Mr. Adelbert Temple of Hopkinton, Massachusetts, writes: "A man sent for me that I might have a look at an owl that was staying around his place. On looking it over and catching it in my hands, it proved to be a Richardson's Owl." Mr. H. A. Torrey of East Sandwich, Massachusetts, wrote that his son walked up to a Richardson's Owl sitting on a limb and caught it in mid-air as it flew. A lady correspondent saw a peculiar "bunch of feathers on her clothesline." When she picked it off, she found that she held in her hands a Richardson's Owl. Many of these birds are so stupid or sleepy by daylight that they may be captured thus, if approached silently. The Eskimos in Alaska, according to Dr. Nelson, believe that this owl cannot see by day, and have named it *"tuk-whe-ling-uk"* the blind one. Some authors seem to believe that this owl cannot see by daylight. But even if it sees only indifferently well by day, it is the exception among owls, as most of them see remarkably well then.

Apparently there is a more or less irregular migration of this species; otherwise it would not be found so frequently in northern Maine, where it is not known to breed. But the bird apparently never goes so far south as does the Snowy Owl and rarely is found in considerable numbers within the boundaries of the United States. Little is known of its food which is supposed to consist principally of mice, insects and small birds.

ECONOMIC STATUS. — See page 188.

Cryptoglaux acádica acadica (GMELIN). Saw-whet Owl.

Other names: ACADIAN OWL; SAW-FILER.

Plate 47.

DESCRIPTION. — Smallest New England owl; unmistakable; much like Richardson's, but much smaller than that or the Screech Owl; no ear-tufts, head large, wings long, tail short; feet feathered above to claws. *Adults (sexes alike)*: Much less white on top of head and hind neck than in Richardson's Owl; white marks on top of head mostly narrow shaft-lines instead of spots, and brown of upper plumage usually ruddier; tail marked with *three rows of white spots* (each feather having two spots in each row, one on each web of the feather), and tipped white; below, white with a buffy tinge, streaked and dappled with peculiar light chestnut-brown; wing linings mostly white or whitish; brows and space in front of eye usually mostly white or whitish, except a blackish spot in front of inner corner of eye; face white or grayish, tinged brownish, laterally marked with radiating lines of dusky, and framed below by a brown neck-band which is separated from streaking of breast by a white half-collar on throat; legs and feet unmarked; iris yellow; bill and claws black; under sides of toes yellowish-flesh-color. *Young in first winter plumage*: Like adults, but center of face and forehead mostly white and color of upper plumage more ruddy. *Young in juvenal plumage*: Unlike adults, except wings and tail; above ruddy chocolate-brown with no white marks except on flight-feathers and tail, where spotted and barred with white like adults; throat and breast lighter brown than upper plumage; rest of lower plumage tawny-buff or cinnamon-buff unmarked. *Downy young*: "Covered with reddish down" (C. J. Maynard).

MEASUREMENTS. — Length 7.00 to 8.50 in.; spread 17.00 to 20.50; folded wing 5.00 to 5.90; tail 2.50 to 3.25; bill .68 to .75; tarsus .75 to 1.00. Sexes near same size, but variable. Female usually somewhat larger than male.

MOLTS. — Juvenal plumage is acquired by complete postnatal molt in the nestling; this plumage (except flight-feathers, tail-feathers and primary coverts which are like adult), is shed in August, and brown first winter plumage with white face (as adult) is assumed in September; adults have complete molt (August to November), and may have partial molt in spring.

FIELD MARKS. — Smallest New England owl; much smaller than Screech Owl or Richardson's Owl; no ear tufts; resembles Richardson's Owl somewhat except in size, but lighter, and top of head with white streaks instead of white spots; bill black, instead of yellow.

VOICE. — Sharp whistles resembling saw filing; a sound like the "faint tones of a distant bell " (Audubon); a metallic ringing sound, continuous, suggesting saw filing; a whistling *whurdle-whurdle-whurdle-whurdle*, long and uninterruptedly, not ringing or metallic and not suggesting saw filing; *skreigh-àw, skreigh-àw, skreigh-àw*, given at frequent intervals in sets of three, like the filing of a large mill-saw (Wm. Brewster); a rasping, querulous *sa-a-a-a-ay*, bearing only the most distant resemblance to saw filing and a low mellow *cook* (W. L. Dawson); the autumnal call, four whistles in quick succession *hew-hew-hew-hew* (Brewster); also a sound resembling the muffled or choked squawking of a chicken; when disturbed at nest, a peculiar cry similar to that of a startled Robin (D. Gale); a soft *co-co-co, co-co-co* several times repeated (Fanny Hardy Eckstorm). *Young:* A noise like a dog sniffing the air (Otto Behr); a shrill, bat-like, squeaking; after molt a new cry — a series of five or six low, chuckling whistled calls (Brewster).

BREEDING. — In woods or forests; wooded swamps often preferred. *Nest:* Commonly in hole in tree, deserted nest of flicker or other woodpecker or knothole or other natural cavity of dead tree or stump; occasionally in abandoned nest of larger bird or squirrel; rarely in cavity among rocks; in most cases eggs are laid on chips or dead wood in bottom of hole, sometimes on a slight lining of grass or feathers. *Eggs:* three to seven; .95 to 1.00 by .87 to .90 in.; nearly oval or rounded ovate; white and chalky; illustrated in Bendire's, "Life Histories of North American Birds," Vol. I, Plate XII, Fig. 7. *Dates:* March 31 to April 30, central New York; April 4 to May 1 (July 3), Massachusetts; April 6, New Hampshire; April 15 to May 21, Maine. *Incubation:* Period apparently about 21 days; by female. One brood yearly.

RANGE. — Most of North America, north to near northern part of Canadian Zone. Breeds chiefly in Canadian and Transition zones from extreme southern Alaska, British Columbia, Alberta, Manitoba, northern Ontario, central Quebec, New Brunswick and Nova Scotia south (in mountains) to California, central Arizona, New Mexico and Colorado, and to southern Nebraska, east-central Missouri, northern Illinois, north-central Indiana, Ohio (Pennsylvania and Maryland in mountains) and Connecticut; in winter south to southern California, Mexico and Guatemala, casually to Louisiana, Tennessee and Georgia.

DISTRIBUTION IN NEW ENGLAND. — *Maine, New Hampshire and Vermont:* Uncommon resident, more common in northern Maine; not uncommon migrant or winter visitor. *Massachusetts:* Rare resident and irregularly common winter visitor. *Rhode Island:* Not uncommon winter visitor; not known to breed. *Connecticut:* Rare resident and irregular winter visitor.

SEASON IN MASSACHUSETTS. — Rare resident; most common in severe winters.

HAUNTS AND HABITS. The little Saw-whet Owl, the smallest of all our eastern nocturnal birds of prey, is about the size of a Towhee, but its long, broad wings and its heavy coating of loose downy feathers which fit it to endure intense cold, give to it a larger appearance. Owing to its nocturnal habits, its reticence and its extremely retiring disposition in daylight, it is not seen often except during those severe winters when hundreds appear searching for food wherever it may be found. Then they sometimes enter farm buildings for shelter or perhaps in search of mice, and many are captured. The note of this owl which sometimes is harsh and creaky, resembling saw filing, may be so softly intoned at other times as to bear little resemblance to that nerve-racking sound, and the bird has the power of ventriloquizing so that the softened call seems faint and far away.

PLATE 47

PLATE 47

HAWK OWL
Page 235

ADULT

SCREECH OWL
Page 214

ADULT
GRAY PHASE

ADULT
RED PHASE

RICHARDSON'S OWL
Page 209

ADULT

SAW–WHET OWL
Page 211

ADULT

All about one-third scale.

Louis Agassiz Fuertes

While its notes frequently are uttered during the mating season in February, March and April, when few people are in the woods, the bird is ordinarily more quiet after the eggs are laid, and even if its voice is heard then, it is commonly attributed to some other creature. It hunts silently at night, and during the day retires to some dark evergreen thicket or a hole in a tree to sleep away the hours of sunlight. Hence it is more common than many a day bird that is more often seen. In support of this view Mr. William Brewster said that according to the testimony of Alva Coolidge, a trustworthy guide, these owls may be heard everywhere in the forest about Lake Umbagog in February and March, most frequently just before daybreak, but often throughout the night. The saw-filing season, he says, reaches its height in March, but the call may be continued intermittently through May and even to the first part of June. After that the birds are silent most of the time, and the summer visitor to the forest rarely hears one and almost never sees one.

While I have observed small owls in the woods many times at dusk, I have seen and fully identified the Saw-whet Owl alive but once. Many specimens have passed through my hands, but I know little of the habits of the bird from personal observation. Dull and sleepy though it may be in daylight, at dusk it becomes an active, animated forest elf. Its courage is great, as it has been known to attack and kill rats much larger than itself; to kill and devour small squirrels; and even to fly at the head of a man who came near its young. Mr. E. Cutting of Lyme, N. H., tells how a Saw-whet Owl got into his barn and killed a number of full-grown pigeons. Dr. Coues tells a tale on the authority of Gentry that one of these owls lived in a hollow tree with a red squirrel in perfect amity.

Wood mice form the principal food of this owl. In winter in the great coniferous forests of Canada much of the snow is upheld on the branches of the trees in such a way that there are spaces here and there close to the trunks where there is little snow. There the wood mice come out at night from their hiding-places under the snow, and there the little owl perched in the branches above them awaits their coming; but if for any reason owl-food is scarce or hard to obtain, as sometimes happens in severe winters with deep snow, the little owls must move south or perish. At such times, as in the winter of 1922–23, when Acadian Owls were abundant in New England, there is a great influx of these birds from the north. By the time they reach a milder clime, many of them are too emaciated and exhausted to hunt or even to eat. They seem to lose all interest in life, and seek only a quiet retreat in which to die. Others more hardy or less exhausted survive to return, with the advent of spring, to the land of their nativity.

Dr. Fisher reports on the stomachs of 22 birds of this species: 1 contained a sparrow, 17 had taken mice, 1, an insect and 2 were empty. These birds were winter visitors. In summer many insects are eaten. Dr. Warren reports that of seven stomachs of this species taken in summer and autumn, six contained only insects and the seventh a mouse and a spider.

ECONOMIC STATUS. No exhaustive study of the food habits of this owl have been made but most of the evidence thus far adduced is in its favor.

Ótus ásio asio (LINNÆUS).   Screech Owl.

Other names: MOTTLED OWL; RED OWL.

Plate 47.

DESCRIPTION. — Head large, with large, prominent, but not very long ear-tufts; eyes large; wings long and rounded; tail very short; toes only sparsely feathered or bristled; two phases of plumage. *Adults, gray phase:* Above, brownish-gray, mottled, dappled and streaked with dusky or blackish and lighter gray; many black or blackish shaft-streaks, most numerous at top and back of head; a whitish stripe along outer webs of scapulars, another from near bend of wing to ends of greater coverts, and a white bar along ends of outer greater coverts; flight-feathers and tail broadly barred dusky; primaries darker than rest of upper plumage, their outer webs with several distinct whitish, buffy or pale brownish spaces; below, white or grayish-white, streaked with broad, dark shaft-lines, much widened on breast, giving off numerous dark, narrow, wavy cross-bars; middle of belly, ventral region and under tail-coverts little marked, but leg feathers buffy and unmarked except on tarsi, which are brokenly barred brownish or dusky; face pale grayish, mostly finely mottled and darkest near inner corners of eyes, disks framed on sides with blackish, a brownish streak from above eye to and along outer edges of ear-tufts; under wing-coverts chiefly whitish, pale brownish or buffy, more or less marked dusky. *Adults, red phase:* Markings similar, but ground color of upper plumage light chestnut-red or bright rust-red, and comparatively little marked with dusky above or below, except in shaft-streaks of varying width; some barring on flight-feathers and tail-feathers; chestnut-red extends more or less on lower plumage.   Fleming says: ("Birds of Toronto") that red phase usually occurs for several years in succession and then disappears.[1] *Young in first winter plumage:* Like adults, but in reddish phase the color is not so clear and markings more prominent; in gray phase the body plumage sometimes is redder.   *Young in juvenal plumage:* Flight-feathers and tail-feathers in most cases like gray adults but some are much like red adults; nearly all the rest of the plumage shows colors similar to adults, but is downy and loose; ear tufts showing, but shorter; plumage barred narrowly grayish and reddish, or grayish and dusky.   *Downy young:* Nearly pure white.

MEASUREMENTS. — Length 6.50 to 10.00 in.; spread 18.00 to 24.00; folded wing 6.10 to 7.30; tail 2.90 to 3.70; bill .80 to .95; tarsus 1.05 to 1.35; weight 4 to 6 oz. (E. H. Eaton); female 5 to 7 oz. (B. H. Warren); usually larger than male.

MOLTS. — Juvenal plumage, except flight-feathers, tail-feathers and primary coverts, which are like adults, is molted in late summer or autumn, and young birds become much as adults; in second autumn after another molt they are as winter adults; adults have one complete molt in late summer and autumn.

FIELD MARKS. — Size, not so long as a Robin, usually much wider, but can appear very slim at will; the only little New England owl with *ear-tufts;* color generally either light reddish-brown or brownish-gray with streaked breast.

VOICE. — A long, tremulous, wailing call usually descending toward the end, somewhat resembling the cry of a young raccoon; another long, tremulous call all on one key; also a variety of lower calls inaudible at a distance.

BREEDING. — In open woods and among forest, shade or old orchard trees. *Nest:* A hollow tree, a nesting box or some nook in an old building, lined with such rubbish as may lie therein, as straw or a few leaves and feathers; often in old woodpecker hole.*   *Eggs:* Commonly 3 to 5, rarely 7 and up to 9; 1.25 to 1.55 by 1.16 to 1.35 in.; nearly oval, often approaching spherical; white, usually smooth but occasionally rough shelled; illustrated in Bendire's "Life Histories of North American Birds," Vol. I,

---

[1] Auk, Vol. XXIV, 1907, p. 74.

*There is a record of a Screech Owl raising young in one compartment of a martin box, the martins themselves occupying the other compartments (Bird-Lore, Vol. XXVII, 1925, p. 109).

Plate XII, Fig. 8. *Dates:* April 9 to 20, Virginia; April 7 to May 5, southern New England. *Incubation:* Period 21 to 25 days (Authors); by one sex or both. One brood yearly.

RANGE. — Eastern North America, chiefly in Transition and upper Austral zones, from extreme eastern North Dakota, southern Manitoba, Minnesota, Wisconsin, northern Michigan, southern Ontario, northern New York, southern Quebec, Maine, New Brunswick, Prince Edward Island and Newfoundland south to northeastern Oklahoma, northern Arkansas, central Illinois, Tennessee and North Carolina, and west at least to Oklahoma, eastern Kansas and eastern South Dakota. Breeds over most of its range. Along the south Atlantic and Gulf coastal regions and in the west other races of *Otus asio* take the place of this northern and eastern form; at least 14 races have been described.

DISTRIBUTION IN NEW ENGLAND. — *Maine:* Rather common to rare resident in settled country and open hard woods, particularly rare in northern coniferous forests. *New Hampshire:* Rather uncommon resident, rare in the northern mountainous regions. *Vermont:* Rather uncommon resident, more common at lower elevations of southern part. *Massachusetts, Rhode Island and Connecticut:* Common resident.

SEASON IN MASSACHUSETTS. — Permanent resident, most generally distributed in winter.

HAUNTS AND HABITS. Out of the wisdom of the ages Pliny produced among other wise sayings the following: "The Scritch Owl alwaies betokeneth some heavie newes, and is most execrable and accursed. In summer he is the very monster of the night, neither singing nor crying out cleare, but uttering a certaine heavie groane of doleful mourning, and therefore if it be seene to flie abroad in any place it prognosticateth some fearefull misfortune." This dictum was promulgated far away and long ago, but our Screech Owl of New England has inherited both name and reputation. Many superstitious folk still believe that this little owl is an ill-omened fowl. Its silent, ghostly flight and its mournful night-cries have given it a place among the powers of darkness in the minds of the simple and unlearned. Many still shudder whenever they hear its plaintive, long-drawn-out wail, which, though it seems to carry a note of sadness, is merely a love song, unappreciated, except, perhaps, by the ears for which it is especially intended. Its mournfulness so impressed Thoreau that he characterized the lugubrious lay in his journal as follows: "It is no honest and blunt *tu-whit to-who* of the poets, but without jesting a most solemn graveyard ditty, — but the mutual consolations of suicide lovers remembering the pangs and the delights of supernal love in the infernal groves. And yet I love to hear their wailing, their doleful responses, trilled along the woodside, reminding me sometimes of music and singing birds, as if it were the dark and tearful side of music, the regrets and sighs that would fain be sung. . . . They give me a new sense of the vastness and mystery of that nature which is the common dwelling of us both. 'Oh-o-o-o-o that I had never been bor-or-or-or-orn!' sighs one on this side of the pond, and circles in the restlessness of despair to some new perch in the gray oaks. Then 'That I never had been bor-or-or-or-orn!' echoes one on the further side, with a tremulous sincerity, and 'bor-or-or-orn' comes faintly from far in the Lincoln woods."

Many people still believe that this doleful wail is prophetic and foretells disaster, disease or death. The little Screech Owl of the south is known in Louisiana as the "Shivering Owl"; and along Bayou Lafourche when its notes banish sleep, and the resourceful "Cajun" wishes to ward off the ills that he believes otherwise sure to follow, he must arise from his couch and turn his left shoe upside down.   Then the cries are sup-posed to be stilled.   This charm does not work, however, on the lower Mississippi, where one must turn his left trouser or "pants" pocket inside out.[1]   The latter plan is believed to be effective by many colored brethren on the South Carolina coast, where a piece of iron thrown into the fire also is regarded as efficacious.   The belief prevails there that trouble or even death will befall an inmate should one of the owls alight on the roof of the house and utter its prophetic notes.[2]   Even in canny, practical New England super-stition still lives, for Mr. F. B. White tells us that not many years ago "one that took up its residence for a few days in a church tower, was credited with foretelling — if not indeed causing — the death of a citizen of dignity, domiciled next door."[3]

Your Screech Owl lives in an old neglected orchard, often near a brook, where it can find a hollow in the heart of some ancient tree which serves it for a retreat during the hours of daylight; there also is a plentiful supply of food for its young in the shape of mice and insects, with sparkling water for bathing, for this little owl delights in a daily or nightly bath.   It was in such an orchard that I first met this bird of darkness.   As a small boy it was my custom to spend many hours before and after school in the fields and woods, and so, coming home one night in the gloaming and passing beneath some old apple trees, I was alarmed by a loud snapping just behind my head.   I turned quickly and gazed upon empty air.   There was nothing to be seen within my field of vision that could by any possibility have produced that sound.   Again, but more alertly, I resumed my way when snap-snap-snap sounded once more almost under my hat brim.   Turning instantly I saw the form of a little gray owl gliding swiftly and silently on expanded wings to alight near by on a horizontal limb in an opening among the trees.   Quick as a flash it turned to face me, and, as the glow from the western sky lighted its fore-front showing its great startled eyes and its broad head and wide-set ears, it seemed like some ancient forest gnome with long, pointed, white beard hanging down between the converg-ing dark stripes on its dappled breast.   As I gazed at it in amazement, again behind me sounded a snappy beak as a little red owl charged me from behind.   I realized then that this must be a pair of Screech Owls with young which they were trying to defend, and next day I searched the locality for the nest and eggs or young, but did not find them, for, as I learned later, another boy had been before me.

When taken young from the nest the Screech Owl makes a beautiful and interesting pet.   Care should be taken, however, not to keep young owls (even from the same nest) together, for eventually the little cannibals may eat one another, and finally there may be left only one survivor of the brood, sitting piously on his perch and blinking in the most honest way at his owner.

The Screech Owl is a nocturnal bird.   It rarely stirs abroad before dusk, and if an

---

[1] Arthur, S. C.: The Birds of Louisiana, 1918, p. 51.
[2] Wayne, Arthur T.: Birds of South Carolina, 1910, p. 83.
[3] Birds of Concord, New Hampshire, 1924, p. 45.

intruder molests it or its nest in the daytime, it is likely to remain inert or even to simulate death. If, however, anyone imagines that the bird cannot see in daylight, he should watch one fly into a hole in an apple tree when pursued by the noisy jays. Mr. Harry Hathaway describing this says that the owl "went into it like a bullet." I once had a tame Screech Owl that could see a hawk in the sky in bright sunlight long before it came within range of my vision; and whenever this owl, sitting on the window sill, began to wabble its head about and gaze skyward, we knew that a hawk or some other large bird had come within its ken. In captivity this species will catch and eat anything in the daytime as freely as at night. This owl may seem dull and stupid in daylight, but when the shades of night have fallen, it is a changed being, and then if it has young, it may attempt to intimidate intruders on its nesting grounds. Newspaper stories of "flocks of owls" attacking villagers are derived from this habit. The attacking birds sometimes go beyond mere bravado and actually strike the enemy.

For several years a pair of Screech Owls raised young in a nesting box in the pine woods beside my summer cottage. The young in their first flight usually alighted on the dwelling. Their parents became accustomed to our presence and paid little attention to us, but one evening one of my daughters who had come to visit her parents came out under the trees in a white dress. Immediately the adult owls struck at her head, one after the other repeatedly, and though she ducked and dodged, I could see that they barely missed her, and that their wings stirred her hair as they passed over. Several times they swept within an inch of her head, but after that night they never molested her, though they continued to feed the young in trees near by until about four weeks after they left the nest. While the young were in the nest, the parents fed them mostly mice and insects and afterwards chiefly insects, as we could see them nightly and watch the feeding in the dusk. The young began to give peculiar calls soon after they were out of the nest, some of which resembled the distant, faint, hoarse squalling of a hen, others were somewhat like the yowling of a tom-cat, others were husky imitations of their parents' usual tremulous call. The old birds meanwhile answered with their wail or called *ou ou*. Such a variety of sounds apparently indicating pain or despair coming from the depths of a dark pine wood at evening would be likely to fill the minds of the ignorant and superstitious with fear or foreboding. The calls of the young gradually lost their husky quality as the fledglings grew older.

One call of the Screech Owl which I have never seen described and have heard from but one individual is the only cry that could possibly merit the term "screech." It resembled the note of the siren whistle, beginning low and full and gradually rising without the usual tremolo until it ended in a shrill shriek. The bird that delivered this remarkable utterance was a resident of Concord, Mass., and Mr. Brewster and myself heard it there one season only. One of my note-books contains the following record of the occurrence: "Nov. 4, 1903. Last night at dusk I heard a new sound from the birch field. It resembled much the first notes of a siren whistle — rather long and with a sharp, distinct, rising inflection. Brewster and I both heard it later, but could not place it. Brewster thought it an owl of some kind. Tonight just before dusk I heard it again in the woods south of the house. I called G's attention to it, when it changed by degrees to the ordinary wail of the Screech Owl with tremulous delivery and falling inflection. Brewster also heard it and we all three agreed that the bird must be a Screech Owl." After that it was heard for some time and seen, though never very distinctly.

This species is not supposed to be migratory, but there seems to be a more or less irregular migration from the northern part of its range in winter. Probably it wanders southward at that season from bleak and inhospitable regions in search of food. Many of the owls that appear in Massachusetts in winter are starving, and in some seasons a number are found dead of starvation. Dr. John B. May found a Screech Owl in a nesting box at Cohasset, Massachusetts on November 20, 1923 — a year of much owl migration. The bird was much emaciated. It could not have starved in that region at that time, with no snow on the ground and an abundant food supply. It must have come from some less favored region. He placed a numbered band on its leg. In another box 50 feet away Dr. May found a headless half-grown rat. Five days later the owl was found in this second box, in company with the remains of a meadow mouse, a white-footed mouse and a leopard frog. The bird was no longer emaciated.

Birds of this species appear in autumn and winter in Massachusetts localities where they are not seen in summer, but they may have wandered only a few miles from their breeding places. Mr. Harry Hathaway banded a Screech Owl near Providence, Rhode Island, on March 14, 1920. This bird was caught January 9, 1921, only three miles from the place where it was banded. Screech Owls appear to be more numerous here in winter than in summer, which may be accounted for by the season's increase or by migration from the north. Many of the smaller owls are killed and eaten during the winter by larger species, which may account for the reduction in their numbers noticed in spring. I once found in the stomach and gullet of a Barred Owl the greater part of a Long-eared Owl, while in the stomach of the latter were some remains of a Screech Owl.

The Screech Owl gets its sustenance chiefly from mice and insects. It is very destructive to field mice, house mice, cutworms, grasshoppers, locusts and other pests. It eats many noxious nocturnal moths and many beetles — seems, in short, to have a marked predilection for destructive insects. Usually it seems to kill only small numbers of birds and seldom troubles poultry or game-birds. All one season I watched a pair that were rearing a brood near my cottage. We found in and about their nesting box feathers from several Blue Jays, others from a male Red-winged Blackbird and the wing of one Robin. All the pellets and other refuse from their food that season showed only remains of mice, shrews and insects. We concluded that the destruction of the Blue Jays was a benefit as there were too many of them, and they fed to some extent on the eggs and young of other birds. While the owls were there, the mice did no damage in our young orchard, but two years later their box fell down and was not replaced for the next two years. The second winter mice girdled nearly all our apple trees. The next year a number of boxes were erected. The owls returned and we had no trouble from mice thereafter. Dr. A.

A. Allen had an experience quite different from ours with a pair of these owls that fed many birds to their young.[1] On occasion, also, the Screech Owl destroys many English Sparrows.

Dr. A. K. Fisher reports on the stomach contents of 255 Screech Owls as follows: 1 contained remains of poultry; 38, other birds; 91, mice; 11, other mammals; 21, lizards; 4, batrachians; 1, fish; 100, insects only; 5, spiders; 9, crawfish; 7, miscellaneous matter; 2, scorpions; 2, earthworms; 43 were empty. Dr. B. H. Warren was informed by Mr. L. M. Turner that his examination of Screech Owl stomachs revealed that their food consisted mainly of large insects, such as beetles and grasshoppers, and many mice, and Dr. Warren himself found in examining 27 stomachs, taken principally in winter, that 20 had taken mice and insects; 5, small birds; and 2, small birds and insects. He remarks that when insects are abundant, the bird feeds mainly on them, and that it is chiefly in winter when other food is scarce or when the young require much food that it takes birds. Professor Aughey dissected 8 of these owls in Nebraska during locust invasions and in their stomachs found 219 locusts, 2757 other insects, 2 mice and 1 small bird. The one that had eaten the bird contained also 32 locusts and 8 other insects. In addition to the small mammals, birds and insects destroyed, Screech Owls occasionally get spiders, crawfish, a few small fish, small snakes, small frogs, snails, millipedes and earthworms.

ECONOMIC STATUS. The Screech Owl apparently is a useful bird, destroying many young rats, house mice, field mice and injurious insects. It rarely troubles game birds or poultry though it has been known in rare cases to kill the Bob-white and Woodcock, and occasionally in winter one may get into a dovecote and kill doves. At this season it has been known rarely to enter a fowl house and attack fowls, which, however, it is seldom able to kill. In one instance reported by Dr. A. A. Allen, during 45 days when a pair of these owls were watched, 77 small birds were brought to their young. This was in a bird sanctuary where birds were abundant, and it did not decrease the bird life in the sanctuary as there was a slight increase in the number of birds there at the end of a year. Doubtless, however, that increase would have been greater without the influence of the owls. The birds fed to the young were chiefly adults.[1] Probably this was an exceptional case but some Screech Owls get the habit of reaching into bird-houses and pulling out young birds. Apparently Screech Owls should not be encouraged to take up their habitation in a bird sanctuary.

Búbo virginiánus virginianus (GMELIN). Great Horned Owl.

Other names: CAT OWL; HOOT OWL.

Plate 46.

DESCRIPTION. — Distinguished from other, large, native owls by conspicuous ear-tufts, the others having none; large, powerful, robust; bill and feet powerful; wings long, broad and rounded at tips; tail rather short; feet feathered to claws. *Adults (sexes alike, but variable in size and color):* Above, mottled, speckled and vermiculated with brownish-black on a dull grayish, grayish-brown or ochraceous

[1] Auk, Vol. XLI, 1924, pp. 1–16.

ground; the darker color usually predominates on top of head and on back; flight-feathers barred with light and dark colors, and tail crossed by about seven bands of dusky or blackish; both wing and tail show dusky mottling on the lighter bars; throat white, which often extends down centre of breast; rest of under plumage ochraceous, buffy or tawny, mostly barred narrowly blackish and dappled or striped black lengthwise on breast; legs and feet more or less marked usually, but sometimes feet unmarked; face usually chiefly tawny or rusty, bordered by blackish; bill and claws black; iris bright yellow to pale yellow or straw. *Young in first winter plumage:* Like adult, but usually more rufous on middle of back, on wings, tail and lower plumage. *Young in juvenal plumage:* Flight-feathers and tail much as in adult, otherwise buffy or tawny, barred dusky; face edged blackish. *Downy young:* White or yellowish-white, which later becomes barred dusky-brown and face edged black; chin and throat remain white; iris changes from grey to pale yellowish as young bird grows.

MEASUREMENTS. — *Male:* Length 18.00 to 23.00 in.; spread about 35.00 to 52.00; folded wing 13.00 to 15.25; tail 7.00 to 9.00; bill 1.20 to 1.60; tarsus 1.20 to 1.30. *Female:* Length 22.00 to 25.00 in.; spread about 53.00 to 60.00; wing 15.00 to 16.30; tail 6.90 to 8.70; bill 1.50 to 1.95; tarsus 1.40 to 1.60. Female usually much the larger. Weight of male about 3 lbs. to 3 lbs. 8 oz.; female up to 4 lbs. 8 oz.

MOLTS. — Juvenal plumage is acquired by complete postnatal molt in the nestling; there is an incomplete postjuvenal molt in summer, flight-feathers and tail are retained, and when first winter plumage is assumed they form a part of it; in this plumage young bird appears much like adult and does not molt again until its postnuptial molt in summer and autumn, following the first winter, when apparently it becomes as adults, but many require another year for full maturity; adults have one complete molt (postnuptial).

FIELD MARKS. — Size larger than Red-tailed Hawk, with even greater wing spread; seen in flight may be recognized by great size, dark color, apparently shortened foreparts and lack of visible neck; rarely seen sitting except near nest.

VOICE. — Commonly a deep-toned hoot; *hŏŏ-hŏŏ-hoo-hŏŏ-hŏŏ-hooo'*, *hŏŏ'*, *hoo'*, *hŏŏ-hŏŏ*, *hoo'* or *hŏŏ*, *hŏŏ-hoo*, *hoo hoo* or some such grouping of syllables in similar refrains; "when the 'hoos' are uttered in a low tone, the sound is like a distant factory whistle" (J. A. Farley); more rarely a powerful blood-curdling shriek; a loud *waugh'-hoo*, first syllable accented, and with rising inflection; also many short jabbering or laughing tones; "a single soft cooing sound, quite dove-like — 'oo-oo-o,' with no aspirate quality" (H. K. Job).

BREEDING. — Commonly in heavy timber, in well-watered forests, especially in deep swamps or near some large stream or body of water. *Nest:* Rarely builds its own nest; frequently the deserted domicile of hawk or crow from 10 to 90 feet up; nests of Red-tailed or Red-shouldered Hawks are frequently chosen; rarely in hollow tree; more rarely in crevice of rocks and still more rarely on ground on small island or tussock surrounded by water;* rather rarely lined with down from the mother's breast and a few feathers. *Eggs:* Usually 2, rarely 3, very rarely 5; 2.15 to 2.33 by 1.70 to 2.00 in.; rounded ovate approaching oval or spherical; dull white, thick shelled and granular; pores large; illustrated in Bendire's "Life Histories of North American Birds," Vol. I., Plate XII, Fig. 12. *Dates:* Late November and early December, Florida; late January to middle February, Virginia; February 17 to April 20, Massachusetts; March 11 to 23, northern New England.† *Incubation:* Period variously given from 21 to 30 days, probably about 28 days; by both sexes. One brood yearly.

RANGE. — South central and southeastern Canada and east central and eastern United States, from southern Ontario and southern Quebec south to the Gulf coast and Florida and west to Wisconsin, southeastern Minnesota, Iowa, southeastern South Dakota, eastern Nebraska, eastern Kansas, Oklahoma and eastern and southern Texas; farther west and north it is replaced by other races of the species; accidental in Ireland.

---

* Cases are recorded where a Horned Owl had young on hay in a mow. See Auk, Vol. XLII, 1925, p. 444; and Vol. XXXVII, 1920, p. 309.

† An early nesting record for the Madison region, Wisconsin, was February 11, 1923, in zero weather!

DISTRIBUTION IN NEW ENGLAND. — Generally not uncommon; most common in heavily wooded regions, as in Maine; rare resident in Rhode Island; uncommon in Connecticut.

SEASON IN MASSACHUSETTS. — Permanent resident; most conspicuous when hooting in late winter.

HAUNTS AND HABITS. The Great Horned Owl is the most morose, savage and saturnine of all New England birds. We can hardly wonder that certain Indian tribes regarded this fowl as the very personification of the Evil One, or that they feared its influence and regarded its visits to their dwellings as portentous of disaster or death. Brewster writes as follows of the Great Horned Owl: "Despite his dignified bearing and handsome plumage, the Great Horned Owl does not make a pleasing addition to the aviary, for of all New England birds he is perhaps the most irredeemably morose and untamable. Even a Rattlesnake is scarce less amenable to kindly human advances, but whereas it may resent them with active and perhaps fatal aggression, the Owl will be no more than coldly unresponsive provided he is not touched. Much of what is doubtless his true nature may be read in his staring, yellow-girdled eyes. Soulless at all times, they express either vacuous or sullen indifference when he is resting undisturbed; malignant resentment, should he be annoyed or threatened; bloodthirsty lust, when his gaze is fixed on coveted prey. Yet he is not addicted to quarrelling with other large birds, even when closely confined with them, or to killing beyond his need for food. Such forbearance might redound more to his credit were it less obviously the outcome of mere selfish distaste for needless exertion of every kind. If he be ever moved to affection for any living creature, except, perhaps, for his mate, with whom he is accustomed to pair for life, the existence of such emotion is certainly not betrayed by any outward sign." [1]

The Great Horned Owl is not only the most formidable in appearance of all our owls, but it is the most powerful. The Great Gray Owl and the Snowy Owl may appear larger but the Great Horned Owl exceeds them in courage, weight and strength. Indeed it little regards the size of its victim for it strikes down geese and turkeys many times its weight, and has even been said at times to drive the Bald Eagle away from its aery and domicile its own family therein. In one case the owl laid its eggs in a cavity in the side of an eagle's nest and both families occupied the same habitation.[2] Recently a correspondent wrote to me saying that a Horned Owl had struck the claws of both feet into the back of his large collie dog. This bird may have been misled by a white patch on the dog, as the white on the back of a skunk is its favorite mark. Any white moving object is likely to attract the attention of this owl at night and bring on an attack, and it may be that old Bubo strikes at the white head of the eagle during the hours of darkness when the larger bird is at a disadvantage. Dr. William Wood wrote to Dr. Merriam the story of a man who was riding on horseback at night through a large tract of woods and wearing a white beaver hat, when something struck his head with such force that it took his hat, and for a time he feared that the top of his head had gone with it. The attack was noiseless and the poor man, thinking that he was pursued by Satan himself, fled at top speed

---

[1] Brewster, William: Birds of the Lake Umbagog Region of Maine, Part 2, 1925, pp. 386–387.
[2] Jacobs, J. Warren: Wilson Bulletin, Vol. XX, 1908, p. 103.

for about three miles. I came very near to a similar experience in the autumn of 1918. One night before retiring, while wearing a white canvas hat, I stepped out behind my cabin in the Wareham woods for a little gymnastic exercise. I had barely begun the calesthenics when just above my right ear there sounded a startling *waugh* followed by a string of vituperative owl language which drifted swiftly away toward a pine tree on the edge of the woods where some guinea-fowls were wont to roost. The wings of that owl must have almost brushed my ear, yet no sound of them was audible. Probably the great bird, watching from the top of some tall pine, had seen my moving hat in the moonlight, and as he shot over the cabin roof had realized his mistake just in time.

Sometimes when the nest of the Horned Owl is disturbed, the bird attacks the intruder and inflicts painful wounds, though usually it is extremely careful not to trust itself by daylight within gunshot of a human being. Mr. M. A. Carriker, Jr. relates that when he climbed to a nest containing well grown young, the female attacked him so suddenly that he had barely time to throw up his gloved hand before his face when she struck it with terrific force tearing the glove, severely lacerating the hand and almost causing him to lose his hold on the tree.[1] Another intruder at the nest of one of these birds was struck a stunning blow on the back of the neck by the female with such force that he was dazed for an instant as well as wounded, having received six slashes from her powerful claws.[2] Mr. F. N. Whitman is still another climber who has suffered terrific blows from a ferocious pair of these dangerous birds which nearly broke his grip on the branch besides leaving him cut and bleeding.[3]

My lifelong friend, Mr. John A. Farley, who is responsible for the correction of some errors which otherwise might have appeared in this volume, has studied closely the nesting of this owl but only once was he molested by the bird. While climbing to a nest he was struck a hard blow from behind. The powerful talons of the owl penetrated his overalls and heavy winter clothing and drew blood. Mr. John F. Carleton also informs me that he was struck from behind under similar conditions by one of these birds. Mr. H. H. Pitman and Mr. Howard Jones also record similar attacks. Mr. Pitman was struck and wounded three times.[4] Dr. Frank Overton recounts the continual attacks of a specially vindictive pair of Horned Owls, and gives a striking series of close-range pictures taken on these occasions.[5] In my experiences at the nests of these birds no attack was ever made. The mother bird usually disappeared at once and did not return; but one dull day in early March I had climbed to a nest on a great oak near Lake Quinsigamond and had stowed safely in my pocket the two newly-hatched young, when the powerful mother, who had been circling the tree, suddenly swooped down, alighted on a limb within a few feet of my face, and, leaning forward until she hung almost head downward, stared directly into my eyes with an expression of such fiendish ferocity that I prepared

---

[1] Proceedings of the Nebraska Ornithologists Union at its first Annual Meeting, 1900, p. 33.
[2] Murie, O. J.: Wilson Bulletin, Vol. XXXIV, 1922, p. 168.
[3] Bird-Lore, Vol. XXI, 1919, pp. 18–20.
[4] Bird-Lore, Vol. XXVII, 1925, pp. 94–96.
[5] Natural History, Journal of American Museum Natural History, Vol. XXI, 1921, pp. 175–184.

to defend myself. She soon swept away again, however, and continued her restless circling. Mr. William F. Lisk, who has found many nests of the Horned Owl tells of a night watchman in a woolen mill who was accustomed to pass through a grove of pine and other trees on the banks of Swift River near his home. He was attacked there one day in May by a large bird which struck him on the head and shoulders repeatedly. He picked up a stick to defend himself, but this proved to be rotten and useless, and the bird fairly drove him out, so that he ran toward home, beating the bird off with his hands. Mr. Lisk says that the bird was undoubtedly a Great Horned Owl that was heard hooting there. Probably it had fledged young somewhere near. Mr. Joseph B. Underhill tells of a female Great Horned Owl (whose mate he had caught and confined) that attacked him and struck him a stunning blow on the forehead, inflicting wounds and drawing much blood.[1]

A Horned Owl has been known to flutter over the ground like a Ruffed Grouse uttering short "wailing" notes and beating the ground with one wing and then the other, as if wounded, as a protest against the climbing by an intruder to its nest with young.

If taken *early enough*, young Horned Owls sometimes make interesting and tractable pets.[2] A young bird of this species, confined at the rooms of the Worcester Natural History Society, was so heavy that his mere weight made his sharp claws sink into one's wrist. Yet he was the gentlest of pets, uttering continually his peeping cries.

The Horned Owl is swift and skillful on the wing and threads its way with ease among the trees of the forest. Only one case has come to my notice where it has struck an object inadvertently. Dr. E. H. Perkins, writing from Unity, Maine, says that he heard a sudden noise outside the house, and the next morning he went out and picked up a dead owl of this species. The bird appeared to have been confused by a lighted window and had struck the building.

The courtship of the Horned Owl is a curious performance. The male goes through peculiar contortions, nodding, bowing, flapping its wings and using, meanwhile, the choicest and most persuasive owl language. One motion which seems common to all owls is a rotary movement of the head which is raised to the full length of the neck, then swung to one side and dropped as low at least as the feet, and then swung to the other side and raised again, giving the owl a ludicrous appearance. Whatever may be said about the fierceness and ferocity of owls, no one can accuse them of being unfaithful to their young. Mr. Farley tells me that more than once he has found the nest well lined with a handsome, yellow mass of warm feathers from the mother's breast which seemed analogous to the downy lining of a duck's nest. She sits closely on her eggs during the cold days and long nights of late February and early March. Often the snow covers both her and the nest and then if she is driven away by an intruder, the nest will be found covered with snow surrounding the imprint of her body, showing where she has faithfully outstayed the storm. The young remain in the nest and continue to grow for one long month, and during all that time they are well cared for and provided with a quantity

[1] The Young Oölogist, Vol. I, 1885, p. 152. [2] Bird-Lore, Vol. XXIII, 1921, p. 293.

of food.   Mr. Ned Dearborn tells a tale which shows both parental finesse and devotion. Two young birds were taken from the nest and placed on the ground below, in the hope that their parents would come near enough to be shot.   Soon an owl was heard hooting near by, and one of the watchers started in pursuit of the bird.   The hooting gradually receded as the man with the ready gun advanced.   Presently the man who remained behind was surprised to see one of the parents swoop to the ground and bear off one of the young in its talons, regardless of the unready gun which roared far behind her.[1]

In January and February these owls become vocal.   Later in the year the birds are less vocal, but now and then, especially in autumn, their hooting may be heard.   The following is taken from my notes of September 5, 1904, when I was staying at one of the Brewster cabins on the Concord River : "Tonight just after dark as I sat in the cabin a sound came from down river like someone trying to imitate a dog, which was baying on the other shore; then it changed to higher, gabbling tones, gradually coming nearer, and sounding more like the talk and laughter of a boatload of women coming up the river. Soon it was followed by the unmistakable *hŏŏ-hŏŏ, hōō', hŏŏ-hōō'* of the Great Horned Owl.   I stepped out of doors and answered it and the bird soon came quite near.   I then went indoors, and it alighted on one of the trees above the cabin where it remained for some time, conversing with me in owl language.   That bird made more peculiar and diverse sounds than I have heard from any other owl; for awhile its vocalizing was confined to soft cooing tones like *wu woó* and *wu wa*.   Then, becoming bolder it launched forth a volley of interrogative *wahoos* and double hoots that were startling when coming from a distance of less than twenty yards.   I answered occasionally and the bird kept up its hooting for half an hour.   The upward slide of its loud *waugh-hoo* was inimitable ; beginning at C the note *waugh* ran up to F at its ending followed by the emphatic *hoo* which fell again to C.   Also it called *wau-hoo' hoo ooo, oo-oo* without the rising inflection, or *wu waugh?-hoo-hoo-hoo, hoo-hoo, ho, hoo-hoo*, etc.   To me this was the principal event of the day."

One moonlit night the owl began hooting away off in the swamp nearly a mile away and every hoot was answered by the note of a male Black Duck across the river.   The hooting came nearer and nearer and the drake answered, until suddenly the call of the owl boomed out directly over the cabin roof.   From then on that drake kept very quiet.

In August, 1920, as I lay on the ground beside a small lake west of Waquoit Bay listening to numerous mosquitoes in conclave just outside my netting, a pair of owls began their hooting in the darkness.   Answering their calls I soon enticed them to the trees above me.   One was a particularly deep-toned hooter.   The other, probably the male, seemed to be a light-weight.   I have noticed in other cases that one of a pair, presumably the female, has a much deeper voice than the other.

In the forests of northern New England we usually hear the Horned Owl hooting in the swamps but sometimes they are on the mountains.   A case of this kind occurred in western Massachusetts during the winter of 1919–20.   European Hares had been intro-

---

[1] Birds of Durham and Vicinity, 1903, p. 50.

duced by some one in eastern New York near the Massachusetts line and had increased rapidly in numbers and spread into western Massachusetts where they had become a serious pest to the farmer and orchardist. In November and December of 1919 a flight of owls came into that region and Mr. Walter Pritchard Eaton told me that numbers were heard about the mountain in Sheffield. There they preyed upon the hares. He said that the mournful hoot of these great owls began about 3.30 P.M. in December and continued until late at night all along the wooded mountain side. He had heard as many as four at once near his house. These owls overran the region and many returned the next winter. The following spring European Hares were very scarce in that country.

The Horned Owl is a nocturnal bird, most active in the dusk of the evening and on moonlit nights, but it may be heard hooting at times at midnight in the "dark of the moon." It hunts at night, yet it can see perfectly in the daytime. It will hardly allow a man to come within gunshot in daylight, though under the protection of darkness it may come very near him. The best opportunity to see one by day is to advance upon it when it is mobbed by the noisy angry Crows. Then by keeping behind trees and moving up quickly while the Crows are calling, one may rarely get a glimpse of the owl. But it always starts before the Crows, which, no sooner do they see the owl go, than they follow in their usual uproarious pack. The bird often hunts just before dusk on dull days, and on very dark days it may be out before the middle of the afternoon. I remember once looking down from a cliff on the side of a mountain at Mount Desert upon an owl hunting over the meadows below. This was about 4 P.M. and the view of the owl's back and wings as it quartered over the land like a Marsh Hawk hunting for mice was all that could be desired.

Horned Owls are not regarded as migratory, but in winter they often leave regions where suitable food is scarce and go where it can be found. They are not always successful in this search, however, and now and then one is found starved and frozen in the snow. Such specimens when discovered are very much emaciated. Mr. H. A. P. Smith writing from Digby, Nova Scotia, March 14, 1923, says that a Great Horned Owl was found there sitting upright in an apple tree frozen stiff. Probably his tightly clinched talons froze to the limb and held him there in death; but the bird would not have been frozen had it had food enough to keep up the animal heat in its body. In this species the extensor (fused) tendons of the leg which retract the toes and clinch the claws pass through a groove in the tarso-metatarsus and then into and through a hole in the bone, as a rope passes through a pulley-block. The tendons are thus held firmly in place as they pass over and through what in the human being would be the heel. When the leg is bent and drawn up the tendons also are drawn tight, clenching the toes and driving in the talons. Thus when the owl settles down on a limb, its toes and talons lock round it and hold the bird firmly in sleep or as in the above case even in death. This arrangement of the tendons and their connection with the machinery of the toes forms a powerful equipment with which to strike its prey. When the bird strikes a victim, the force of the blow alone tends to bend the legs, contract the tendons and drive the claws into a vital part. In addition to this the powerful muscles of the legs are brought into play to force the talons home. Thus its speed, weight and muscular power all combine to give the bird the force to overcome animals many times its own weight.

Horned Owls migrate usually from regions where food is scarce in winter and thus escape starvation. Probably there is some migration of these birds every year from the northern parts of their range toward more southern regions. In some seasons of scarcity this migration increases to considerable proportions. Says Mr. E. O. Grant writing on November 12, 1924, "There were lots of Great Horned Owls coming in before I left township 11, range 16, Aroostook County, Maine." Major Mark Robinson wrote November 20, 1921 from Algonquin National Park in the highlands of Ontario. "We observed quite a migration of owls November 2 and 3. The woods were ringing with their hooting. They were gone on the fourth." The spring migration northward is not so evident as the fall exodus. Many of these northern birds are shot by gunners in autumn and winter and many more are taken in traps, especially around game farms. As many as 50 or 75 of these owls are taken in some years about a single game farm. When pressed by hunger they will eat any small mammal that they find in a trap and often they are caught at such times in baited traps. Miss Florence Pease in a letter to me in 1918 said that in the previous winter a large owl was reported in Conway, Massachusetts with a steel trap on one leg and that in 1919 one alighted on a factory in Connecticut in a similar plight, causing so much excitement in the factory that the works were shut down.

Every living thing above ground in the woods on winter nights pays tribute to the Great Horned Owl except the larger mammals and man. Ordinarily when there is good hunting this owl has a plentiful supply of food, and when there is game enough it slaughters an abundance and eats only the brains; but in winter when house rats and mice keep mostly within the buildings, when woodchucks and skunks have "holed up" and when field mice are protected by deep snow — then if rabbits are scarce and starvation is imminent, the owl will attack even the domestic cat, and usually with success. A farmer brought me a Great Horned Owl one winter day that had killed his pet tom cat on the evening of the previous day. The cat was out walking in the moonlight on one of his usual expeditions in search of unattended females, when the farmer heard a wail of mortal agony and opening the door saw Mr. Cat in the grasp of the owl. Before he could get his gun and shoot the bird the cat was no more. Its vitals had been torn out. Usually the noiseless flight of the owl enables it to take the cat by surprise and seize it by the back of the neck and the small of the back, when all is soon over; but if the cat is not taken by surprise and is quick enough to turn on the owl, the episode is likely to have a different ending. Sometimes the owl "wakes up the wrong customer" as the following incident related to me by Mr. J. A. Farley clearly shows:

"Mr. Zenas Langford, for many years superintendent of streets in the southern part of Plymouth, tells me that a few years ago in the Pine Hills, he came upon a Horned Owl in trouble with a black snake. As he went along the cart road, the two suddenly 'fell into it.' Plainly the owl had caught the snake, but the reptile had twisted itself around the bird so that it was unable to fly, and fell to the ground with its prey. Mr. Langford says that the owl had grasped the snake about six inches below its head, but the part of the snake below the owl's talons had twisted itself around the bird tightly. There was at least one light turn around the owl's neck. Mr. Langford could not see that the snake had bitten the owl, which however, was nearly exhausted. The owl nevertheless had not relaxed its hold on the snake. Neither of the creatures had given up. Mr. Langford killed the snake, which measured 4 feet. The owl was so weakened and helpless that it could not fly; it seemed to have been choked. Mr. Langford wrapped it in a blanket, took it home, kept it for a week and then let it go." The porcupine, also, does not yield up his life, without doing all the harm possible. Witness the Horned Owl, liberally besprinkled with porcupine quills, which was shot in the Province of Quebec in December 1907, and reported by Rev. G. Eifrig.[1]

Horned Owls kill and eat many skunks, and seem to care little for the disagreeable consequences of attacking these pungent animals. Many of the owls that I have handled give olfactory evidence of the habit. They kill both wild and domesticated ducks, picking them up skillfully out of the water at night, and no goose is too large for them to tackle. Occasionally, however, the owl comes to grief in its attack on some water-fowl. At Lanesboro, Massachusetts, in February, 1918, one was found floating dead in a pool with a duck that it had killed. No one knew the details of this midnight tragedy. It may be that the owl was weakened by hunger and was unable to rise from the water. Where hens, chickens and turkeys are allowed to roost at night in the trees, many fall victims to this owl, which is said to alight on the branch beside its chosen prey, crowd it off the limb and then strike it in the air. Some guinea hens roosting in trees on my farm disappeared in some such manner. Usually the owl does not stop to eat his victim on the spot but bears it away.

Mr. A. A. Cross of Huntington informed me that in December, 1918, one of his neighbors left a live guinea hen in a sack and it disappeared. The next day he found the remains of the fowl in the orchard. The sack had been torn open and about half of the bird had been eaten. Two traps were set near it and the next night a splendid specimen of the Great Horned Owl was taken.

In eating its prey this owl usually begins at the head and eats backward. The birds are plucked, but small mammals such as mice and rats are swallowed whole, head first. Mr. E. O. Grant says that he saw an owl strike a Ruffed Grouse in a bush and bear it away without even checking his flight. "The owl flew up a stream with a stream of feathers trailing in his wake. I think," says Mr. Grant, "that he must have had that bird pretty well plucked before he had gone 60 rods." The Horned Owl is no respecter of persons. It kills weaker owls from the Barred Owl down, most of the hawks and such nocturnal animals as weasels and minks. It is the most deadly enemy of the Crow, taking old and young from their nests at night and killing many at their winter roosts. Game

[1] Auk, Vol. XXVI, 1909, p. 58.

birds of all kinds, poultry, a few small birds, rabbits (especially bush rabbits), hares, squirrels, gophers, mice, rats, woodchucks, opossums, fish, crawfish and insects are all eaten by this rapacious bird.   It is particularly destructive to rats.   Mr. E. O. Niles tells of a nest of this owl on his farm containing two young owls and several dead rats. On the ground below the nest were the bodies of 113 rats, recently killed, with their skulls opened and the brains removed.   When we find young in the nest of one of these owls, they are well supplied with game.   Mr. H. O. Green writes that he found remains of a skunk, a Crow and a pheasant at one nest and Mr. Joseph Peters says that the parent birds that supplied another nest brought black ducks, rabbits, rats, snakes, a Red Phalarope, a Virginia Rail, two Woodcocks, a Bob-white, a Northern Flicker, a Pheasant and some small birds.   In eating their food the fierce young birds grasped the game firmly in the talons and tore at it with their beaks.   They began their feast on the larger birds and mammals by consuming the head and then working backward through the carcass.   Of 127 stomachs of Great Horned Owls examined by Dr. A. K. Fisher, 31 contained poultry or game birds; 8, other birds; 13, mice; 65, other mammals; 1, a scorpion; 1, fish; 10, insects and 17 were empty.

ECONOMIC STATUS.   In the wilderness the Great Horned Owl exerts a restraining influence on both the game and the enemies of game, for it destroys both and thus does not disturb the balance of nature.   But on the farm or the game preserve, it cannot be tolerated.

Bubo virginianus palléscens STONE.   Western Horned Owl.

NOTE.   Mr. F. B. White (in The Auk, Vol. XLIII, 1926, p. 377) records a bird under the above name, now in the collection of Mr. C. F. Goodhue, taken at Boscawen, N. H., October 15, 1909.   This bird was identified by Mr. Goodhue who writes to me that he compared it with a specimen of the Western Horned Owl.   Recently Mr. White took the bird to Mr. James L. Peters, of the Museum of Comparative Zoölogy at Harvard College who examined it carefully, compared it with other specimens, and now makes the following statement : " Size and coloration typical of birds of southern Alberta south to Colorado that should be called *occidentalis* (Stone), but since the American Ornithologists' Union does not recognize *occidentalis*, the bird was correctly recorded as *pallescens* by Mr. White."

Mr. Robert Ridgway, who follows Mr. H. C. Oberholser in recognizing *occidentalis* describes it as follows: "Much paler than B. v. virginianus with grayish and buffy predominating on upper parts, the under parts more extensively white, with black bars narrower ; legs and toes buffy to nearly white, usually immaculate or nearly so ; size larger."   I know of no other clearly authentic record of this race in New England.

The range given for this bird in the A. O. U. Check-List, 3rd edition, 1910, follows : Western United States (exclusive of the higher mountains) from eastern Oregon, Montana, Minnesota, south to southeastern California, Arizona, New Mexico, western Texas and northeastern Mexico.   This range includes also that of the Pallid Horned Owl to which Mr. Ridgway, again following Oberholser, gives the name *Bubo virginianus pallescens* (Stone), and which is similar to *Bubo virginianus occidentalis*, but smaller.

Doubtless the molts, field marks, voice, breeding, haunts and habits and economic status of this owl are similar to those of the Great Horned Owl.   No field marks can be given which would certainly distinguish the bird from the Arctic Horned Owl.

Bubo virginianus subárcticus Hoy. Arctic Horned Owl.

DESCRIPTION. — Similar to Great Horned Owl in size and shape. *Adults (sexes alike)*: Above, white or very pale in ground color, with markings similar to those of Great Horned Owl, but much paler and more restricted. Below, white with dark markings comparatively few and sometimes obsolete; legs and feet white or very pale buffy.

MEASUREMENTS AND MOLTS. — Similar to those of Great Horned Owl.

FIELD MARKS. — Size and shape of Great Horned Owl but much paler; typical specimens almost as white as some Snowy Owls.

VOICE. — Similar to that of Great Horned Owl.

BREEDING. — Chiefly in coniferous forests. *Nest:* Usually in coniferous tree, sometimes in deciduous tree or on a cliff. *Eggs:* Indistinguishable from those of Horned Owl. *Dates:* April 1 to 22, southern Mackenzie. *Incubation:* No details.

RANGE. — Chiefly north central Canada. Breeds probably north to tree limit from the Mackenzie Valley and west coast of Hudson Bay south to northern Alberta, southwestern Saskatchewan, central Manitoba and northern Ontario; south in winter to Idaho, Nebraska, Minnesota, Wisconsin, northern Illinois, southern Ontario, New York and New England.

DISTRIBUTION IN NEW ENGLAND. — Rare, irregular straggler in winter; probably not so exceedingly rare as the records indicate. Records: *Maine:* Brownfield, 1886, bird now in collection of the Portland Society of Natural History.[1] Portland, Dec. 6, 1869, presented alive to Portland Society of Natural History, said to have been taken in Maine. Recorded by A. H. Norton, under name *B. v. arcticus* (Proc. Portland Society of Natural History, Vol. II, 1897, p. 103) and very likely is *B. v. wapacuthu*.[2] Massachusetts: Waltham, November 30, 1867, specimen taken by C. J. Maynard and prepared for Museum of Comparative Zoölogy,[3] now in collection of Boston Society of Natural History; Cambridge (Mount Auburn Cemetery), December 4, 1917, female taken by an employee, now in collection of Boston Society of Natural History;[4] Somerville, November 26, 1918, male found dead, now in collection of Boston Society of Natural History.[5]

LABRADOR HORNED OWL AND ARCTIC HORNED OWL

HAUNTS AND HABITS. The Arctic Horned Owl migrates in winter from the northern part of its range, and when there is a dearth of owl food in northern Canada, many individuals may reach the northern United States. They appear in the middle west and more rarely in New England. Such an invasion occurred in the winters of 1916–17 and 1917–18 and between the latter year and 1921 I heard of a number of specimens in the hands of taxidermists, taken in New England, which probably were referable to this subspecies, but as I had no opportunity to compare them with typical specimens, and as

---

[1] Knight, O. W.: List of Birds of Maine, 1897, p. 69.
[2] Allen, Glover M.: Auk, Vol. XXXVI, 1919, p. 369; and Norton, Arthur H.: *in litt.*
[3] Morse, A. P.: Birds of Wellesley, 1897, p. 23.
[4] Allen, Glover M.: Auk, Vol. XXXVI, 1919, p. 368.
[5] *Ibid.*, pp. 368–369.

the identification of the various races of the Horned Owl and their intermediates is rather difficult, I have not recorded any of them. Some of them may have been referable to a western race.

In the winter of 1923–24 there was an influx of white or pale Horned Owls into Maine and also some very dark ones (as at Machias in fall of 1923), but not one of these specimens came into my hands. Both the northern and western birds intergrade with *virginianus*. The Arctic Horned Owl is a forest species, and, so far as now known, its habits are similar to those of our well-known native bird, but it may be more given to migration.

Bubo virginianus heterocnémis (Oberholser). Labrador Horned Owl.

DESCRIPTION. — Similar to Great Horned Owl, but much darker; blackish-brown above, finely marked with gray, with very wide dusky bars below; face dark rather than russet or tawny, and feet much deeper in color than in *virginianus*.

MEASUREMENTS. — Similar to those of Great Horned Owl and probably Molts, Voice and Breeding also.

NOTE. A specimen of this race, taken in Maine, near Portland, and given in March, 1870, to the museum of the Portland Society of Natural History was recorded at the time as a Dusky Horned Owl, *Bubo virginianus saturatus*. *Asio magellanicus heterocnemis*, Labrador Horned Owl, was described by Oberholser in Volume 27 of the Proceedings of the United States National Museum, 1904, p. 187, and this form is included in the third edition (1910) of the Check-list of the American Ornithologists' Union, as *Bubo virginianus heterocnemis*.

RANGE. — Northern Ungava and Labrador; casual in New England. Mr. Oberholser gives the range of his new subspecies *neochorus*, Newfoundland Horned Owl (18th Supplement to A. O. U. Check-list — Auk, Vol. XL, 1923, p. 519), as Newfoundland and Nova Scotia. He says: "It [a single adult from Truro, N. S.] is evidently of the same race, and indicates that the range of *Bubo virginianus neochorus* extends to Nova Scotia. It is entirely possible also that birds from the neighboring areas of New Brunswick and northern New England, where occur many grayish individuals which we have heretofore referred to a supposed dark grayish phase of *Bubo virginianus virginianus*, belong to the present new race. Such birds should, therefore, now, undoubtedly be carefully compared with the present new form."

DISTRIBUTION IN NEW ENGLAND. — *Maine:* Portland, bird killed many years earlier, given in March, 1870, to the Portland Society of Natural History. Referred in 1897 (Proceedings Portland Society of Natural History, Vol. II, 1897, p. 103) by Arthur H. Norton to race *saturatus*, as then understood; "no doubt this, too, is an example of the subspecies *heterocnemis* and came from the North"; [1] Scarborough, adult female taken about February 7, 1918, and received in the flesh on the 9th by Curator Thomas A. James of the State Museum at Augusta, Maine, and now in collection of Boston Society of Natural History.[2] *Massachusetts:* Marshfield, male taken about December 22, 1917, on Hen Island near edge of salt marsh by Wilbur Ewell.[3] *Connecticut:* Black Hall, bird shot in November, 1917, by R. Beecher Huntley.[4]

---

[1] Allen, Glover M.: Auk, Vol. XXXVI, 1919, p. 368; and Norton, A. H.: *in litt.*
[2] Allen, Glover M.: Auk, Vol. XXXVI, 1919, p. 367.
[3] Lamb, Charles R.: Auk, Vol. XXXV, 1918, pp. 233–234.
[4] Bishop, Louis B.: Auk, Vol. XXXVIII, 1921, p. 586.

Nýctea nyctea (LINNÆUS). **Snowy Owl.**

Other names: SNOW OWL; WHITE OWL; ARCTIC OWL.

Plate 46.

DESCRIPTION. — Very large; fully as large as Great Horned Owl, heavier than Great Gray Owl; head rounded, without ear-tufts; wings long and broad; tail slightly rounded; feet fully feathered to and beyond toe tips. *Adult male:* Pure white with more or less reddish-brown or dark grayish-brown barring above, and less or pure white below; rarely unmarked, but often with very few markings; iris light yellow or straw; cere greenish; bill and claws bluish-horn blackening toward tips. *Adult female:* Usually white, but with many more markings than male and often much darker; face, chin, throat, wing linings and axillars, legs and sometimes middle of breast and belly, region about vent, and under tail-coverts, unmarked; feet unmarked or nearly so; top of head and upper plumage from neck to tail usually heavily spotted and barred with slaty-brown or dusky; some birds are so heavily marked as to appear quite dark; face always white; a slight tinge of yellowish-brown on back. *Young male in first winter plumage:* Much like adult female, but with a small patch of heavily barred feathers in middle of nape. *Young female in first winter plumage:* More heavily barred and mottled dark brown, both above and below, than first winter male or adult female. *Young in juvenal plumage:* Above and below, generally dusky brown, the feathers (of very loose texture) tipped and speckled grayish-white; face and chin white with brown feather-tips, wing-feathers and tail-feathers like adults, but tips of tertials from buffy-white above, (white below) to dusky-brown or "deep, sooty-grayish" darkening with age; primary coverts mottled brown and a brownish tinge on back.

MEASUREMENTS. — Length 20.00 to 27.00 in.; spread 54.00 to 66.00; folded wing 15.50 to 19.00; tail 8.27 to 10.59; bill 1.25 to 1.60; tarsus 1.80 to 2.50. Female usually larger than male. Weight 3 lbs. to 4 lbs., 8 oz.; a large female weighed 5 lbs.

MOLTS. — Juvenal plumage, except wing-and-tail-quills and primary coverts, appears to be molted early in autumn; by the next autumn a complete molt is succeeded by a plumage practically as adult. Adults have one complete postnuptial molt (summer and autumn).

FIELD MARKS. — Fully as large as Great Horned Owl; variable, but largely white, and in flight, seen from below, looks very white; distinguished from White Gyrfalcon by apparent lack of neck, larger head and more rounded wing tips; seen in flight looks whiter than Arctic Horned Owl; some Barn Owls appear very white if seen from below, especially in flight, but the Barn Owl is a summer visitor while the Snowy Owl is seen rarely before November or December.

VOICE. — Few details; apparently a silent bird with us; I have heard it give a rather weak, whistling, intermittent cry.

BREEDING. — Usually in open, barren country, rarely where there are trees. *Nest:* A mere depression in soil, on hillock or hillside or slight elevation in the tundra; occasionally a shelf of a rocky cliff. *Eggs:* 4 to 10 or 11; 2.16 to 2.55 by 1.72 to 1.90 in.; somewhat more elongated than those of Horned Owl; white, with smooth surface; some have "corrugated lines" running lengthwise (Bendire); illustrated in Bendire's "Life Histories of North American Birds," Vol. I, Plate XII, Fig. 19. *Dates:* May 26 and into June on Arctic islands. *Incubation:* Period about 32 days; by female. One brood yearly.

RANGE. — Northern part of Northern Hemisphere. Breeds as far north as land is known, and south to northern British Columbia, central Mackenzie, central Alberta, northern Manitoba, northern Ungava (northern Quebec), and to about latitude 53° Labrador; south in winter to South Carolina, Georgia, Gulf states, Texas and California; accidental in Bermuda; in Europe south in winter to France, Switzerland, Caspian and Black Seas, and in Asia to northern India and Japan.

DISTRIBUTION IN NEW ENGLAND. — Uncommon to rare migrant and winter visitor, chiefly in open lands, irregularly common, principally coastwise.

SEASON IN MASSACHUSETTS. — October 12 to April 12 (May 20).

HAUNTS AND HABITS. My first acquaintance with the Great White Owl as a bird of New England came about as follows — three boys, ages twelve to fourteen, of which I was one, used to go hunting together accompanied by two hounds belonging to neighbors and one muzzle-loading double-barreled shotgun borrowed from an indulgent father. One snowy day Bob came rushing into the house crying excitedly that there was a big white owl on a tree in the old orchard. In the excitement that followed, the gun was loaded somehow and Bill with the deadly weapon at the ready, crept softly through the newly fallen snow toward that owl, keeping well behind the tree trunks. Finally he crouched and sighted the piece, taking long and careful aim. In the silent interval that followed a cap snapped sharply. At that startling sound the owl spread its great white wings and launched its form upon the snow-laden air, followed by the roar of the other barrel, and flapped away into the dim obscurity of the fast falling snow. In the excitement and haste of loading that gun both charges of shot had been poured into the right barrel and all the powder into the left.

My most satisfactory observation of the Snowy Owl is recent. The following description is taken from my note-book: "November 17, 1926. Last Sunday and Monday great flights of Brants came down the Massachusetts coast and small groups of Snowy Owls were seen moving along the shore. All yesterday and the previous night a southerly gale was blowing, and storm warnings were up along the coast. Yesterday in the gale I went to Yarmouthport and at night we drove before the wind across Barnstable Harbor and were washed ashore in a dory at Sandy Neck. All night the gale howled and roared. Rain dashed against the window panes before we slept, but with daybreak the wind 'hauled' to the westward, and the sun rose on one of the most perfect days of the year. The wind, which usually blows there, had moderated somewhat, but still the wind-driven sand swept up the westerly slopes of the taller dunes, streamed off their tops like smoke, and rattled on one's clothing like tiny hailstones.

" What a contrast the bird life of Cape Cod presents at this time of the year to that of the mainland. There it is at its lowest ebb, while here birds are abundant. On the bay, about 500 yards from shore, gulls may be seen in countless myriads, mile upon mile, as far as the telescope can bring them into view. Up the shore to Sandwich and where the beach curves toward Plymouth their white breasts flash in the sunlight upon the dark blue water. Their presence in such untold multitudes may be accounted for by the vast numbers of squids cast up all along the shore — food for a million gulls.

" Flocks of Brant pass high overhead, bound south toward Muskeget or east toward Monomoy. Bunches of scoters, sheldrakes and Old-squaws speed by before the wind, and now and then a few Black Ducks. Great Loons, Red-throated Loons and Grebes float near the shore. Gannets are fishing in the bay. Among the dunes flocks of Horned Larks and Snow Buntings flit by, and with them a few Longspurs. Myrtle Warblers, Flickers and Catbirds move about in the thickets, and a sharp-winged Pigeon Hawk swoops down from the sky on the wings of a driving gale — and is gone. A great flock of Starlings moves on to the southward. Sanderlings run along the shore. Here are more birds than one can often see in one day in Massachusetts, but I disregard them and pass on, for the object of my quest is the Snowy Owl.

"Tramping over the dunes I climb to the tops of the highest and scan the country for patches of white. Most of these prove to be pieces of newspaper that the gale has carried here and lodged among the bushes; but one seen imperfectly through the tracery of little twigs may be an owl. As I tramp toward that suspicious object, there is a flutter of great white wings over the dune top and the bird is gone from my sight forever. It is a wild one, and toil as I will through shifting sands, I search for it in vain. Passing to the northward nearer the beach and on up the interminable sands of the Neck, another suspicious object is seen. It is stationary, but on a nearer approach it spreads great wings, swings over to leeward and alights about 100 yards away on a low ridge facing me and the sun. The telescope brings the bird up close and as I am partly hidden by the beach grass of a near ridge, she soon forgets me and sits at ease in the blazing sunshine — a monstrous great female Arctic Owl with her white plumage darkly barred, a face as white as snow, and great yellow eyes wide open and staring as she turns her head from side to side, now forward and now back, watching the birds in the sky. Soon she leaps over the top of the ridge and out of my field of vision. My stalking is a failure, as she has the wind of me and can hear the least motion. Before I have lessened the distance to 60 yards, she is on the wing and away to another dune where she sits with her great body in profile and her face turned full upon me. Her expression is savage; her eyes have a tigerish glare. At my first forward motion she is up and away, moving with long slow flaps, her ample wings bending well down with each stroke. Occasionally she sails with or athwart the wind. Now she rises high over the bay, and some of the complaining gulls follow her, but although they could easily overtake her, they do not dare to approach too near. Now she swings toward me and from her far height swoops diagonally downward into the wind and straight at my face. She is upon me in a moment, but at my first motion she turns and, passing a few yards to one side, alights on the top of a dune.

"Three cawing, busybody Crows have seen her swoop and have followed her down. As the first one darts at her, she crouches ready to spring at him, but the crafty black rascal has seen the glare of her eyes and sheers wide of that dune top. The Crows continue to plunge at her, but they never come within reach of her spring and as she disregards them absolutely and entirely, they soon tire of their dangerous game and move on.

"Now she sees something in the sky — probably some great bird — as she begins those curious motions of her head that owls always make when they espy a large hawk or eagle far up in the blue vault. Whatever she sees there is beyond my ken, for I can find nothing there even with the binoculars. Oh for the eyes of an owl! Those who imagine that owls cannot see in the daytime should watch her now as she follows that phantom shape across the sky far beyond human vision. Twice I have had her within easy gunshot, but had I killed her I would have missed her reception of the Crows and that eery following of that unknown form across that cloudless sky."

The Snowy Owl is a bird of the open. It alights commonly on the ground and I never knew one to sit in a tree except in the case above described. But the bird does this at times.[1] In a letter written to me on January 19, 1914, Mr. R. J. Gregory of Princeton tells of one that appeared in his neighborhood and perched in an apple tree, where it was seen to devour another bird which it had caught. When it had finished the bird, it calmly descended to the ground and washed its face in the snow, pushing its head through the snow "in a manner similar to the way cats have been known to act." Feathers left on the snow proved that it had eaten a Meadowlark. Along the coast where Snowy Owls are occasionally much more common than they are in the interior they usually alight and feed on knolls or on the tops of dunes. Mr. Freeman B. Currier wrote to me of a Snowy Owl that was first noticed on the snow in an open field because of several noisy Crows that were darting down at it. The owl appeared to disregard the Crows, but when the observers got within about 100 yards of the bird, it flew to a distant knoll. It was followed from knoll to knoll and at each place where the owl had alighted, "a collection of duck's feet, bones, feathers, wings and fur" was found, which seemed to show that the bird had been accustomed to feed there. Evidently the Snowy Owl chooses the tops of knolls so that it can overlook the surrounding country and watch for approaching enemies, for this owl usually is somewhat shy, and as it can see as well by day as by night, it can discover a human intruder afar off. This owl often sits down, resting on its breast, or stands with its body slanting forward at an angle of about 45 degrees. In New England it prefers large marshes, pastures and open lands where it can command an unobstructed view of its surroundings. Hence, during its migration, its numbers are greatest on the salt marshes and islands along the coast.

Apparently a few Snowy Owls reach Massachusetts in every winter but only on rather rare occasions does the species become common. One of the greatest flights that I have seen occurred in the autumn of 1876, when one man found six on a little island near Cape Ann, and another saw fifteen one foggy morning on an island near there and killed nearly half of them; some of the New England taxidermists had from 50 to 150 birds each that winter. Most of these birds were in a half starved condition and probably were driven south by the dearth of food in the north.[*] In the winter of 1876–77 the migration of Snowy Owls into the Northern United States was general.

Mr. J. H. Fleming, of Toronto, estimated that at least one thousand of these owls were killed in Ontario alone during another great flight that occurred in the winter of 1901–02, when many owls were killed in New England.[2] They were unusually abundant again in the winter of 1905–06,[3] and another considerable flight occurred in the fall and winter of 1922–23.

In the winter of 1906–07 they were abundant in Manitoba.[4] Mr. Deane quotes

[1] Cameron, E. S.: Auk, Vol. XXIV, 1907, p. 269.

[*] An observer reports that on the Iowa prairies "the smaller and whiter birds come in cold winters, the darker and larger ones in warm winters." (Bulletin Nuttall Ornithological Club, Vol. VIII, 1883, p. 237.)

[2] Deane, Ruthven: Auk, Vol. XIX, 1902, pp. 271–283; and Fleming, J. H.: *ibid.*, p. 400.

[3] Deane, Ruthven: Auk, Vol. XXIII, 1906, pp. 283–298.   [4] Deane, Ruthven: Auk, Vol. XXIV, 1907, pp. 217–219.

Mr. J. H. Fleming and Mr. P. A. Taverner. Mr. Taverner, writing from Detroit, notes that the owls taken in his district were very white; and Mr. Fleming also writes that the flight in his locality, although not large, was remarkable for the wonderful whiteness of the birds. Mr. Taverner holds that the whiteness of these birds shows that they came from a different geographical source than previous flights, and adds: "The only place I know of where white birds are at all common is the Canadian Northwest."

Commander Donald MacMillan informs me that some of these owls remain in northern Greenland all winter, living on northern hares. Wherever food becomes scarce, these owls must leave the region in winter or starve. The Snowy Owl is warmly clad to withstand the cold, and its keen vision serves it well both day and night, as it needs must through the long, Arctic, summer day.

In the north it subsists largely upon mice and lemmings. It takes many ptarmigans also and sea-fowl along the coast. It captures birds on the wing much after the manner of the Gyrfalcon as its flight is strong and swift. It has been known to catch fish. Audubon describes how one lay down on the edge of a deep water hole, and watching its chance snatched a fish from the water.

ECONOMIC STATUS. The Snowy Owl is a necessary factor in the economy of nature in boreal regions, where its numbers always assemble to check any sudden invasion of those extremely prolific mammals — field mice and lemmings. Dr. Leonhard Stejneger found the stomach of one so crammed with the remains of mice that "probably it contained at least ten or fifteen." When these birds arrive in the United States, they seem to prefer mice to any other food when these can be obtained. Dr. A. K. Fisher reports as follows on the stomach contents of 38 birds, all but 5 of which were taken in the United States: 2 contained game birds; 9, other birds; 18, mice; 2, other mammals; and 12 were empty. The birds taken were sea-birds or water-fowl except one small finch and one Prairie Hen. What we know of the food of the Snowy Owl indicates that it is more beneficial than injurious. It kills few domestic fowls and takes few game-birds in the United States, except in hard winters when mice are sheltered by deep snow. Then it may become destructive to ducks and sea-fowl along the coast.*

Súrnia úlula cáparoch (MÜLLER). Hawk Owl.

Plate 47.

DESCRIPTION. — Eyes rather small, wings ample, but not reaching nearly to tip of tail, which is long and much graduated; markings variable, but bird unmistakable; toes completely feathered like those of Snowy Owl. *Adults (sexes alike)*: Dark brown above, spotted white, the brown darkest on foreparts — almost black on top of head, where each feather has a small central spot of white; face pale gray or

---

* In a recent letter, Mr. C. L. Hauthaway gives the details of a series of interesting observations and experiments with Snowy Owls. A number of these birds when shot had in their stomachs only remains of mice, but they were shot in the act of killing ducks. He found by experiment that Snowy Owls tore away the skin and feathers of their bird victims, eating only flesh and no bones, thereby making it a difficult task for the investigator to identify bird remains in their stomachs, while, on the other hand, they swallowed skin, bones and fur of mice thus making it easy to identify the remains of that part of their food. Should this prove to be their usual method we may have to revise somewhat our estimate of the economic status of the species as determined by stomach examinations.

grayish-white, nearly surrounded by a broad blackish border; large blackish spot beneath bill, some black in front of eye; three blackish areas on back of neck, one in center and two on sides, marked off by intermediate areas of white spots; scapulars and wing-coverts much spotted with white, and flight-feathers so spotted on inner and outer webs as to give impression of narrow white bars on blackish background; tail narrowly barred and tipped with white; below, white, brownish-white or buffy-white, everywhere narrowly barred brown or burnt umber; a partial, white half-collar on upper breast; legs very narrowly barred and feet little marked; under wing-coverts and axillars barred like sides; exposed part of bill yellow or yellowish; iris yellow. *Young in first winter plumage:* Like adult, but wing-feathers and tail-feathers eventually more worn and perhaps more faded and paler at tips. *Young in juvenal plumage:* Plumage not quite so loose in texture as in young of most other owls; above mainly dark, brown but dull grayish-buff prevails on top of head and on hind neck, where feather-tips are thus colored, feathers of back and scapulars indistinctly tipped same; lores and ear-coverts brownish-black, rest of face whitish; below, whitish, shaded across breast with sooty-brownish, the rest rather broadly and indistinctly barred sooty-brownish; wings and tail like those of adult.

MEASUREMENTS. — Length 14.50 to 17.50 in.; spread 31.00 to 34.00; folded wing 8.25 to 9.82; tail 6.80 to 7.50; bill .80 to .90; tarsus .90 to 1.21. Female averages larger than male.

MOLTS. — Juvenal plumage acquired in nest by complete postnatal molt; in summer and early autumn juvenal plumage is shed, except flight-feathers and tail-feathers, which are retained with ensuing winter plumage until after first nuptial season, when by complete molt bird becomes as adult; adults apparently have one complete molt in summer and early autumn.

FIELD MARKS. — Size smaller than Crow, about that of Short-eared Owl, but color much darker; flight resembling that of falcons; wings rather short and pointed; tail rather long for an owl and much graduated; the only New England owl that is *narrowly barred across both breast and abdomen;* a rather dark, plump bird that usually alights on tops of tall trees and commonly sits not upright as do most owls, but with its body inclined forward, and frequently jets its tail, raising it quite high and lowering it rather slowly; at times, however, this owl sits bolt upright in the conventional owl attitude.

VOICE. — A chattering hawk-like note (N. F. Ticehurst); "a low whine"; male, a far-reaching rolling trill (Grinnell); a whistle "*tu-wita-wit, tuwita-tu-wita, wita, wita*"; a screech, "*sh-wee*" and one like "*que-reek*" the first syllable drawn out, the other emphasized; when nest is disturbed, protesting notes *rike rike rike rike* and an "occasional *whir-u, whir-u,* while flying" (A. D. Henderson).

BREEDING. — In pine and spruce forests of boreal regions. *Nest:* None; eggs laid on decaying wood in hollow top of stump or in hole in tree, deserted nest of other bird or rarely in recess in face of cliff; a few feathers often found about the eggs. *Eggs:* Virtually indistinguishable from those of Short-eared Owl (see page 198); illustrated in Bendire's "Life Histories of North American Birds," Vol. I, Plate XII, Fig. 18. *Dates:* From early April to mid-May but eggs taken *once* on June 14, northern Canada. *Incubation:* Period unknown; chiefly by female. One brood yearly.

RANGE. — Northern North America. Breeding in Canadian and Hudsonian zones and north to tree limit from Alaska to Ungava (northern Quebec), south to southern British Columbia, northern Washington, Montana casually (and probably northern Idaho), southern Alberta, northern Saskatchewan, northern Manitoba, southeastern Labrador and probably Newfoundland; south in winter to Washington, Nebraska, Missouri, northeastern Mississippi (casual), northern Illinois, (?) Michigan, southeastern Indiana, Ohio, Pennsylvania (very rarely), and New Jersey; casual in the southern part of its range; accidental in Bermuda and the British Isles.

DISTRIBUTION IN NEW ENGLAND. — Rare, irregular, fall and winter visitor in Maine, New Hampshire, Vermont and Massachusetts (occasionally common in parts of Maine); "an unparalleled" flight in October and November, 1884, in northern Maine and New Hampshire (Brewster); [1] casual or accidental winter visitor in Rhode Island and Connecticut.

SEASON IN MASSACHUSETTS. — November 16 to March 25.

---

[1] Auk, Vol. II, 1885, p. 108.

HAUNTS AND HABITS. Our Hawk Owl, an American race of a world-wide species, probably is one of the rarest of the northern owls in southern New England. During the great owl flight of 1922–23, when Richardson's Owls were commonly reported, and Snowy Owls were seen all along the coast, Hawk Owls were not reported in southern New England, and our only news of them came from correspondents in northern New England and the Provinces.

The Hawk Owl is a rare and irregular visitor to Massachusetts; otherwise it would be reported more often, as it is a conspicuous bird because of its size, its comparative tameness and its habits of hunting in daylight and perching conspicuously on the very topmost twigs of a tall tree or on the top of a dead stub in broad daylight or before the dusk of evening has obscured the scene.

This bird is so bold that it seems to have little fear of man, and takes no pains to keep out of gunshot. Several persons report that, when ascending to a nest, they have been attacked by one of the birds. Dr. Joseph Grinnell says that when he tapped on a tree containing a nest, the male, which was on the nest, flew out and away for about thirty yards, then turned and flew at his head, which it struck with full force, knocking his cap twelve feet and inflicting three slashes on his head, where its claws drew blood — a very plain hint that the bird disapproved of callers. Mr. A. D. Henderson, while chopping into a nest in Alberta, was struck several times on the head by the female. His heavy hat was knocked off, and once her claws penetrated his clothing and scratched the skin.[1]

This species follows the rule of the boreal owls in migrating southward in autumn from the most northern part of its range, and when food becomes scarce in its customary winter range, it must necessarily move still farther south. Such scarcity of food probably accounts for its occasional appearance in some numbers in the northern United States. The food of the Hawk Owl consists mainly of lemmings and mice (sometimes shrews), but it kills weasels also and young hares, and often takes Ptarmigans. It has been seen to kill and carry off a Ruffed Grouse.

ECONOMIC STATUS. The Hawk Owl undoubtedly is of considerable importance in the north in holding in check irruptions of mice and lemmings, but it is usually so rare in New England as to be of little consequence here.

NOTE. Dr. Brewer notes in the Nuttall Bulletin (Vol. II, p. 78) that of two fine males of the Hawk Owl taken at Houlton, Maine, one is in the plumage known as *Surnia ulula* and thought to be exclusively palæarctic. This opens up an interesting question of distribution, but it seems impossible at this late day to trace the specimen referred to. The only American record for the European Hawk Owl is St. Michael's, Alaska (casual), and even this is doubted by Mr. Ridgway.

Speótyto cuniculária hypogǽa (BONAPARTE). Burrowing Owl.

DESCRIPTION. — Head rounded, without ear-tufts, facial disk incomplete; wings rather long, tail very short, legs, especially tarsi, long, slim and slightly feathered; tarsi only sparsely feathered in front, toes nearly bare; coloration variable, but pattern invariable. *Adults (sexes alike)*: Above dull grayish-brown, profusely spotted with whitish, buffy or yellowish, these spots arranged in rows on wings and give the

---

[1] Oölogist, Vol. XXXVI, 1919, p. 62.

appearance of barring on closed flight-feathers, which are actually barred in some cases; face whitish or stained brownish; eyebrows, chin and throat white, with a narrow dark brown partial collar across lower throat; below, white or yellowish-white, barred or cross-spotted brown from neck to region of vent; under wing-coverts and axillars tawny-white; "iris yellow"; bill light greenish-yellow; cere and claws blackish; "feet dull brown" (N. S. Goss). *Young in first winter plumage:* Virtually as adults. *Young in juvenal plumage:* Above mostly plain grayish-brown, except wings and tail which when developed are about as adults; upper tail-coverts and large space on wing-coverts, and all lower plumage chiefly plain buffy to isabella-white; chin and throat much as in adult, but the collar unspotted.

MEASUREMENTS. — Length 9.00 to 11.00 in.; spread 22.50 to 24.00; folded wing 5.80 to 8.00; tail 3.00 to 3.50; bill .55 to .70; tarsus 1.50 to 1.80. Sexes about the same size, male often larger.

MOLTS. — Juvenal plumage acquired in nest by complete postnatal molt; in June, July and August young birds apparently begin to shed juvenal plumage, which in autumn is replaced by first winter plumage; molting material examined not sufficient to determine later molts.

BURROWING OWL

FIELD MARKS. — Size about that of Screech Owl; a little, long-legged, short-tailed, ground owl, brown, spotted with white above; and white, cross-spotted or barred with brown below; rarely, if ever, alights in trees or bushes.

VOICE. — A chattering note in flight; alarm note *tzip-tzip*, love note, "a mellow sonorous and far-reaching *coo-c-o-o*, the last syllable drawn out" (Bendire); hooting is very similar to note of Yellow-billed Cuckoo (Coues).

BREEDING. — On prairies. *Nest:* A burrow in ground, from five to 10 feet in length with a chamber at end lined with grass or rubbish. *Eggs:* 6 to 11 (7 often is a full complement); about 1.30 to 1.35 by 1.05 to 1.18 in.; usually rounded ovate; white, usually rather smooth-shelled; rather more pointed and glossy than owls' eggs in general; illustrated in Bendire's "Life Histories of North American Birds," Vol. I, Plate XII, Fig. 14. *Dates:* Early April, California; middle April, Oregon; up to June 15, Utah; July 1, Colorado. *Incubation:* Period about 3 weeks (Bendire); probably by both parents. One brood yearly.

RANGE. — Unforested parts of southwestern Canada and western United States, Mexico and Central America (including islands along the Californian and Mexican coasts). Breeds from southern British Columbia, southwestern Saskatchewan, southern Alberta, southern Manitoba and Minnesota south to southern Lower California, through Mexico to Guatemala, and in Panama; ranges east to western Minnesota, western Iowa, southeastern Nebraska, Kansas, western Oklahoma and Louisiana; migratory north of Oregon, South Dakota and Colorado; accidental in Alabama, Indiana, New York, Massachusetts and New Hampshire.

DISTRIBUTION IN NEW ENGLAND. — Accidental visitor in Massachusetts and New Hampshire. Records: *Massachusetts:* Newburyport, May 15, 1875, specimen taken by H. Joyce and J. K. Clifford, placed in mounted collection of the Museum of Comparative Zoölogy at Harvard College,[1] and now in collection of Boston Society of Natural History. *New Hampshire:* Dover, about Feb. 20, 1922, one found dead in a barn by Patrick Carroll, and preserved in the collection of George F. Wentworth who identified it. The bird apparently died of starvation and was found soon after death.[2]

HAUNTS AND HABITS. The comical, slim-legged, little Burrowing Owl is a rare straggler in the east, and its occurrence here is so fortuitous that one wonders whether the three specimens taken in New York and New England had not escaped from captivity. There

---

[1] Deane, Ruthven: Rod and Gun, Vol. VI, 1875, p. 97.

[2] Bulletin Audubon Society of New Hampshire, Vol. I, No. 4, April–May–June, 1922 (extract from the Manchester Union), and White, F. B.: Auk, Vol. XLIII, 1926, p. 377.

is no evidence, however, that they were ever caged. This owl is the only North American species which habitually lives underground, and it seems to be dependent on the presence of prairie dogs or ground squirrels, which provide burrows for its accommodation. Where prairie dogs are exterminated the owls which accompany them also disappear. The burrows of the prairie dog are large enough for the owl. Those of the ground squirrels or spermophiles are not, but the bird is capable of enlarging them and preparing them for its own purposes. There has been much nonsense written about the happy families of prairie dogs, rattlesnakes and Burrowing Owls, all living together in the same burrow. The owl seems to be fully capable of defending its domicile against either marmot or rattlesnake, and doubtless drives out either of these animals if they show any disposition to molest the nest. It is a "nocturnal animal with fairly good day-vision, yet distinctly embarrassed, uncertain and confused when the eyes are exposed to bright sunlight" (Dr. Casey A. Wood).[1]

An interesting biography of the Burrowing Owl is given in Bendire's "Life Histories of North American Birds" (Vol. I, pp. 395–400).

ECONOMIC STATUS. This owl is largely nocturnal; it feeds chiefly on small injurious mammals and insects and rarely molests birds. It is, therefore, a useful bird wherever its colonies become established.

ORDER COCCYGES. CUCKOOS, ETC.

Number of species in North America 11; in Massachusetts 3.

This order contains several groups of birds bearing little outward resemblance to one another, but all having certain common characters. The feet are picarian, syndactylous, or zygodactylous, and the hind toe is always present. The order includes suborders *Cuculi*, Cuckoos, *Trogones*, Trogons, and *Alcyones*, Kingfishers, only the first and last of which are represented in New England.

SUBORDER CUCULI. CUCKOOS.

Number of species in North America 7; in Massachusetts 2.

This suborder contains birds having, besides the characters of the order, the "spinal feather-tract forked in the scapular region," a nude oil gland and no after-shafts.

FAMILY **CUCULIDÆ.** CUCKOOS, ANIS, ETC.

Number of species in North America 7; in Massachusetts 2.

This is a very extensive group, almost cosmopolitan. In birds of this family, as in all birds of the suborder, the feet are zygodactylous or yoke-toed (two toes in front and two behind) by reversion of the fourth toe. Usually they have ten tail-feathers. They

---

[1] Auk, Vol. XXXVII, 1920, p. 612.

are long-tailed and chiefly tree birds though a few are terrestrial. The bill is very variable in size and shape, but always down-curved at the tip and always more or less compressed. The young are practically naked when hatched, and remain in the nest until fledged. The family includes the tree cuckoos, the anis and the road-runners or ground cuckoos. Most of these birds are modestly or darkly colored, but there are some exceptions among Old World species. Over two hundred species have been recognized.

SUBFAMILY **COCCYZINÆ**. AMERICAN CUCKOOS.

Number of species in North America 3; in Massachusetts 2.

This subfamily, recognized by the American Ornithologists Union, is ignored by many ornithologists who consider that the differences between American and Old World Cuckoos are not important enough to warrant this subdivision. The American Cuckoos, however, differ rather strikingly from the common cuckoo of Europe in having the tarsus naked, the feathers of the rump and upper tail-coverts shorter and much less copious and the lower plumage immaculate where that of the European bird is barred.

Coccýzus americánus americanus (LINNÆUS). Yellow-billed Cuckoo.

Other names: RAIN CROW; CHOW-CHOW.

Plate 48.

DESCRIPTION. — Bill rather long, convex above and down-curved at tip; wings moderate and rather pointed; tail longer than wing, rounded and graduated for at least ⅓ of its length; leg-feathering long and loose, like that of a hawk, only a little of upper tarsus feathered. *Adults* (*sexes alike*): Above plain grayish-brown or olive-brown with a bronzy gloss, usually passing into grayish on forehead, and becoming darker over ear-coverts; outer webs of primaries usually more or less tinged with rufous, and sometimes nearly cinnamon-rufous, inner webs of primaries and part of those of secondaries partaking of a similar tinge for much of their length; middle pair of tail-feathers (rarely 2 middle pairs) colored like back, but sometimes dusky or blackish terminally; other tail-feathers black or blackish with faint bluish or greenish gloss, growing grayish-brown at bases, each of them very broadly tipped white; white tips increasing in length from inner to outer tail-feathers where white extends up most of outer web; sides of head, up nearly to eyes and ear-coverts white like under plumage which, however, shows some grayish tinting on throat (rarely sides of head and all under plumage light gray) and sometimes a shade of buffy on under tail-coverts; wing linings and axillars "buffy-white to pale pinkish-buff"; bill chiefly slaty-black above (lower part of side of upper mandible from base to near tip yellow), yellow below, except black tip; iris dark brown, eyelids yellow, naked skin about eye grayish; legs and feet pale bluish-gray to bluish-olive. *Young in first winter plumage:* Similar to adults, but tail somewhat resembles that of juvenal plumage; outer tail-feathers duller, less blackish or more grayish-brown, with white spots less sharply defined; naked skin about eye pale yellow. *Young in juvenal plumage:* Similar to adult but duller; dark, lateral tail-feathers never black but merely dusky or dull grayish-brown, and white tips not sharply defined; a tawny shade on throat and breast.

MEASUREMENTS. — Length 11.00 to 12.70 in.; spread 15.50 to 17.00; folded wing 5.40 to 5.95; tail 5.50 to 6.35; bill .95 to 1.01; tarsus .85 to 1.00. Weight 2⅛ oz. (B. H. Warren).

MOLTS. — Juvenal body plumage and most wing-coverts appear to be molted (August to October), but juvenal wing-quills and tail-feathers appear to be retained during first winter; immature birds, appar-

PLATE 48

PLATE 48

BLACK–BILLED CUCKOO
Page 244

ADULT

YELLOW–BILLED CUCKOO
Page 240

ADULT

BELTED KINGFISHER
Page 248

ADULT MALE

ADULT FEMALE

All about one-half scale.

Louis Agassiz Fuertes.

ently, become as adults sometime during the following spring; adults apparently have two complete (?) molts (July to October and January to March or April); no winter specimens examined.

FIELD MARKS. — Our cuckoos are slightly longer than the Robin — long slender birds, brown above with greenish gloss and white or grayish-white below; this species distinguished from Black-billed Cuckoo by rufous on flight-feathers which often may be seen in the field, and by black tail-feathers with their large conspicuous white marks; these white markings much smaller and less conspicuous in Black-billed Cuckoo; yellow of lower part of bill not very noticeable, but may be seen in good light.

VOICE. — Much like that of Black-billed Cuckoo, but perhaps notes of yellow-billed species are a little louder and often deeper in tone; many notes of one species difficult if not impossible to distinguish from those of the other; both have various calls. "The common call of this bird is a long series of notes beginning fast and retarding toward the end. The first notes are simple, but the last ones are slurred down and sound like '*kow.*' The whole call is like *kakakakakakaka ka ka ka ka ka ka kow kow kow kow kow kow kow kow.* The *retarded* time and harsher quality are different from the Blackbill" (Aretas A. Saunders); some joint notes like *c-rick-k-k-k-k;* a low *noo-coo-coo-coo* also *cow-cow-cow* several times repeated, other syllables resembling *ough, ough, ough,* slow and soft, some reminding one of the *kloop-kloop* of Bittern, a note like the *kiuh-kiuh-kiuh* of flicker, a low, sharp *tou-wity-whit* and *hweet hwe,* the last in the nesting season (C. Bendire); a series of loud, explosive gutturals resembling *kuk-kuk, kuk-kuk,* repeated many times, ending with *kyow kyow,* repeated 2 to 6 times; occasionally a low liquid *coo, coo, coo,* resembling a note of Least Bittern (E. H. Eaton); a series of explosive notes *cook, cook, cook, cook, cook, cook, cook, cook, cook,* delivered rather slowly, *rallentando et diminuendo* (W. L. Dawson); *krow-krow-krow-krow-krow; kru-kru kru-kru kru-kru* (E. A. Samuels); *Gr-r-r-r-olp, cowlp, cowlp-olp-olp,* with little if any variation in tone and a voice seemingly as deep as that of a heron (Schuyler Matthews); its longest deliverance (the "song") begins abruptly with loud, "woodeny" notes, *kek-kek-kek* which run off into *cows;* its loud "woodeny" *cow-cow-cow* is almost at times like a human voice (J. A. Farley).

BREEDING. — Usually on farm lands; in edge of woods and near or in orchards (often old) or in dense thickets such as frequently border roadsides and fields; also in swampy woods. *Nest:* Usually a shallow platform of sticks, twigs (often large and covered with lichens — when nest may be bulky although poorly made), rootlets, strips of bark, etc., sometimes built on abandoned nest of some other bird, often slightly lined with straws, catkins, blossoms or pine needles; usually in low tree or thicket from four to 10 feet from ground, rarely 20 feet or more high. *Eggs:* 2 to (rarely) 6 more rarely 8; 1.10 to 1.30 by .75 to .90 in.; oval or elliptical; light, bluish-green, sometimes slightly mottled or clouded with darker or over-washed with whitish; illustrated in Bendire's "Life Histories of North American Birds," Vol. II, Plate V, Fig. 1. *Dates:* Eggs sometimes laid in late April in southern states; May 20 to June 30, Massachusetts (July 9, 2 eggs, Canton); June 4 to July 10, Vermont. *Incubation:* Period 14 days (Burns); probably by both sexes. Usually one brood in the north, but sometimes double-brooded in the south.

RANGE. — Eastern North America, Middle America and northern South America. Breeds in eastern North America, chiefly in Austral zones, from North Dakota, Minnesota, Wisconsin, northern Michigan, southern Ontario, southern Quebec, New Brunswick and Nova Scotia south to northeastern Mexico, Gulf coast and southern Florida and west to South Dakota, Nebraska, eastern Colorado and Oklahoma; in migration south through eastern Mexico, and Central America, the West Indies and (casually) the Bermuda Islands; winters in Venezuela, Colombia, and western Ecuador; some breeding West Indian birds said to be of this form, but they are probably of a southern race that breeds there (a western race inhabits the far west); accidental in Greenland, British Isles, Italy and Belgium.

DISTRIBUTION IN NEW ENGLAND. — *Maine:* Rare summer resident, chiefly in extreme southwestern part. *New Hampshire:* Rare summer resident, chiefly in southern parts and lowlands. *Vermont:* Uncommon to rare summer resident, mainly at lower elevations. *Massachusetts:* Rather uncommon summer resident generally, rare or wanting in some western highlands, more common in southern and eastern parts. *Rhode Island:* Summer resident, irregularly common. *Connecticut:* Common summer resident; irregularly abundant.

SEASON IN MASSACHUSETTS. — (May 4) May 9 to September 26 (October 13).

HAUNTS AND HABITS. Asked to describe a cuckoo, a schoolboy answered that it was "a bird that imitates the cuckoo clock." The American cuckoos answer the first part of this description but not the last. The European Cuckoo is not only the cuckoo of the Bible, of Shakespeare and European literature but also the cuckoo of the clock. It resembles the common American cuckoos somewhat in form, but not in color or notes. The subject of this biography probably is the most widely and generally known of American cuckoos.

The Yellow-billed Cuckoo is a harbinger of summer. When the woods and orchards have put on their spring greenery; when the blossom-buds of the moccasin flower and the columbine begin to unfold their petals, then the voice of the cuckoo is heard in the land. If the season is early, then a few may appear earlier; but when spring is backward, individuals of the species may be still moving northward on June first. The cuckoo is a graceful, elegant bird, calm and unperturbed; it slips quietly and rather furtively through its favorite tangles and flies easily from tree to tree in the orchard, keeping for the most part under protection of the leaves, which furnish excellent cover for its bronzy, upper plumage, while the shadows of the foliage tend to conceal the whiteness of its under parts. It has a way also of keeping its back with its greenish satiny reflections toward the intruder in its solitudes, and while holding an attitude of readiness for flight it sits motionless, and its plumage so blends with its leafy environment that it does not ordinarily catch the eye. In the meantime it turns its head and regards the disturber with a cool, reserved, direct gaze, looking back over its shoulder, apparently unafraid and giving no indication of nervousness or even undue curiosity; but if the observer approaches too closely, the elegant bird slips quietly away, vanishing into some leafy, cool retreat where it may enjoy the silence and solitude, dear to the woodland recluse. This calm, quiet, secretive bird is far more often heard than seen. Indeed it would be rarely seen were it not for its rather loud unhurried notes. These, frequently repeated, apprise the world of its presence.

The cuckoo has acquired the reputation of a weather prophet. Some of the country people believe that when the bird becomes vociferous, rain will surely follow, and probably there is some foundation for the belief.

Once our cuckoos undoubtedly were birds of the forest and woodland thicket, but they have adapted themselves in some measure to civilization, for the reason, perhaps, that they find an abundant and easily obtained food supply in our orchards. Most fruit trees normally harbor caterpillars of which cuckoos are fond, and in seasons when caterpillars are abundant cuckoos may breed in the orchard or near it, or on occasion they may nest in a village shade tree or even in a city park.* According to Brewster this species is a familiar bird in the Cambridge region of eastern Massachusetts and is given to frequenting cultivated grounds near houses. He says further: "Its favorite summer haunts are apple orchards, brushgrown lanes and roadsides, causeways shaded by willows, and dense thickets near water." With us the numbers of this species fluctuate consider-

---

* Now and then cuckoos make a nest in the most exposed situations where people are continually passing and repassing.

ably from year to year. Doubtless a plague of those hairy caterpillars on which they feed tends to increase their numbers for the time being.*

I have not seen the courtship of this cuckoo nor have I found any adequate description of it. Late nesting is the rule, as nests with eggs are not found very commonly in New England until June. The nest is so flat that now and then an egg rolls out or is brushed out by the parent in leaving the nest. Eggs are frequently laid at considerable intervals after incubation has begun, so that young of several sizes may be found in a nest, together with an egg or two, fresh or incubated. The most interesting part of the development of the young is the process of feathering. The nestlings are provided with a black, tough, leathery-appearing skin, and each feather as it grows is encased in a black, pointed sheath, giving the callow youngster the appearance of being clothed in quills like the "fretful porcupine." On the day that the fledgling leaves the nest a seeming miracle occurs. In a few hours the sheaths burst open, and the young bird goes forth into the world properly clothed in a plumage resembling that of its parents. Young cuckoos have been found in the nest as late as September 13.

The cuckoo has the reputation of laying its eggs in the nests of other birds, but this is true only to a very limited extent of the species now under consideration, though the European Cuckoo is truly parasitic in this respect. The Yellow-billed Cuckoo and the Black-billed species each occasionally deposit an egg (or eggs) in the nest of the other † and perhaps more rarely in that of the Robin or some smaller bird, but this is unusual. The Yellow-billed Cuckoo was accused by Wilson, Nuttall and Audubon of the habit of eating the eggs of other birds, but I have never been able to get any direct evidence of this habit, which may, however, be attributed to the Black-billed Cuckoo.

When autumnal caterpillars are scarce about the region where cuckoos have nested, some of them begin to move southward by or before July 20. If fall webworms are abundant, some remain much later in infested regions to feed upon these pests, and cuckoos are seen not infrequently through the month of September. After that they usually become scarce in New England, as most of them are then moving toward South America.

The Yellow-billed Cuckoo feeds very largely on injurious insects. To quote from one of my former works:

"The cuckoos are of the greatest service to the farmer, by reason of their well-known fondness for caterpillars, particularly the hairy species. No caterpillars are safe from the cuckoo. It does not matter how hairy or spiny they are, or how well they may be protected by webs. Often the stomach of the cuckoo will be found lined with a felted mass of caterpillar hairs, and sometimes its intestines are pierced by the spines of the noxious caterpillars that it has swallowed. Wherever caterpillar outbreaks occur we hear the calls of the cuckoos. There they stay; there they bring their newly fledged young; and the number of caterpillars they eat is incredible. Professor Beal states that

*In the spring of 1892 (a great tent-caterpillar year in eastern Massachusetts) Yellow-billed Cuckoos were almost as common as "Black-bills."

† A cuckoo's nest was found with seven eggs — three Black-billed and four Yellow-billed (Oölogist, Vol. XXIX, 1912, p. 314) and in another case the two species were found sitting side by side on a mixture of their eggs.

two thousand, seven hundred and seventy-one caterpillars were found in the stomachs of one hundred and twenty-one Cuckoos, — an average of more than twenty-one each. Dr. Otto Lugger found several hundred small hairy caterpillars in the stomach of a single bird. The poisonous, spined caterpillars of the Io moth, the almost equally disagreeable caterpillars of the brown-tail moth, and the spiny elm caterpillar, are eaten with avidity." [1]

The chief utility of cuckoos lies in their apparent fondness for hairy caterpillars and their ability to dispose of large quantities of these destructive insects. Many other birds eat such caterpillars when these larvæ are very small and others take larger ones, but cuckoos take them at all stages and seem to enjoy it. When, in time, the inside of the bird's stomach becomes so felted with a mass of hairs and spines that it obstructs digestion, the bird can shed the entire stomach-lining, meanwhile growing a new one — a process that would be beneficial to some unfeathered bipeds could they compass it. The following, taken from the reports of the late F. H. Mosher, one of my former assistants, who was detailed to observe the enemies of the gipsy moth and the brown-tail moth, will give some idea of the numbers of such pests eaten by this species. Mr. Mosher, a competent observer, watched a Yellow-billed Cuckoo eat 41 gipsy caterpillars in fifteen minutes, and later he saw another consume 47 forest tent caterpillars in six minutes. This species of cuckoo was present most of the time at localities infested by caterpillar pests and ate them almost constantly. Dr. Amos W. Butler says that he has known these cuckoos to destroy every tent caterpillar in a badly infested orchard and tear up all the nests in half a day. [2] This species frequently feeds on or near the ground, and there gets an enormous number of locusts and other pests. In summer and autumn it feeds to some extent on small wild fruits, such as the raspberry, blackberry and wild grape.

ECONOMIC STATUS. As the Yellow-billed Cuckoo feeds largely on some of the worst insect pests known, as it eats very little fruit and no grain, and is not known to be seriously harmful to other birds, its status as a beneficial bird seems fully established.

Coccyzus erythrophthálmus (WILSON). Black-billed Cuckoo.

Other names: RAIN CROW; COW-COW.

Plate 48.

DESCRIPTION. — Formed much like the Yellow-billed Cuckoo, but somewhat more slender, and tail-feathers not nearly so broad as those of Yellow-billed Cuckoo. *Adults* (*sexes alike*): Above olive-brown with a bronzy gloss similar to that of the Yellow-billed Cuckoo (perhaps a little brighter), becoming more grayish on forehead, loral and ear regions; tail-feathers with dull white tips (except middle pair which may show very narrow white tips), preceded by a broad dusky bar, which is more conspicuous on under side than on upper; under plumage and lower part of side of head white, tinted with buffy or buffy-grayish on chin, throat, lower parts of head and upper breast, and with brownish or buffy on under tail-coverts; bill mostly black, pale grayish-blue basally below; iris dark brown or hazel; naked skin around eye bright red; legs and feet pale bluish-gray or grayish-blue. *Young in first winter plumage:* Similar to adults, but tail resembling juvenal. *Young in juvenal plumage:* Similar to adults, but upper

---

[1] Useful Birds and Their Protection, 1913, p. 264.   [2] Report of the State Geologist of Indiana, 1897, p. 824.

plumage more brownish, the feathers mostly with narrow whitish tips, and more strongly suffused with pale brownish-buffy below; white tips of tail-feathers less distinct, and dusky bars faint or obsolete; naked skin about eye yellow. "Born with rudimentary down which never unfolds."[1]

MEASUREMENTS. — Length 11.00 to 12.70 in.; spread 15.00 to 16.75; folded wing 5.12 to 5.70; tail 5.50 to 7.00; bill .92 to 1.15; tarsus about .85 to .95.

MOLTS. — Apparently similar to those of Yellow-billed Cuckoo (see page 240).

FIELD MARKS. — Size near that of Yellow-billed Cuckoo; lack of both the conspicuous, large, black and white markings on the tail and of rufous, usually, on wing, as well as its black bill, distinguish it from Yellow-billed Cuckoo; the Brown Thrasher resembles it in size and shape, but is more rufous, and has a streaked and spotted breast, where the cuckoo is always unmarked.

VOICE. — Similar to that of Yellow-billed Cuckoo; while the "songs" of the two species are very different, it is doubtful if the two birds can be distinguished certainly from each other by all their notes; the Black-billed Cuckoo's "song" is similar to that of the Yellow-billed (see p. 241), but is commonly prefaced by an introductory soft *pruh* instead of the loud, abrupt, woodeny *keks*; many of the "Black-bill's" notes seem softer, not so heavy and deep as those of the other species; young as well as adults utter fragmentary notes; a rattling call *kow kow kow kow* sometimes kh′ kh′ kh′ kh′ kh′ kah; a peculiar, raucous, guttural call *errattŏtoo* or *worrattŏtoo* (Nuttall); a soft *coo coo* repeated several times (C. Bendire); the alarm note *cuck-a-ruck* (Olive Thorne Miller) or *buck-a-rock, buck-a-rock* (O. W. Knight). "The commonest song is a series of two to five note phrases, repeated over and over, many times. Usually one note of the phrase is accented. The phrases are repeated in perfectly even time, note *retarded*. A common two note phrase is *kucka kucka kucka* repeated over many times. Three note phrases would be *kakucka kakucka kakucka*, with the middle note accented. Others would have the first or last note accented, or the second or third or some other note of five. This spring I heard a bird giving this sort of call. It had been calling some time, perhaps fifty times or more, when I began to count. I counted 219 calls before the bird ceased, all in perfectly even rhythmic time. The other performance of the Black-bill sounds like *krakika kuh kuh kuh kuh kuh kuh kuh kuh kuh*. All but the first phrase in even time. I have heard this from a bird near the nest that had young" (Aretas A. Saunders); other notes similar to those given by Yellow-billed Cuckoo; sometimes a bird utters the usual *kuk-kuks* while on the nest; also a sound like that made by a woodpecker tapping on a tree; a bird at a nest with young continually "moaned" (a soft note) and also once or twice "chucked," besides uttering very loudly the familiar *pruh-cuo-cuo-coo-o-o* (J. A. Farley).

BREEDING. — Similar to that of Yellow-billed Cuckoo but Black-bill is more partial to lowland thickets, and nests less often in apple trees. *Nest:* In shrub or clump of briars or toward the end of some rather low tree-branch; sometimes on ground; usually from 2½ to 10 feet from ground; built like that of Yellow-billed Cuckoo of sticks and twigs largely and lined with leaves and catkins. *Eggs:* 2 to 6, very rarely 7 or 8, commonly 4; .98 to 1.50 by .70 to .92 in.; similar to those of Yellow-billed Cuckoo, but usually smaller and darker and more nearly oval; sometimes marbled with a darker shade than the general color; illustrated in Bendire's "Life Histories of North American Birds," Vol. II, Plate V, Figs. 3 and 4. *Dates:* May 20 to August 29, New England. *Incubation:* Period 14 days (Burns); by both sexes. One brood yearly in the north; in the south two may be reared.

RANGE. — North, South and middle America. Breeds in temperate eastern North America north to the southern border of the Canadian Zone, from southeastern Alberta, southern Saskatchewan, southern Manitoba, northern Wisconsin, northern Michigan, southeastern Ontario, southern Quebec, New Brunswick, Prince Edward Island and Nova Scotia south to northern Oklahoma, northern Arkansas, southern Illinois, eastern Tennessee, Georgia and southern South Carolina and west to central Montana and eastern Colorado; south in migration through Mexico and Central America; winters in South America from Venezuela and Colombia to Peru; casually Bermudas, Cuba (one record), Tobago and Trinidad; accidental in Azores, Ireland and Italy.

---

[1] Herrick, F. H.: Journal of Experimental Zoölogy, Vol. IX, 1910, pp. 169–233. Life and Behavior of the Cuckoo.

DISTRIBUTION IN NEW ENGLAND. — Common summer resident, except on highest elevations and in deepest forests.

SEASON IN MASSACHUSETTS. — May 4 to October 8 (October 21).

HAUNTS AND HABITS. The Black-billed Cuckoo is in many respects almost a counterpart of its yellow-billed congener; but it is even more slender and graceful, the markings of the tail differ, the bill lacks any tinge of yellow and the bird is somewhat more retiring and perhaps less vociferous. The present species may be more given to night-wandering, as its voice is heard more frequently at night than that of the "Yellow-bill." Otherwise the two are almost identical in appearance and habits and they haunt the same places, and occupy much the same range, except that the "Yellow-bill" is normally a more southern bird. The development of the "mailed" young in this species is similar to that of the "Yellow-bill." The Black-billed Cuckoo is the more common generally of the two species in New England, especially in the northern part of the region, while the yellow-billed bird may be at times most numerous locally in the southern portion. In the latter part of the last century the "Yellow-bill" was regarded as the most abundant of the two in southern New England, but more recently there seems to have been a change in this respect. There are some very early records of the Black-billed Cuckoo in Massachusetts, but for the most part it does not arrive here in numbers until about the beginning of the third week in May. It migrates at night, and on some warm May morning its call may be heard almost anywhere among our hills.

There is incontestable evidence showing that this bird occasionally drops an egg in the nest of some smaller bird and that the young cuckoo eventually crowds out the rightful occupants of the nest, but this is exceptional as our cuckoos as a rule are very faithful parents.* Both species incubate, and both care for the young and often will attempt to entice the intruder away from the vicinity of the nest. When once out of the nest, the young before they can fly climb cleverly. Mr. J. L. Davison, of Lockport, New York, says that on June 17, 1882, he found a Black-billed Cuckoo and a Mourning Dove sitting together on a Robin's nest. The nest contained two eggs of the cuckoo, two of the dove and one of the Robin.[1] A peculiar case is reported by Mr. J. A. Farley who found a Black-billed Cuckoo's nest placed on the ground beside the nest of a Veery. The two nests were distinct although so near as to be scarcely separated by the width of the hand. When the nest was approached, the Veery always flew first. The cuckoo sat very close.

Though cuckoos are included in the same order as kingfishers, the plumage of the two families is quite different. That of the kingfishers is tough, hard and waterproof, while that of the cuckoos is delicate and will not shed water so well. Probably cuckoos dislike to get very wet. Miss J. Olivia Crowell, of Dennis, reports that after a heavy thunderstorm, she saw a cuckoo sitting on top of a fence within a few yards of her window

---

* A cuckoo whose nest with young was in an apple-tree, was very brave; she flew back again and again to the nest, with wide-open bill and ruffled plumage, coming close in real hawk style" (J. A. Farley).

[1] Forest and Stream, Vol. 33, September, 1889, p. 164.

Photograph by Daniel D. McDavid

Fig. 50. — Nest and Eggs of Black-billed Cuckoo

Courtesy of Eugene W. Schmidt

Page 245

Photograph by Edwin L. Jack

Fig. 51. — Nestling Kingfishers Developing Juvenal Plumage

Page 251

and spreading out its bedraggled wings to dry in the sun. This brought to mind the old song, one verse of which runs:

> "'Tis raining, 'tis raining,
> 'Twill wet the cuckoo.
> All gay are the flowers,
> Green the grass too."

In seasons when caterpillars of any species are abundant, cuckoos usually become common in the infested localities. They follow the caterpillars, and where such food is plentiful, the size of their broods seems to increase. During an invasion of forest tent caterpillars in Stoneham, Massachusetts, in May, 1898, Mr. Frank H. Mosher watched one of these birds that caught and ate 36 of these insects inside of five minutes. He saw another in Malden eat 29, rest a few minutes and then take 14 more. In July, 1899, he reported a family of these birds in a locality infested with the gipsy moth, and said that they were eating large quantities of gipsy caterpillars. In June, 1895, Mr. Henry Shaw reported great numbers of these cuckoos in Dorchester feeding on the same pests. The late Professor Walter B. Barrows, of Michigan, an extremely conservative ornithologist, is responsible for the statement that in several instances remains of over 100 tent caterpillars have been taken from a single cuckoo's stomach. The Black-billed Cuckoo, because more common than the Yellow-billed, is the species that most commonly attacks this insect in New England orchards. During an invasion of army worms, Professor S. A. Forbes found that 95 per cent of the food of this species consisted of that caterpillar.[1] The examination of 46 stomachs of Black-billed Cuckoos reported upon by Professor F. E. L. Beal, of the Biological Survey at Washington, showed remains of 906 caterpillars, 44 beetles, 96 grasshoppers, 100 sawflies, 30 bugs and 15 spiders.[2] The Black-billed Cuckoo seems more inclined to go to the ground than is the other species, though it is rather seldom seen there. It seems to be fond of wet places, and feeds more or less in such localities on aquatic insects and other small aquatic forms of life. There is some evidence which convicts individuals, at least, of robbing the eggs of other birds. Several species, the Robin in particular, show dislike toward the cuckoo, and often chase it away from the vicinity of their nests.

ECONOMIC STATUS. The Black-billed Cuckoo is, on the whole, one of the most useful birds of farm and orchard and deserves full protection.

SUBORDER ALCYONES. KINGFISHERS.

Number of species in North America 3; in Massachusetts 1.

This suborder includes both the fish-eating kingfishers and those that subsist mainly on other food, and contains no other families.

---

[1] Transactions Illinois State Horticultural Society, Vol. XV, 1881, p. 129.
[2] United States Department of Agriculture, Farmers Bulletin No. 54, 1898, p. 5.

FAMILY **ALCEDINIDÆ.** KINGFISHERS.

Number of species in North America 3; in Massachusetts 1.

SYNDACTYL FOOT
OF KINGFISHER

This family is syndactylous with three toes before and one behind, *third and fourth toes united.* The bill is long, large, usually straight, rarely hooked and quite acute. The tongue is rudimentary. There are no aftershafts and usually a tufted oil gland. The head is very large with rather large eyes. The wings are ample; the tail rather short. The feet are very small and weak and the legs also small and short, the tarsi extremely short. The soles of the middle and outer toes are as one for about half their length; the inner toe is always short, rudimentary or (in two genera) wanting. The family is nearly cosmopolitan and contains about 200 species. Some are chiefly fish eaters; others are insectivorous.

Céryle álcyon álcyon (LINNÆUS). **Belted Kingfisher.**

Other names: KINGFISHER; LAZY-BIRD.

Plate 48.

DESCRIPTION. — Bill longer than head, large, heron-like, but nostrils basal and head feathered to nostrils; head large, with double-pointed crest; wings ample, pointed; tail rather short, of 10 feathers; feet, very small. *Adult male:* Above (except white collar around neck), band across upper breast, and sides under wings grayish-blue with black shaft-streaks; feathers of top of head and crest and two middle grayish-blue feathers of tail have wider black median streaks; alula, primary coverts and primaries and all but two middle tail-feathers black; flight-feathers (and sometimes wing-coverts) spotted and marked and tail barred with white; white spot before eye; below (except breast-band and sides) white; axillars, wing linings and basal parts of inner webs of primaries chiefly white; bill black, brownish-black or slaty, sometimes paling or bluish toward base; iris dark brown; legs and feet bluish-gray or livid slate. *Adult female:* Similar, but with a band of cinnamon rufous (sometimes incomplete) across lower breast beneath the dark band, separated from it by white of breast. *Young in juvenal and first winter and summer plumage:* Similar to adults but breast bands all more or less brown or rusty; some young males show second (rufous) band as in female (or traces of it) on sides of breast.

MEASUREMENTS. — Length 11.00 to 14.75 in.; spread 21.00 to 23.00; folded wing 6.00 to 6.50; tail 3.50 to 5.00; bill 1.75 to 2.25; tarsus about .44. Weight 5 to 6 oz. (E. H. Eaton); a small female 4 oz. (B. H. Warren). Sexes of similar size, but very variable.

MOLTS. — The young have no nestling plumage but are hatched naked, and juvenal-winter plumage develops, like that of cuckoos, in sheaths; when these sheaths burst, the bird is fledged in a plumage resembling adults but with neckband brown or its feathers edged brown; some young birds apparently become as adult after partial prenuptial molt in spring; after postnuptial molt in succeeding autumn, all birds become as adult; adults apparently acquire winter plumage by complete postnuptial molt beginning, apparently, in August.

FIELD MARKS. — Size larger than Robin, but smaller than pigeon; large, long, straight, pointed bill and large crested head; grayish-blue above, white below with one or two dark bands across breast; flight peculiar, with two moderate wing beats alternating with a few very fast ones.

VOICE. — A long, harsh rattling cry, difficult to describe; said to resemble the sound of a watchman's rattle or the rackety, ratcheted, wooden whirligig that children use as a plaything, often sounded when in flight, and when disturbed or alarmed; occasionally, as when disturbed at nest, a peculiar creaking sound (F. H. Herrick).

BREEDING. — Usually near water or not very far from it, in either forested or unforested land, in the wilderness or in civilized communities, wherever it is not molested. *Nest:* In a hole (about four inches in diameter) excavated by the birds in side of bank or bluff, running in nearly horizontally from three to 15 feet, usually about four or five, often straight or nearly so, sometimes with a turn near inner end (may be in a very low bank if nothing else is available); "nest," an enlargement at inner end of excavation; sometimes a bed of sticks, leaves and grasses, usually fish scales, bones, etc.; nest very rarely in hollow tree. *Eggs:* Five to eight, rarely 10 to 14; 1.10 to 1.46 by 1.04 to 1.21 in.; usually short ovate or rounded ovate; white and glossy; illustrated in Bendire's "Life Histories of North American Birds," Vol. II, Plate I, Fig. 3. *Dates:* May 14 to June 6, Massachusetts. *Incubation:* Period 16 to 17 days (W. L. Finley); chiefly by female, "by both parents" (Audubon). One brood yearly, possibly two in the south.

RANGE. — Eastern North America, middle America, and northern South America. Breeds in eastern and central North America from northwestern Mackenzie, northern Manitoba, central Quebec, southern Labrador and Newfoundland south to western Texas, Gulf coast and southern Florida, and west to North Dakota, Nebraska and Oklahoma; winters from Massachusetts, southern Ontario (casually), Ohio, Illinois and Nebraska south through eastern Mexico (west to Chihuahua), Yucatan, Central America and West Indies to Trinidad, British Guiana, Venezuela and northern Colombia; also to Bermudas; accidental in Azores and in Ireland; another subspecies occupies extreme western North America.

DISTRIBUTION IN NEW ENGLAND. — Common summer resident near ponds, lakes, streams and coasts, throughout the territory; rare winter resident or visitor from southern Maine, New Hampshire and Vermont southward.

SEASON IN MASSACHUSETTS. — Permanent resident; most common May to October.

HAUNTS AND HABITS. Both the generic and specific names of the Belted Kingfisher translate "kingfisher." The first is derived from the Greek, the second from the Latin. Thus we have *Ceryle alcyon*, a Kingfisher of Kingfishers. Why he is called a kingfisher we can only surmise. He is a master fisher and he wears a kind of crown, but the bird that originally was named kingfisher had no such head-piece as our bird displays. Alcyone, daughter of Æolus, was fabled to have been transformed into a kingfisher, when out of devotion to her shipwrecked husband, Ceyx, she threw herself into the sea. In ancient times the kingfisher was believed to nest on the sea when the waves were stilled; hence the term "halcyon days."

This wild, grotesque "tousled-headed" bird is a common sight along our waterways. Its nesting holes may be seen on or near almost any stream with high banks, usually where the bank has been cut away abruptly by the stream, rarely in a low sloping bank covered with sod through which these birds dig easily. Mr. Herbert F. Moulton of Ware, Massachusetts, tells me that he found a kingfisher's nest in a plowed field on a hillside. The entrance was made in a "dead furrow." A hole in a perpendicular bank or cliff is much the safer dwelling-place, as it is inaccessible to most of their enemies. The kingfisher, however, is a fierce fighter and can use its strong bill to good advantage in defending its home, striking out wickedly at an intruder. A friend, now a public official in Alaska, has recently recalled my attention to an experience that I had many years ago with a

Kingfisher on Puget Sound. While exploring some islands I discovered many holes near the top of the precipitous sides. These holes proved to be the domiciles of Belted kingfishers and Rough-winged Swallows. In order that I might reach them, my friend with several sailors went around to the top of the bluff, while I remained on the strand. A rope was then let down to me and held by the sailors above while I climbed up it and made a hitch about my body, and then with one hand explored the interior of the holes. Soon one of my fingers was nipped as by a pair of pincers, and as I pulled it from the hole a kingfisher hung by its bill from the digit. The sailors seeing my comical predicament laughed so that they loosened their hold on the rope. My friend says that he never will forget the expression of my countenance when that rope began to slip.

When the river ice begins to break up in March, a few kingfishers appear here and there in the interior. Probably these are birds which have wintered along our southern coast-line, and which take the earliest opportunity to revisit their summer haunts. Most of the wintering birds, however, may be found along the shores of southern New England from the New York line to Cape Cod.* There they go into winter quarters in December, especially about river mouths where at that time the little frost-fish come in, and there they remain, unless extreme cold locks rivers and shores in ice. It is late April or early May, however, before the bulk of the great northward flight of kingfishers arrives. May is the month of mating and nesting. Except during the breeding season the Belted King-fisher is a solitary bird. Then, however, he becomes more than chummy, and seeks the society of some double-belted bird who, if he finds favor in her sight, may become the mother of his chicks. When the conjugal arrangement has been satisfactorily completed, the pair begin to dig. Apparently the male is even more diligent at this task than the female, as his beak is usually more scarred by contact with stones and gravel than that of his mate. The time occupied in the task of excavation varies from two to ten days, depending somewhat on the depth of the hole and the character of the soil. Sand or gravel banks are chosen usually, but occasionally a burrow is made in hard clay, which is less common here than more friable soil. The excavation is made by the beaks of the birds, and the soil is removed with their feet, and scratched out to fall where it may. Generally the hole is made near the top of the bank where it is least accessible to four-footed enemies, and it is carried slightly upward, insuring good drainage and a safe sod roof. Apparently the male leaves most of the duties of incubation to the female, while he often utilizes his surplus energies in digging one or two shorter holes near the first. The "nest" is a rounded chamber at or near the end of the burrow and frequently just beyond where it makes a short turn. When the numerous chicks have hatched, the parents, who are very devoted, must keep busy to furnish sufficient food for so many hungry and rapidly growing mouths. The male takes for his fishing ground a certain section of the stream, along which he flies from one perch to another in regular sequence while patrolling his demesne. Certain dead limbs along his fly-way are favorite watch-towers from which he scans the stream for fish and the surrounding country for intruders. If

*Sometimes the species winters about Boston and at various northern *inland* points as well.

any person trespasses upon his bailiwick, he flies before the interloper, passing from station to station, until he reaches the farthest limit of his fishing ground and then, making a wide detour, he returns to near the starting point. If another kingfisher trespasses upon his domain, there is immediate reaction and there ensues literally a rattling fight in the air which continues until the intruder beats an ignominious retreat.

While the kingfisher seems to love rapid waters, he is by no means confined to their neighborhood, for he lives by large lakes also and along the sea-coast and even upon sea islands. There, where there is fishing aplenty for all, he does not so jealously guard his territory. Three pairs nested one year on one small island not very far from Woods Hole, Massachusetts. In fishing, the kingfisher either dives directly from his perch into the stream below or flies along above the water until he sees his prey, when, hovering above it until satisfied that he can make a strike, he partly closes his wings and shoots down like an arrow, headfirst into the water.* If successful, he rises with a tiny fish in his bill, he turns it head foremost, and swallows it at once; or if the fish is larger than his usual catch, he takes it to a branch, post or rock and beats it vigorously, holding it first by one end and then by the other, until it has been reduced to a tractable condition, when he takes it by the head and swallows it head first. If the fish is a little too large to be swallowed easily, the bird is compelled to assume a rather strained, uncomfortable position until the extremely rapid process of digestion enables him to engorge and dispose of that part of his meal which at first protrudes from his beak. The indigestible bones and scales of fish are ejected as pellets. Often before the young are fledged, the continual passing of the parents to and fro in their feeding operations wears two grooves, one on either side of the hole, where their little feet have padded down or worn away the soil. The young kingfishers are naked at first, then covered with bristly feather-sheaths, and finally they become rather comical short-tailed replicas of their parents. My friend, Mr. William L. Finley, thus characterizes the young bird:

"A young kingfisher seems to grow like a potato in a cellar, all the growth going to the end nearer the light. He sits looking out toward the door and, of course, his face naturally all goes to nose. Everything is forfeited to furnish him with a big head, a spear-pointed bill, and a pair of strong wings to give this arrow-shaped bird a good start when he dives for fish. Of course, he seems top-heavy in appearance. His tiny feet are deformed and hardly large enough to support him. I am sure a kingfisher would not pretend to walk, but he is built for a professional fisher and is a success at the business."[1] Juvenile kingfishers usually do not attempt to fly until they are large and strong enough to make their first flight a success. Mr. Finley found a kingfisher's burrow a mile from their usual fishing place. He watched the young, and believes that when they emerged from their nest, they flew nearly all the way "at one try." They must be able to fly well at once to keep from falling in the water, but kingfishers are provided with waterproof plumage and can swim on the surface if need be. The adults fish day and night.

---

* Kingfishers sometimes escape hawks by diving under the water (Auk, Vol. XLII, 1925, p. 585). See also page 168 in the present volume. [1] Finley, William L.: American Birds, 1913, p. 140.

Sometimes the devoted parent miscalculates the size of the youngster's gullet.   Mr. Milton S. Lacey writes to me that he saw three little kingfishers sitting side by side. One of them had a "flat-fish" which he was manipulating in a desultory half-hearted manner as if he had no real expectation of ever getting it down.   The others looked on with somewhat indifferent interest as if to say "we've tried it and it can't be done."

When the young birds leave the nest, they keep near together for awhile, still fed by the parents, until they learn to fish for themselves; then they separate and remain solitary ever after, except in the breeding season.   Inexperienced young birds sometimes get into the most unlikely places.   Miss Annie F. Towne, of Topsfield, informed me that a friend in Ipswich heard early one morning a great commotion behind her fireboard, and on removing it, was greatly surprised to find that a young kingfisher had come down the chimney into the fireplace.   When released it flew around the room.   The kingfisher now is said to have a new enemy in the introduced Starling, which sometimes "jumps the kingfisher's claim" and occupies its burrow.   It seems more probable that the Kingfisher burrows occupied by the Starling have been first deserted by their original owners.

The principal food of the Belted Kingfisher under ordinary circumstances is believed to be fish, but it does not depend entirely on this diet.   In the west when its favorite streams dry up, it readily subsists on other food.   It takes some mice, many frogs, lizards and newts, crawfish and other crustaceans, many water-insects and such large terrestrial insects as grasshoppers, crickets and the larger beetles, and it has even been known to eat fruit in times of necessity.*   Mrs. Mary Treat watched one that commonly fished near her windows and observed that when the water was too rough to fish, the bird went to "a sour-gum tree (*Nyssa aquatica*)" and greedily devoured the berries, afterward regurgitating pellets of the seeds in the same manner in which it ejects the scales and bones of fish.[1]   Mrs. Gene Stratton Porter examined the food remains which lined the nest of a Kingfisher and found about one-tenth of them to be nearly equally divided between berry-seeds and the hard parts of grasshoppers.   She also says that every summer the Kingfishers that fished around the lake shore near her cabin came into the wild cherry trees and ate the fruit.[2]   Probably they also feed on mussels — the so-called freshwater clams.   According to Dr. B. H. Warren, Mr. B. M. Everhart found a Kingfisher lying on the bank of a stream unable to fly, its bill clasped by a large fresh-water mussel.   Dr. Warren stated that he had heard of other similar instances.[3]

ECONOMIC STATUS.   The food and feeding habits of the Belted Kingfisher have not been fully investigated.   Anglers believe it to be a destructive enemy of trout, and where tame trout are bred in large numbers in artificial pools, doubtless the Kingfisher may destroy many of them if permitted.   The species cannot be tolerated in the neighborhood of a fish-hatchery.   In some states it is not protected by law.   Probably, however, this

---

*A case is reported where a Kingfisher devoured "calmly" the newly hatched young of an English Sparrow (Journal, Maine Ornithological Society, Vol. VII, 1905, p. 46).

[1] Bendire, Charles: Life Histories of North American Birds, Vol. II, 1895, pp. 36–37.
[2] Homing with the Birds, 1919, p. 126.
[3] Birds of Pennsylvania, 1890, p. 163.

is a mistaken policy as the bird may be more beneficial than detrimental to trout in streams under natural conditions. There its food seems to consist largely of minnows which are known to be destructive to trout spawn. This bird also destroys numbers of water-beetles some of which are known to feed on spawn or small fry. Probably it destroys other insect enemies of fish. The mice and grass-eating insects on which it feeds surely count in its favor, and the bird probably deserves protection by law, except about fish hatcheries.

ORDER PICI. WOODPECKERS, WRYNECKS, ETC.

Number of species in North America 24; in Massachusetts 9.

This order includes birds not very closely related, but differing considerably from birds of all other orders, and gathered conventionally by systematists into a large group under one heading. The family *Picidæ* is the only subgroup of the order represented in North America and therefore the only one that need be considered here.

FAMILY PICIDÆ. WOODPECKERS.

Number of species in North America 24; in Massachusetts 9.

Birds of this arboreal family are peculiarly specialized for climbing and pecking. The bill is very strong and hard, usually straight, and adapted for chiseling wood; the skull is dense, compact and strong. The primaries are ten, the first short or in some cases spurious. Tail of ten very stout, rigid, pointed feathers and two rudimentary ones lying concealed at its base. The shafts of these feathers are stout and pointed for use as a support in climbing; for which the feet also are formed, with two toes in front and either one or two behind. The following passages are taken from one of my former works:

FOOT OF THREE-TOED WOOD-PECKER

FOOT OF HAIRY WOOD-PECKER

"These modifications of the foot and tail assist the bird in climbing perpendicularly and in clinging to the bark of trees. While climbing or feeding, the two pairs of toes with their strong, sharp claws enable the bird to grip the bark and hold on, while the strong, sharp-pointed quills of the tail serve as a brace or support. The bird is thus more fully equipped for climbing than a telegraph lineman. The claws and tail take the place of the man's hands and spurs. But the Woodpecker's tools for drilling into the wood and extracting its living food are more wonderful than its climbing apparatus.

"If any one who had never heard of a Woodpecker were to be told that the bird drilled holes into the solid wood by beating its head against a tree, he would be likely to regard the story as fiction.   Nevertheless, that is very nearly what the Woodpecker actually does.   The highly specialized apparatus that will permit of such constant hammering of beak and head against the trees without producing concussion of the brain, or the least inconvenience or injury to the bird, is certainly among the most wonderful features of bird anatomy.

"A moment's reflection will convince any one that, unless the Woodpecker's skull were built on an unusual plan, it could not withstand such hard and continuous hammering.   If we watch a Woodpecker drilling, we shall see that he draws back his head and body to the greatest possible distance from the tree, and then strikes with all his force, sending his strong beak powerfully into the wood.   The skull of the typical Woodpecker is very thick and hard.   Its connection with the beak is strong, but at the same time springy, and somewhat jar-deadening.   The membrane which surrounds the brain is very thick and strong.

"Maurice Thompson says that no person can doubt, after an examination of Woodpecker habits, that the birds are hard of hearing.   He apparently believes that the continual concussion has deadened this sense.   However this may be, it has not interfered with the bird's sight, which seems preternaturally keen.

"The bill is shaped somewhat like a stout chisel, and is used as one.   It strikes out small chips, and so drills its way, if necessary, even to the heart of the tree ; but the most highly specialized organ of the Woodpecker is its tongue, which serves as an accessory to the bill in bringing to light the deep-lurking enemies of the tree.   The subjoined cut of the Woodpecker's skull (see cut) shows the tongue slightly protruding from the open beak.   Ordinarily the tongue lies in the depression of the lower mandible.   It is slender, nearly round, and its upper surface is covered with very minute spines, directed backward ; its tip is as hard as horn, with many strong barbs, which make of it a weapon more effective in its way than a fish spear.   The machinery for thrusting it forth is most perfect.   The bone of the tongue, called the hyoid, has two branches which pass downward and backward from the lower jaw, up and around the back of the head, and over the top of the skull, where they either pass into the nostrils and so on in channels down toward the end of the upper mandible of the beak, or, turning to one side, coil themselves about the bony part of the eyeball.   These branches of the hyoid are enclosed in sheaves which fit into a groove on the top of the skull.   By means of this apparatus the tongue may be extended so that, in the Hairy Woodpecker, it may reach an inch and a half beyond the end of the bill.   The tongue is propelled forward at need by powerful muscles, so that when the bird has drilled to the burrow of a boring beetle it can open the beak

SKULL OF WOODPECKER

slightly, protrude the tongue, spear the insect and draw it out and into the mouth. Birds which possess such implements for the destruction of boring insects must be immensely serviceable to man, for borers are difficult for man to control.

"The utility of Woodpeckers is now quite generally recognized by foresters, and by entomologists who study forest insects. Dr. A. D. Hopkins, the most active and experienced forest entomologist in the United States, is quoted by Dr. E. P. Felt as asserting that Woodpeckers are the most important enemies of spruce bark beetles, and appear to be of inestimable value to the spruce timber interests of the northeast. Dr. Hopkins also states that Woodpeckers are the principal enemies of the destructive sap-wood borers.

"It is sometimes argued that Woodpeckers are of little use as protectors of trees, since they never dig into living wood. This reasoning is based on an error, due to lack of careful observation. Nuttall speaks of a Flicker that dug a nest hole eighteen inches deep in a green sassafras. Dr. Hopkins figures a section of a living tree in which a hole four inches long, two wide, and five deep had been made by Woodpeckers in their search for boring larvæ. According to the annual wood rings around the entrance of the cavity, the tree recovered and lived at least fifteen years after the bird captured the borers. The work of Woodpeckers on living trees does not ordinarily attract much notice. They seldom need to dig far into live trees for borers, for most species that infest live trees are found during a part or all of their lives just under the bark or in the sap-wood not very far from the surface; and the Woodpecker can drill a small hole into the burrow, insert its open beak, and with its tongue spear and extract the insect. The wound soon heals, leaving no noticeable trace. A Woodpecker may thus reach insects at a depth of from one to four inches, according to the size of the bird. Dead trees, however, are riddled with borers in all their parts, and the birds are obliged to delve deeply to find them; therefore, the work of the birds in dead trees is most noticeable." [1]

The genus *Picoides* is the only one represented in North America with but three toes. Woodpeckers are nearly cosmopolitan in wooded regions of the world but are not found in Madagascar or the Australian region. About 425 species and subspecies have been recognized. Woodpeckers nest normally in holes in trees, most of which they excavate, and lay rather numerous, white, rounded, glossy eggs on the chips in their nesting holes.

ECONOMIC STATUS. The chief value of the woodpeckers consists in the fact that when they find a tree infested with borers, they are likely to keep at work upon it until no more larvæ can be found. Thus they often save the tree, and check an incipient outbreak of borers. Woodpeckers so engaged sometimes destroy parasites of boring insects. Such destruction of useful insects by these birds is of little consequence, for when the birds destroy the grubs, the parasites are not needed. When the birds are too few in numbers to prevent an increase of boring insects, the parasites also have a similar immunity from the attacks of birds, and so are free to exert their influence in restraining

---

[1] Useful Birds and Their Protection, 1913, pp. 245–248.

the borers.   If woodpeckers should eat an undue number of parasites, they might then be doing harm ; but such cases probably seldom occur.

The woodpeckers are useful also in providing homes for other birds.   Most woodpeckers each year hollow out from the wood a home for their young, and rarely, if ever, use it more than one season.   Some species, of which the Downy and the Hairy Woodpeckers are familiar examples, also excavate holes to which they retire for shelter during winter nights.   The larger woodpeckers often make deep holes in dead trees, while digging out large borers or colonies of ants.   When the carpenter birds are through with these cavities, they are used sometimes as nesting places by other birds that are unable to excavate for themselves.   The deserted nests of the Downy Woodpecker are used by the House Wren, the Black-capped Chickadee or even the Tree Swallow ; those of the Hairy Woodpecker may be used by Bluebirds, Purple Martins, or Tree Swallows ; those of the Northern Flicker by the Screech Owl and the Wood Duck.   The excavations made by woodpeckers in securing insects are often used by the Black-capped Chickadee or the House Wren.

Woodpeckers are absolutely dependent upon trees, as trees furnish them food, shelter and nesting places.   Nearly all the food of most woodpeckers is found in trees, though some get a part of their food from the ground or from other plants   Woodpeckers are indispensable to the welfare of trees as they feed on destructive tree insects which most of the time are secure from the attacks of other birds.   On the other hand woodpeckers injure live trees more or less in their search for insects by boring holes through the bark and into the wood as a surgeon injures his patient with the knife.   Woodpeckers, however, do not close the wounds that they make as does the surgeon, and every wound in a tree invites the entrance of fungi and other tree enemies.   However, the injury done by the bird surgeons is usually insignificant compared with the benefits conferred by them, as borers if not removed often kill the tree.   The only serious injury done to trees by woodpeckers is confined to a single genus *Sphyrapicus*, the true sapsuckers.   These birds take large quantities of sap and often impair the quality of the timber, and sometimes destroy enough of the cambium layer to weaken or kill the tree.

Dryóbates villósus villosus (Linnæus).   Hairy Woodpecker.

Other names: SAPSUCKER ; BIG SAPSUCKER.

Plate 49.

DESCRIPTION. — Bill stout and straight, about as long as head with thick tuft of corn-colored, buffy or buffy-white, basal bristles covering each nostril ; wings ample, first primary very short, virtually spurious.   *Adult male:* Black above with white stripe over eye running back and broadening to a red band (sometimes divided by black) on back of head, and another white stripe below eye broadening at ear-coverts and running nearly to back of neck, which is black ; broad stripe down back, rows of spots on wing-coverts and flight-feathers (giving the appearance of bars when wing is closed), all lower plumage and three outer tail-feathers white, inner one of these three sometimes marked black, 2d sometimes has black mark and the outer may have a very little black ; bill dark grayish-horn, or bluish-horn, darkening

PLATE 49

PLATE 49

HAIRY WOODPECKER
Page 256

Adult Female

DOWNY WOODPECK

Page 261

Adult Female

Adult Male

Adult Male

All about one-half scale.

toward end, but whitish at extreme tip ; iris reddish-brown ; legs and feet grayish, tinted with blue or olive. *Adult female:* Like male, but lacking red on back of head, which is replaced by white (usually divided at back by black). *Young in first winter plumage:* Similar to adults, but white markings sometimes tinged yellowish, red of back of head sometimes duller. *Young male in juvenal plumage:* Similar to adult female but black crown more or less spotted reddish, pinkish, yellowish or bronzy, forehead often spotted with white, and white markings in some cases tinged yellowish. *Young female in juvenal plumage:* Similar to young male, but crown uniform black in some specimens. Both sexes variable, some have white spots on crown.

MEASUREMENTS. — Length 8.50 to 10.50 in.; spread 15.00 to 17.50; folded wing 4.50 to 5.07; tail 3.00 to 4.00; bill 1.10 to 1.36; tarsus .86 to 1.00. Weight 2½ oz. (B. H. Warren). Female the smaller.

MOLTS. — Nestling is hatched naked and grows no down; juvenal plumage develops before bird is fledged; this is molted completely in late summer (late July and August), and in first winter plumage bird becomes virtually as adult; adults have some molt of body feathers, wings and tail in spring and a complete postnuptial molt in autumn (July to September).

FIELD MARKS. — Size slightly smaller than Robin, with much shorter tail; a black and white bird, white below, striped and spotted with white above, wings barred with rows of white spots, a broad white stripe down back; distinguished from smaller Downy Woodpecker (which also has a white stripe down the back) by relatively *larger, longer bill* and unmarked white outer tail-feathers; latter cannot be seen unless tail is spread somewhat.

VOICE. — A high, sharp, rather metallic *chink* or *click;* its cries much louder than notes of Downy Woodpecker; more like a *huip, huip,* its whinny or rattling call, *trrui, trrui* (C. Bendire). A "Hairy" uttered both the loud note *cheerk* and the chatter while on the wing; the species occasionally utters notes in succession which resemble the Flicker's *wick-a-wick-a-wick;* they are very noisy after the young hatch and continually scold an intruder with their *cheerks* and rolling *chirrs* (J. A. Farley); an unusual note sounds like *koowick, koowick, koowick, quick quick quick quick quick* (A. A. Saunders); another is an odd quavering ventriloquial whistle (Kathleen M. Hempel).

BREEDING. — Chiefly in woods, more rarely in orchards or fields. *Nest:* A hole in dead or living tree or in dead branch of living tree, from 5 to 60 feet up, excavated by the birds, with no lining, except a few chips in the bottom; entrance usually a nearly round hole less than 2 inches in diameter; excavation gourd-shaped, from about 8 to 16 in. deep. *Eggs:* 3 to 5, rarely more, usually 4; .70 to 1.02 by .64 to .75 in.; shining white. Illustrated in Capen's "Oölogy of New England," Plate XIV, Fig. 9. *Dates:* April 20, Illinois; April 22 to May 30, Massachusetts. *Incubation:* Period 14 days (Burns); by both sexes. One brood yearly.

RANGE. — Upper Austral and Transition zones over northeastern United States and southeastern Canada, extending into lower parts of Canadian Zone. Breeds over most of its range from Central Manitoba, southeastern Ontario, southern Quebec, New Brunswick and Nova Scotia south to central Texas, central Arkansas, southern Illinois, southwestern Kentucky, northern Alabama, central North Carolina, southwestern and central Virginia and west to South Dakota, eastern Colorado, and northwestern Texas; other races of this species occupy a large part of the remainder of the continent.

DISTRIBUTION IN NEW ENGLAND. — Common resident in Maine, New Hampshire and Vermont, breeding chiefly in forested sections; rather uncommon winter visitor and less common summer resident in Massachusetts; very rare summer resident on Cape Cod and in some adjacent parts of the state; uncommon winter visitor and rare summer resident in Rhode Island and Connecticut.

SEASON IN MASSACHUSETTS. — Permanent resident; more common in winter than in summer in southeastern section.

HAUNTS AND HABITS. The Hairy Woodpecker is the embodiment of sturdy energy and persistent industry. Active, cheerful, ever busy, its life of arduous toil brings but one reward, a liberal sustenance. It sometimes spends nearly an hour of hard labor in digging out a single borer, but commonly reaches the object of its quest in much less time. Notwithstanding great and strenuous activity the bird keeps in good condition. It is a bird of verve; even its loud wing-beats (*prut-prut-prut*) are diagnostic. This woodpecker is not very common in Massachusetts, but in the hardwood forests of Maine it may be seen in autumn in considerable numbers. Groups of half a dozen or more birds, each group probably a family party, may be met with at that season scattered through the woods, exploring crevices in the bark and rapping away on the trunks and limbs as if their very lives depended on the success of their undertaking. They are a little shy, but by striking a stick against a tree trunk, in imitation of their tapping, the traveler may succeed in attracting their attention and causing them to draw near. These family groups often are accompanied by Downy Woodpeckers, Nuthatches, or Chickadees, all of which are conservators of the forest, as these birds continually search over the trees for insects which destroy the leaves, bark or wood.

As winter approaches many Hairy Woodpeckers leave their forested breeding grounds and appear in orchards and villages and in parts of southeastern Massachusetts where they are almost unknown in summer. Their numbers increase considerably also in the southern parts of their range, which indicates a considerable migration. Mr. J. McI. Terrill of St. Lambert, Quebec, tells me that usually the few local breeding birds of this species disappear in early autumn and others (a very noticeable wave) appear toward the end of October or in early November. During the winter, in its search for food, the Hairy Woodpecker often becomes a familiar bird about farmsteads, and though normally more shy than the Downy Woodpecker, it may be attracted in winter to any place where people feed the birds.

During the inclement season it is said to require a sheltered place in which to sleep and, like the Downy Woodpecker, to excavate a hole in a tree for a sleeping chamber, but there is evidence that it does not always seek such shelter, as the late Charles E. Bailey and myself watched one for several winter evenings in a grove, clinging upright against a tree trunk in the usual woodpecker position. Night after night, the bird was there at dusk, remained there until dark, and was there also at daybreak each morning in precisely the same place.[1]

In early spring the movement northward and back to the forest begins, and Major Mark Robinson, a ranger in the Algonquin National Park in the highlands of Ontario, writing to me on March 11, 1920, said that about April 1, the larger northern form of the Hairy Woodpecker left his region and that on the 10th he first noticed the smaller race which was by no means so tame as were the usual winter resident birds. He has noted a similar movement in subsequent years.

On bright March days this bird begins to practise what is either a love song, a challenge, a call to its mate, or all combined. This is no vocal music but instead a loud drumming on some resonant dead tree, branch, or pole. This long roll or tattoo is louder than that of the Downy Woodpecker, not quite so long, and with a slightly greater interval

---

[1] Useful Birds and Their Protection, 1907, p. 260.

between each succeeding stroke. It takes a practiced ear, however, to distinguish between the drumming of these two species. In courtship the male chases the female from tree to tree with coaxing calls, and there is much dodging about among the branches and bowing to each other before the union is consummated. The tree selected for nesting is often very large and tall, and usually the trunk or branch chosen is dead at the heart, although otherwise apparently sound. Rarely the birds excavate their home from sound live wood.

Mr. Farley reports that he found in Lynnfield, Massachusetts, a Hairy Woodpecker's nest in a *thrifty, sound, young oak*, eight or nine inches in diameter. The nest hole was 12 feet up and the cavity inside was much enlarged. The birds had taken out the entire heart of this *green* tree. "I could hear the clamor of the young in the hole," he says, "while still on the ground at the foot of the tree."

As the young develop in the nest their outcry grows in volume until like that of young Flickers it may be heard at some distance from the tree. The entrance to the hole is barely large enough to admit the workers. If not disturbed, these birds seem to evince an attachment to some particular tree and come back to the old home year after year, making a new hole each time until the tree, usually decayed at the heart in the beginning, is no longer tenable. Both birds work at the excavation and take turns at digging and in carrying away the chips which they scatter about at a distance, though some are spilled on the ground beneath the hole and over a small space near by.

It is somewhat of a mystery how the woodpeckers are able to tell the exact location of a boring larva beneath the bark or wood. Some of the larger grubs may be heard without difficulty, as they cut away the wood with their strong jaws, but many smaller ones make no audible sound. Maurice Thompson asserts that the Hairy Woodpecker strikes its bill into the wood and then holds the point of one mandible for a moment in the dent thus made. He believes that the vibrations produced by the insect in the wood are then conveyed through the beak and skull of the bird to its brain; but this does not explain how the same bird can drill unerringly into the very spot where a grub or ant lies dormant and motionless in winter. The only plausible explanation of this feat seems to be that the delicate sensibilities of the bird enable it by sounding with its beak to fix the exact spot at which the body of its prey fills the burrow. The tapping of the beak may enable the bird to locate the grub by sound, somewhat as the carpenter by striking on the wall of a room with a hammer can find the position of a timber hidden under laths and plaster.

"This woodpecker is quite destructive to hairy caterpillars, and feeds its young on noxious larvæ of many species. It also attacks the pupæ or chrysalids of many injurious moths, among them those of the gypsy moth. Moths that hibernate in cocoons during the winter are particularly exposed to the attacks of this woodpecker. Dr. F. M. Webster states that he saw one of these birds peck through the cocoon of the *cecropia* moth, and devour the contents. On examining more than a score of these cocoons, he found only two uninjured by the bird. Ants, grasshoppers and spiders are eaten." [1]

---

[1] Useful Birds and Their Protection, 1913, p. 259.

Certain of the wood-boring beetles taken by this bird are harmless for the most part as they work chiefly in decayed wood, but there are others that attack living trees, and the bird does not discriminate between them. It takes many injurious caterpillars, and is particularly destructive to pupæ of moths that produce voracious, leaf-eating caterpillars such as the gipsy and the *cecropia*. It eats weevils, ants, caterpillars, bugs, plant lice and scale insects, locusts, grasshoppers and crickets, spiders and millipeds.

A habit of this bird which appears to have been observed but once is recorded by Bendire:

"Mr. V. A. Alderson, of Marathon County, Wisconsin, publishes the following interesting statement in the 'Oölogist' (Vol. VII, July, 1890, p. 147): 'Last summer potato bugs covered every patch of potatoes in Marathon County (being my home county), Wisconsin. One of my friends here found his patch an exception, and therefore took pains to find out the reason, and observed a Hairy Woodpecker making frequent visits to the potato field and going from there to a large pine stub a little distance away. After observing this for about six weeks, he made a visit to the pine stub, and found, on inspection, a large hole in its side, about 15 feet up. He took his ax and cut down the stub, split it open, and found inside over 2 bushels of bugs. All had their heads off and bodies intact.' Now, why did the Woodpecker carry the bugs whole to the tree and only bite off and eat the heads, which could have been done in the potato field?" [1]

This bird has learned to eat meat and fat in winter, probably by feeding on the skinned carcasses of animals left in the woods by hunters and trappers. It may be readily enticed anywhere by fat, meat or suet, hung on the trees in winter. According to Professor F. E. L. Beal the food of this woodpecker is 77.67 per cent animal and 22.33 per cent vegetal. The latter includes a few grass seeds, hazel nuts, beech nuts, wild berries and a small proportion of the inner bark and cambium of trees. Mrs. Susan K. Squires of Fredericton, New Brunswick, saw a Hairy Woodpecker place a butternut in a crevice of the bark and hammer it, but finally it dropped the nut which it had crushed completely, but it had failed to pierce the shell.

ECONOMIC STATUS. The Hairy Woodpecker is a useful bird. It has been known to eat a little corn, but is quite as likely to take the corn worm or the corn borer. The wild fruit that it eats is mostly such as is not fit for human consumption. It is not a sapsucker. If it subsists on sap at all, it is taken in very limited quantities, as several other birds sip a little now and then around maple-sugar camps (see "Haunts and Habits" of Downy Woodpecker, p. 268). The bird deserves perpetual protection as a conservator of the forest.

NOTE. **Dryobates villosus leucómelas** (BODDAERT). **Northern Hairy Woodpecker.**
This larger, lighter race may occur rarely in winter in northern New England. It has been reported more than once, but I have never seen a specimen actually taken within the limits of this territory; some taken in winter in northern Maine seem to be intermediate between this form and *Dryobates villosus villosus*.

---

[1] Bendire, C.: Life Histories of North American Birds, Vol. II, 1895, p. 47.

Dryobates pubéscens mediánus (SWAINSON). Downy Woodpecker.

Other names: DOWNY; LITTLE SAPSUCKER.

Plate 49.

DESCRIPTION. — A black and white woodpecker closely resembling the Hairy Woodpecker (see page 256), but much smaller with shorter bill (shorter than head) and with three white *outer tail-feathers barred sparingly with black;* male with red on back of head, which is lacking in female; "bill bluish-black; iris dark red; feet bluish-green" (Audubon); claws light bluish, black at ends. *Young male in juvenal plumage:* Similar to adult male, but without the red band on back of head; more or less feathers on top of head tipped red, black plumage duller, white markings often more yellowish and lower plumage sometimes streaked on breast and sides. *Young female in juvenal plumage:* Similar to male but often without red on top of head; all nestlings *supposed* to have red on crown which, in some cases, disappears very soon in female. Crown very variable in both sexes.

MEASUREMENTS. — Length 6.25 to 7.15 in.; spread about 10.92 to 12.25; folded wing 3.50 to 4.04; bill .55 to .80; tarsus .70 to .90. Weight 1¼ to 1½ oz.

MOLTS. — The molts of this species might be expected to be similar to those of the Hairy Woodpecker but no spring specimens were found in molt. Juvenal birds were found molting into first winter plumage in August; adults were in postnuptial molt in July and August.

FIELD MARKS. — See field marks under Hairy Woodpecker.

VOICE. — A common call note *pwit pwit* terminating with *tchee tchee tchee,* "rapidly repeated"; another (when two are chasing one another) reminds one of the *kick-kick* of a Flicker but not so loud (C. Bendire); when searching for food a low *pshir pshir,* a shrill cry like a whinny, descending rapidly.

BREEDING. — In orchards, among shade trees, in open woods, more rarely in large forests. *Nest:* A hole excavated by the birds in tree from 5 to 50 feet up; entrance, round or oval about 1.25 in. in diameter, enlarging inwardly into a gourd-shaped hole 6 to 10 in. deep. *Eggs:* 4 to 6, rarely 7 or 8; white, similar to those of Hairy Woodpecker but smaller; .65 to .75 by .50 to .62 in.; illustrated in Bendire's "Life Histories of North American Birds," Vol. II, Plate I, Fig. 24. *Dates:* May 15, Connecticut; May 20 to June 21, Massachusetts; May 27, Maine. *Incubation:* Period 12 days (Burns); probably by both sexes. One brood yearly.

RANGE. — Resident in Upper Austral Zone and parts of Transition Zone of eastern North America, from southern Virginia, western North Carolina, eastern Tennessee, southern Illinois and Indiana, northern Arkansas and central Kansas north to North Dakota, Minnesota, Michigan, southern Ontario, southern Quebec and Nova Scotia; westward to central Nebraska, South Dakota, North Dakota and eastern Montana.

DISTRIBUTION IN NEW ENGLAND. — Common resident, except at altitudes above 3,000 feet; in Rhode Island more common in winter than in summer.

SEASON IN MASSACHUSETTS. — Permanent resident.

HAUNTS AND HABITS. The sprightly little Downy, smallest of our woodpeckers, is an admirable bird. It sports no gay plumes and sings no song, but it is a model of patient industry and perseverance, and though it may take a little sap from some maple tree occasionally in early spring, the small amount that it requires will never be missed. It is found commonly throughout most of New England wherever trees grow, and, unlike the Hairy Woodpecker, it may be seen more often usually in settled cultivated districts than in great forests. It delights in orchards, scattered shade trees, and the borders of woods. It may be found in the lowest swamps or on the mountain tops though it may become scarce at an altitude of more than 3,000 feet.

After a mild winter its courting may begin in March, but if the spring is backward not until late April or early May. Then two males often may be seen following a female about. When one male, with spread wings, and the female have taken up a position on a limb facing each other and ready for the preliminaries, the other male comes in between and interrupts the ceremony, and thus the ancient comedy is reënacted with small results and little advancement for either ardent suitor. The female may be something of a flirt, and may seem to encourage first one and then the other. In such case the rivals for her affection may be kept in suspense for a week, but when the fickle one finally makes her choice, there is little delay in beginning the domestic arrangements. First, however, there may be rather a protracted hunt for a suitable location. A dead stub or some branch that is decayed at the heart is usually chosen. Often the birds nest in an apple tree, rarely in a building. Mr. Laurence B. Fletcher informs me that in a boat-house at Marblehead about six feet above high-water mark, a pair of these birds bored through the outer wall just above a door and a little to one side. The boards were an inch thick and the building was sheathed inside. In the space between the inner and outer walls, the female laid her eggs on a two by four inch joist some three feet below the opening, which faced the harbor. Residences stand all about the boat-house and the locality is much frequented. Here a woodpecker family was reared and successfully launched into the outer world.

This little bird can chisel out sound wood, and it has been known to cut through concrete. Mrs. W. F. Eldredge of Rockport, writing to me in the spring of 1919, said that one of the birds had made a nest hole through the cement that had plugged a cavity in a hollow limb. Probably in this case the cement was not so well "tempered" as it should have been. When a tree that suits the pair has been found, excavation is begun immediately. In a few days a gourd-shaped hole has been dug, provided the wood is decayed enough to be easily excavated, but otherwise a week may be occupied in the task. Occasionally the spot is not well chosen, and progress is stopped by some large, hard knot. In this case the birds give over their task, and begin anew in a more favorable spot. The entrance to the nest is almost perfectly round and just large enough to enable the occupants to squeeze in and out; not a fraction of an inch to spare is allowed. Here the snow-white eggs are laid and the young are reared until fledged. When hatched they are ugly, blind, naked, helpless and dumb, with an enlargement of the gape, seen in all young woodpeckers. As they grow and their eyes open, they become vociferous, so much so that their insistent cries for food may be heard at a little distance from the tree — a kind of "shrill twitter, now rising, now dying down like a breath expelled." When the young are fledged, they follow the parents about until they learn to find food for themselves. Then the family may roam through woods and orchards in company for a time, but finally they separate, and during the winter Downy seems rather to shun its own kind, regardless of family ties. Quite commonly, however, one may be seen with some band of Chickadees and Nuthatches, and with these birds it is likely to frequent any locality where people are feeding birds with suet or other materials suitable for woodpeckers.

As winter comes on, there is more or less migration of the Downy Woodpecker from the northern part of its range to the southward, and from higher to lower altitudes. Some ornithologists have regarded the species as non-migratory. This may be true in respect to individuals in a large part of the range of the species, but Major Mark Robinson says that early in October most individuals of the species leave his station in Algonquin National Park in the highlands of Ontario, and that before winter sets in they disappear and are seen very rarely or not at all during the winter. In the more southern and less elevated parts of Ontario the Downy Woodpecker is common throughout the winter.

Wherever this bird spends the winter, it finds or makes a snug retreat wherein it sleeps on cold winter nights. Often it excavates a cavity in some decayed tree, at the cost of three or more days of hard labor, or it may find an unoccupied nesting hole of some woodpecker, a hollow tree or a bird-house or nesting box in some sheltered situation. An individual occupied all winter a nesting box only five feet from the ground in my yard. The bottom of the box had a lining of sawdust. The bird entered this box daily from 4.12 to 4.30 P.M. eastern standard time, and left it from 7 to 7.20 A.M. daily, according to the length of the winter days. Its comings and goings were almost as well regulated as the hands of the clock. Some of my correspondents also have observed this bird lodging through the winter in such a box. It is one of the birds known to take a snow bath.

In winter "Downy" lives chiefly upon insect enemies of trees. Wherever it works, bits of bark and lichens scattered on the snow give evidence of its diligence. In early spring, however, like several other arboreal winter birds and squirrels it may now and then take some sap from the flowing maples. Hence the popular name Little Sapsucker, which has some foundation in fact, though this bird's work, unlike much of that of the true sapsuckers, seems to cause no injury to the trees. Several ornithologists have published statements denying that the species takes sap, and some are positive that it never makes perforations in the bark of trees similar to those made by true sapsuckers. Therefore it is necessary here to introduce some evidence to the contrary.

Alexander Wilson, often called the Father of American Ornithology, was (in 1808) the first to call attention to the sapsucker-like habits of the Downy Woodpecker in the following words:

"In fall he is particularly fond of boring the apple trees for insects, digging a circular hole through the bark, just sufficient to admit his bill, after that a second, third, etc., in pretty regular horizontal circles round the body of the tree; these parallel circles of holes are often not more than an inch, or an inch and a half, apart, and sometimes so close together that I have covered eight or ten of them at once with a dollar." [1] Audubon (1831) was the first to notice and report the liking for sweet sap displayed by the Hairy Woodpecker [in the following words: "I often saw this bird perforate sugar cane stalks and take with evident enjoyment the sweet juice thus set flowing," but he does not attribute a similar habit to the Downy Woodpecker. Nuttall did not follow Wilson in the

---

[1] Wilson, Alexander, and Bonaparte, Charles Lucien: American Ornithology, or the Natural History of the Birds of the United States, Vol. I, 1832, p. 161.

belief that the Downy Woodpecker was always in quest of insects, for he says: "The circles of round holes which it makes with so much regularity around the . . . trees are no doubt made for the purpose of getting at the sweet sap which they contain." Again he says: "In the month of February, 1830, I observed these borers busy tapping the small live trunks of several wax myrtles (*Myrica cerifera*); and these perforations were carried down into the alburnum, or sap-wood, but no farther. . . . On examining the oozing sap I found it to be exceedingly saccharine, but in some instances astringent or nearly tasteless." [1.] In 1866 Dr. Henry Bryant of Boston, a well-known ornithologist of his day, published the following: "It has long been known that some of our smaller woodpeckers pick out portions of the sound bark of trees, particularly of apple trees, where there are no larvæ and apparently no inducement for them to do so. . . . They [the holes] are generally seen in circles round the limbs or trunks of small irregularly rounded holes, and in this vicinity are made almost exclusively by the Downy Woodpecker (*P. pubescens*) aided occasionally by the Hairy Woodpecker (*P. villosus*)." [2]

In 1869 Dr. J. A. Allen, who in his day was regarded as one of the most eminent American naturalists — one whose writings were everywhere considered authoritative, wrote "the perforations in the bark of trees, forming transverse rings, and commonly attributed almost solely to the Yellow-bellied Sapsucker, are chargeable also to the Downy and Hairy Woodpeckers"; and he asserted that they might often be seen engaged in the operation.[3] Mr. H. D. Minot evidently did not believe in the sapsucking habit, for he says ". . . they extract wood-borers and other insects from the wood. For this purpose they dig out small circular holes of about the size made by a large awl, and with these often encircle a large tree."

It is noticeable that in all the above statements except that of Nuttall there is no direct evidence. Assertions are made, but the authors do not give the observations on which they are based. I purpose now to submit the evidence of those who have observed the Downy Woodpecker in the act of making pits in the bark similar to those made by true sapsuckers, and actually taking sap or cambium from the tree.

In "Useful Birds and Their Protection" (1907) I published the following statement regarding the Downy Woodpecker: "In many cases it perforates the bark of apple trees with small roundish holes less than an inch apart disposed in parallel rings." Before that time I had seen the bird apparently working at these holes in a region where thousands of such perforations could be seen and where I had never observed a sapsucker though at that time I was out collecting daily, but I could not be certain that the Downy was the original maker of them. I relied on my friend, the late Chester A. Reed, who said that he had watched the bird at close range and seen it make the holes in perfectly sound bark. Having known Mr. Reed well for years and having worked with him in the field, I had the utmost confidence in any statement that he made regarding his observa-

---

[1] Chamberlain, Montague: A popular Handbook of the Ornithology of the United States and Canada, based on Nuttall's Manual, 1891, Vol. I, pp. 453, 454.

[2] Proceedings, Boston Society of Natural History, 1866, Vol. X, pp. 91, 92.

[3] Memoir, Boston Society of Natural History, 1869, Vol. I, p. 499.

tions. In American Ornithology (1903) he made the following statement: "You have probably noticed rows of tiny holes extending nearly around some apple trees. These are the work of the Downy in his search for the insects which, if left to do their work unhampered, would soon increase in numbers so as to devastate every orchard." [1] This again is a mere statement of what he evidently believed to be a fact, but it is not evidence. In 1906, however, he published this experience. His article was unsigned, but after his death his father, Mr. C. K. Reed, publisher of the magazine, assured me that his son wrote it. In it occurs the following statement: "Last fall I watched a Downy busily at work hammering on the trunk of an apple tree. He would pound away for half a minute steadily in one spot and then hitch sideways about an inch and repeat the operation; when he had completely encircled the tree he dropped down about his length and made another ring around the trunk. The marks left on the tree were identical with those that I had supposed were made by the Sapsuckers." [2] He saw nothing to indicate that the bird was getting insects, sap, or cambium from their perforations, only that it made them.

In 1920 having in mind the preparation of this volume I asked my many correspondents to watch carefully in the spring and see what bird made these parallel rings of perforations. Several of them wrote later that they had seen the Yellow-bellied Sapsucker making these pits; others said that they had seen the Downy or the Hairy Woodpecker, apparently making such holes, but were not certain whether the bird was not working at holes already made by the Sapsucker. Major Mark Robinson of Algonquin National Park, Ontario, wrote that on February 2, 1920, he saw a male Downy Woodpecker in a small yellow birch making a ring of holes along one side of the trunk about 6 inches below a knot hole, or "cat face," at a distance of about 8 feet, and watched the bird for some time. On April 11 he wrote that he had examined carefully the holes that he reported as made by the Downy Woodpecker, and found that some insect had bored into the trunk of the tree. This woodpecker evidently was drilling for insects.

Mr. J. K. Jensen, a Danish field ornithologist of long experience, formerly of Westwood, Massachusetts, wrote that he had actually seen the Downy Woodpecker make the small pits so often seen in apple, maple and birch trees, and believed that it was the author of most of these holes.

My old friend, Mr. C. J. Maynard of Newtonville, in a letter dated October 24, 1920, said that he had seen the Downy Woodpecker making rings of holes about a tree, and that there was an old wild apple tree back of Prospect Hill, Waltham, on which he remembers seeing the Downy at this work. Mr. Norman P. Woodward of Worcester, Massachusetts, writing to me November 17, 1919, asserted that there was an old pear tree in his yard that was full of little holes made by woodpeckers, and that he had often seen the Downy Woodpecker drilling these holes, never long at one hole but moving from hole to hole and giving half a dozen pecks with its bill. He had never seen in either spring or autumn any signs of sap running from the holes.

---

[1] American Ornithology, Vol. III, 1903, p. 94.
[2] American Ornithology, Vol. VI, No. 2, February, 1906, p. 39.

Miss Nina G. Spaulding wrote from Jaffrey, New Hampshire, on March 12, 1920, that she watched a Downy Woodpecker on an old apple tree pecking some small round holes. After the bird left she found the freshly made pits. Mr. William J. Trudell of Huntington, Massachusetts, sent me the next autumn the following note: "On November 13, 1920, while rabbit hunting, I came into a small apple orchard on the Russell watershed, known as the Ritch Farm. I was standing under one of the apple trees waiting for a sign of game, when I heard a Woodpecker at work over my head. I took my glasses and saw it was a Downy. It was about 8 feet from me and I plainly saw it make a series of round holes horizontally on a limb, and I am positive it was making the original holes and not opening up old holes. I am not sure whether the bird was securing food, but I think it was, as there is no sap in the tree as late as that." Later Mr. A. A. Cross of Huntington sent me a section of the branch on which Mr. Trudell had seen the woodpecker at work.

On comparing this section of the branch of an apple tree with another on which were similar pits that a Yellow-bellied Sapsucker was seen to make, we find that in both cases the majority of the pits were either nearly circular in form or horizontally elliptical. Those made by the Downy were deeper than those made by the Yellow-bellied Sapsucker for the reason that the branch on which the latter worked was larger, with thicker bark. In all cases the latter penetrated the bark to the wood. In most cases the Downy did the same; there were three particulars in which the pits differed. The sapsucker's pits averaged larger, varied much more in size and form, and exposed more wood at the bottom of each pit. Neither penetrated the wood. Several of the pits made by the sapsucker tended toward a rectangular shape and two were over half an inch in length; the longest diameter vertical; the longest elliptical pit made by the Downy was less than $\frac{1}{4}$ in. long at its outer diameter. The pits made by the Sapsucker were as large where they reached the wood as at the surface, while those made by the Downy were much smaller where they reached the wood than at the surface. The first might have injured the tree, the second did not.

Mr. Charles J. Anderson of Springfield, Massachusetts, writing April 26, 1922, says: "This last March I noticed a Downy Woodpecker always stopping to peck at a high branch of a maple tree in the yard. He made a ring of small holes around the branch. Later on when sap began to run I saw it coming down from holes on three different branches. I saw chickadees drinking the sap."

Sapsuckers do not always follow the plan of circular rows. Sometimes the drillings are scattered rather promiscuously as is the case with many made by the Downy Woodpecker. Two observers reported having seen the Downy making vertical rows of perforations. The following note from Mr. R. A. Gilliam of Dallas, Texas, shows how this was done: "December 5, 1920, I saw two Downy Woodpeckers on the stem of a honey locust, just below where the first limbs branch off, industriously boring into what I knew, even without a glass, was perfectly good bark. They kept at this for at least twenty-minutes before I was compelled to disturb them. I found they were going entirely through the cambium, the incisions or holes being about one-eighth inch in diameter, and possibly one-fourth inch apart up and down the tree, then one would start another run about one-fourth inch to the side." These rows of vertical perforations evidently were similar to those made by a Yellow-bellied Sapsucker, watched by Frank Bolles.[1]

On January 25, 1922, Dr. Joseph Grinnell, the eminent California ornithologist, editor of the Condor, who, with Mr. Tracey I. Storer, had been investigating the fauna of the Yosemite Valley, wrote to me as follows regarding the work of the western sub-species of the Downy Woodpecker, *Dryobates pubescens turati*, the Willow Woodpecker: "A pair of Willow Woodpeckers proved to be regular tenants of Curry's apple orchard on the floor of Yosemite Valley. They or their ancestors had evidently worked there for some years, with the result that most of the 150 trees in the orchard showed marks of their attention, and many of the trunks were fairly riddled with the somewhat Sapsucker-like drillings. On November 8, 1915, two of us made a study of the site, with findings as follows:

"A measured area 6 inches (15 cm.) square, 4 feet (130 cm.) above ground on a trunk 12½ inches (32 cm.) in diameter contained 17 fresh pits and 30 old ones, of last year's digging or older. These pits were horizontally elliptical, each about 2.5 by 4 m. in surface extent, thus distinctly different in size and shape from true Sapsucker drillings. They were arranged in irregular horizontal rows, with spaces of 6 to 14 m. between individual pits and 3 to 8 cm. between rows. On this particular trunk, the pits occurred over a vertical distance of 41 inches (105 cm.), so that there were about 2,100 pits in all on this one tree. Limbs less than 4 inches (10 cm.) in diameter were not usually found to have been worked upon. However destructive this drilling would seem to be, it does not seriously affect the vitality of the trees; the pits are but 4 to 5 cm. deep, penetrating only the outer layers of the bark, which after a time scale off. We should judge that all evidence of this woodpecker's work is removed in natural process within about three years. The wood seems to be not damaged at all as is the case with most true Sapsucker work."[2]

There is little in all the above evidence to indicate the object of this drilling. It is safe to assume, however, that in most cases of this kind the birds are not seeking insects, but rather fragments of the inner bark or the cambium (the layer between bark and wood), or else they are drilling for sap. In the "Food of Woodpeckers of the United States," by Professor F. E. L. Beal, the stomach contents of 3,453 woodpeckers including sixteen species, are recorded. Professor Beal reported that nearly all members of the woodpecker family ate some cambium.[3] The quantity found in the stomachs of sapsuckers, however, is much greater than that found in other species. There seems to be little evidence available regarding the sapsucking habits of other woodpeckers. In 1873 Mr. C. A. White saw Red-headed Woodpeckers pecking holes in sugar maples on the campus of

---

[1] Auk, Vol. VIII, 1891, p. 258.
[2] Grinnell, J., and Storer, T. I.: Animal Life in the Yosemite, 1924, pp. 318–319.
[3] Biological Survey, Bulletin No. 37, 1911, p. 11.

Iowa University and watching the birds closely afterwards, "became convinced that they were sucking the sap and that they had pecked the holes for the purpose of obtaining it." [1]   Mr. F. Stevens (quoted by Bendire) [2] and Dr. Joseph Grinnell [3] record the sap-drinking habits of the California Woodpecker.

Notwithstanding the fact that little seems to be known to ornithologists regarding the sap-drinking habits of birds, farmers who have maple orchards tell us that while sugaring in early spring, Downy and Hairy Woodpeckers, nuthatches and squirrels, commonly take sap.   The first trustworthy evidence, however, that I obtained regarding the tapping of trees for sap by the Downy Woodpecker was in 1899, when my assistant, the late Charles E. Bailey, on April 6 watched one for several hours.   His report reads: "At 12.30 I found a Downy Woodpecker, and watched him till 2.45; he took three larvæ from a maple stub, just under the bark.   He next tapped two small swamp maples, four and six feet from the ground, and spent most of the time taking sap.   He tapped the tree by picking it a few times very lightly; it looked like a slight cut, slanting a little. The bird would sit and peck the sap out of the lower part of the cut.   The cut was so small the sap did not collect very fast.   The bird would go and sit for a long time in a large tree and not move, then it would come back and take more sap.   It did this three times while I was watching it.   It did not care to take any food but the sap.   I could get within six feet of the bird without any trouble when it was taking sap.   It then left and went into a large tree, and I lost it; but if I had stayed by the tree it tapped I think it would have come back before night, as it had done before when I was watching it. It was gone half an hour at one time." [4]   Mr. Bailey cut off and brought to me the limbs, the bark of which was perforated by this bird. . . .   The perforations passed through the bark to the wood but did not enter it and they do not in the least resemble in shape those ordinarily made by the Yellow-bellied Sapsucker.   This was an isolated observation, made incidentally by the one man detailed to get information on the food habits of the bird, but in 1920 and 1921 when a number of observers were on the lookout for sapsuckers this habit was noted again.

Mrs. Arthur Caswell of Athol wrote that three Downy Woodpeckers had been "very busy tapping the maple trees" near her windows and that they took "long deep draughts" of sap "after filling up on the suet fastened to the trunks."   She said that through the middle of the day the sap dropped freely from the holes made by the woodpeckers, and that little icicles of sap were formed during the night.   Miss Alice P. Terry of New Bedford wrote that on February 26, 1921, she saw a Downy Woodpecker tapping a maple tree by boring holes in a ring around a branch.   Mr. Edmund P. Brown of Belfast, Maine, wrote to me on August 27, 1922, that he saw the Downy Woodpeckers making and revisiting fresh pits in the bark of a locust tree.   When revisiting the holes he said "they inserted the bill in each one."

---

[1] American Naturalist, Vol. VII, 1873, p. 496.
[2] Bendire, Charles: Life Histories of North American Birds, Vol. II, 1895, p. 115.
[3] University of California Publications in Zoölogy, Vol. V, 1908, pp. 65, 66.
[4] Annual Report, Massachusetts State Board of Agriculture, 1900, pp. 48–49.

Many of the pits made by the Downy Woodpecker are the result of its search for insects, which apparently it never fails to find when they are the object of its quest, but there was no evidence in the specimen of the work of this bird sent me by Mr. Cross that the pits in the bark had been made in quest of insects. Sap evidently was not the object as sap was not flowing at the time. There was no sign of the work of bark beetles or other insects. Apparently the holes were made as are many of those made by true sapsuckers in quest of the tender inner cambium layer. The small size of the bottoms of the pits indicates that the bird takes a very small bit of cambium from each hole while the true sapsuckers enlarge the bottom of the pit and take more.

Having now presented the evidence that the Downy Woodpecker has sapsucking habits, I will leave the reader to judge for himself whether a case against the bird has been made out, and will consider the effect produced by its activities. I have never been able to find any evidence that this work of the Downy Woodpecker injures the trees. In fact it seems to benefit them and increase their growth, perhaps because it slightly weakens the bark and so gives the trunk more chance for growth, or because it stimulates growth as removing the outer bark with a scraper often does. Alexander Wilson, who took great pains to study the effect of the drilling of the Downy Woodpecker declared that uniformly he found that the trees marked with its rings of pits thrived best and were most productive.[1]

In searching for and securing the insects on which it feeds, the Downy Woodpecker shows its greatest skill. In this work it is a model of industry and perseverance. It is the self-appointed guardian of orchards neglected by their owners, and there its work is most effective. It seems to be especially happy in going over such orchards, perhaps for the reason that the trees always harbor many varieties of insects. It taps on the shaggy bark and locates beneath the scales the cocoons of the codling moth, parent of the apple worm and drives its bill into the vitals of its victim. The bird lays the side of its head to the bark and apparently listens for the movements of the deadly borer; then with a few smart taps it penetrates the outer bark and hales the fellow forth. It discovers the wingless females of the canker-worm moth crawling up the bark on the way to deposit their eggs; it destroys weevils, caterpillars, ants, plant lice and bark lice. That Downy can be exceedingly active and swift if necessary can be vouched for by those who have seen him whip round a limb to escape the rush of a hawk. One would think it difficult for him to go down a tree backward with much speed, but he can skip down the trunk in this fashion quick enough to catch a grub that he has dropped. The following extract from "Useful Birds and Their Protection" shows the great utility of this bird in protecting shade and forest trees from insect enemies:

"When the Metropolitan Park Commission first began to set out young trees along the parkways near Boston, some species of trees were attacked by numerous borers; but the Downy Woodpeckers found them out and extracted the grubs, saving most of the trees. . . .

---

[1] Wilson, Alexander, and Bonaparte, Charles Lucien: American Ornithology, Vol. I, 1832, pp. 185–186.

"The untiring industry of this bird and the perfection of its perceptive powers may be shown by the experience of Mr. Bailey. On March 28, 1899, a Downy Woodpecker that he watched climbed over and inspected one hundred and eighty-one woodland trees between 9.40 A.M. and 12.15 P.M., and made twenty-six excavations for food. Most of these holes exposed galleries in the trunks or in high branches where wood-boring ants were hiding. The openings that the bird drilled in piercing one of these tunnels in a branch some thirty-five feet from the ground are shown in [1] . . . . . . It had uncovered dormant black ants, and in each case had pierced their burrow at the exact spot where they were gathered. These wood-boring ants often gain an entrance at some unprotected spot on a living tree, and so excavate the wood of the trunk that the tree is blown down by the wind. This Woodpecker acts as a continual check on the increase of such ants.

"The delicacy of that sense of touch or audition by which the bird was enabled to locate those motionless insects in their hidden burrow must ever command our admiration, unendowed as we are with such delicate perceptive powers."[1]

The Downy Woodpecker searches out the pine weevil which kills the topmost shoot of the young white pine and so causes a crook in the trunk of the tree, unfitting it for the lumber market. It picks into the galls of goldenrod stalks and robs them of their grubs, and works on mullein heads, picking open the brown seed-cases to get at grubs also. It sometimes even goes to the ground to pick up tent caterpillars. It also destroys the corn-borer. The vegetal food of the Downy Woodpecker consists of a few buds and petals of flowers, wild berries and seeds, frozen apples, beechnuts, acorns, hazelnuts, a very little corn, possibly a few cherries and a little cambium.

Economic Status. Professor F. E. L. Beal of the Biological Survey, United States Department of Agriculture, reporting on the food contained in 723 stomachs of this species, found that 76.05 per cent of the food consisted of animal matter and 23.95 per cent of vegetal; the animal matter consisting chiefly of noxious insects, and the vegetal matter mainly such as to be of little or no importance economically. It would be difficult to find a bird more useful and less harmful than the Downy Woodpecker. It should have complete protection at all times and places.

Picoídes árcticus (Swainson). Arctic Three-toed Woodpecker.

Other names: BLACK-BACKED, THREE-TOED WOODPECKER.

Plate 50.

Description. — Bill about as long as head, stout, straight and very wide at base with black tufts covering nostrils; foot with hind toe wanting, and outer toe reversed as in all woodpeckers; form otherwise similar to that of Hairy Woodpecker. *Adult male:* Above, black with more or less bluish gloss; top of head with large yellow patch extending from forehead over crown; forepart of forehead, narrow stripe behind eye (sometimes wanting) and broad stripe running below eye and ear white, beneath the latter a more or less distinct black stripe; most of flight-feathers spotted with white in transverse rows on outer webs, giving the appearance of five or six narrow white bars on closed wing; below, chiefly white, barred

---

[1] Useful Birds and Their Protection, 1907, p. 253.

PLATE 50

PLATE 50

ARCTIC THREE–TOED WOODPECKER
Page 270

THREE–TOED WOODPECKER
Page 274

Adult Female

Adult Female

Adult Male

Adult Male

All about one-half scale.

Louis Agassiz Fuertes

on sides and flanks with black; four middle tail-feathers black, the rest mostly white, often with considerable black on 3rd; bill dark slate above, usually lighter below; iris reddish-brown to dark claret; legs and feet slate or slate-blue. *Adult female:* Similar, but yellow on top of head wanting and replaced by black. *Young in juvenal plumage:* Similar to adult male, but duller, and yellow crown-patch smaller and paler or sometimes wanting in female, but *supposed* to be always present in nestling female.

MEASUREMENTS. — Length 9.00 to 10.20 in.; spread 14.00 to 16.00; folded wing 4.50 to 5.50; tail 3.40 to 3.82; bill 1.20 to 1.60; tarsus .65 to .75.

MOLTS. — Young bird in nest assumes juvenal plumage which is probably completely shed in autumn, and first winter plumage, which seems identical with that of adults, assumed; adults have complete autumnal molt; only one molting (?) spring specimen examined; this had lost three tail-feathers May 23.

FIELD MARKS. — Size larger than Hairy Woodpecker, much smaller than Flicker; a "dark" bird — *i.e.* dark for a woodpecker; distinguished from other New England woodpeckers by black back without central white stripe; male shows large yellow spot on top of head.

VOICE. — "A sharp, shrill *chirk, chirk*" (Manly Hardy); call, or alarm note resembling that of Kingfisher (E. O. Grant); a call much like *w-e-e-a* frequently uttered, shrill and clear (O. W. Knight); a loud single call, like *click, click* (Charles B. Floyd); a low, single note *pert, week* or *tup* (Grinnell and Storer); a subdued *chip* at frequent intervals on occasion (F. H. Kennard), "as male was about to alight (near nest with young), female spread her wings and uttered a *whe-e-e-ee*. This call, which was at its loudest at its middle point, rose and then fell to the same pitch at which it was begun"; resembled the Flicker love-making (Lawrence Achilles); its chipping note was more like the Hermit's *chuck* than a woodpecker's note; it had also a cackling note (J. D. Smith).

BREEDING. — In coniferous forests, mostly spruce, larch, fir and cedar. *Nest:* A hole in live or dead tree or stub, beveled on lower edge, diameter of entrance about 1¾ to 2 inches, expanding to gourd shape and from 9 to 18 in. deep, lined with a few chips at bottom, and in some cases a little moss. *Eggs:* Usually 4, sometimes 5 or 6; .88 to 1.01 by .69 to .80 in.; ovate; white and moderately glossy; illustrated in Capen's "Oölogy of New England," Plate XIV, Fig. 11. *Dates:* May 23 to June 10, northern New York and New England. *Incubation:* Period about 14 days (Bendire); by both sexes. One brood yearly.

RANGE. — Northern North America, chiefly in Canadian and Hudsonian zones. Breeds from central Alaska, Yukon, southern Mackenzie, northern Manitoba, northern Ontario, southern Ungava (Quebec) and southern Labrador south to central-eastern California (in the Sierra Nevadas), northern Wyoming, South Dakota, northern Minnesota, northern Michigan, southeast central Ontario, northern New York, Vermont, central New Hampshire, Maine and Nova Scotia; south in winter erratically to Nebraska, southeastern Iowa, northeastern Illinois, northern Ohio, Pennsylvania, southeastern New York, Massachusetts, Connecticut and Rhode Island; accidental in northern Florida.

DISTRIBUTION IN NEW ENGLAND. — *Maine:* Rare to uncommon resident in northern and western counties; uncommon to common winter visitor. *New Hampshire:* Rare resident in northern part of state and above 3,000 feet in White Mountains and probable resident on some of the more southern mountains; uncommon winter visitor. *Vermont:* Rare resident in northern part and on higher mountains; occasional winter visitor. *Massachusetts:* Uncommon to rare winter visitor; occasionally well distributed; casual in summer, may breed casually on Mt. Greylock; recent summer record, Pelham, male seen June 30, 1921, at a distance of less than 12 feet.[1] *Rhode Island:* Very rare, irregular, winter visitor. *Connecticut:* Rare, irregular, winter visitor.

SEASON IN MASSACHUSETTS. — September 28 to May 23 (June 12, summer).

HAUNTS AND HABITS. The dark, sturdy, Arctic Three-toed Woodpecker comes to us in winter from dense coniferous Canadian forests. Comparatively few breed in north-

---

[1] Nice, Mrs. M. M.: *in litt.*

ern New England and although they are rarely seen in summer in western Massachusetts, we have no record of breeding in the state. While with us it seeks white pine woods that have been killed by fire, or isolated dead pine trees. The first or second year after trees have been killed by fire these woodpeckers come into a pine wood in numbers in pursuit of bark-beetles and wood-borers. In winter they usually work quietly, though at times they are vociferous. As a rule they are unsuspicious, and anyone may walk up close to a bird and watch it work. Mr. E. O. Grant tells me that while he was cutting into a dead tree, one of these birds, posted about six feet above his head, kept its position for several minutes. This species very often begins to work on the trunk near the foot of a tree; it sounds the bark with direct blows, and then, turning its head from side to side, strikes its beak slantingly into and under the bark, and flakes it off. It often works long on the same tree and barks the whole trunk in time, only occasionally working on the branches. Thus it exposes channels of bark-beetles and the holes made by borers. When the bird remains motionless, it is well concealed against the blackened bark of the burnt trees. It seems deliberate in its movements and appears to do its work thoroughly, as it often remains five to ten minutes on the same spot and then shifts only a little distance. In early autumn, while the grubs are still at work on the tree, it lays its head against the tree, at times, turning it first to one side and then to the other as if listening. In its summer home it does not always nest in trees. Major Mark Robinson, of Algonquin National Park, Ontario, reports that in the summer of 1922 a pair cut into a telephone pole and raised young in the cavity, and the next winter a male bird enlarged the same hole and occupied it. Mr. Charles L. Whittle informs me that this bird is very noisy and conspicuous on its breeding grounds. It climbs to the tops of tall trees there and calls loudly and often.

DIAGRAM OF LOWER MANDIBLE OF NESTLING ARCTIC THREE-TOED WOODPECKER. After Bates.

The cartilaginous process which widens the gape of many young birds, and which may be seen in the young of the flicker (Fig. 52, opposite page 293), reaches a high development in the present species. The late Frank A. Bates made a drawing of this peculiar formation as found on the living young of the Arctic Three-toed Woodpecker. This drawing was reproduced in his " Lake, Field and Forest," [1] and a copy of it may be seen in the appended cut. This process shrinks as the young one grows, and finally disappears when the bird is fully fledged. This woodpecker may appear in Massachusetts every winter in very small numbers, as I have records of individuals almost yearly for the past decade. Only an occasional winter, however, brings it in numbers.

It is difficult to determine exactly what causes these unusual migrations. They are not forced by inclement weather, for one at least has occurred in a mild winter. A scarcity of the seeds of coniferous trees, on which many arboreal birds feed in winter, apparently does not affect them, as they have come in a year of an abundant food supply,

[1] Lake, Field and Forest, 1899, p. 149.

when Pine Grosbeaks and Crossbills remained in the north. It seems probable that the unusual invasions of the species into New England follow summers when its food has been unusually abundant. An excessive food supply tends to fecundity, and overbreeding naturally compels expansion and induces migration, whether among the lower animals or humankind. Since the above was written, Mr. Josselyn Van Tyne has published a paper regarding the unusual flight of this species in 1923 [1] in which he advances a similar explanation. He says that between 1909 and 1914 there was an irruption of the spruce budworm in eastern Canada and Maine which resulted in the death of many trees and a consequent increase of bark-beetles and borers, followed by an increase in the number of these woodpeckers. On the other hand a scarcity of the usual food supply may cause migration. A wet season with few fires in the woods or a scarcity of insects (such as the spruce bud-moth) that kill trees might, later, cause a migration. When these periodical invasions occur in southern New England, the species is well distributed far and wide in autumn, but fewer return north in spring, and thus possibly congestion in the north is relieved by the casualties incident to migration, until another particularly favorable breeding season occurs. A great irruption of these birds occurred in the autumn of 1860. During the following winter Mr. George O. Welch often saw as many as six or eight at once in a piece of fire-killed pine timber in Lynn. Probably this never would have been recorded had not Mr. Brewster interviewed Mr. Welch and published the facts.[2] Probably there have been greater and lesser movements of this kind both before and since, but competent observers were few and there was no one to give publicity to these occurrences. In recent years with many observers in the field and hundreds of them reporting often, we have been able to get records of such movements. In the autumn of 1923, many of these birds appeared in Aroostook County, Maine, coming before the end of summer. Mr. E. O. Grant reported in October that they had been "about as common" there as the Hairy Woodpecker or the Downy. By late October they were distributed generally over northern New England and Massachusetts and a few had entered Rhode Island and Connecticut. Some appeared here in succeeding winters. In the autumn of 1925, there was a lesser movement, and many returned through New England in the spring of 1926. In the autumn of 1926 another considerable southward migration occurred.

Besides the insect food taken by the Arctic Three-toed Woodpecker which in quantity exceeds three-fourths of all its aliment, it takes some nuts or acorns, a little wild fruit, and about 10 per cent of its food is cambium from living trees.

ECONOMIC STATUS. The fact that this bird seems to feed largely on dead trees might indicate that it is of no economic value. It is well known, however, that if bark-beetles and wood-borers increase unduly, as they will if unchecked, they attack living trees. Professor F. E. L. Beal estimates that one of these woodpeckers will destroy annually over 13,000 wood-boring grubs. When the woodpeckers gather from afar to feed among dead trees, they must constitute a very potent check on the undue increase of these borers.

---

[1] Auk, Vol. XLIII, 1926, pp. 469–474.   [2] Bulletin of the Nuttall Ornithological Club, Vol. VIII, 1883, p. 122.

Picoides americânus americanus BREHM. Three-toed Woodpecker.

Other names: AMERICAN THREE-TOED WOODPECKER; BANDED-BACKED THREE-TOED WOODPECKER; "LADDER-BACK."

Plate 50.

DESCRIPTION. — Similar in shape to the preceding species. *Adult male:* Similar to adult male of Arctic Three-toed Woodpecker, but with more white and less black; above, black or bluish-black, marked with white; nasal tufts grayish, narrowly streaked black; forehead streaked black and white, often, more or less similar streaking about crown which is yellow; sides and back of head and back of neck mostly bluish-black to below eye and ear-coverts where a broad white streak runs back; an indistinct or broken wide streak of blackish from gape down side of jaw; sometimes a distinct, narrow line of white running from eye back over ear-coverts, and widening to a white patch on side of neck; *back, rump and upper tail-coverts distinctly marked with rather broad bars and cross-spots of white;* outer webs of primaries and some secondaries spotted with same, these spots appearing like irregular bars on closed wing, secondaries and tertials more or less marked (principally on inner webs) with white; two outer tail-feathers mostly white for terminal half or more, with some black markings and stained yellowish ends, white on the third less extensive, middle tail-feathers black or mostly black; below, white, but sides and flanks rather broadly barred black, and sides of breast also marked with broken bars or streaks; bill and feet grayish (or slate), feet sometimes with a greenish cast; iris claret-brown to dark red. *Adult female:* As male, but lacks yellow on crown, which usually is streaked with black and white, but sometimes entirely bluish-black. *Young in juvenal plumage (sexes similar):* Like adults, but with more or less yellow on crown in both sexes, usually less in female than in male.

MEASUREMENTS. — Length 8.00 to 9.75 in.; spread 13.00 to 15.25; folded wing 4.00 to 5.00; tail 3.00 to 3.75; bill 1.00 to 1.25; tarsus .60 to .75.

MOLTS. — Probably similar to those of Arctic Three-toed Woodpecker; no molting specimens examined.

FIELD MARKS. — Size near that of Hairy Woodpecker; distinguished from all other native woodpeckers by black and white barring down middle of black back; works commonly on dead spruce trees.

VOICE. — A call-note much like that of Arctic Three-toed Woodpecker; also a "squealing prolonged sound" similar to that made by a Yellow-bellied Sapsucker (Bendire); "a loud *quip* or *queep*, also shrill chatters"; well grown young in nest very noisy, may be heard 100 yards away (J. A. Farley).

BREEDING. — In northern coniferous forests, largely in timber killed by insects, fire or water. *Nest:* A hole, excavated by the birds, bevelled on lower edge, about 10 or 12 inches deep with entrance about 1½ inches in diameter, in spruce, larch, balsam or cedar tree, lined only with a few chips. *Eggs:* Usually 4; .90 to .95 by .65 to .70 in.; nearly elliptical to ovate; white; illustrated in Capen's "Oölogy of New England," Plate XIV, Fig. 12. *Dates:* Late May to June 8, northern New York; *Incubation:* Period probably about 14 days; by both sexes. One brood yearly.*

RANGE. — Canadian and Hudsonian zones of North America, chiefly east of the Rocky Mountains. Breeds in forested parts of its range north to about tree limit, from southern Mackenzie, northern Manitoba, northern Ungava (Quebec) and northern Labrador south to southern Manitoba, northern Minnesota, central Ontario, northern New York, northern Vermont, northern New Hampshire and central Maine and west to central Alberta and central southern Mackenzie; south irregularly in winter to southeastern British Columbia, central eastern Idaho, southern Wisconsin, northern Michigan, southern Ontario and Massachusetts; its place is taken in Alaska and in the western mountains by two other races of the species.

---

* Dr. C. Hart Merriam announced the first eggs of this bird known to science. The nest (June 4, 1878) was 8 feet up. (See Bulletin Nuttall Ornithological Club, Vol. III, 1878, p. 200.) A nest found in New Brunswick by Mr. J. A. Farley was also low down.

DISTRIBUTION IN NEW ENGLAND. — *Maine:* Rare resident in northern parts and on high elevations; rare to common winter visitor. *New Hampshire:* Rare resident in northern part of state and in mountains above 3,000 feet, south to Sandwich range; rare winter visitor. *Vermont:* Rare winter visitor and rarer resident.* *Massachusetts:* Rare and irregular winter visitor. One summer record for Williamstown (see Haunts and Habits below).

SEASON IN MASSACHUSETTS. — Autumn, winter and early spring.

HAUNTS AND HABITS. The Three-toed Woodpecker and the Arctic Three-toed are not rightly named, as the latter is a bird of more southern distribution than the former and neither of them are really Arctic birds. They should be known respectively as the Banded-backed Three-toed Woodpecker and the Black-backed Three-toed Woodpecker. These names, even now often used, distinguish them at once. They occupy for the most part the same region, take similar food and have similar habits, except that the Three-toed Woodpecker is perhaps more closely confined to the spruce growth or its neighborhood than the black-backed species. This may affect somewhat the winter distribution of the Three-toed Woodpecker in southern New England, where most of the spruce woods have been cut off and replaced by deciduous trees.

A small per cent of the food of the Three-toed Woodpecker consists of cambium. Probably most of this is taken in summer on its breeding-grounds, but Miss Caroline E. Hamilton of Greenfield, Massachusetts, observed in late September an individual that remained in a yard from daylight till dark, making the rounds of the trees and remaining longest on the fruit trees at the tiny holes attributed to Sapsuckers. She said that the bird seemed to find good food in these pits, and it may have been eating some of the cambium. Mr. Charles L. Whittle found that the behavior of this bird on its breeding-grounds was in strong contrast to that of the Arctic Three-toed Woodpecker. The former, he says, was very quiet and fed mostly from the ground to ten feet up the trunk. It moved slowly and its pecking was almost inaudible.

Mr. J. A. Farley reports that a pair of "Ladder-backs" whose nest he found in New Brunswick fed their young "daintily" rather than by the "stabbing" method so common with woodpeckers.

There is reason to believe that the Three-toed Woodpecker once bred more commonly in northern New England than it has since the original spruce growth was cut. There is still some old spruce left on Saddle Mountain and its highest peak, Mt. Greylock, near Williamstown, Massachusetts, where in August, 1919, Mr. William J. Cartwright, a careful observer, reported that he saw a pair of Three-toed Woodpeckers and two young feeding on a grub-infested tree. The birds were there for several days; the young were nearly full grown but were still fed by the adults. The birds were quite tame, could be closely approached and all their characteristic markings were noted. Their loud rattling notes, uttered frequently, attracted the attention of passersby. Several other

---

*Mr. G. H. Ross of Rutland has found both species of Three-toed Woodpecker on Mt. Pico in Sherburne, and Mr. Geo. L. Kirk, also of Rutland, found on June 12, 1912, a male *P. Americanus* apparently breeding on Mt. Horrid in Rochester. Mr. Kirk writes: "It is his (Mr. Ross') and my belief that these woodpeckers bred occasionally throughout the higher Green Mountains before the heavy growths of spruce were cut off, say prior to the late eighties."

observers saw them. This is the only summer record of this bird in Massachusetts that has come to my attention.

Mr. E. O. Grant, a faithful correspondent of Patten, Maine, travels over a considerable region and north into southern Quebec, spending much time in the woods. On March 6, 1922, he wrote that the spruce budworm had killed about thirty per cent of the spruce in that region and nearly all the fir, and that among the dead trees he saw hundreds of both the three-toed species, together with nearly equal numbers of Downy Woodpeckers and Hairy Woodpeckers. Food for the birds was very plentiful, as bark-beetles and spruce-borers were numerous. When an invasion of caterpillars strips coniferous trees and thus exposes their trunks and branches to the hot summer sun, bark-beetles attack and virtually girdle them with numerous tunnels beneath the bark; borers get in and sometimes most of the trees die. The woodpeckers, concentrating on these dead trees from all the forest round about, help to keep down the undue increase of bark-beetles and borers which, if they became too numerous, might attack some live trees. Mr. Grant believed that the birds were mating, as they were in pairs, and probably a number of them nested in that region in that year.

Economic Status. The Three-toed Woodpecker is a useful bird in the forest, but is too rare in most of New England to be of much service here.

Sphyrapícus várius varius (Linnæus). Yellow-bellied Sapsucker.

Other names: SAPSUCKER; YELLOW-BELLIED WOODPECKER.

Plate 51.

Description. — Bill about as long as head, not quite so stout as in the foregoing species, ridge curved slightly, and nasal tufts less dense; wing with very short first (spurious) primary; tail long-pointed. *Adult male in breeding plumage:* Above, black (with much greenish-blue gloss) much varied with white; *forehead and top of head "poppy-red" or crimson,* bordered on sides and behind by black (very rarely a narrow red crescent on nape similar to that on Red-naped Sapsucker but narrower), white stripe back from eye round nape broadening there into a band, another from white nasal tuft along jaw and side of neck; back spotted black and white, black often prevailing in center, white on sides; rump and tail-coverts black and white, white usually prevailing in center, black on sides; tail black, inner webs of middle tail-feathers white with several cross-spots or bars of black and narrow white edges to two outer feathers; scapulars and wings black, with large, longitudinal, white patch along wing-coverts, rows of white spots on outer webs of primaries and secondaries, tertials black and white toward ends and all other quill-feathers tipped narrowly white. *A large crimson throat-patch surrounded by black* which extends down on upper breast, forming large black patch, rounded posteriorly; elsewhere below chiefly brownish-white on sides and flanks where marked with V-shaped spots of black; under tail-coverts white or whitish, sometimes with a few black marks; bill usually blackish-brown; iris brown; legs and feet greenish-gray to olive-green. *Adult male in winter plumage:* Similar to breeding plumage but with most of the light-colored markings of back, neck and head light yellowish-olive or "light buffy yellowish-brown"; bill, sides and flanks more brownish and other under plumage deeper (more brownish) yellow. *Adult female:* Similar to adult male, but crimson of throat replaced by white and that of top of head restricted (or replaced entirely) by black; this feature very variable; in some individuals top of head black spotted with whitish; others variously marked there with yellow and crimson or "brownish-

PLATE 51

PLATE 51

NORTHERN PILEATED WOODPECKER
Page 281

ADULT MALE

YELLOW–BELLIED SAPSUCKE
Page 276

ADULT MALE

ADULT FEMALE

ADULT FEMALE

All about one-half scale.

Louis Agassiz Fuertes

orange." *Young in juvenal plumage (sexes similar)*: Without black on breast and usually no red on top of head; wings and tail as in fall adult; throat usually whitish, but in some males more or less red on both head and throat; elsewhere below yellowish-white obscured more or less by dusky cross-bars on each feather.

MEASUREMENTS. — Length 7.75 to 8.80 in.; spread 14.31 to 16.00; folded wing 4.62 to 5.20; tail 2.90 to 3.30; bill .80 to 1.08; tarsus .70 to 1.00. Weight (1 specimen) 1¾ oz. (B. H. Warren). Female smaller than male.

MOLTS. — According to Brewster, this species wears its juvenal plumage a long time, some birds taken in October and November still retaining some of it; probably there is a complete molt of this plumage, and birds are found molting all through winter and spring until June, when, apparently, all become as adults; adults have a molt of body feathers, especially about throat (January to spring) and complete molt in late summer and autumn.

FIELD MARKS. — Size nearly that of Hairy Woodpecker; our only woodpecker with forehead and top of head red, and upper breast black. *Male:* Distinguishable from all other New England Woodpeckers by *red crown and throat, large longitudinal patch of white on black wing and black* upper breast. *Females and young:* Lack the large crimson patch on throat; young recognized by their yellowish tints; their black wing with longitudinal white patch on coverts, like adults, and their general resemblance to adults in shape and habits.

VOICE. — A plaintive querulous squealing cry; "a sharp note like *huwy*," a whining *whäee;* other sounds resembling calls of Blue Jay and others those of Red-shouldered Hawk; in mating season *hoik-hoik* repeated a number of times (Bendire); call to mate at nest a low *yew-ick yew-ick*, spring call a ringing *cleur* repeated 5 or 6 times (Brewster); the cry, heard at a distance, is very hawk-like; besides his ordinary *squeal* the Sapsucker has some shorter notes, one of them like *click* often repeated; besides the "Red-shoulder" squeal, bird has other loud notes, utterly unlike the "squeal" and apparently belonging to the mating season (J. A. Farley); usually a rather silent bird in Massachusetts, especially in autumn, but noisy on its breeding grounds.

BREEDING. — In either coniferous, deciduous or mixed woods or in more open farm lands, often in swampy tracts near ponds or rivers where timber has been killed by flowage, or on islands in lakes or sea. *Nest:* A cavity excavated by both sexes in dead tree or stub, telegraph pole or even in sound wood in live tree; often large dead birches are chosen; entrance from 12 to 40 feet high, circular, from 1.25 to 1.60 inches in diameter, cavity usually gourd-shaped and from 6 to 18 in. deep, usually about 12. *Eggs:* 5 to 7; .81 to .92 by .64 to .69 in.; ovate to elliptical ovate, occasionally elliptical oval; white, slightly glossy; illustrated in Capen's "Oölogy of New England," Plate XIV, Fig. 13. *Dates:* May 18, Illinois; May 26, New York; May 15 to June 8, Maine. *Incubation:* Period probably about 14 days; by both sexes. One brood yearly.

RANGE. — Eastern North America, Mexico, West Indies and Central America. Breeds mainly in Canadian and Transition zones from central Mackenzie, northern Manitoba, northern Ontario, southern Quebec and Cape Breton Island south to central Missouri (casually), Iowa, central Indiana, northern Ohio, southern New York, northern New Jersey and western Massachusetts (casually Connecticut) and in Allegheny Mountains to southwestern North Carolina and west to Alberta, central North Dakota and western Iowa; in winter from Iowa and Michigan through northern tier of states to Massachusetts and south through Mexico and Central America to Costa Rica; also to Bahamas, Cuba and other West Indies, and Bermudas; casual in eastern Wyoming and eastern Colorado; accidental in southern Greenland.

DISTRIBUTION IN NEW ENGLAND. — *Maine:* Common migrant and common summer resident over most of the state. One winter record.[1] *New Hampshire:* Common migrant, and common summer resident in northern half up to about 3000 feet; not common summer resident in southern part; accidental in winter. *Vermont:* Common migrant and common summer resident, except in extreme southern

---

[1] Auk, Vol. XXXIV, 1918, pp. 353–354.

part where less common; accidental in winter. *Massachusetts:* Uncommon migrant, rather uncommon to rare summer resident in western counties, and casual in winter in eastern counties in mild seasons. *Rhode Island:* Uncommon migrant. *Connecticut:* Rare spring and uncommon fall migrant; casual in summer and winter; two breeding records (Winsted).

SEASON IN MASSACHUSETTS. — April 1 to May 10 (summer); September 10 to November (winter).

HAUNTS AND HABITS.   There is something mysterious about the movements of the Yellow-bellied Sapsucker in New England.   In some parts of the three northern states it is the most common woodpecker in the breeding season, but it is usually uncommon or rare in migrations in most parts of southern New England.   I remember particularly

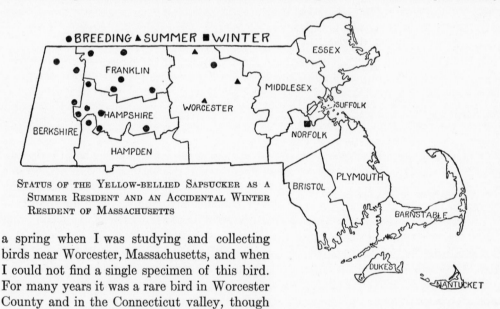

STATUS OF THE YELLOW-BELLIED SAPSUCKER AS A
SUMMER RESIDENT AND AN ACCIDENTAL WINTER
RESIDENT OF MASSACHUSETTS

a spring when I was studying and collecting birds near Worcester, Massachusetts, and when I could not find a single specimen of this bird. For many years it was a rare bird in Worcester County and in the Connecticut valley, though not so rare near the coast.   Either the majority of birds that breed in northern New England and the Maritime Provinces pass through southern New England in the night, or they keep well out of sight.   Nevertheless Dr. J. A. Allen said years ago in his Catalogue of Birds of Springfield,[1] that "they breed plentifully on the hills in western Massachusetts, twenty or thirty miles west of Springfield."

Enough of them visit these states to leave their marks on our orchards, and very rarely we hear of a tree that they have actually injured by persistently denuding it of small bits of bark; but I have heard of only one such case in 20 years in eastern Massachusetts. There never are sapsuckers enough here to do much harm.   My own experience with them here would indicate that they are usually hunting insects, going rapidly over the timber and passing quickly from tree to tree, working north or south according to the

---

[1] Proceedings, Essex Institute, 1864, p. 53.

season. They are addicted largely to the dexterous flycatcher habit and they "bound," as it were, through the air from one tree to another.

The sapsucker is a bird of temperament — of marked individuality. "A pair, seen busily getting insects for their young in a nest in a near-by sugar orchard in Rowe, did no woodpecker work *as such* — *i.e.*, no picking of bark. Instead they gleaned a good deal in and around the foliage of the apple trees in the orchard, like any Oscine that feeds in a tree — but with a most agile flight, with quick leaps and bounds, in and out of and around the tree, sticking 'on to' the bark now and then like any woodpecker; then in half a minute off again, into the leaves, first on one side of the tree and then on the other. They uttered now and then their squealing cry. They were strong, energetic, active birds — their wings often made a noise as they darted (or rather bounded) back and forth between their nest in the sap-orchard and the apple trees in the open" (J. A. Farley).

In the breeding season I have seen the mating birds drumming, and excavating their nesting holes. The young birds in the nest hiss like so many snakes! Mr. Harry E. Woods, of Huntington, Massachusetts, says that he watched a pair feeding their young on insects. Each insect was taken by the bird to a tree on which they had pecked a hole in the bark about the size of a quarter of a dollar where they seemed to soak the insect in sap before feeding it to the young.

The sapsucker, like others of the smaller woodpeckers, often makes a hole for its nest almost too small for the bird to squeeze through. Is this ever done with a purpose? Mr. J. A. Farley tells of a sapsucker's nest that he found in a New Hampshire sugar orchard that may illustrate this point. The nest hole was high up in a dead branch in the center of a large maple. There were three holes on the same side of the stub — one above the other and all within three feet, two of them being new. The top (new) hole was small and the bottom (new) hole was smaller still so that the male sapsucker had great difficulty in squeezing into it. The middle (old) hole was rather larger as would be expected after probable squirrel-occupancy and the action of the elements. The upper hole was tenanted by flying squirrels. "The small size of the new holes may be explained, perhaps, by the fact of the squirrel's presence. Probably the upper hole was dug first by the woodpeckers only to be stolen from them by the squirrels. Then the birds dug the third or lowest hole with still smaller diameter."

The sapsucker, like other woodpeckers, is very fond of drumming on some resonant substance, such as a dry limb, tin roof, eaves-trough or conductor. Mr. D. W. Sweet says that one of its favorite pastimes is to tap on telephone wires and then "listen to the sound of the vibration." Once upon hearing what sounded like a cowbell in the woods, he investigated and found one of these birds tapping on a tin dipper hung on a small hemlock by a spring. He found another bird rapping upon a round disk of tin that had been hung on a tree for a target.[1]

Doubtless like other woodpeckers the sapsucker is fond of its bath. Mr. W. H. Robb, of Montreal, tells me that he observed one on several occasions lying on a shingled

---

[1] Journal of the Maine Ornithological Society, Vol. X, 1908, p. 89.

roof with feathers ruffed and wings spread as if sunning itself or drying its feathers.   He says that the bird was seen each time on the same spot on the roof.

In the south I have seen the sapsuckers' work on the southern pine and have examined many fine trees that they have saved from bark beetles.   Most of the trees in Massachusetts that are marked with their characteristic pits seem not to have been injured thereby. These are chiefly fruit trees, which continue to remain thrifty and bear well.   I refer now to the rings of perforations, somewhat similar to those attributed elsewhere to the Downy Woodpecker.   However, these pits, if driven into the sapwood, may injure its appearance by providing openings for the entrance of fungus growths, and may result in dark spots which detract from its value for ornamental purposes.   But there is another kind of sapsucker work where the bird pecks out larger holes, often roughly rectangular or triangular in shape.   In some cases the bird so injures the bark over large areas that the remaining bark between the holes dries out, and if these punctured areas extend entirely around the trunk, the tree is girdled, and it dies.   Instances of trees killed have been noted in northern New England and also in the south where the species spends the winter. Sometimes valuable shade trees and timber trees are thus destroyed.   It seems that if an individual once gets the habit of visiting a favorite tree, it continues to feast on either insects drawn to it, sap, or cambium (one or all) until the tree either dies or becomes so enfeebled that the bird prefers some more vigorous subject.   Sometimes it clings motionless beside a hole it has made on its favorite birch or maple.   From this hole or boring the sap usually flows freely, dripping frequently or even running down in a little rivulet. Usually there are several punctured trees in a sapsucker "orchard," and the birds, young as well as adults, come to them at frequent intervals throughout the day.   Various other creatures, as hummingbirds, chipmunks and red squirrels, and many insects are drawn to the tree to feast on the sap.   The Yellow-bellied Sapsucker has been seen to eat ice which had formed where sap had trickled down and frozen.   There is an excellent article on the habits of this species by Brewster in the Bulletin of the Nuttall Ornithological Club (Vol. I, 1876, pp. 63–70); another by Dr. C. Hart Merriam (Vol. IV, 1879, of the same bulletin, pp. 1–6); another by Frank Bolles (Auk, Vol. VIII, 1891, pp. 256–270); and another, with excellent cuts showing borings, by C. W. Lovel, and another in Bird-Lore (Vol. XVII, 1915, pp. 301–307).

ECONOMIC STATUS.   The annual injury to trees caused by sapsuckers in the United States is so serious that my friend, Mr. W. L. McAtee, of the Biological Survey, has estimated it at one and a quarter million dollars.   This damage is caused more by injury to the wood which impairs its value as lumber than by the actual destruction of trees which probably is serious only locally where sapsuckers are numerous.   This injury also is divided among four forms of sapsuckers of which the Yellow-bellied Sapsucker seems to be the chief offender because of its wide distribution.   In New England, however, the chief injury occurs on the breeding grounds of the species in the three northern states, and I have no information that it is serious even there except locally to a few trees.   The bird is not common enough in southern New England to commit any serious depredations.

Phlœótomus pileátus abietícola (Bangs). Northern Pileated Woodpecker.*

Other names: BLACK WOODPECKER; LOG–COCK; BLACK COCK OF THE WOODS.

Plate 51.

DESCRIPTION. — Largest New England woodpecker; bill as long as head or longer, broader than high at base, nostrils concealed by tufts; head not unusually large, conspicuously crested, and neck small by comparison; wings ample; tail bent downward at tip; prominent scales on front of tarsus and upper sides of toes. *Adult male:* General color very dark, dusky sooty-brown or brownish-black, some feather-edges almost slaty; tufts over nostrils corn color or whitish; forehead, whole top of crested head and wide stripe from base of lower mandible along side of jaw poppy-red, rather narrow stripe from above eye to near nape, another wider from base of upper mandible, which, beginning at nostril-tufts and passing below eye, widens toward back of head where merged into a wide stripe down side of neck and breast, chin, throat, large conspicuous markings on primary coverts and outer secondaries, all axillars, wing linings, basal half of primaries and tips of some outer ones, white; white on throat, primaries and under wings often tinted more or less yellowish or pale yellow; feathers of sides and flanks margined terminally white; rest of plumage, including stripe from near nostril-tufts to and under eye, widening behind eye and narrowing toward back of head, dusky brownish-black, somewhat lighter below; bill dark slate to slaty-blue above, usually lighter below; iris pale or light yellow to cream yellow or orange; scales of legs and feet black. *Adult female:* Similar to male, but whole forehead and forepart of crown olive-brown or grayish-brown, about half of terminal part of crest red, and red stripe along jaw replaced by dusky. *Young male in juvenal plumage:* Similar to adult male, usually more white tips to feathers below, but red of head paler and duller and that of forepart of crown and of jaw less uniform; general color of dark plumage lighter and more sooty. Some show a few pale feather-tips on back. *Young female in juvenal plumage:* Similar to young male but forehead and forepart of crown and jaw more like those of adult female; fore crown with paler edging at end of each feather.

MEASUREMENTS. — Length 16.38 to 19.50 in.; spread 28.00 to 30.05; wing 8.50 to 10.00; tail 6.50 to 7.50; bill 2.10 to 2.65; tarsus 1.20 to 1.40. Weight 10 to 16 oz. Female smaller than male.

MOLTS. — Young hatched naked; juvenal plumage develops in the nest. Adults have a complete postnuptial molt (August to September). No evidence of spring molt in birds examined.

FIELD MARKS. — Size larger than Dove, approaching Crow; appears black with long red crest, slim neck, white stripe on head and neck and white markings in and under wing, which are conspicuous in flight which is either on one plane or (if the bird so wills) undulating like that of Flicker, but in longer undulations and with less up and down motion; "white wing-area shows so plainly that one may often discover the bird flying at a distance by the heliostatic flashes of white" (T. Gilbert Pearson).

VOICE. — An oft-repeated cry like the *wicker* or *wake-up* of the Flicker, but a little louder and a little more musical and given a little more slowly; ordinary call a loud *cäck-cäck-cäck* (Bendire); note of anger or alarm *ha-hi, ha-hi;* a love note *a-wuck a-wuck* (H. Nehrling); a loud *kuk kuk* (Manley B. Townsend); a loud, repeated call *kŭ, kŭ, kŭ, kŭ* (A. C. Bagg); not so high-pitched as Flicker's call (J. A. Farley).

BREEDING. — Usually in forests of heavy timber, but often in second growth, deciduous, coniferous or mixed woods. *Nest:* A hole excavated in a trunk or stub from 12 to 60 feet from ground with entrance 3 to 4 inches in diameter, cavity extending down from 12 to 30 inches, lined with chips or rarely a little sand also. *Eggs:* 3 to 6; small for size of bird, 1.23 to 1.50 by .90 to 1.04 in.; usually ovate; white and very glossy; egg of Pileated Woodpecker illustrated in Bendire's "Life Histories of North American Birds," Vol. II, Plate I, Fig. 5. *Dates:* May 1 to 25, New York; May 17, Vermont; May 11 to 28, Maine. *Incubation:* Period 18 days (Burns); probably by both sexes. One brood yearly.

RANGE. — Forested regions of eastern and central North America in Canadian, Transition and north-ernmost upper Austral zones, from southern Mackenzie, northern Manitoba, northern Ontario, southern

---

* Feathers of *pileum* elongated and erectile. In other words, a Crested Woodpecker.

Quebec, Nova Scotia and Newfoundland south to Iowa, northern Indiana, northern Ohio, West Virginia, Pennsylvania, New Jersey, Connecticut and Rhode Island and west to Alberta, Montana, western South Dakota and eastern Nebraska. Breeds in forests of most of its range; little southward migration in winter, even in the north.

DISTRIBUTION IN NEW ENGLAND. — *Maine:* Common to very rare resident according to locality; most common in wilder or heavily forested regions. *New Hampshire:* Rare resident in southern more open lands; not rare in northern forested hills. *Vermont:* Rather rare resident, found mostly in forested hills. *Massachusetts:* Uncommon to rare resident in north-central and western wooded sections; casual or accidental winter visitor in southeastern parts. *Rhode Island:* Casual or accidental winter visitor; a single record on Block Island. *Connecticut:* Very rare resident in western forested hill country; less rare winter visitor in same region.

SEASON IN MASSACHUSETTS. — Permanent resident as noted above; may appear *anywhere in winter*, but not yet reported on Cape Cod.

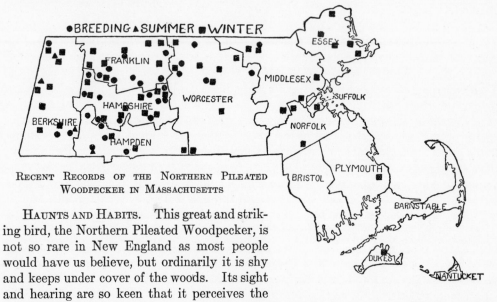

RECENT RECORDS OF THE NORTHERN PILEATED WOODPECKER IN MASSACHUSETTS

HAUNTS AND HABITS. This great and striking bird, the Northern Pileated Woodpecker, is not so rare in New England as most people would have us believe, but ordinarily it is shy and keeps under cover of the woods. Its sight and hearing are so keen that it perceives the approach of a man at a distance and slips quietly away before it is seen, and its notes so closely resemble those of the Northern Flicker that few people recognize them, and so the bird escapes notice.

To see this fine bird to advantage one should rise with the lark and embark upon some slow stream that flows through its favorite haunts. Such a place may be found in the lower reaches of Sandy Stream near where it empties into Little Carry Pond, in the great woods of Somerset County, Maine. A slow-flowing watercourse, its borders clogged with duckweed and lily pads, it lies calm and clear at daybreak on a September morning, unruffled by the light breeze that barely fans the cheek. The east fore-shore is low and swampy and screened by water brush. Skeletons of dead trees show bleached and white against the dark green background of the spruces whose slim spires rise high against the rosy light of coming dawn. The remains of an old beaver-house lie near the low shore. Beyond the farther bank a high ridge looms where grows a forest of spruce, fir, birch, beech and maple, where the trees have clasped great rocks with their gnarled roots and thrust them deep into the crevices of the ledge. Upstream trout leap and play. Deer have waded along the margin, leaving their footprints in the soft earth, and to the east on a low ridge denuded by the lumberman an immense black bear has cleared away the blueberries from many a patch of low bushes. A Canada porcupine comes down to drink at the water's edge. In the woods giant trees lie strewn along the ledge where storm winds have thrown them — their great roots flung high, their tops and branches crushed and torn. Beside these relics of decay springs perennial life from the earth, clothing the rocks in greenery. Here above the murmur of the rising breeze comes the sharp rattle of the great black woodpecker followed by his flicker-like call. Soon the fine bird rises above the tree-tops and alights on a tall slim stub, the remains of a monarch of the primeval forest, towering far above the lesser trees of to-day. Clearly revealed in the rays of the rising sun the bird erects his blazing crest, and, with head drawn far back, scales his watchtower to the very top. Once he opens a wing as if to flash its conspicuous white markings. Then he springs away, and with diagonal flight slides easily down the air to a low tree on the eastern shore, showing the great white area under his wings to fine advantage as he passes over the stream. Now he calls to his mate, and she soon rises above the trees, alights on the same tall stub that he has just left, and goes through a performance similar to his own. In flight the wings are spread for a brief instant while the bird sails; then they are struck swiftly far downward for propulsion. They never seem to rise much above the body, and usually the bird does not undulate in flight like other woodpeckers but steadily keeps to its plane. It can bound through the air, however, at will.

Unless one seeks for a good outlook, he might wander for days in the Maine woods without seeing one of these woodpeckers. However, he need not go to Maine to see the bird, as it is now less rare in Massachusetts than it was ten years ago. With the cutting off of the primeval forests in New England and the later increase of gunners this bird decreased rapidly, but now as it has become accustomed to live among smaller trees and as it is more strictly protected than formerly, it is coming back into the region of its former abundance. Within the past five years the increase in numbers of the "log-cock" has been noticeable, and now there are towns in Massachusetts even east of the Connecticut River where the bird sometimes is more common than the Hairy Woodpecker, and it has become more confiding than formerly, coming into orchards and even to houses where it has been known to help itself to suet hung up for smaller woodpeckers and Chickadees. It has bred in recent years through our northern and western counties east to Middlesex and has even begun breeding rarely again in the hills of northern Connecticut. No doubt the abandonment of many unproductive farms among the hills of New England which have since grown up to woods has had something to do with the recent increase of the species here and elsewhere in its range.

Although this bird is supposed to be non-migratory, probably there is some slight migration southward in autumn and a return in spring. At Algonquin National Park, Ontario, the species increases in winter, while in southern New England near the southern part of its range it seems also to increase in numbers at that season. The fact that the bird has been seen recently on Block Island and Marthas Vineyard proves that it migrates to a limited extent.

In spring the "log-cock" seeks its well-remembered nesting-place. Year after year it returns to the same place to breed. In early spring the bird becomes loquacious and like other drumming woodpeckers rattles away with its bill on some resonant hollow stub or limb. Its masterly roll is one of the notable sounds of spring, but during the breeding season it is quiet and secretive in the vicinity of its nest.

The following graphic description of its courtship was given me in 1921 by the late Miss Inez A. Howe, formerly of the Fairbanks Museum at St. Johnsbury, Vermont: "On the morning of April 23, . . . two Pileated Woodpeckers met in a tree-top, their wings spread at full width, and they danced and balanced before each other and bowed to each other, then they alighted on a branch and apparently fed or kissed each other, and then repeated the performance. Their long necks and the opening and closing wings showing the silvery lining made a pretty sight against the sky; their performances were most charming. After alighting they wheeled in the air and went through the prettiest circles with fluttering wings; you could hardly see the motion of the wings, they moved so rapidly. They kept up their characteristic call. This call is much like the flicker's *wicker wicker*, only louder, clearer, higher in pitch, sharper and more musical. They raised and lowered their crests, which were up high and pointed almost forward when the birds were in the air, but after they alighted the crests were lowered when the birds were in action, and then as they flew, the crests and wings seemed to enlarge to twice their usual size. They went through the performance three times, alighted twice, and the third time, after they circled and sang, they flew off to a higher tree on the hill, perhaps looking for a breeding place."

The Northern Pileated Woodpecker does not always make its nest hole *high* in a tree, although the taking of its eggs is still usually, to quote the late Dr. Elliott Coues, "something of an exploit." It seems rather careless of the safety of its nest, as it scatters many chips beneath the entrance or near by, though it also carries many more to a distance; also it seems rather indifferent when its eggs are taken. Dr. William L. Ralph (quoted by Bendire[1]) tells how a Florida woodpecker of this species deceived him by dropping chips out of the entrance to its nest whenever he came near it, causing him to believe that the excavation was still unfinished, so that when he finally made a closer investigation he found in the nest some young birds nearly grown. The female must have had eggs when he first discovered the nest.

This woodpecker not only digs out a nesting hole in a tree but it excavates another for shelter in winter. The bird is so large, swift and strong that it has little to fear from most hawks and its habit of sleeping in a tree-hole at night probably protects it from

---

[1] Bendire, Charles: Life Histories of North American Birds, Vol. I, 1895, p. 106.

owls in winter. The following incident related to Bendire by Manly Hardy exhibits the quickness of this bird, its fearlessness and its dexterity in avoiding its enemies:

"I once saw a Sharp-shinned Hawk persecute a pair of these Woodpeckers most persistently. They spent considerable of their time on some dead hemlocks close to my camp, and while busily at work the little Hawk would dart at one and follow him with his legs stretched out as if to seize him, all the time uttering a 'ca-ca-ca' to scare him. When the Woodpecker alighted and faced him from behind a tree, the former would also alight close by on some convenient limb, ready to repeat the performance as soon as the other commenced to work again. Sometimes the Woodpecker, instead of flying, would sidle around the body of the tree, and the Hawk would occasionally follow him twice entirely around before alighting to take a rest, only to make a fiercer dash next time. On some days this performance would be continued for at least an hour at a time, and the Hawk seemed to put in all the time he could spare from getting a living in annoying these birds. It was very evident, however, that he dared not seize one, as he easily could have done had he wished to do so. One would hardly think that a Pileated Woodpecker could catch on the side of a tree, swing his body around, and present his bill to the Hawk so quickly, but I saw this done dozens of times. The Sharp-shinned Hawk reminded me of some people who never can bear to see others getting an honest living." [1]

Pileated Woodpeckers are such powerful birds that they can split off large slabs from decaying stumps, strip bushels of bark from dead trees, and chisel out large holes in either sound, dead or decaying wood. They like to strip the bark from dead pines, spruces and especially hemlocks. Their size and strength and their long spear-like tongues enable them to penetrate large trees and draw out borers from the very heart of the tree. In a letter to me Mr. Charles L. Whittle describes as follows the work of a bird of this species in a wild cherry tree near Peterboro, New Hampshire, on September 25, 1920: "I watched a female bird at work for about fifteen minutes. She was directing her attack against a dying and no doubt infested limb. Chips and bark flew in every direction. She scaled the bark off the limb by powerful tangential blows. Finally a favorable point of attack was uncovered which received sledge-hammer blows in rapid succession, the bird swinging her head through an arc of at least eight inches in length. Her whole body was brought into play at times, the feet only remaining motionless; at last the larvæ were uncovered and silence reigned while they were being extracted."

The following passage by Mr. Sanford Richie gives a graphic description of the bird at work:

"But as we pushed farther into the heavy timber growth there suddenly rung out upon the frosty air a sound like the stroke of a woodchopper's ax-driven poll on to the bole of a tree. The familiar sound was repeated at intervals, and cautiously approaching the spot we were soon enabled to locate the author of it in the presence of a magnificent specimen of the Pileated Woodpecker (*Ceophlœus pileatus*). The bird, which was a male, appeared to be engaged in the business of stripping a dead pine of its bark, and we reck-

---

[1] Bendire, Charles: Life Histories of North American Birds, Vol. I, 1895, p. 104.

oned he would soon be out of a job, at least so far as that tree was concerned, if the strips and sheets of bark that covered the snow about the base of the tree afforded any fact, that could be used as a basis for our calculations. He would draw back the head to the fullest extent of the long neck and strike several powerful blows with that heavy wedge-shaped bill which usually resulted in a section of bark starting from the wood, when the bill would be inserted in the cavity as a lever, and a good sized portion of the outer covering of the tree would be removed and allowed to fall to the snow below. Sometimes a smaller loosened section would be caught by its edge with the bill and with a sudden, dexterous jerking movement of the head it would be thrown several feet from the tree." [1]

Says Dr. T. Gilbert Pearson [2] "I once measured a combination chip and splinter more than 14 inches in length."

Though a forest recluse this bird sometimes courts the companionship of other species. Mr. E. O. Grant tells me that he saw one working side by side with a Black-backed Three-toed Woodpecker, and when the smaller bird flew to another tree the log-cock followed it.

The food of the Northern Pileated Woodpecker consists chiefly of beetles and their larvæ, mostly wood borers and ants. They eat enormous numbers of both. Professor Beal records that in three stomachs of this species, ants which aggregate 6,680 were found. These ants are chiefly species like the carpenter ant, which eat the wood of trees, working in from the ground about their roots; therefore this woodpecker is often seen at work on or near the ground at the base of a tree. Other insects such as flies, caterpillars and cockroaches seem to be taken incidentally. The bird eats comparatively little vegetal food, chiefly wild berries, unfit for human food, and blueberries and wild cherries of which it is very fond. Rarely the bird finds a cultivated cherry tree.

ECONOMIC STATUS. The Northern Pileated Woodpecker takes its food chiefly from the forest and does no injury to the farmer or the horticulturist. It sometimes bores large holes into trees, apparently sound, but such trees are infested by borers or ants, and the work of the woodpecker in such a case often saves the tree from complete destruction. Its abandoned domiciles serve as nesting places for the Wood Duck, Bufflehead, Hooded Merganser, and possibly for the Golden-eye also. Therefore it plays a part in the conservation of these game-birds. The bird is useful and picturesque and an asset to any forested region. It should be protected everywhere by law and public sentiment.

Melanérpes erythrocéphalus (LINNÆUS). Red-headed Woodpecker.

Plate 52.

DESCRIPTION. — Bill slightly convex in profile above and below; colors of plumage chiefly in masses, not spotted, barred or streaked as in foregoing species. *Adults (sexes alike)*: Head, neck and part of upper breast bright crimson, margined by a narrow band of black across breast, usually more or less concealed by overlapping red feathers; back, scapulars, wing-coverts, primaries, part of first secondary and tail chiefly black, glossed bluish-black on back, scapulars and edges of wing-coverts (some inner primaries sometimes have white tips); rump, upper tail-coverts, tertials, secondaries, all under plumage from upper

---

[1] The Journal of the Maine Ornithological Society, Vol. V, 1903, p. 32.   [2] Bird-Lore, Vol. XIX, 1917, p. 365.

PLATE 52

PLATE 52

RED–BELLIED WOODPECKER
Page 290

RED–HEADED WOODPECKER
Page 286

IMMATURE

ADULT MALE

ADULT FEMALE

ADULT

NORTHERN FLICKER
Page 292

ADULT FEMALE

ADULT MALE

All about one-half scale.

breast to tail, and tips of all except 2 to 4 middle tail-feathers white; shafts of tertials and secondaries black; white of belly usually tinged yellowish or reddish; shafts and bases of secondaries black, but bases mostly concealed; wing linings mostly white, black on outer edge; bill light-bluish to bluish-gray or lead color, dark at tip and on ridge, lightening toward base, sometimes becoming bluish-white there; iris brown, chestnut or hazel; legs and feet greenish-gray or "olive-blue." *Young in juvenal plumage (sexes alike)*: Unlike adults; red parts of adults replaced by grayish-brown or brownish-gray spotted above and streaked below with darker or blackish (sometimes with more or less red on hind-head or sides of head); back, scapulars and wing-coverts black, the feathers margined and tipped pale gray or brownish-gray; primaries black or blackish; secondaries and tertials chiefly white with one or two blackish bands toward ends; tertials more or less marked or invaded basally with black; white parts below dull or shaded with brownish-gray or grayish-brown; sides and flanks and sometimes breast more or less streaked dusky; otherwise much as adults.

MEASUREMENTS. — Length 8.50 to 9.75 in.; spread 16.00 to 18.00; folded wing 5.00 to 5.70; tail 3.30 to 3.75; bill 1.03 to 1.15; tarsus about .85. Female usually smaller than male.

MOLTS. — There seems to be no distinctive first winter plumage; a complete molt between fall and spring renews the plumage so that gradually red comes in on head, neck and breast, black of black parts becomes more intense, bluish or greenish gloss on back and wing-coverts appears, and the bird in its first spring becomes much as adult though some individuals retain some black on tertials until next autumn; adults apparently have a partial (?) molt in spring and a complete autumnal (August and September) molt.

FIELD MARKS. — Size about that of Hairy Woodpecker. *Adult:* Our only black and white bird *with a red head and neck. Young:* The only native woodpecker with white rump and *upper tail-coverts;* flickers have white rumps but tail-coverts conspicuously spotted black and are much larger.

VOICE. — Call note a loud *tchur-tchur;* when chasing each other a shrill *chärr-chärr,* a harsh rattling alarm note (Bendire); and another like that of the tree-frog, *Hyla arborea* (Otto Widmann); loud calls *quee-o-que-o-queer"* or *yarrow, yarrow, yarrow* (W. L. Dawson); the characteristic *ker-r-r-ruck, ker-ruck-ruck-ruck* (C. Hart Merriam); the voice is quite hen-like in character (J. A. Farley).

BREEDING. — In forests or open woodlands or farming country, wherever trees or standing poles may be found. *Nest:* A gourd-shaped cavity in a dead tree-top, dead branch, stub, stump, post or pole at almost any height from ground; entrance about 1¾ in. in diameter; depth 10 to 18 in. lined with a few chips; on prairies where trees are scarce nests "under the roofs of houses or in any dark corner it can find" (Bendire). *Eggs:* 4 to 6; .90 to 1.15 by .71 to .90 in.; ovate; white and somewhat glossy; illustrated in Capen's "Oölogy of New England," Plate XIV, Fig. 14. *Dates:* May 28 to June 17, southern New England. *Incubation:* Period 14 days (Burns); by both sexes. One brood ordinarily, sometimes two.

RANGE. — Transition and Austral zones from near central Alberta, southwestern Saskatchewan, southern Manitoba, southeastern Ontario, northern New York, New England and (casually) southern Quebec, New Brunswick and Nova Scotia south to northern New Mexico, southern Texas, the Gulf coast and southern Florida and west to southeastern British Columbia, western Montana, Wyoming, Colorado; casually Utah and Arizona; irregularly migratory in northern parts of this range.

DISTRIBUTION IN NEW ENGLAND. — *Maine:* Rare, irregular straggler, chiefly in spring and fall; has bred near Portland,* very rare in winter. *New Hampshire:* Rare, irregular summer and fall visitors mostly in southern part; undoubtedly breeds; a winter record. *Vermont:* Uncommon to rare summer resident eastward but more common in western part, especially in valleys; occasionally a few winter. *Massachusetts:* Rare, irregular visitor at all seasons, breeding casually; less rare summer resident in western counties but apparently decreasing in recent years, formerly much more common. *Rhode Island:* Irregular visitor; has bred. *Connecticut:* Irregular visitor at all seasons and rare summer resident, formerly more common.

SEASON IN MASSACHUSETTS. — May be seen casually at any season, but apparently not a permanent resident.

---

* The first breeding record for Maine, July 4, 1926, Herbert Haven, Maine Naturalist, Vol. VI, 1926, p. 160.

HAUNTS AND HABITS.   The Red-headed Woodpecker is the handsomest and most conspicuous of our woodpeckers.   It is the bird that first excited the ardor of Alexander
Wilson by its splendid colors and inspired him with the ambition to become an ornithologist.

On the island of Naushon there exists to-day one of the last tracts of primeval forest
in New England.   Great beech and oak trees stand as they have stood through the centuries while still older trees, now fallen, lie prone on the forest floor.   There the deer
wander in small bands as they roamed in the days of the red Indian.   So abundant are

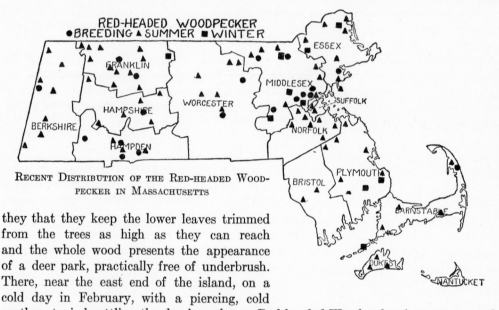

RECENT DISTRIBUTION OF THE RED-HEADED WOOD-
PECKER IN MASSACHUSETTS

they that they keep the lower leaves trimmed
from the trees as high as they can reach
and the whole wood presents the appearance
of a deer park, practically free of underbrush.
There, near the east end of the island, on a
cold day in February, with a piercing, cold
northwest wind rattling the dry branches, a Red-headed Woodpecker in a sunny nook
tapped away as merrily on a dead branch as if summer zephyrs were blowing.

Unlike most woodpeckers the Red-head migrates far and wide.   There is a flight
southward in autumn, but when the beechnut crop is large the Red-heads remain in considerable numbers in the north.   In the autumn of 1881 they were abundant in many
parts of Massachusetts and Connecticut and on Long Island and many remained through
the winter.   They are likely to migrate in any direction toward abundant beechnuts
which are their favorite food.   The primeval beech and oak forest on Naushon probably
was the attraction that had influenced one hardy bird to remain there alone through a
New England winter, while most individuals of the species were enjoying a vacation in
a southern clime.   It seems probable that the Red-head mates for life as pairs are seen
together all winter in their southern retreats.   In the early part of the last century when
my uncle, the Rev. T. B. Forbush, was a boy, this bird was common in Massachusetts as

far east as Worcester County. As he had traveled over the entire country, he was well acquainted with the bird. Nuttall, writing about the same period, said that the bird was "rarely seen in the maritime parts of Massachusetts, but was said to be as common in the western part as in the middle states." It has gradually retired westward. Old residents of Berkshire county informed me that years ago it was once a common breeding bird there, where locally it was not uncommon as late as 1860.* It has grown less and less common meantime in New York State though still regarded as locally common in central-western Vermont, but old residents in the last century said that it was once common throughout that state.

This bird is the most striking of our woodpeckers, clothed in red, white and blue. With the dark blue gloss of its back appearing black at a distance and its colors in masses and strongly contrasted, it is a conspicuous bird. To-day throughout Massachusetts its presence is mostly traditional, and many people still apply the name Red-headed Woodpecker to any woodpecker with red on its head. Here the bird is seen chiefly in open woodlands or among orchard or shade trees. It spends much of its time in the usual woodpecker-like activities and much also in flying to the ground for insects and in fly-catching, for it takes many insects in the air.

It is a rather noisy bird during the breeding season, and often the sexes pursue one another with loud cries and excited flutterings. At times they are active and playful and amuse themselves with drumming on various objects; at other times they are quiet and sedentary. In searching a tree trunk for wood-boring insects this woodpecker gives it a few smart raps here and there, and then turns the head as if to listen. When apparently satisfied it attacks the bark or wood and drills directly to the lurking grub.

The food of the Red-head consists of about one-third animal and two-thirds vegetal matter, and both are eaten at all seasons of the year as they can be obtained. When acorns or beechnuts are abundant, this bird feeds mainly on them, and in the summer and autumn it eats much fruit and some corn. Occasionally it destroys the eggs or young of other birds, but destructive insects constitute the major part of its animal food. It has a habit of storing beechnuts and acorns for future use, tucking them away under loose bark, in cracks, knot holes and cavities of trees where quantities are stored with, occasionally, a little corn. Sometimes insects such as grasshoppers are similarly stored.

ECONOMIC STATUS. Besides several species of wild fruit that the Red-head takes, which are of no economic value, it eats apples, pears, cherries, grapes, strawberries, raspberries and blackberries and sometimes takes quantities of them. Its destruction of the eggs and young of other birds probably seldom is serious. It may occasionally kill a small chicken or duckling or eat the eggs of poultry or consume eggs or young of some game bird, but the evidence to that effect is almost negligible. On the other hand nearly one-third of its food consists of pests, such as borers, May beetles, grasshoppers, ants and

---

* In the early fall of 1894 a flock of about 50 Red-headed Woodpeckers in Springfield "for several days" were literally a "sight to behold." The veteran Robert O. Morris, referring to this visitation, says: "Heretofore these birds have not been observed here except occasionally singly or, more rarely, in pairs" (Auk, Vol. XII, 1895, p. 86).

weevils.   On the whole, although the bird does some damage, its benefactions to mankind probably exceed considerably its injurious habits, and it should not be stigmatized as an injurious bird.

Centúrus carolínus (Linnæus).   Red-bellied Woodpecker.

Plate 52.

DESCRIPTION. — Similar in shape to Red-headed Woodpecker but somewhat larger and quite differently colored.   *Adult male:* Whole top and back of head, nape and back of neck bright poppy-red or scarlet; nasal tufts usually similar in color or paler (sometimes dull whitish or dusky); back, scapulars and wings, except primaries, barred black and white, the white bars usually narrowest; primaries more or less margined white toward tips or tipped white, also white basally; paired white spots on inner and outer webs of secondaries; upper tail-coverts chiefly white; tail black, with one or two outer feathers barred white, inner webs of middle feathers white with black spots, and outer webs with white stripe next shaft; sides of head, and lower plumage usually grayish-white or pale brownish-gray, passing into red in middle of belly and sometimes into pale red on sides of head and on chin, and into white or yellowish-white on flanks and under tail-coverts which are more or less marked with black; some specimens quite dusky below from contact with burnt trees; bill blackish or slaty, sometimes light grayish at base below; iris dark red or brownish-red to scarlet; legs and feet olive or grayish-green, "greenish-blue" (N. S. Goss).   *Adult female:* Similar to male but top of head gray, paling toward bill, and often intermixed with black behind, only nape and back of neck scarlet, nasal bristles and forehead usually tinted reddish; red of belly usually more restricted and much paler (a few individuals sparsely sprinkled below with small black spots).   *Young male in first winter plumage:* Similar to adult male but forehead duller or lacking the scarlet of adult.   *Young female in first winter plumage:* Similar to adult female.   *Young male in juvenal plumage:* Similar to adult female but still duller, browner above, back barring less sharply defined, upper breast with dusky shaft-streaks, hind neck tinged pink and top of head tinged reddish. *Young female in juvenal plumage:* Similar to young male but top of head darker or dusky-grayish; little or no red on belly.

MEASUREMENTS. — Length 8.75 to 10.60 in.; spread 15.00 to 18.00; folded wing 4.00 to 5.50; tail 3.00 to 4.00; bill 1.05 to 1.30; tarsus .75 to 1.00.   Female smaller than male.

MOLTS. — Apparently juvenal plumage is shed completely (August to October) and first winter plumage assumed; there is a partial spring molt, after which young bird becomes as adult; adults have complete postnuptial molt in late summer and autumn (July to September) and probably a partial prenuptial molt in late winter or early spring.

FIELD MARKS. — Size about that of Hairy Woodpecker; the *black and white barred back and wings* and gray under plumage distinguish it from all other New England woodpeckers, not to mention the bright scarlet top of head of male and large patch of same on nape of female.

VOICE. — Call note resembles *tchurr, tchurr* of Red-headed Woodpecker; another more like *chawh chawh* (C. Bendire); a startling *clark* (W. L. Dawson); *churr-churr* or *chow-chow* (A. H. Howell); loud, harsh croaks sounding like *crirrk* (H. Nehrling); a rolling *wor'r'r'roo* very like that of a flicker (Brewster).

BREEDING. — A forest bird, but not confined to forests; breeds also on prairie or other open lands where opportunity offers.   *Nest:* In tree, stump, post or pole, in cavity excavated by the birds, from 16 to 50 feet from ground; entrance about 1¾ inches in diameter; depth about 12 inches.   *Eggs:* Usually 3 to 5, rarely more; .91 to 1.05 by .66 to .76 in.; ovate; dull white.   *Dates:* May 10 to June 6, southern Illinois; May 1 to May 24, Virginia.   *Incubation:* Period 14 days; by both sexes.   Ordinarily 1 brood yearly.

RANGE. — Chiefly Upper and Lower Austral zones of the eastern United States, from southeastern Minnesota, central Wisconsin, southern Michigan, southeastern Ontario, north central New York and

Massachusetts (casually) south to Gulf states, from central Texas to southern Florida and west to southeastern South Dakota, eastern Nebraska, central Kansas, Oklahoma, northwestern and west central Texas; accidental in Arizona, eastern Colorado and northwestern Nebraska.

DISTRIBUTION IN NEW ENGLAND. — Casual or accidental visitor from the south or west to Massachusetts, Rhode Island and Connecticut. Records: *Massachusetts:* Springfield, May 13, 1863, one seen by J. A. Allen; [1] Newton, November 25, 1880, pair seen and female taken by William Adair, recorded by Gordon Plummer; [2] Cohasset, May 28, 1881, male taken by son of Matthew Luce [3] and now in collection of Museum of Comparative Zoölogy; Clinton, July 17, 1896, male seen by Arthur M. Farmer.[4] Cambridge, April 9, 1921, male seen by Morris Brounstein,[5] *Rhode Island:* Providence, 2 birds, now in collection of Boston Society of Natural History. "Providence" — only data, except that Accession 2,680 included 63 New England birds, purchased from G. O. Welch, of Lynn. The purchase was made about June 21, 1880.[6]

G. M. Allen in the "Aves" speaks of this bird in Rhode Island as an accidental visitor; near Providence, two specimens.[7]

Howe and Sturtevant in their Birds of Rhode Island are similarly silent in regard to these two birds saying only that they were taken "near Providence." [8] *Connecticut:* Stratford, October 16, 1842, one seen by Linsley.[9] Suffield, July 30, 1874, female taken by E. I. Shores.[10] Hartford, one killed near there by Dr. Crary.[10]

SEASON IN MASSACHUSETTS. — May to November.

HAUNTS AND HABITS. The Red-bellied Woodpecker is a handsome and conspicuous bird. It makes a good target, and perhaps for that reason it is rather restless, shy and wary. I have seen it only in the south, and there it was usually quick to beat a retreat, but in the northern winter, necessity sometimes drives it to feeding places about houses and it becomes quite domestic, feeding on suet. In Florida it frequently comes into orange groves about the homesteads. In some localities it will pursue its jerky, devious or spiral way up the trunks of the trees utterly regardless of the onlooker; usually, however, when approached it flies away with an undulating motion before the observer is well within gunshot, and it is likely to betake itself to the top of some tall tree at a distance, where it keeps a sharp lookout for danger. There, while hammering away, it utters at intervals a loud and solemn *churr*, always alert and apprehensive. It is rather a noisy bird especially in the mating season. In southern Ontario, at about the same latitude as southern New England, the species seems to be a permanent though not common resident; but in New England the bird is a mere straggler, chiefly during the milder part of the year. It may migrate occasionally, but seems to have no regular migration, and the individuals found outside of the normal breeding range seem to be aimless wanderers. Evidently this bird is another which, like the Red-headed Wood-

[1] Allen, J. A.: Proceedings Essex Institute, Vol. IV, 1864, Communications, p. 53.

[2] Bulletin, Nuttall Ornithological Club, Vol. VI, 1881, p. 120.

[3] Brewster, William: *ibid.*, p. 183.

[4] Osprey, Vol. I, No. 3, 1896, p. 39.

[5] Brounstein, Morris: *in litt.*

[6] Sanford, S. N. F.: *in litt.*

[7] Fauna of New England, List of the Aves, 1909, p. 121.

[8] Birds of Rhode Island, 1899, p. 64.

[9] American Journal of Science and Arts, Vol. XLIV, 1843, p. 263.

[10] Merriam, C. Hart: Birds of Connecticut, 1877, p. 65.

pecker, has retired westward during the last century.   Giraud said that formerly it bred on Long Island, and it was once common in the lower Hudson Valley from which it has virtually disappeared.   According to Mr. E. H. Eaton it is now uncommon and local in western New York.

The food of the Red-bellied Woodpecker consists largely of insects, such as beetles, caterpillars and bugs, and still more largely of vegetal matter consisting of wild fruits, seeds, acorns and occasionally a little corn.   It sometimes damages ornamental palm trees by excavating large holes in them, and it has a habit of boring into oranges, either on the ground or growing on the tree, and eating both juice and pulp.   It feeds somewhat on the ground but does not walk as easily as the flicker.

At Thomasville, Georgia, the Red-bellied Woodpeckers frequently entered the Baldwin bird traps, placed on the ground and baited with bread crumbs, scratch feed, etc.

ECONOMIC STATUS.   As this woodpecker feeds its young chiefly on insects and destroys many tree pests, it deserves protection except perhaps where actually doing injury to the orange crop in Florida.

Coláptes aurátus lúteus Bangs.   Northern Flicker.

Other names: FLICKER; GOLDEN-WINGED WOODPECKER; PIGEON WOODPECKER; HIGH-HOLE; WAKE-UP; HARRYWICKET; GAFFER WOODPECKER; YELLOW-HAMMER; ETC., ETC., ETC.

Plate 52.

DESCRIPTION. — Bill as long as head, somewhat slender for a woodpecker, slightly down-curved, nostrils not entirely concealed by nasal tufts; wings ample; tail rather long for a woodpecker.   *Adult male:* Top of head and back and sides of neck ashy-gray with a crescentic scarlet band on nape; back, scapulars, wing-coverts and most secondaries olive-brown (sometimes grayish) with bars and cross-spots of black; primaries blackish above, shafts and under sides of all flight-feathers chiefly rich yellow with golden gloss below; rump and upper tail-coverts white, latter marked more or less heavily with black; tail black with shafts more or less yellow, golden-yellow below with black ends, some tipped whitish; (individual birds have under side of tail variously marked with black, yellow and white); sides of head, chin, throat and upper breast "deep vinaceous cinnamon" or "lilac brown," with conspicuous black moustache marks on both lower jaws exceptionally showing touches of red; breast with large, wide, black subcrescent; rest of lower plumage similar to throat, but paler, whitening on middle of belly and under tail-coverts and thickly strewn with conspicuous sharply defined black spots, mostly rounded, but angular on under tail-coverts; wing linings yellow or yellowish, paling toward edge of wing, where spotted black; bill slaty blue-black, brownish or dusky, lighter or light bluish below; iris dark reddish-brown or hazel; legs and feet light bluish-gray or light leaden-gray.   *Adult female:* Similar but lacking black moustache marks.   *Young in juvenal plumage:* Similar to adult male, but black bands above broader with more or less red on top of head, and vinaceous parts of head and neck more gray; both sexes have the black moustache patch in this plumage.

MEASUREMENTS. — Length 12.00 to 13.00 in.; spread 18.50 to 21.35; folded wing 5.60 to 6.50; tail 4.00 to 4.85; bill 1.51 to 1.65; tarsus .88 to 1.12.   Weight 4 to 6 oz. (B. H. Warren).

MOLTS. — The nestling is hatched naked and has no down, but grows a juvenal plumage which is much like that of adult; this plumage is molted out completely (June to October), and both sexes go into the first winter plumage (the young female losing the black moustache patch) and become virtually as

Fig. 52. — Northern Flicker Recently Hatched

Showing wing quills starting and the process at gape

Page 292

Fig. 53. — Fledgling Flicker Developing Juvenal Plumage

Showing shrinkage of process at gape

Page 292

adult; adults have a complete molt (June to October) and possibly some incomplete molt of body-feathers in late winter and early spring, but no birds examined showed this.

FIELD MARKS. — Size larger than Robin; its large size, bounding flight and black breast-patch identify it; the yellow under sides of wings and tail show as it flies overhead, and as it flies up from the ground the white rump is conspicuous; no other land bird has such prominent round black spots below.

VOICE. — Call-note a loud *wick wick wick wick;* a high-pitched *ti-err* (Ralph Hoffmann); *ske-er* (Gentry), *zee-ah* (Bendire) or *kee-ah* (Knight); when courting, a note like *yúck-ă-yúck-ă yúck-ă;* this bird has a greater variety of notes than any other New England woodpecker and many different renderings of them are given by imaginative writers. Among others we have *whick-ah, wick-a, wrick-a wicker, a-week, o-week, wichyew, pee-up, pee-on peop, we-cogh, we-cup, weechem, woit-a, flicker, wit-ah hurric ah, whrick-ah, whick-ah, h'witch, yucker, yu-cah, wake-up, tchuck-up, chuck-up, yarrup, pi-ack, pioh, quit-u, hi-to, queah, wy-kle, we-co;* also *clape, klu-ak, cheer, part, cuh, wit, peerit, woit, puir* and *ouit;* most of them repeated more or less.

BREEDING. — Among orchards, shade trees or open woodlands, also in forests. *Nest:* A hole made by the birds in a tree, fence post, a hollow tree, building,* haymow, haystack, stump, nesting box, or hole in a bank or cliff such as those made by Kingfishers or swallows; very rarely a mere hollow in the ground; when a cavity in a tree is hollowed out by the birds, the entrance usually is from two to three inches in diameter and the hole 10 to 24 inches in depth and from $2\frac{1}{2}$ to 60 feet from the ground. *Eggs:* 3 to 20, commonly 5 to 9; .77 to 1.16 by .72 to .87 in.; short or elliptical ovate; white, fine grained and very glossy; illustrated in Capen's "Oölogy of New England," Plate XIV, Fig. 15. *Dates:* April 29, Rhode Island, to June 14, Maine. *Incubation:* Period variously given as 11 to 16 days; incubation may commence with first or last egg; by both sexes. Usually one brood yearly, sometimes two.

RANGE. — [Colaptes a. borealis is recognized in A. O. U. Check-List and occupies all of northernmost part of North America.] Eastern United States and southeastern Canada. Breeds from Nebraska, Iowa, Michigan, southern Ontario, southern Quebec and Newfoundland south to central northern Texas, Oklahoma, central northern Arkansas, central eastern Missouri, south central Illinois, south central and southeastern Indiana, northeastern Alabama, eastern Tennessee, western North Carolina and Virginia; south in winter from the latitude of Nebraska, southern Michigan, southern Ontario, southern New York and southern New England (casually Maine and accidentally Nova Scotia) to southern Texas, the Gulf coast and Florida; casual on Bermuda Islands.

DISTRIBUTION IN NEW ENGLAND. — *Maine:* Common migrant and summer resident; rare winter resident in coastal region. *New Hampshire:* Common migrant and summer resident, except higher mountain slopes; rare winter resident in southern part near coast. *Vermont:* Common migrant and summer resident. *Massachusetts:* Common to abundant migrant; common summer resident; common to rare winter resident, most common in southeastern part. *Rhode Island and Connecticut:* Common to abundant migrant; common summer resident; less common to rare winter resident.

SEASON IN MASSACHUSETTS. — Permanent resident; most common in migration in April and late September and October.

HAUNTS AND HABITS. The flicker is the most generally abundant and well known of all American woodpeckers. It is said that it is known in various parts of the country by fully 125 common names. Country people are almost everywhere familiar with the bird.

When the glad vociferous flickers arrive after a long and severe winter, we feel that surely spring is here. Thoreau recognized the rejuvenating quality in the spring note of

---

* In 1897, in Lynnfield, Massachusetts, flickers made various holes in the side of an unoccupied barn. One foot below one of these holes they laid their eggs on a 5-foot pile of hay which lay on the barn floor and against the side of the barn. When the owner of the barn went inside one day, the flicker flew around wildly and escaped through one of the holes (J. A. Farley).

the bird.   On April 3, 1842, he wrote : "I have just heard a flicker among the oaks on the hillside ushering in a new dynasty.   It is the age and youth of time."   Again he says : "But how that single sound enriches all the woods and fields . . . this note really quickens what was dead.   It seems to put life into withered grass and leaves and bare twigs, and henceforth the days shall not be as they have been."

As the season advances and the wooing of the flicker begins, his cheery, seductive love notes express the very spirit of the spring.   Now comes the season of reproduction and with it the awakening of life in earth, in air, in a million pools, in verdant meadows and slowly greening woods — the teeming vibrant life of coming summer.   We hear "hither and yon" the flicker's loud, oft-repeated cry, gradually lowering in pitch and often given for an almost unlimited number of times.   Next we see the male in the early morning drumming rapidly on some resonant limb or tin roof — too early for the sluggards, who complain of a reveille at such an unseemly hour.   Those who dance all night care not to rise with the birds at dawn.   The drumming is a long, almost continuous roll, and the bird frequently clings to his drumming-post and continues his music for a long time.

The extravagant courtship of the flicker is notorious.   We see a pair together, the female reluctant and coy, the male following her close by from tree to tree.   Slyly he peeks at her from behind a limb ; but soon, becoming bolder, sidles up to her, swinging his head about and displaying the beauties of spread wings and tail as he softly calls " *yúcker yúcker yúcker*."   Next a rival male appears.   Now all is action and excitement ; each vies with the other in exhibiting all his endearing charms to the demure object of his desires.   One takes an elevated position on a branch near her side ; the other, not to be outdone, mounts to a similar place on the other side, and now begins a superlative effort on the part of each suitor to impress her with the glowing splendors of his plumage and the seductive pleadings of his tenderest tones.   With wings open and tails widely spread, they turn and twist about, throwing into their notes the most eager supplication.   They bow and nod, advance and retreat and use every art known to flickers to win the fair one ; but she is obdurate, and so the wooing goes on from day to day.   If she goes to the ground, he follows.   If he presses his suit too boldly at first, she repels him with a sharp jab from her bill.   When finally she faces him or stands by his side and reciprocates, by nodding even perfunctorily, the situation seems more encouraging.   Then he redoubles his efforts to please, sidling around her, posturing, nodding, tossing his head up or swinging it from side to side, and with spread wings and tail, displaying his charms to perfection.   His red nape seems to expand and glow in the sunlight, and his spotted breast swells with renewed ardor.*   When finally the female accepts a suitor, she acknowledges her submission by returning his courtesies in kind.   Later in the season, especially where males are scarce, the females may assume the initiative, two or three seeking the company of a single male.   When such an unusual and complicated situation arises, the females have

---

* Mr. C. W. Leister tells of a particularly ardent male that mounted into the air in jerky spirals for about 350 feet and came down in a similar way to a branch just above the female, there to continue his antics (Auk, Vol. XXXVI, 1919, p. 570).

even been known to do battle for the favors of the male; but usually these affairs seem to be settled amicably, the females merely hitching about and bowing to one another and to the male in turn.   When the happy twain are united, they soon find a location for their home, and both sexes work at the excavation, relieving each other from time to time.   They are so industrious that they sometimes carry on their work far into the night, and soon after daylight their labor begins again.   If they choose a hollow tree or a nesting box for their home, they are likely to hammer away at the inside until they have chips enough in the bottom to make a bed for the eggs.   Therefore, it is well to place some fine chips or coarse sawdust with a little dry earth in the bottom of a flicker box when it is put up. They may use the same domicile for years if not molested.   In their fights with other birds for a nesting hole in a hollow tree, sometimes even the Screech Owl is worsted.[1] There is a case recorded where a flicker, a Bluebird and a Sparrow Hawk occupied holes in the same dead branch.[2]   Flickers have nested (as have wrens) in holes in an old stump in a lion's cage at the Washington National Zoölogical Park.[3]   If robbed of her treasures the female may continue to lay or may first deepen the hole and then lay another set. Mr. Charles L. Phillips tells of a female that laid 71 eggs in 73 days, when they were taken from the nest as fast as deposited, one always being left for a nest-egg.[4]   Both sexes take turns in incubation, and the one on the nest is fed by the other.   They are very affection-- ate, continuing their wooing more or less during the nesting season, and both share in caring for the young.   The young remain in and about the nest about 14 to 16 days, but during the last two of these they may spend much time climbing about outside.   In some cases, however, they seem timid and backward about leaving their natal home, and the parents have to use persuasion and even force to get them out.   As the young in the nest increase in size they become noisy, and if a person taps on the tree, a loud buzzing may be heard from within.   In September when the fledglings have grown strong and able to care for themselves, the southward migration begins.   This continues through October when, after some severe frost in the north, hundreds may be seen migrating by daylight, especially along the coast of Connecticut, where they turn westward and follow the shore.

Most of the flickers that pass the winter in New England seek the vicinity of the sea, though in mild winters an occasional individual may appear anywhere in southern New England.   Near the sea-shore they find bayberries of which they are very fond, and, other food failing, they get some sustenance from the rows of seaweed along the shore.   Usually they retire to some cavity in a tree at night, but during one winter at Wareham one appar- ently slept on the wall of my summer cottage under the eaves, clinging to one of the orna- mental battens in an upright position as it would cling to a tree trunk.   This bird for some unaccountable reason chose the north side of the cottage.   He was there night after night at dusk and also at daylight each morning.   Mr. R. F. Carr tells of a flicker that was accustomed to pass winter nights in a chimney of an occupied dwelling in a

[1] Bird-Lore, Vol. XXVII, 1925, p. 398.
[2] Bird-Lore, Vol. XV, 1913, p. 155.
[3] Bird-Lore, Vol. XX, 1918, p. 158.
[4] Auk, Vol. IV, 1887, p. 346.

thickly settled neighborhood which undoubtedly was a more comfortable roosting place than the north side of my cottage. These cases were very unusual. Commonly in winter flickers drill holes through the walls of vacant buildings in southeastern Massachusetts and sleep inside. Sometimes they become confused while exploring the interior of a furnished cottage, and, unable to find the way out, die there. At different times I have found two dead in my cottage. They had cut away a part of a window sash and damaged the curtain in their efforts to escape. Mr. H. W. Copeland reports that a flicker found shelter during a severe rain-storm by clinging to the side of a post which supported a bird box. The bird kept to the dry side of the post and the bottom of the box formed a roof over its head. Ned Dearborn says:[1] "In fierce winter weather flickers frequently cling to the lee side of a good-sized tree for shelter from high winds."

The flicker occasionally manifests considerable curiosity. On October 7, 1916, I landed from my skiff on the bank of the Agawam River, near the head of tidewater. In a dark grove of white pines I heard the sound of wings brushing against the branches, and six Night Herons flapped awkwardly away. As I emerged from the woods, another, a young bird, flew across the river and alighted in the top of a great dead tree on the farther shore. This was a Crow's watch tower, and there the black rascal already had taken his accustomed stand. Immediately a curious flicker followed the heron, and, alighting on a limb near it, hopped back and forth in great excitement, examining the ungainly heron. Soon the Crow, becoming alarmed at my presence, summoned the black rabble of the flock by his loud outcries, and then the dark sentinel and the heron both spread their pinions in alarm and departed, but as I seated myself beneath a tree that curious flicker came back across the river as if to see what all the fuss was about. She alighted on a fence post in front of me in full sunlight, her black cravat glowing like satin, and there she scanned me, first with one eye and then with the other, to her heart's content. Finally she flew to some trees at my right, where, with the sun at her back, she could get a better view unobserved.

The flicker is very fond of ants which form a large part of its daily food whenever they can be found; hence this bird is often seen on the ground investigating ant-hills, and in autumn while the family keeps together, from five to ten birds may be started from the ground in the same field. While on the ground they run a few steps and stop, run a few more and stop, much in the manner of the Robin, but when they find an ant-hill they spend considerable time there. While thus engaged they often allow a near approach. As they fly off when startled, they are likely to utter a curious purring sound, and they display their white rumps, thus proclaiming their identity.

The number of ants eaten by flickers is surprising. Prof. F. E. L. Beal found over 5,000 very small ants in the stomach of one bird and over 3,000 each in two others. One hundred flickers' stomachs examined contained a similar quantity of ants, but the number in each was less, because the ants were of larger species. The flicker destroys small numbers of ground-beetles; bugs, grasshoppers and crickets are eaten more freely.

[1] Birds of Durham, 1903, p. 55.

Caterpillars (as *C. disstria*), flying larvæ, spiders, myriapods and crustaceans make up a small part of its animal food, which forms 60.92 per cent of its sustenance for the year; against 39.08 per cent which is vegetal, and consists of a little corn, a small amount of cambium, a little weed seed and a large quantity of wild fruit with occasionally cultivated cherries.[1] In late summer and autumn this bird seems to be very fond of wild cherries and the fruit of the Tupelo or sour-gum (*Nyssa sylvatica*). In winter the fruit of the bayberry and that of the poison ivy are favorites.

ECONOMIC STATUS. Various opinions are expressed regarding the economic status of this bird. Professor Walter B. Barrows opines that "on the whole the insect food of the Flicker does it little credit and its vegetable food does not help the record much." He bases his opinion largely upon the fact that ants form its chief insect food, and apparently he does not consider ants destructive. His experience with ants has been at variance with my own. Ants riddle posts set in the ground or any timber or lumber resting upon or in contact with the ground. They destroy the sills of buildings set close to the ground and often ruin living trees, especially such as have a few dead roots. They infest lawns and buildings, destroying grass on the lawns and food in the house, and are difficult to eradicate. They sometimes eat alive the young of certain ground-nesting birds. They are very prolific and require a severe check upon their numbers. Otherwise they would become unbearable pests. Mr. William Dutcher wrote as follows regarding the economic value of the flicker:

" If the flicker had no other valuable economic quality it would deserve protection because it is the enemy of the ant family, fifty per cent of its food for the year being of these insect pests. Ants, besides being wood-borers, care for and perpetuate plant-lice or aphids, which infest and are very destructive to vegetation in all parts of the country to the very serious loss of the agricultural interests. Professor Comstock says in his 'Manual of the Study of Insects,' p. 157:

" ' It is easy to see what benefit ants derive from this association with plant-lice, and how they should learn that it is worth while for them to care for their herds of honey-producing cattle. Little has been done, however, to point out the great benefit that accrues to the plant-lice from this relationship. It seems fair to assume that the plant-lice are greatly benefited, else why has the highly specialized apparatus for producing the honey-dew been developed?

" ' Writers long ago showed that ants protect plant-lice by driving away from them lady-bugs and other enemies. Recently, however, Professor Forbes has demonstrated that, in certain cases at least, a more important service is rendered. In his studies of the corn plant-louse, he found that this species winters in the wingless, agamic form in the earth of previously infested corn-fields, and that in the spring the plant-lice are strictly dependent upon a species of ant, *Lasius alienus*, which mines along the principal roots of the corn, collects the plant-lice, and conveys them into these burrows, and there watches and protects them. Without the aid of these ants, the plant-lice were unable to reach

---

[1] Beal. F. E. L.: Bulletin No. 37, United States Department of Agriculture, Biological Survey, pp. 52–58.

the roots of the corn. . . . Ants take very good care of their cattle (aphids), and will carry them to new pastures if the old ones dry up. They also carry the aphid-eggs into their nests and keep them sheltered during the winter, and then carry the young plant-lice out and put them on plants in the spring.'"[1] The flicker is one of the few birds that destroy the pernicious European corn-borer (*Pyrausta nublalis*) which now threatens the corn crop of this country. The bird should be protected and fostered.

ORDER MACROCHIRES. GOATSUCKERS, SWIFTS, ETC.

Number of species in North America 28; in Massachusetts 5.

Plate 53.

This is a composite group, including a number of suborders and families having certain affinities. The only suborders of this order represented in New England are *Caprimulgi* or goatsuckers, etc., *Cypseli* or swifts and *Trochili* or hummingbirds. These suborders differ quite widely from each other in many respects, but they are alike in having small and rather weak feet, and alike also in another part of their structure — the long, terminal portion of the wing. As they take almost all their food while in flight, they have developed that part of the wing which corresponds to the hand in man. Hence the name of the order, *Macrochires*, which may be translated freely as "birds with long hands."

SUBORDER CAPRIMULGI. GOATSUCKERS, ETC.

Number of species in North America 6; in Massachusetts 3.

Goatsuckers first received their name from a popular belief that a European species obtained its sustenance by relieving goats of their milk — a belief without foundation in fact. As these birds feed almost entirely on flying insects, the only apparent ground for this notion lies in the facts that they have large soft mouths, and that they fly around domestic animals in pasture, because of the insects that these creatures put to flight from grass or shrubbery.

FAMILY CAPRIMULGIDÆ. GOATSUCKERS, ETC.

Number of species in North America 6; in Massachusetts 3.

In this family the bill is exceedingly small and weak, but the mouth is enormous, the gape opening far back under the ears. The head is large, the skull being very wide, thus resembling those of rapacious birds. In fact the goatsuckers show anatomical affinity to the owls. They have similar soft plumage, noiseless flight, large eyes and nocturnal vision. The nostrils are exposed and rounded, with a raised border which, in some cases, becomes tube-like. In many species feather-shafts resembling bristles

---

[1] Educational Leaflet No. 5, National Committee of Audubon Societies.

grow on either side of the head above the mouth, and extending outward thus increase the efficiency of this perfect insect trap by broadening its scope. The plumage is provided with aftershafts and the oil gland is nude. The wings are long in most cases and ample with ten primaries; the tail medium with ten tail-feathers; the feet exceedingly small; the toes are shortened (outer toe very short with only four phalanges, hind toe exceedingly short, middle toe longer than other front toes, claw usually pectinate), all of them being webbed toward their bases. The colors are modest and protective, as they must be with birds which incubate their eggs and brood their young unhidden on the ground. Most of the species, which are largely nocturnal or crepuscular, have loud, impressive, peculiar night-cries. Their food consists chiefly of insects taken on the wing, though some of the larger species occasionally catch and swallow small birds. The family is common to both the Old World and the New. Goatsuckers inhabit temperate and tropical regions; Over 100 species have been described.

ECONOMIC STATUS. The members of this exceedingly useful family obtain their sustenance largely by devouring injurious insects.

Antróstomus carolinénsis (GMELIN). Chuck-will's-widow.

DESCRIPTION. — Largest goatsucker in the United States; bristles on sides of mouth have *lateral filaments;* wings long, tail rounded, legs feathered in front nearly to toes; inner side of claw of middle toe comb-like with prominent pectinations; *extremely variable in markings;* some individuals much darker than others. *Adult male:* Above generally dark wood-brown with rather heavy streaks or dashes of black, sparingly disposed in lines on top of head, with lesser streaks of same elsewhere above, where sprinkled with minute specks of black on ground color varying from tawny to yellowish-gray, with many fine vermiculations also of black; posterior scapulars and tertials usually lighter and grayer than back and marked with large black spots; wing-coverts, secondaries and tertials centrally black, edged whitish or tawny, primaries and their coverts mainly black with broken tawny cross-bars or cross-spots, secondaries and tertials mostly similar, but markings finer; four middle tail-feathers tawny, irregularly cross-spotted and vermiculated with black, central black spots giving effect of barring, inner webs of three outer tail-feathers largely white above (which is replaced by tawny on under side) with darker tips, and outer webs mottled black and tawny; below, ochraceous (especially toward tail) becoming buffy on throat and darker on breast, more or less streaked, cross-waved and barred with blackish; a whitish or buffy band across lower throat, wing linings tawny, black-barred; bill blackish or brownish; iris dark brown; feet brownish. *Adult female:* Similar to adult male, but lacking white on inner webs of tail which are tawny, marbled with black, also three outer tail-feathers on each side sometimes broadly tipped tawny and sprinkled with small black spots; bill brownish; feet and legs dull bluish (J. W. Atkins); bill black, light at base; legs brownish; iris light blue (G. Wurdemann). *Young in first winter and juvenal plumages (sexes alike):* Similar to adult female in pattern and colors; band across lower throat indistinct or obsolete, and lower plumage generally barred with black on a light brownish-buffy ground. *Downy young:* Pale yellowish-brown or buffy, darker on shoulders and cheeks.

CHUCK-WILL'S-WIDOW SHOWING LATERAL FILAMENTS ON BRISTLY FEATHERS AT SIDES OF MOUTH

MEASUREMENTS. — Length 11.00 to 13.25 in.; spread 24.50 to 25.50; wing 8.00 to 8.90; tail 5.40 to 6.50; bill from tip to feathers of forehead .30 to .45; tarsus .60 to .75. Female rather smaller than male.

MOLTS. — Young goatsuckers are clothed when hatched, or soon after, with a light down which is succeeded by a juvenal plumage sometimes lighter in color than that of adults; in autumn they molt into first winter plumage like that of female adult; adults have a complete postnuptial molt in autumn completed late in the year; apparently there is no spring molt.

FIELD MARKS. — Longer than Whip-poor-will, and nearly twice its bulk; resembles it closely in color, but band on throat not so pure white as in Whip-poor-will.

VOICE. — A loud, bold, whistle ("Chuck-will's-widow"), resembling that of Whip-poor-will; many people fail to distinguish the difference, and attribute both calls to the same bird; first three syllables nearly equal in cadence, "wid" being accented and emphasized, last note about half length of first; among southern people where the bird is common, its cry is rendered "Twixt-hell-and-white-oak" or other similar phrases, usually ending in "white oak"; also a single "quak" when startled and flushed (A. T. Wayne).

BREEDING. — Commonly in deciduous woods; occasionally on rocky, bushy hillsides. *Nest:* None; eggs deposited on dry leaves in woods or on bare ground. *Eggs:* 2; 1.30 to 1.58 by .95 to 1.08 in.; usually nearly oval, both ends shaped almost alike; usually rich cream to pure white, glossy, marbled and spotted with different shades of drab, lavender and pearl-gray, overlaid or intermixed with spots of various shades of brown and tawny; sometimes irregular lines appear; very variable; illustrated in Bendire's "Life Histories of North American Birds," Vol. II, Plate I, Figs. 8 and 9. *Dates:* April 14, Florida; May 23, Virginia. *Incubation:* Begins when first egg is laid, second deposited several days later (A. T. Wayne); by both sexes (probably chiefly by female); period unknown. Probably but one brood yearly.

RANGE. — Lower Austral and part of Upper Austral zones, chiefly in eastern United States, and Tropical Zone to northern South America. Breeds from southeastern Kansas, central Missouri, southern Illinois, southern Indiana, West Virginia and southern Maryland south to central southern Texas, coast of Gulf states and Florida; migrates through eastern Mexico; winters from southern Florida, Bahamas, and West Indies to Panama and northern Colombia; accidental north on Atlantic coast to Connecticut, Massachusetts, Nova Scotia and southeastern Ontario.

DISTRIBUTION IN NEW ENGLAND. — Accidental visitor. Records: *Massachusetts:* Revere, dead specimen found in a barn, December, 1884, which was caught in October by a cat, now in the collection of Boston Society of Natural History.[1] East Boston, October 13, 1915, bird shot by N. Hagman, now in mounted collection of Boston Society of Natural History.[2] *Connecticut:* New Haven, bird taken alive by Decatur Morgan, May 19, 1889, recorded by A. H. Verrill.[3]

HAUNTS AND HABITS. This great goatsucker, the largest of the family in North America, is a mere straggler in New England. I have seen and heard it only in Florida, where it is common and where its loud and rather mournful notes frequently are heard at dusk and on moonlit nights. At times its call is repeated so rapidly that the syllables almost merge into one. It is an ardent wooer, swelling and strutting like a turkey-cock, and it is very devoted to its young. It frequents forests and is said to rest during the day in hollow trees, except in the season of incubation. It is fond of dark and shady woodlands, especially where the branches hang low, and it rarely stirs abroad until the sun

---

[1] Osgood, Fletcher: Auk, Vol. II, 1885, p. 220.
[2] Brooks, W. Sprague: Auk, Vol. XXXIII, 1916, p. 328.
[3] Ornithologist and Oölogist, Vol. XIV, 1889, p. 96.

has set. Its loud notes usually cease when the young have hatched, and it migrates southward during August. Its food consists largely of destructive insects, but occasionally it catches small birds from the size of a hummingbird to that of a swallow. These birds, taken on the wing, are snapped up in the mouth of the Chuck-will's-widow and swallowed whole.

ECONOMIC STATUS. See page 299.

Antrostomus vociferus vociferus (WILSON). Whip-poor-will.

Plate 53.

DESCRIPTION. — Similar in form to Chuck-will's-widow, but much smaller; bristles at sides of mouth without lateral filaments, pectinations on nail of middle toe less prominent; legs feathered in front nearly to feet. *Adult male:* Similar to adult male Chuck-will's-widow, brownish and grayish above, the brown predominating; much mottled and otherwise marked with blackish; top of head more or less grayish, finely vermiculated and narrowly streaked with black, streaks heaviest near center; scapulars grayish with a row of large black markings at both their upper and lower edges; both webs of flight-feathers spotted and marbled with yellowish or tawny, which grows grayer toward tips; primaries appear barred when wing is closed; middle pair of tail-feathers with irregular bars of blackish; a white patch occupying more than a third of the three outer tail-feathers on each side extending to their tips (this patch buffy on under side of tail), and increasing in size from outer feathers inward; in most specimens the white of tail-feathers edged tawny or buffy; lores, cheeks, chin and throat barred tawny (or brownish) and blackish; *a white band across lower throat*, sometimes tinged more or less with light buff; elsewhere below marked with pale grayish-brown and pale brownish-buff, spotted, finely vermiculated and narrowly barred dusky; axillars and wing linings tawny and dusky; bill and iris brown; feet reddish-purple, scales and claws blackish; "legs and feet light purplish flesh color seamed with white" (Wilson); "iris bluish-black; bill and claws black; legs and feet grayish-brown" (N. S. Goss). *Adult female:* Usually a little lighter above and grayer on head than adult male; white on three outer tail-feathers wanting, these feathers broadly tipped buffy, and throat-band narrower and more buffy (may be rarely white).[1] *First winter plumage:* Similar to adult. *Young male in juvenal plumage:* Outer tail-feathers, primaries and primary coverts like those of adult male, otherwise quite different; back, wing-coverts and scapulars "deep brownish-buff" or tawny, sparsely marked with black; below pale buffy, barred narrowly more or less with dusky. *Young female in juvenal plumage:* Similar to young male but tail like that of adult female. *Downy young:* Covered with pale buffy or yellowish-brown down (See Fig. 55).

MEASUREMENTS. — Length 9.00 to 10.30 in.; spread 16.00 to 19.40; folded wing 5.75 to 6.90; tail 4.10 to 5.00; bill .36 to .55; tarsus .60 to .69. Weight (one specimen) 2 oz. (B. H. Warren). Female usually smaller than male.

MOLTS. — Down of nestling is replaced during summer by juvenal plumage; this is shed (beginning in July or August) and winter plumage is assumed closely resembling that of adult; adults have complete postnuptial autumnal molt.

FIELD MARKS. — Length about that of Robin but appears much larger with larger, longer wings; a brown bird, easily distinguished from Nighthawk when seen in good light by its shorter wings not reaching tip of *rounded tail;* Nighthawk's wings reach beyond tip of *forked tail* and Nighthawk is darker and more gray and shows large white spot on spread wing; Whip-poor-will usually rises from a dark, shady place on ground in woods, and feeds at night by low, short flights; Nighthawk rises from the open and often flies high by day or night.

---

[1] Loomis, Leverett M.: Auk, Vol. X, 1893, p. 152.

Voice. — Beside the usual "whip-poor-will" it has a soft *chuck*, coming before the "whip" and often given separately; one bird began calling like any Whip-poor-will, but after about half an hour he began to stutter as if excited; he called whip-whip-whip-poor-will and kept calling faster and faster until he was saying whip-whip-poor-poor-will-will (Blanche B. Chase); "another stammering Whip-poor-will seemed to have difficulty at times in getting out the will; he says whip-poor-whip-poor-whip-poor-will; again he says whip-whip-whip-poor-whip-poor-will and so on" (S. D. Robbins); also "a low grunting" like *däck-däck* and another like *zue-see zue-see* (C. Bendire); it sounds like the croaking of some small species of frog; *wuck a wuck*, also a peculiar purring *aw-aw-aw-aw* (O. W. Knight); a low murmuring sound in flight (Audubon); cry of the fledged young, *pe-ugh* in a low, mournful tone (Nuttall); female calls her young with a gentle *coo*.

Breeding. — Commonly in a country more or less wooded and usually on the outskirts of forests, in a growth of dry mixed woods or young saplings or bushes, also among rolling, wooded hills, about ponds or along streams, usually on well-drained land. *Nest:* None; eggs laid in a very slight depression on leaves or bare ground (See Fig. 54). *Eggs:* 2; 1.09 to 1.25 by .75 to .90 in.; nearly oval; white, more or less glossy, blotched, spotted and traced or lined with different shades of brown, drab, lavender, lilac and gray; rarely one is almost unspotted; illustrated in Bendire's "Life Histories of North American Birds," Vol. II, Plate I, Figs. 10 and 11. *Dates:* From May 10 to 21, Virginia; May 18 to June 9, Massachusetts. *Incubation:* Period 14 days (Audubon); 17 days (Burns); 19 days (Geo. C. Atwell); probably chiefly by female; male said to assist.

Range. — Eastern parts of United States and southern Canada, west to eastern edge of Great Plains and south to Salvador and Costa Rica. Breeds from southern Saskatchewan, central Manitoba, southern Ontario, southern Quebec, New Brunswick and Nova Scotia, south to northeastern Texas, central Arkansas, northern Alabama, northern Georgia and northwestern South Carolina, and west to eastern parts of North Dakota and South Dakota, central Nebraska, central Kansas, and eastern Oklahoma; winters from South Carolina, southern Georgia, and southern Texas south through eastern Mexico to Guatemala, Salvador, and at least casually to Costa Rica; accidental in Porto Rico and Colorado.

Distribution in New England. — Common summer resident except on higher elevations of northern New England; varying much in abundance locally from year to year.

Season in Massachusetts. — (April 4) April 22 to October 3 (October 21).

Haunts and Habits. In calm, still summer nights when under the soft light of the full moon the dark plumes of the pines stand motionless against the sky, the loud sweet notes of the Whip-poor-will ring through the forest shades and resound among the fells. On such a night long ago, having addressed an audience in Barre, Massachusetts, I rode through the woods for miles toward Gardner, where another engagement called me the next morning. As the buggy rolled along the darkened roads, Whip-poor-wills were calling from every direction. The air fairly vibrated, and the woods were resonant with their outcries. The dark-eyed French-Canadian driver, listening, shook his head solemnly and peering furtively about as if in apprehension said "Ah don' lak' hear dem fellar. Dey say dey breeng bad luck — dem er *woodchuck*." His words voiced a feeling prevalent among the more ignorant and superstitious of the country folk, some of whom believed that if the Whip-poor-will called on the door-stone, its visit presaged sickness or death. It is natural to suspect those who move silently in darkness; and birds which, like the owl or the Whip-poor-will, fly soundlessly by night from place to place and are so concealed by the shades of evening that they are never seen distinctly are likely to be at least misunderstood. Since man became man he has feared the evil that stalks in the

Fig. 54. — Eggs of Whip-poor-will in Situ
Page 302

Fig. 55. — Downy Young Whip-poor-wills
Page 301

PLATE 53

PLATE 53

NIGHTHAWK
Page 306

Adult Male

CHIMNEY SWIFT
Page 310
Adult

WHIP–POOR–WILL
Page 301

Adult Male

All about one-half scale

Agassiz Fuertes.

dark, but a creature so harmless as the Whip-poor-will should never be regarded with suspicion or alarm. When one of these birds comes from the woods to alight on the roof-tree or on the door-stone, it should be a welcome visitor even though its plaintive calls may banish sleep for a short time.

Whip-poor-wills often appear in the evening about country dwellings in pursuit of nocturnal insects, such as moths, beetles and mosquitoes, which are attracted to the buildings by the lights. While I slept unsheltered nightly for a week in the Concord woods, rolled in my blanket, with only a head-net hung to a branch overhead to protect me from mosquitoes, I noticed each morning upon awaking just before daylight that something fluttered softly about my head. The sound was like that produced by a large night-moth, but soon I heard something strike the ground a few feet away, and then a well-known cluck convinced me that my visitor was a Whip-poor-will. The bird came nightly while I remained in the woods, and each morning before daylight it flew around my head-net until it had caught all the mosquitoes there. Never at any other time have I been able to detect a sound from the wings of a Whip-poor-will.

From regions about the Gulf of Mexico the Whip-poor-wills come up by night, arriving in southern New England unheralded in late April or early May. As soon as they have rested from their journey the males announce their presence in the woods or thickets by their calls. Here the latter part of May sees the mating and nesting at its height. Major Charles Bendire who watched a pair of these birds from a small out-building gave the following account of the Whip-poor-will's wooing.

"I happened to be in a little outbuilding, some 20 feet in the rear of the house at which we were stopping, early on the evening of the 24th, about half an hour after sun-down, when I heard a peculiar, low, clucking noise outside, which was directly followed by the familiar call of 'whip-poor-will'. . . . Directly alongside of the small outbuilding previously referred to, a barrel of sand and lime had been spilled, and from the numerous tracks of these birds, made by them nightly afterwards, it was evident that this spot was visited regularly, and was the trysting place of at least one pair. Looking through a small aperture, I saw one of the birds waddling about in a very excited manner over the sand-covered space, which was perhaps 2 by 3 feet square, and it was so much inter-ested in its own performance that it did not notice me, although I made some noise trying to fight off a swarm of mosquitoes which assailed me from all sides. Its head appeared to be all mouth, and its notes were uttered so rapidly that, close as I was to the bird, they sounded like one long, continuous roll. A few seconds after his first effort (it was the male) he was joined by his mate, and she at once commenced to respond with a peculiar, low, buzzing or grunting note, like 'gaw-gaw-gaw,' undoubtedly a note of approval or endear-ment. This evidently cost her considerable effort; her head almost touched the ground while uttering it, her plumage was relaxed, and her whole body seemed to be in a violent tremble. The male in the meantime had sidled up to her and touched her bill with his, which made her move slightly to one side, but so slowly that he easily kept close alongside of her. These sidling movements were kept up for a minute or more each time; first one would move away, followed by the other, and then it was reversed; both were about equally bold and coy at the same time. Their entire love-making looked exceedingly human, and the female acted as timid and bashful as many young maidens would when receiving the first declarations of their would-be-lovers, while the lowering of her head might easily be interpreted as being done to hide her blushes. Just about the time I thought this courtship would reach its climax, a dog ran out of the house and caused both to take flight." [1]

When the birds have paired, the female chooses some retired spot in the woods or beneath dense shrubbery and usually deposits her eggs on the dead leaves that in such places cover the ground. If the bird is undisturbed, the young are hatched and reared in the same spot, but if too much troubled by visitors the mother may carry either eggs or young to some other location. Mr. J. H. Bowles says "several years ago I flushed a Whip-poor-will that rose with a baby bird clutched firmly between his thighs." [2] If surprised with her young she flaps, tumbles and flutters about the intruder with open mouth and whining or guttural cries and feigns a broken wing or other hurt and thus endeavors to draw attention away from her treasures. Often she *clucks* angrily; sometimes in her excitement she seems to forget that a Whip-poor-will should always sit lengthwise on a branch and time after time alights crosswise on a horizontal limb, which merely indicates that birds do not always follow the rules of action that we lay down for them. Apparently the Whip-poor-will rarely if ever hunts food for its young in the daytime, but as the shades of night begin to fall, it rises from the ground or from some horizontal limb along which its body has lain all day, simulating an excrescence of the tree, and begins to flutter and dart about, now low and close along the ground, now just over the shrubbery or among the tree-tops, sailing and wheeling in long graceful curves or doubling and twisting in erratic flight, in pursuit of its favorite insect prey. As the male bird darts and turns, using his quickly spread tail as a rudder, the white of the outer tail-feathers flashes sharply for a brief instant here and there, as the tail opens and closes. Now and then he alights, but instead of resting, pours forth his repeated whip-poor-will until the woods ring again. This call may be heard occasionally after sunrise, but it is given chiefly in the evening and in the morning on the approach of daylight; yet in full moonlight it may be heard at any time during the night. In the mating season he often continues to enunciate this cry until it would seem that he must drop from exhaustion, turning about occasionally or moving to another perch and sending forth his call to a different point of the compass. Dr. C. W. Townsend has recorded 664 calls without a break and then the bird paused for only a few seconds and began again.[3] Mrs. E. S. Fowler informs me that Mrs. Charles Preston of Tamworth, New Hampshire, counted 700 consecutive repetitions. John Burroughs, however, made a count which so far as I know exceeds all others. He records that he heard a bird "lay upon the back of poor will"

[1] Bendire, Charles: Life Histories of North American Birds, Vol. II, 1895, p. 148.
[2] Nidiologist, Vol. II, 1895, p. 113.
[3] Supplement to the Birds of Essex County, Massachusetts, 1920, p. 121.

1088 blows with only a rarely perceptible pause here and there, as if to take breath. Such excessive calling is very unusual; even one hundred consecutive calls is a large number. Sometimes four or five birds close together will give a lively concert for several minutes. When close to the performers we may hear a soft short *cluck* or *chuck*, just before the "whip." Provided with a night glass I have watched this bird call at dusk, at a distance of about eight feet. The tips of the wings commonly drop a little below the tail which is raised slightly. With each *cluck* the head is thrown back, with each note the tail is raised and lowered slightly, and with each complete "whip-poor-will" the shoulders move as if in the effort of expelling the sound, the strongest expulsion coming on the accented "will." The bill and mouth as I saw them were only slightly opened.

As the season wanes, and the young birds leave the place of their nativity, they soon learn to run and hide. In late summer the calls of the male are seldom heard, though he may be heard again occasionally in September before all depart for the south. A light-colored, flat, open space seems to attract Whip-poor-wills on moon-lit nights; they will alight on a bare ledge in a pasture or on the wide farmhouse door-stone. Mr. Stanley H. Bromley of Southbridge, Massachusetts, tells me that a farmer there placed a large tray of dry wood ashes on the ground, and Whip-poor-wills came there at night to dust in it. This is a common habit. They also alight in the roads at night. Many a driver of a motor car has been puzzled to see a large red eye glowing in the rays of his headlights and has stopped his car and found a Whip-poor-will sitting in the road. Its eye always shows red in the glare of the light. In daylight in its shaded retreats the Whip-poor-will blends into its surroundings so as to be virtually invisible to the human eye until it moves, which it rarely does, until in danger of being trodden upon, when it flutters along for a few rods and again disappears. In the woods it is fairly safe, though no doubt preyed upon by owls; but when the country becomes thickly settled, Whip-poor-wills are likely to disappear. Cats and dogs destroy their eggs and young, and too often the adults become targets for the hunter's gun. There are many localities now in eastern Massachusetts where the call of the bird is never heard, where formerly it was a common sound.*

The food of the Whip-poor-will consists mainly of nocturnal insects. Night-flying moths, among which may be found some of the greatest pests of the forest, form a large part of its sustenance. In its food list we find cutworm moths, cranberry moths and practically all the larger moths whose caterpillars destroy the leaves of trees. The bird also takes ants, grasshoppers, potato beetles, May beetles or "June bugs," mosquitoes, gnats and many other winged insects and the eggs of insects.

ECONOMIC STATUS. The Whip-poor-will is an animated insect trap. Its wide mouth and the long "bristles" about it, fit the bird especially for the capture of the larger nocturnal winged insects, which the smaller day birds cannot eat. It consumes quantities of them. Mr. E. H. Eaton writes that he found 36 moths in the stomach of one Whip-poor-will. This bird should be carefully conserved.

---

* The Whip-poor-will used to sing almost in the heart of Keene, New Hampshire (J. A. Farley).

Chordeíles virginiánus virginianus (Gmelin). Nighthawk.

Other names: BULL-BAT; MOSQUITO HAWK; PORK-AND-BEANS; BURNT LAND BIRD.

Plate 53.

DESCRIPTION. — Similar to Whip-poor-will in form, but wings much longer, tail slightly forked, bristles about mouth wanting, plumage a little more compact, legs not so fully feathered in front and colors of upper plumage generally darker and grayer. *Adult male:* Above sooty-blackish with faint greenish gloss, irregularly spotted and marbled with buff and pale buffy-gray and whitish; top of head largely blackish, spotted sparsely and irregularly with buffy; light grayish broken stripe from bill over eye and ear-coverts; primaries and tail dusky or blackish, four or five of the former crossed near middle by a large conspicuous white spot; tail crossed near end by narrow, white, interrupted band and also by other bands of grayish, buffy-grayish or very dull whitish; a wide white band crosses upper throat (sometimes including chin), extending backward under ear-coverts; lower throat and upper breast dark sooty-brown with cinnamon or brownish-buff spots anteriorly, the spots becoming paler or whitish on upper breast; rest of under plumage including wing linings and axillars rather narrowly cross-barred with sooty-blackish and whitish; bill blackish; iris blackish-brown or brownish-black; legs and feet grayish-brown or dusky. *Adult female:* Similar to adult male but white spot across primaries smaller, without white band on tail, upper plumage of a lighter appearance than male and white throat-patch usually buffy or buff. *Young in first winter plumage:* Similar to adult female. *Juvenal plumage:* Similar to adult female, having no white band across tail, but without any well-defined, light throat-patch, though this may be suggested or replaced by blackish and buffy bars; paler above, barring below more extensive, extending from bill to tail; breast lighter than in adults; whitish margins around tips of all primaries; wings and tail shorter than in adult and plumage somewhat looser. *Downy young:* Dark brownish, spotted and tipped irregularly above with grayish or in some cases rufous and yellowish.

MEASUREMENTS. — Length 8.25 to 10.00 in.; spread about 21.00 to 23.75; folded wing 6.75 to 8.90; tail 3.25 to 4.80; bill .20 to .30; tarsus .45 to .65. Female smaller than male.

MOLTS. — The grayish nestling down is very quickly replaced (July or early August) by juvenal plumage; some show molt of body plumage in September but not of wings or tail; apparently there is a partial or complete prenuptial molt in spring when young become as adult; adults seem to have a complete molt or possibly two incomplete molts in autumn and winter or early spring as the entire plumage is shed before they return to New England; not enough winter specimens available to trace this winter molt fully.

FIELD MARKS. — Size about that of Whip-poor-will but wings longer, more pointed, and tail forked rather than rounded; flight usually higher than that of Whip-poor-will and a large *white spot shows in each dark wing* like a hole through it; the white throat band of nighthawk crosses high on throat while that of Whip-poor-will crosses lower down near upper breast.

VOICE. — A single harsh note, described by various authors as *peent, scaipe, scape, ch-eek, speek, mueke, squeak, peep, beard, aëk,* etc., according to the imagination of the writer; the note varies somewhat, and when heard close at hand seems double; hence the two syllable attempts to imitate the cry such as *peesquăw, mizard, aëk-aëk, beé-ak or speé-yah;* the latter, given by Dr. C. W. Townsend, resembles a real note of the bird; it reminds one of a common note of the Woodcock usually uttered on the ground, but the Nighthawk calls more commonly when on the wing.

BREEDING. — In open upland fields or moors, often on land burned over, in rocky pastures and in cities. *Nest:* None; eggs laid on bare rock, gravel, open ground, in open spaces among shrubbery or on flat gravelled roofs of buildings.* *Eggs:* 2; 1.09 to 1.32 by .80 to .90 in.; nearly elliptical; very variable in color and markings; most New England eggs show a very light ground color varying from creamy-

---

* A nighthawk once laid her eggs between the rails of a track (Bird-Lore, Vol. XXVII, 1925, p. 251); another nested in a deserted Robin's nest (Journal of the Maine Ornithological Society, Vol. X, p. 25).

white to olive-gray. Typical specimens may be described as follows: grayish-white, spotted and blotched more or less, with browns, drab and lilac; illustrated in Bendire's "Life Histories of North American Birds," Vol. II, Plate III, Figs. 1 to 3. *Dates:* May 10, South Carolina; May 20 to June 5, Virginia; June 5 to 15, Massachusetts, and June 15 to July 4, Maine. *Incubation:* Period about 16 days (Bendire); by both sexes. One brood yearly.

RANGE. — North America to southern South America. Breeds from northern Yukon, central Mackenzie, northern Saskatchewan, northern Manitoba, northern Ontario, central and eastern Quebec and western Newfoundland south to northwestern Washington, southwestern Alberta, southern Manitoba, northeastern Oklahoma, northern Arkansas, southern Illinois, southeastern Tennessee, central northern Georgia and southern Virginia, and in the United States west to edge of Great Plains in western Minnesota, eastern South Dakota, eastern Nebraska and eastern Kansas; west in migration to eastern Alaska and east to Bermuda Islands; winters in South America from Venezuela and Colombia to Brazil and Argentina; straggles northward to Melville Island, Arctic Ocean.

DISTRIBUTION IN NEW ENGLAND. — Common migrant and common summer resident, somewhat locally distributed in rather open lands; shuns highest elevations of northern New England; breeds rarely in coastal region of southeastern Massachusetts and Rhode Island and rather rarely in Connecticut.

SEASON IN MASSACHUSETTS. — (March 16 to 30, April 20) April 25 to October 6.

NOTE. The March records of the Nighthawk need some explanation. For years we have received occasional very early records of this bird but ignored them, believing that a note of the Woodcock had been mistaken for that of the Nighthawk, but in March, 1925, so many reports of the bird came in that they could not be disregarded. On March 14, 1925, Mr. O. R. Robbins, Pleasant Lake, Nova Scotia, during a heavy rain with high wind heard a Nighthawk, and, going out, flushed the bird from the ground or near it. He could see the bars on its lower plumage and the white spots on its wings. Mr. E. W. Schmidt, of New Britain, Connecticut, wrote that on March 16, two days later, five Nighthawks appeared on a farm there, pursuing insects about an apple orchard. They remained there until the 22nd, when they disappeared. Mr. Bartol Parker wrote on the 29th from Framingham, Massachusetts, that Mr. Elton Clark and his son had seen one there almost daily since the 17th and had heard its cry. Miss Louise B. Pratt, of Middleboro, Massachusetts, heard, as she believes, several individuals flying very high on the evening of March 19. On the evening of the 29th Mrs. W. P. Richmond, of North Middleboro, heard the call of the Nighthawk many times and afterwards heard two others. She also has a record of one both heard and seen March 25, 1921. These people all know the bird and its notes. Others reported hearing Nighthawks in flight. These birds in migration fly in large flocks along the seaboard and large river valleys, especially in the fall. Mr. Arthur T. Wayne says that on September 6, 1905, flights of Nighthawks were passing along the coast of South Carolina in such numbers that their dense flocks obscured the sky and that they extended over a space (so far as he was able to ascertain) of 15 miles from east to west. A flight of these birds may have been moving north from South America in mid-March, 1925, and some of them may have been blown out to sea and carried north on the wings of a cyclonic storm that raged up the coast about that time. The action of such storms and their effect on flights of birds is explained in the introduction to Volume I of this work.

HAUNTS AND HABITS. The Nighthawk is a wonderful bird. It wanders in migration from the islands of the Arctic Ocean to southern South America. It feeds and flies indifferently at any hour of the day or night, being able apparently to see and catch flying insects in brightest sunlight or on clear nights. It has an enormous stomach which requires quantities of food to supply its remarkable digestion, and thus furnish energy to sustain it in tireless flight. Its mouth, like that of the Whip-poor-will, opens far back under its ears and forms a yawning trap to engulf unwary insects, while its long and powerful wings enable it to overtake them with ease.   It lays its eggs on the ground, on a ledge or on the flat roof of a building, exposed to the blazing summer sun, where it seems as if the young bird must be roasted alive, but nevertheless it seems to reproduce its kind with fair regularity.

In late April or early May the Nighthawks, coming up from the south, usually appear in southern New England.   In backward seasons, however, their migration through this region continues until June.   In mating the courtship is mostly an aërial performance, for the Nighthawk is preëminently a fowl of the air.   In the mating season the male often rises to a considerable height and then falls swiftly, head first, with wings partly closed, until near the earth, when, spreading his wings, he turns upward, producing with his vibrating primaries a resounding boom which may be heard at a considerable distance.

The eggs so closely resemble the rock, earth or gravel, on which they rest, and the young so simulate in appearance clods or horse droppings covered with mold that they seem to escape the eyes of their enemies.   The mother sitting on her eggs is almost invisible, as her plumage blends into the colors of her environment, and she will sit there with eyes nearly closed until almost trodden upon.   Sometimes she will refuse to leave, but with spread wings will make a noise like a spitting cat.   If she is brooding young, she may leave them, and rush hissing at the intruder with her great mouth wide open.   As she charges forward, almost hidden, as it were, behind that yawning cavity, she must present a fearsome front to any small or timid creature.   There is something menacing and snake-like about that swiftly advancing open countenance.   But if the bold front fails to daunt the enemy, she may resort to artifice and limp along the ground like a wounded bird, fluttering slowly ahead of her pursuer.   If he fails to follow she may fall across the top of a low stump or rock and lie there as if at her last gasp with head down and one wing hanging as if broken, meantime uttering doleful cries, while the young lie flat and motionless.

The Nighthawk usually sleeps during the brighter part of the day, resting upon the ground, a rock, a fence rail or a bough.   Usually it sits silent on a large limb, where it might be mistaken for an excrescence or a bunch of gray lichens.   During the nesting season, however, it keeps very irregular hours; frequently it hunts in daylight, and may sleep in the darker part of the night, but at times it is heard on the wing far into the night. Breeding in cities is a comparatively recent custom and dates from the introduction of flat, tar and gravel roofs.   These arid spaces seem to suit the bird, and it hawks about high over the city roofs, seeking its insect prey.

The young are fed chiefly by regurgitation, though they have been seen to explore the open mouth of the parent bird in search of food.   They can withstand considerable heat, but Dr. A. O. Gross records a case where a young one succumbed to the heat during a hot wave when the temperature on an unsheltered gravel roof rose to 140°.[1]

Late in August the southward movement of the Nighthawks begins, and it continues intermittently through the greater part of September.   The birds are seen commonly

---

[1] Bulletin of the Northeastern Bird-Banding Association, 1926, p. 42.

passing southward along some river valley in numbers from a score to a hundred or more in loose scattered flocks, flying about in a leisurely manner at no great height above the ground or water, and catching insects as they go. These flocks sometimes rest during a part of the day, either on the ground or in trees on rough and rocky land, and if undisturbed begin their journey toward evening, first filling their stomachs as they go. I have seen Nighthawks resting on the limbs of trees during a migration period. Mr. A. W. Bowers, of Royalston, Massachusetts, noted that when blasting began on road work in the north part of that town on September 3, 1926, three great flocks of Nighthawks, apparently startled by the explosions, arose from the wooded or bushy ground, hovered about for a time and then joined in one large flock and passed on.

It seems probable that a large part of the migration takes place at night, after the birds have fed, when they rise to a great height. Mr. Frank S. Gifford, of Brimfield, Massachusetts, says that he counted 37 birds that appeared, having apparently descended from a considerable height to a point near his position, on September 8, 1926, and that they stayed near him, feeding, for forty-five minutes, sailing around about fifty feet above the ground. Then they rose in the air to "the point of invisibility."

When the flocks are feeding, they do not always move southward, and sometimes they have been observed to travel in exactly the opposite direction. There are certain routes over water which are followed by them, and which often take them far off from the direct southwesterly course. But the general movement trends southward.

The food of the Nighthawk apparently consists entirely of insects. Its large stomach often is packed with them, and its gullet also and even its mouth may be filled with them when about to feed its young. Usually it is difficult to determine with what they are fed, unless (as in a case mentioned by Professor Herrick) the food consists of a mass of living, glowing fireflies. The late Professor Harvey of the Maine State College found remains of 500 mosquitoes in a Nighthawk's stomach. In the stomach of another 1800 winged ants were found and in still another 60 grasshoppers. Its insect food is so varied that it is impossible to enumerate it. Apparently it takes any insect that flies, from tiny gnats to the largest moths. Probably it eats some useful parasitic insects, but a bird that destroys such quantities of first-class pests is entitled to its share of useful insects.

ECONOMIC STATUS. The Nighthawk is believed to be one of our most useful birds. It gourmandizes on such pests as the Colorado potato beetle and the cotton-boll weevil. Nevertheless thousands of these birds have been shot, particularly in the south, by people who enjoy killing any bird that is large enough to make a good target. The bird should be protected everywhere at all times.

SUBORDER CYPSELI. SWIFTS.

Number of species in North America 4; in Massachusetts 1.

This suborder contains but one family, the characters of which are as those of the suborder and are given below.

Family **MICROPODIDÆ.** Swifts.

Number of species in North America 4; in Massachusetts **1.**

Swifts receive their name from their remarkable power of flight. They are believed to be the swiftest birds that fly. In North America they seem to form a connecting link between the nighthawks and the hummingbirds. They have not the long, slender bill of the hummingbird, but a rather short, small, triangular bill and a large, wide mouth, thereby approaching the nighthawks and the swallows, but in the form of the skeleton, the shape of the wings, the small feet and similar anatomical conformation swifts and hummingbirds are much alike. The wings are long, slim and pointed; the hind toe is elevated, reversible or turned sidewise or forward or the four toes tend toward an arrangement in pairs. There is a nude oil-gland. The salivary glands are remarkably developed, and the gummy saliva is used in the construction of the nest. In some species the nest is composed entirely of dried saliva which forms the celebrated "edible birds' nest." The plumage in most cases is hard but in several Indian species it is softer, approaching in texture that of the goatsuckers. The North American swifts are divided into two subfamilies, mainly on account of a difference in the structure of the feet. In this volume we have to do with only one of these, the *Chæturinæ.* All swifts are insect-eating birds and take their prey while in flight. The young are hatched naked.

Economic Status. Swifts, feeding as they do entirely or almost entirely on flying insects, are believed to be very useful birds.

Subfamily **CHÆTURINÆ.** Spine-tailed Swifts.

Number of species in North America 3; in Massachusetts 1.

This subfamily has the front toes cleft to base, the hind toe not reversed, but sometimes reversible, and the tarsi covered with naked skin. The shafts of the tail-feathers project naked, stiff and attenuated beyond the webs, and are used, as are the strong shafts of the tail in woodpeckers, to aid and support the birds in clinging to vertical surfaces. There are more than thirty species so specialized.

Chætúra pelágica (Linnæus). **Chimney Swift.**

Other names: CHIMNEY SWALLOW; CHIMNEY-BIRD.

Plate 53.

DESCRIPTION. — Bill very small, mouth large and deeply cleft; eyes very large; wings longer than bird; tail short, even or slightly rounded, with spiny tips of shafts projecting like needles beyond the webs; legs short, feet with hind toe elevated above level of others; claws rather long and sharp-pointed. *Adults (sexes alike):* Above dark, sooty olive-brown with some gloss, becoming lighter grayish-brown on rump, upper tail-coverts and tail; feathers of top of head darker centrally; wings sooty-blackish, the inner webs of flight-feathers fading into grayish-brown toward edges; sides of neck and all of lower plumage plain grayish-brown, becoming considerably paler on throat, chin and cheeks; bill black; iris

FIG. 56. — NEST AND EGGS OF CHIMNEY SWIFT IN CHIMNEY

Page 311

FIG. 57. — NEST AND EGGS OF KINGBIRD

Page 327

dark brown; legs and feet brownish-black. *Young in first winter and juvenal plumage:* Much like adults (feathers of rump and upper tail-coverts are paler, with lighter edges in the nestling).

MEASUREMENTS. — Length 4.75 to 5.60 in.; spread about 11.98 to 12.65; folded wing 4.85 to 5.25; tail 1.61 to 2.00; bill .20 to .25 from tip to feathers of forehead; tarsus .41 to .55. Female usually smaller than male.

MOLTS. — Young hatched naked, but juvenal plumage develops (July to September) and bird becomes fully fledged; there may be an incomplete molt of body feathers in late summer and autumn, but no sign of this was noted, so juvenal plumage may be retained until spring; no winter specimens were available for examination; complete prenuptial molt beginning in late winter or early spring is followed by a plumage as adult; adults apparently molt twice a year, a complete postnuptial molt in autumn and a partial (possibly complete) molt in spring.

FIELD MARKS. — Size about that of Tree Swallow; sooty bird, almost always seen in flight; flies swiftly, often high, with long wings and looks like a flying cigar; occasionally spreads a rather short fan-shaped tail; seen most commonly at morning and evening.

VOICE. — A loud *chit, chit, chit* or similar notes, run together at times in a chittering cry often prolonged in flight; young utter a loud hiss when disturbed, otherwise a *cheep*.

BREEDING. — Normally in wooded regions, but now wherever a suitable nesting place is available. *Nest:* A "half-saucer-shaped structure" of twigs, stuck together ("varnished") with dried glutinous saliva of the bird and glued in same manner to inside of chimney (from near top to 22 feet below it), unoccupied dwelling, inner wall of barn or shed, near eaves, or inside of a hollow tree, well or cistern. *Eggs:* 4 or 5, rarely 6; .69 to .85 by .50 to .55 in.; elongate ovate to cylindrical ovate; white and moderately glossy; illustrated in Bendire's "Life Histories of North American Birds," Vol. II, Plate I, Fig. 25. *Dates:* May 24 to June 18, Missouri; June 3, Pennsylvania; June 10 to July 1, Rhode Island; June 15 into July, Maine. *Incubation:* Period 18 to 22 days (authors); 16 days (C. MacNamara); by both sexes. One brood yearly.

RANGE. — Eastern North America and middle America. Breeds over most of its range in North America from central Alberta, southeastern Saskatchewan, central Manitoba, central Ontario, southern Quebec, and Newfoundland south to Gulf coast and central Florida, and west to Great Plains, in east central Montana, Nebraska, Kansas, Oklahoma and eastern Texas; migrates through Mexico to Guatemala; winter range not known but probably Central America; casual in the Bermudas; accidental in southern Greenland, and New Mexico.

DISTRIBUTION IN NEW ENGLAND. — Common migrant and common to abundant summer resident.

SEASON IN MASSACHUSETTS. — (April 18) April 25 to October 5 (October 13 and 16).

HAUNTS AND HABITS. Some people call this bird the chimney sweep; but it does not sweep chimneys. It sweeps the skies. In all New England there are few farming regions or country villages where any watcher of the sky, gazing from his pillow through his matutinal window, cannot see the swifts rapidly drawing disappearing lines across the blue. Zigzags and long curves intersect one another as the merry birds drive through the fresh morning air with quivering wings and shrill twitterings — erratic avian missiles seeking luckless winged insects in the over-arching skies.

Swifts are well named. Probably there are no swifter birds. Even the stooping falcon can rarely if ever overtake one. Their speed has been estimated at unbelievable figures, and it has been said that in their ordinary avocations they travel a thousand miles a day. Such statements, however, cannot be verified, and we must be content to watch them with no accurate knowledge of their greatest speed or the length of their daily pathways through the "illimitable air." The swift is essentially a fowl of the air. When its growing young are clamoring for food, it keeps the air much of the time, from the first indication of morning light in the east until nightfall. So far as we know, it never rests on ground or tree limb, and it sleeps clinging to a perpendicular wall in chimney, well, cistern, cave, building or hollow tree, or very rarely to a tree trunk, woodpile or some such upright outer surface. Virtually all its outdoor life is passed in the air. It lives in the air and probably sometimes dies there. Mr. Freeman B. Currier tells me that one of his friends found a Chimney Swift dead in the street, with its wings outstretched and rigid as in flight, and that he himself has found them dead in the same way. The bird is as free as the winds. Its courtship is an aërial one. The first comers reach Massachusetts usually in late April. Later the males may be seen chasing the females about the sky in sport or earnest with down-bent wings and cheerful cries.

When the birds are mated, they commence breaking dead twigs off the trees for their nest, by flying swiftly against a twig and grasping it in their feet or bills as they pass. Often they are unable to tear the twig loose or even to break it, but each bird perseveres until the nest is finished. Twigs are glued first against the inner wall of tree, cave, chimney, well or building by the copious sticky saliva of the birds, and others are then attached in the same way to these first. Mr. Otto Widmann, who watched a breeding pair during three seasons, says that the building of the nest requires about 18 days, and that egg laying begins before the nest is finished.[1] Such work is successful only in dry weather and if much rain occurs the building of the chimney nests is long delayed, and sometimes copious rains later dissolve the gluey substance and precipitate nest and eggs or young to the bottom of the chimney. Miss Stella M. Davis wrote to me on July 29, 1922, that she had been watching a pair through a hole in a chimney directly opposite their nest. The sexes relieved each other during incubation. "Each bird" she wrote, "gave a low call when it entered the chimney; the bird on the nest rose then, hovered an instant while the incoming bird slipped on to the nest, then flew out. Both birds, sitting side by side, facing toward the bricks, occupied the nest at night." When the young birds are about two weeks old, they leave the nest and usually cling to the chimney wall below it where they are fed by the parents until they can fly. Swifts prefer large old-fashioned chimneys for nesting places, and usually occupy such as are unused during the summer. One season, however, a pair built a nest in the chimney of Mr. Brewster's cabin at Concord and brought up a brood successfully, even though a wood fire was built often in the fireplace less than six feet below the nest. The little domicile was so situated over the front of the fireplace that a draught of pure, cool air passed constantly by it when the fire was burning, and the birds did not suffer from smoke or heat. By placing a mirror in the back corner of the fireplace we were able to watch the feeding of the young.

The swift's upward flutterings, downward swoops and quick zigzags commonly are executed in pursuit of fast flying insects, but these birds are extremely playful and many aërial evolutions appear to be the manifestation of a frolicsome spirit. Once while watch-

---

[1] Bendire, C.: Life Histories of North American Birds, Vol. II, 1895, p. 180.

ing some Cedar Waxwings hawking for insects over a river, I saw a Chimney Swift chase them as if with evil intent. The frightened Cedarbirds quickly sought refuge in the nearest tree. Evidently the swift was in play, as it could not possibly have swallowed a bird larger than itself, nor could its weak bill have greatly injured the waxwing. Indeed swifts seem to be entirely harmless, and so far as I know, they are not in the least quarrelsome and have never been known to injure any other bird. They seem fearless, however, as they pay little attention to hawks and they keep the air during the approach of the most violent thunder-storms and tempests. They seem to enjoy riding the storm. If, however, a storm comes on toward night bringing on premature darkness, the swifts are very likely to betake themselves to their chimneys as they do at nightfall.

Once I saw one driven to cover by a hail storm. The hail had beaten it almost to the ground, when it sought the protection of a porch or covered doorway, in which I had already found shelter from the storm, and it attempted to alight on the door within a short distance of my head. Then, apparently finding this refuge unsafe, it fared forth again, braving the storm. This swift bathes and drinks while on the wing, and very rarely one dips in too deep and cannot rise from the water. Mr. Thornton W. Burgess sends the following note: "On June 1st, 1922, while fishing at Moosehead Lake my attention was drawn to a curious object flopping shoreward about 100 yards out. I presently recognized it as a Chimney Swift. It came steadily in with a series of flops, and I picked it up on the shore. It was taken into the kitchen of the hotel and dried off and then set free, when it flew away with no sign of injury. Apparently the bird had in some way swooped low enough to become thoroughly wet and thus unable to fly. This is the only explanation I can give of its curious predicament." Large numbers of Chimney Swifts roost at night in the capacious chimneys of certain large buildings, such as school-houses or factories. The male birds sleep in such dormitories more or less throughout the summer, and when the young are fledged many of them follow their parents to these roosting places. It is an interesting sight to see a swarm of swifts retiring at nightfall into such a place of refuge. This happens more or less at the migration periods.* Hundreds and sometimes thousands gyrate and play about over the chimney, forming a funnel-shaped flock, and finally one by one they raise their wings and drop quickly into it until the whole swarm is at rest. In some remote places their flocks still descend into great hollow trees to pass the night. Audubon, who effected an entrance into one of these hollow trees and examined the roosting birds by artificial light, estimated that 9000 were sleeping in that tree. In all their evolutions there seems to be no interference; no collisions occur, and they seem to live in perfect harmony. The first birds to enter arrange themselves in a row near the top, and the later entrants perch in tiers below.

Chimney Swifts are more or less crepuscular as well as diurnal; that is, they go abroad at early morning and evening, seeming to prefer half-twilight to broad day. Therefore dull and cloudy weather suits them well; but they fly in bright sunlight, and may be

---

* "A Chimney Swift Invasion" — Under this title Bird-Lore (Vol. XXIV, 1922, p. 210) publishes an account of an invasion by many migrating swifts of the chimney and fireplace of a house in Kingston, New York.

seen during warm days far up in the sky chasing insects that rise high on such days. At times swifts seem to be on the wing far into the night, as their cries come down to us from the darkness.* Evidently then their large dark eyes can penetrate the gloom of night. Swifts are believed to feed entirely on flying insects, but my experience in watching them inclines me to the belief that they sometimes take small caterpillars that, spinning down on long threads from the branches of trees, are blown about by the wind, and they may even pick one occasionally from the leaves.

The glands which supply the so-called saliva used in building their nests are very much enlarged in spring, but after the nests are built these shrink rapidly, and the space that they occupied forms two cheek pouches in which the swift can pack a quantity of small insects. Hawking about the sky, it fills these pouches and then descends the chimney to feed its young, to which it seems exceedingly devoted.

Mr. C. J. Maynard, who gives an excellent description of the habits of this species, tells how a Chimney Swift lost its life in a burning building in the attempt to reach its young. "When the swifts enter a narrow flue," he says "they proceed in a singular manner; balancing themselves for a moment over the opening and elevating their wings to the utmost, they will settle downward, but a too rapid descent is avoided by oscillating the body from side to side. When ascending, the wings are vibrated rapidly, causing a noise which resembles distant thunder. They are very devoted to their offspring and I once observed a touching display of this. A house in the chimney of which a pair of these birds had a home, was on fire, the roof had fallen in, thus the flames were leaping upward with fury and the intense heat caused all in the immediate vicinity to withdraw, when I observed a Chimney Swift circling high over the burning pile; it paused above the chimney which contained its young, balanced itself for a moment, and, to my astonishment, dropped quickly with the usual rocking motion, into a flue which was surrounded by bricks that were fairly glowing with heat. This extreme devotion to its young must have caused its death as it did not appear again; in fact, it could not have lived a moment in the furnace which it entered." [1]

In cold, rainy weather which clears the air of flying insects and causes caterpillars to seek shelter, the Chimney Swift perforce must starve. When they cannot obtain their food from the air, both old and young must perish. In June, 1903, southern New England was visited by an almost unprecedented series of rain-storms and low temperatures. From June 7 to 27, inclusive, the temperature rose above 70 degrees on only four days and dropped below 50 on eight. It rained more or less on sixteen of the twenty days, with severe storms on the 12th, 15th and 21st, when over three inches of rain fell. After the storm three wheelbarrow loads of dead Chimney Swifts were removed from the base of a great mill chimney or smoke-stack in North Billerica, Massachusetts, and bushels of these birds' bodies were said to have been removed when the pit at the base of a large

---

* In the extreme northern parts of their range in Canada, where the summer days are very long, they are said to retire before nightfall.

[1] Birds of Eastern North America, 1896, p. 399.

chimney at Clark University, Worcester, was cleaned out. Swifts which roosted in great numbers in a tall smoke-stack adjoining the State Hospital grounds at Taunton perished similarly. These swifts not only roost in great hollow trees and large chimneys, but also nest in some numbers in such places. Dead swifts were found all over southern New England and dead swallows and martins as well. I published a full account of the occurrence in the fifty-first annual report of the Massachusetts State Board of Agriculture. Since that time two similar storms have taken place in New England, but they were not as prolonged, and the destruction of birds, though great, probably was much less than in 1903.

ECONOMIC STATUS. As Chimney Swifts live chiefly on flying insects, including large numbers of *Diptera*, they are believed to be very beneficial. Mr. W. L. McAtee who has investigated the food of the species for the Biological Survey says that it gets many bark beetles (*Scolytidæ*) "the most serious enemies of our forests" and other injurious insects and he considers it "largely beneficial to the agricultural interests of the country." [1]

Those who believe that Chimney Swifts are likely to infest a house with bed-bugs should read the report on this insect by Professor Otto Lugger, in which he shows that the bugs found in "swallows" nests belong to similar species but cannot exist long outside the "swallows" nest.[2]

SUBORDER TROCHILI. HUMMINGBIRDS.

Number of species in North America 18; in Massachusetts 1.

This suborder contains but one family, entirely American and characteristic of the Neotropical region. The characters of the suborder are necessarily the same as those of the family.

FAMILY TROCHILIDÆ. HUMMINGBIRDS.

Number of species in North America 18; in Massachusetts 1.

This family contains the smallest birds known. Osteologically they resemble the swifts, and like them the oil gland is nude, but they have small mouths and long attenuated bills, while the tongue somewhat resembles that of a woodpecker, being long, round and capable of considerable protrusion. The tongue is virtually a sheathed double-barreled tube, and is connected by a muscular arrangement with the hyoid bone, so that it can be thrust far out beyond the end of the bill, as in woodpeckers. It is supposed to be used in sucking sweets from deep flowers.

These little birds are known at once by their small size, long bills, the humming noise made by their wings, and their remarkable powers of flight. Probably few, if any, birds can surpass the speed at which they can dart through the air. In many ways this is the most remarkable group of birds in the world. Small size and brilliancy of changing

---

[1] Bird-Lore, Vol. XIII, 1911, pp. 117–118.
[2] Second annual report of the Entomologist of the State Experiment Station, University of Minnesota, 1896, pp. 199–200.

iridescent colors due to refraction of light caused by feather-structure, are their chief characteristics; only one species is known to be over five inches in length. There is considerable diversity in the shape of the tail in hummers. They are found over both American Continents from Alaska to Patagonia, but the great majority of species are tropical. The number of species approaches 500, of which about 20 have been found within the limits of the United States, but only one has been authentically recorded from New England.

ECONOMIC STATUS. Hummingbirds are generally believed to subsist entirely on the nectar of flowers, but some of them feed mainly, if not wholly, on the insects of forest trees and all of them take a considerable proportion of insect food. Like the bees they distribute more or less pollen and so assist in fertilizing flowers. They are harmless and useful birds.

Archilochus colubris (LINNÆUS). Ruby-throated Hummingbird.

Plate 54.

DESCRIPTION. — *Adult male:* Tail forked, of narrow tapering feathers; above, including middle tail-feathers, golden bronze-green; wings and outer feathers of tail purplish-dusky or slaty; a tiny white spot behind eye; throat metallic, changeable ruby-red; chin and sides of head to below eyes blackish; tuft on either side of rump and on thigh white; rest of under plumage mostly brownish-gray, lightening to whitish or brownish-white on upper breast, and darkening on sides where overlaid by metallic green like that of back; iris dark brown; bill, legs and feet black. *Adult female:* Similar to adult male but not so brilliant; tail not forked, but rounded; three outer tail-feathers broadly tipped white; sides of head below eyes dusky; chin, throat and other lower plumage chiefly grayish or whitish. *Young male:* Similar to adult female, but white-tipped tail often slightly forked, throat streaked with dusky, sometimes with a few ruby feathers, and upper plumage with lighter margins. *Young female:* Similar to adult female.

MEASUREMENTS. — Length 3.07 to 3.95 in.; spread 4.00 to 4.75; folded wing 1.50 to 1.90; tail .90 to 1.25; bill .50 to .83; tarsus .15 to .20. Female sometimes larger than male.

MOLTS. — Little is known regarding the molts of this species, as winter specimens in the molt are few; young are hatched naked and the first plumage shows some down filaments; apparently molting in the young begins in October, when young males show some red on throat; in spring, young birds apparently are as adults; adults have a complete molt some time between autumn and spring.

FIELD MARKS. — In New England where no other species of hummingbird has been found, this bird is unmistakable; plate 54 shows male and female in characteristic positions in the air.

VOICE. — "Shrill squealing sounds like *chic-we-we-a*" frequently and rapidly repeated when fighting (C. Bendire); short repeated chirps or squeaks; an excited chippering; no record of this after breeding season (Bicknell).

BREEDING. — In orchard and other trees about cultivated lands and in open woodlands or dense forests. *Nest:* A lovely little cup lined with plant down and covered outwardly with bits of lichen (rarely with small bits of bark), saddled on a small limb and resembling a knot when seen from below; from 3 ft. to 30 ft. from ground; dimensions about 1½ inches in outside diameter and 1¼ inches in outside depth. *Eggs:* 2; .48 to .57 by .33 to .36 in.; usually elliptical-oval; white; illustrated in Bendire's "Life Histories of North American Birds," Vol. II, Plate I, Fig. 27. *Dates:* April 24 to May 20, South Carolina; May 1 to 14, District of Columbia; May 24 to June 15, Massachusetts.* *Incubation:* Period 14 days (Burns); by female. One or two broods yearly.

---

* A nest with one egg May 18, 1905, at Branchport, New York (Oölogist, Vol. XXXVII, 1920, p. 60).

PLATE 54

PLATE 54

RUBY–THROATED HUMMINGBIRD
Page 316

Adult Female

Adult Male

Flower — Blue Vervain

All about two-thirds scale.

Louis Agassiz Fuertes

RANGE. — Eastern North America and middle America. Breeds from northeastern Alberta (probably), central Saskatchewan, southern Manitoba, southern Ontario, southern Quebec and Cape Breton Island south to west central Texas, the Gulf coast and central Florida; winters from middle and southern Florida and southern Texas south through eastern and southern Mexico and Central America to Panama; accidental in Alaska and central Labrador; casual in migration to the Bermudas and Cuba.

DISTRIBUTION IN NEW ENGLAND. — Common migrant and common summer resident in most of the region; less common summer resident locally and on highest elevations.

SEASON IN MASSACHUSETTS. — (April 25) May 1 to October 15.

HAUNTS AND HABITS. The Ruby-throated Hummingbird is in some respects the most remarkable bird of New England. As Minot says "America may well boast of a treasure which no other country possesses." When the first settlers landed on these shores, they had never seen a hummingbird. Therefore, some of the chroniclers who set down in ink "true relations" regarding the New Land included the tiny bird among the marvels of the country. Some of their descriptions are more picturesque than accurate. William Wood, writing in 1634, informs all and sundry that "The Humbird is one of the wonders of the Countrey, being no bigger than a Hornet, yet hath all the demensions of a Bird, as bill, and wings, with quills, spider-like legges, small clawes: For colour she is as glorious as the Raine-bow; as she flies, she makes a little humming noise like a Humble-bee: wherefore shee is called the Humbird." [1]

Thomas Morton, writing two years earlier, gives us the following illuminating account: "There is a curious bird to see to, called a humming bird, no bigger than a great beetle: that out of question lives upon the Bee, which hee eateth and catcheth amongst Flowers. For it is his custome to frequent these places. Flowers he cannot feed upon by reason of his sharp bill which is like the poynt of a Spanish needle, but shorte. His fethers have a glosse like silke, and as hee stirres they show to be of a chaingable coloure: and has bin, and is admired for shape, coloure and size."

This little bird seems to have few effective enemies. He is too agile and swift for them. At times when he is not feeling truculent, he may allow some of the larger birds to chase him away from their nests, but I have seldom heard of the catching of a hummingbird by another bird. Rarely is he followed far. Now and then an inexperienced Starling will follow one for a long distance, perhaps mistaking it for a moth, but the hummer easily evades its pursuer. It contends more or less with the bees for the nectar of the flowers, and sometimes visits a beehive and inserts its bill into the entrance, possibly in search of sweets. Miss Mabel Tilton, of Vineyard Haven, reports that on May 22 a hummingbird was seeking food from the blossoms of an early shrub, and that every time he visited it he first cleared it of all the bees, dashing at them and driving them away. Sometimes this bird has a savage battle with the "bumblebees" which are reluctant to leave its favorite flowers. The tiny hummingbird is a mighty warrior, with greater strength and speed in proportion to its size than any other bird that flies. The flight

---

[1] New England's Prospect, 1634, p. 31.

muscles of its breast are relatively immense, and it is possessed of such spirit that it does not hesitate to attack any bird, no matter what its size, when occasion seems to require it. Kingbird, hawk, crow or eagle, all alike quickly feel the effects of the hummingbird's displeasure. It has even been known to drive to cover a pompous Plymouth Rock rooster. Its needle-like bill is an irritating little weapon and not to be despised when driven forward by its sturdy humming wings.* Those little wings beating so fast that eye cannot see their motion nor camera depict them, carry it on long migrations, as the species ranges from Hudson Bay to Panama. Some of the Ruby-throats must cross wide stretches of ocean. They must pass over at least 600 miles to reach the Bermudas and 500 miles to cross the Gulf of Mexico to Yucatan and Central America.

Ruby-throated Hummingbirds appear generally in New England when the cherry trees are in blossom, and sometimes a considerable number may be seen buzzing about one blooming tree — their wings giving forth a sound as if giant bees were swarming. The males come first, and when the females arrive their wooing soon begins. Hummingbirds always are quick, but during the mating season the pugnacious males are so dashing and impetuous that the eye can hardly follow their movements, which in their battles are so rapid that the details are confusing. In courtship the female flees and the male pursues. They vanish like shooting-stars, and the dénouement seldom is witnessed by human eye; but when the male displays his beauties before a female that is sitting demurely on a twig, his movements may be readily descried. He seems able to perform any acrobatic feat in the air. He can charge toward her with amazing speed until almost upon her; then suddenly stop and, hanging in mid-air, back away. His most remarkable feat, however, is to swing before her as if hung from an invisible rod like the "lob" of a mighty pendulum, swinging from side to side with breath-taking speed in a segment of a vertical circle thus: ∪ . The radius of the swing may vary with different individuals from three to forty feet or even more. Some birds rise much higher at one end of the segment than at the other, thus: ∪ and often one rises vertically at each end, forming a broad U, thus: ∪ or a vertical half circle. Sometimes the male takes only two or three of these swings; or he may execute fifteen or twenty. Usually the female is sitting near the very bottom of his swing or just below it, and as he flashes back and forth close before her or just above, his gorget glows like fire. Miss Caroline E. Hamilton watching one said that "presently he alighted, and his ruby throat seemed fairly ablaze, but gradually grew dimmer until it seemed its ordinary red." This change may have been caused by a change of position of bird or feathers which might cause the light to reflect from them at a different angle. During the swinging performance the male often makes an unusual humming with its wings and continues chippering or twittering, though some of its notes are so fine that they rarely can be heard by human ears. Now and then a hummer

---

*Hummingbirds, however, have to face many dangers. If they flutter too near the surface of the water they may be seized by big fish (Bird-Lore, Vol. XXIV, 1922, p. 94). They may be blown into the sea by a storm during migration, and some have been found dead (as have other small birds), caught by the strong burrs of the burdock.

is observed to shoot up into the air vertically for fifty feet or more and back again. Probably this also is a manifestation of sexual passion.

After mating, the male apparently becomes a gay wanderer with nothing to do but to enjoy himself or to chase other birds. He spends much time sitting on a particular twig, which he chooses for his watch-tower and resting place, and dressing his plumage, while his mate builds the nest and rears the brood. Very rarely does the male seem to take any interest in the proceedings, though occasionally one may be seen about the nest, and it is said that he sometimes carries building material, but I have not observed this. Having once chosen a nesting site the birds apparently return to the same spot year after year, but I believe that each year a new nest is built. Once I found four nests within a few yards of each other, two of them evidently deserted nests of previous years.

In building the nest the female chooses a limb or twig often sheltered above by leaves or branches, and then collects silky or downy fibers from various plants and trees, such as the down from ferns and milkweed and that from undeveloped oak leaves which she fastens in place with spider's web or that of the tent-caterpillar. With such material she fashions her nest, collecting bits of wet lichens from the trees and attaching them to the outside as the nest rises, so that when finished it appears like a small knot covered with tree lichens. She works expeditiously, flying directly on to the nest with a bit of material, and in another instant off again like a winged bullet.

The hummingbird does not always show good judgment in placing its nest. Set astride a small limb, "like a saddle on a horse," oftentimes this small limb is smooth, as on a pear or an apple tree. In this case a gale may so thrash the limb about that the little nest will become loosened on its slippery foundation and finally will blow off. Occasionally bits of bark are used instead of lichens. In building the nest she sits in it, shaping it to her body and working with both bill and feet; often the eggs are laid before the nest is completed, and the female frequently may be seen to add to it even after the young are hatched; in this case, the nest may often appear two-storied on the outside on account of the different colored lichens used. When the little thing is done, it is the softest, warmest and most lovely cradle imaginable for her tiny white eggs, which are about the size of small white beans. The time required to build it varies much according to the weather, but usually it takes about a week.

Under "Breeding" 14 days is given as the period of incubation, but this may vary somewhat, as I have records of a 13-day period. Audubon gives a week and Mr. Wilbur Smith, of South Norwalk, Connecticut, tells of two eggs, the first laid on June 2, and the second June 4, both of which hatched on June 15, eleven days after the last egg was deposited. The eggs are large for the size of the bird, and are not always laid on consecutive days, one or two days often elapsing between the production of the first and second. There is a great variation in the time that the young remain in the nest. This period has been given by different writers as from 6 to 18 days. It may be possible that in the south or during a hot wave in the north, when the female can safely leave her young without danger of chilling them, that she may procure enough food for them to develop wings to the flight stage in a short time; but my New England records of this period run from 14 to 28 days. Usually the young require no urging to go when the time comes, but Mr. Smith says that in one case the mother grasped the bill of a young bird in her own and tried to pull it off the nest. Failing, she left it, and then the young bird flew to a bush not far away where the mother soon found it. Miss Isabella McC. Lemmon, of Englewood, New Jersey, had an exceptional view of young hummingbirds. She says in Bird-Lore: "The little things . . . lay flat on the bottom of the nest, with necks outstretched; they were a little less than an inch in length, dark slate-color, with a little yellowish fuzz on the bodies, exceedingly thin necks, three-cornered heads and short yellow bills. The eyes were closed. Two days later the fuzz had grown so that the bodies were nearly hidden by it, though the heads were still bare, and the bills were almost twice their original length." When they were nine days old she noted: "The young Hummingbirds nearly fill the nest. They are much browner than at first, and the fuzz does not seem to have grown much, if any. They have, however, quantities of tiny pin-feathers like needle-points, on the heads as well as the bodies, and the bills are nearly a third of an inch in length. The eyes are still closed. Four days later both had their eyes open and a few of the pin-feathers were breaking. Their later growth was so rapid that two days made a decided difference. Several days before leaving they were well feathered, showing the head and white throat over one edge of the nest and the white-cornered tail at the other. They flew July 1, having been respectively 21 and 22 days in the nest."

Hummingbirds appear to be such irritable, darting, erratic creatures that it seems rather surprising to find them coming to feed at regular hours, but Mr. E. O. Grant tells me that during one summer a female came at regular intervals to a window-box of flowering plants, and that she did not vary three minutes from the noon hour each day. The bird was looked for at that time daily, and came as the children came to their noonday meal. The male also came regularly about four o'clock for about six weeks. This went on for two seasons.

The mother is very devoted to her young while they are in the nest and vigorously attacks any bird that comes near them. Mrs. Julie D. Abbott reports that a hummingbird built a nest at Nonquit on the top of a pine cone on a slight branch of a pine tree and during a storm on August 24th, she clung bravely and desperately to the tossing nest, endeavoring to cover and protect her young. The second brood sometimes matures quite late in the season. Miss Mary I. Tufts, of Lynn, records a nest at Plymouth containing two young with eyes still closed August 28, 1924. These birds could not have been two weeks old.

Hummingbirds are very susceptible to cold; therefore, in cool, rainy weather the female must brood her young almost constantly, at least until they are well feathered, and cannot procure sufficient food for them to insure rapid growth. Even if she could leave them as usual at such times, the insects would be more difficult to find and she could not procure as much food as usual. Hummingbirds feed to a considerable extent on flying insects. Mrs. J. J. Piper reports that in the last week of September, 1922, she saw a large swarm of "white flies" near the house, and that a hummingbird darted into the center of the swarm and seemed to be spearing them with his long extensible tongue. It may be that the tongue is used in catching insects in the same manner in which the flicker catches ants. The food of the young is believed to consist of small, soft-bodied insects, swallowed and partially digested by the mother, and then regurgitated into the gullet of her offspring. The following from my notes taken when standing beside a nest, built about four feet from the ground in an apple tree, describes my impression of the young birds and the manner in which they are fed.

"How perfect are these little fledgling wanderers, in their tiny, moss-covered cup, shaded from the southern sun rays by the green leaves which overhang and surround the nest. Their dainty new feathers, of but a few days' growth, have been touched by the tender mother's breast alone or the gentle dew of heaven. Their inscrutable, brilliant dark eyes flash quick glances all around; no motion escapes them. One leans forward from the nest and attempts to pick a moving aphis from the limb. Their whole bodies throb quickly with the fast-surging tide of hot life pulsing through their veins. Now, with a boom like a great bee, the mother suddenly appears out of the air as she darts almost in my face. I am standing within two feet of the nest, and she hangs on buzzing wing, inspecting me, then perches on a limb just above my head, then on another a few feet away, her head raised and neck craned to its fullest extent. Buzzing about from place to place, she inspects me, until, satisfied, she finally alights on the edge of the nest at the usual place, where her constant coming has detached a piece of lichen and trodden down the fabric of the edge. The little birds raise themselves with fluttering wings, and the parent, rising to her full height, turns her bill almost directly downward, pushes it into the open beak of the young, and by working her gullet and throat discharges the food through the long, hollow bill as from a squirt gun." [1]

On the day the young hummingbirds leave the nest, they have learned to strike at insects within reach, and when they go they fly swiftly and surely to some perch not far away, apparently well equipped to care for themselves, but the mother feeds them for a time — sometimes while both are on the wing. During the last part of the nesting period the young are fed more or less with soft insects, not regurgitated, but held in the bill of the parent and passed to that of the young, but probably regurgitation is the rule until the very day of flight. Hummingbirds delight in bathing, but I have never known one to enter the water. They bathe in the rain or in dew by flying and fluttering among the wet leaves on the trees and shaking the drops off on their plumage or by flying in and out of the spray from a waterfall, a fountain, a garden hose or a lawn sprayer. They are quite fearless and often fly into the spray while a person is holding the hose, or feed from flowers held in the hand; and in such cases have been known to alight on an extended finger. They seem particularly attracted by red, orange or pink flowers. Among the blossoms much favored by their attention are those of the trumpet-creeper, bee balm, tiger-lily, painted-cup, scarlet salvia, cardinal-flower, scarlet runner, fuchsia, caragana, pelargonium,

---

[1] Useful Birds and their Protection, 1907, p. 243.

delphinium, columbine, gladiola, canna, azalea, ragged-sailor, jewel-weed, catnip and nasturtium.   By planting these in profusion the presence of hummingbirds may be assured.   Perhaps the caragana has the greatest attraction.   Anything red, however, seems to have charms.   Mr. Manly Hardy told of camping on an island on the Maine Coast where the red shells of cooked lobsters were lying about, and he said that a hummingbird came "out of the fog one day and darted down at those shells, moving about from one to another" as if loath to leave them.[1]   Even red noses may sometimes attract them.   Dawson desires to know why one of them should have hovered for more than 20 seconds before his nose.   This was in pre-prohibition times, and he avers that the rich tint of his proboscis was due only to "honest sunburn." [2]   Artificial flowers made of red cloth with small vials of sugar and water concealed at the base of each are used successfully to attract hummingbirds and will lure them even into open windows.

With the first frosts of autumn hummers begin to leave us.   They can stand but little cold, and now and then in late September one is picked up chilled and apparently dying. If warmed and fed, however, some of them recover.   As September wanes most of them depart for the tropics.   This species subsists to some extent on the sap of maple and other trees.   It follows the Sapsucker and visits his pits for this purpose.   It also takes nectar from flowers, but its food consists largely of small insects, which it takes from flowers and plants, from the bark and leaves of trees, and from the air.   Those who have examined stomachs of these birds have found many of them well filled with insects and very small spiders.[*]

ECONOMIC STATUS.   See page 316.

ORDER PASSERES.   PERCHING BIRDS.

Number of species in North America 333; in Massachusetts 148.

This is by far the greatest group of related birds.   It includes most of the small birds of North America.   In this order the hind toe is always present, and placed so low as to be perfectly adapted for grasping a perch.   It is never turned forward and cannot be so turned.   The feet are never webbed as is the case with many birds of other orders.   The bill, wings and tail vary considerably in size and shape, but the bill is always covered with a hard and horny envelope.   Birds of this order are all altricial, in contradistinction to many members of the lower orders which are præcocial — that is, the young of *Passeres* are hatched naked, blind and helpless and are brooded, fed and cared for in the nest until they gain strength enough to leave it; while in præcocial birds, such as plovers, snipe, ducks, grouse and bob-whites, the young are covered with down when they first break

---

[1] Bendire, Charles: Life Histories of North American Birds, Vol. II, 1895, p. 194.

[2] Dawson, W. Leon: The Birds of Ohio, Vol I, 1903, p. 335.

[*] Miss Althea R. Sherman in her paper on Experiments in feeding Hummingbirds during Seven Summers, in which she details the results of experiments with bottles of sugar and water, comes to the conclusion that female hummingbirds like a saccharine diet (Wilson Bulletin, Vol. XXV, 1913, p. 153).

the shell and are able to leave the nest and feed themselves almost at once. The naked young of *Passeres* produce first a loose downy covering which is replaced in the nest by juvenal plumage. This is molted more or less completely in late summer or autumn. The adults molt completely in autumn and some have either a partial or complete molt in spring. "*Passeres* are primarily divisible into two groups, commonly called suborders, mainly according to the structure of the vocal organ — the lower larynx or *syrinx*" (Coues). These two groups are *Oscines* or singers, and *Clamatores* or songless birds.

SUBORDER CLAMATORES. SONGLESS PERCHING BIRDS.

Number of species in North America 32; in Massachusetts 14.

Nearly all the *Passeres* composing this suborder have the tarsi covered both before and behind with variously arranged scales. They have ten fully developed primaries; although the first may be somewhat shorter than the second, it is at least two-thirds as long. Some birds of this suborder sometimes produce musical notes, and some of them imitate songs of other birds, but as a rule the singing apparatus is not developed.

FAMILY **TYRANNIDÆ**. TYRANT FLYCATCHERS.

Number of species in North America 31; in Massachusetts 14.

This family is American. It is one of the largest and most characteristic groups of birds peculiar to the New World. The North American members of the family have ten primaries, with the first long or even longest (never spurious nor very short), and twelve tail-feathers. The legs are short, the feet small and weak; the neck is short and the head large, wide and sub-crested; the bill is broad and flattened at its base, tapering to a point, and the upper mandible is abruptly bent down at the end and usually notched where the bend begins. The nostrils are near the base of the bill, small, round and slightly veiled by bristly feathers, and the mouth and gape are wide and large with bristles on each side, usually well developed and sometimes so long as to extend nearly to the end of the bill. Birds of this family frequent largely the open spaces, watching for their prey chiefly from a perch, but catching it for the most part in the air. They are agile and quick upon the wing, turning and twisting readily. Their pugnacity and tendency to tyrannize somewhat over other birds has given to the family its name. There are about four hundred species.

ECONOMIC STATUS. As the flycatchers feed almost exclusively on insects, devour many pests and rarely injure any of the products of the farm and garden, they are generally regarded as beneficial. They destroy some useful insects such as bees and parasitic flies, but probably do no appreciable harm in that way. Only a small part of this family is represented in New England, but its species abound in the American tropics.

Muscívora tyránnus (LINNÆUS). Fork-tailed Flycatcher.

DESCRIPTION. — Wings long with three *outer primaries* (of adults) *deeply notched and abruptly narrowed at tip; tail much longer than wing and very deeply forked.* Adult male: Top and sides of head (down to lower jaw) and back of neck black, a *large*, concealed crown-patch of bright yellow; back and scapulars light gray which becomes dark, dusky or blackish on upper tail-coverts; tail black, the outer tail-feather broadly edged white basally for about half its length; wings very dark grayish-brown, most of the coverts and flight-feathers edged light gray or white; region of lower jaw and all under plumage including axillars and wing linings whitish; inner webs of flight-feathers yellowish-white (broadly) at edges; bill black; iris dark brown; legs and feet brownish-black or black. *Adult female:* Similar to male or as male; but usually both yellow crown-patch and outer tail-feathers shorter. *Young in juvenal plumage:* Resembling adults, but tail much shorter, sometimes barely forked; black of head replaced by grayish-brown; black of tail duller than in adult; gray of upper plumage duller and more brown; outer three primaries not notched or emarginated; cap dusky or brownish with pale edges; darker and more brownish above than adults and edges of wing-coverts more brownish; no crown-patch.

FORK-TAILED FLYCATCHER

MEASUREMENTS. — Length 12.00 to 15.75 in.; folded wing 4.10 to 4.75; tail 9.00 to 10.00; bill .55 to .70; tarsus about .65. Female usually smaller than male.

MOLTS. — Juvenal plumage produced by complete postnatal molt in the nestling; first winter plumage acquired by an apparently complete postjuvenal molt which appears to extend through winter, as molting specimens were found in December, January and February; probably a prenuptial molt also; in any case spring birds are as adult; adult has postnuptial and prenuptial molt, both of which may be complete.

FIELD MARKS. — A long-tailed gray flycatcher not as large as Kingbird or Scissor-tail, but tail black and even longer and more deeply forked than in Scissor-tail, *black cap coming down below eyes*, and under plumage white.

VOICE. — "Its various chirping notes" have "a hard, percussive sound, which Azara well compares to the snapping of castanets" (C. Bendire).

BREEDING. — Nest in trees at no great height; built mostly of soft materials such as wool, soft grass and fine rootlets. *Eggs:* Usually 4; about .88 by .65 in.; rather ovate, rather sharply pointed at small end; light cream or white, spotted and blotched about large end with shades of chestnut.

RANGE. — Southern Mexico, Central America, Lesser Antilles and most of tropical and subtropical South America, to plains of Argentina, Uruguay and northern Patagonia; accidental in Mississippi, Kentucky, New Jersey, Maine, Massachusetts and Bermuda.

DISTRIBUTION IN NEW ENGLAND. — Accidental in Maine and Massachusetts. Records: *Maine:* Marion, December 1, 1908, bird shot by G. H. Graham, preserved by an Indian guide and taxidermist, identified and recorded by O. W. Knight.[1] *Massachusetts:* Gay Head, Marthas Vineyard, October 22, 1916, bird seen by Francis A. Foster, and recorded by him.[2] As Mr. Foster had every opportunity to observe this bird carefully, no one who knows his qualifications for such observation will doubt the record, especially as the bird is unmistakable. If the rule of basing the first record in a state on a specimen taken and preserved is adhered to, however, this record will not stand.

---

[1] Auk, Vol. XXVII, 1910, pp. 80, 81.   [2] Auk, Vol. XXXIV, 1917, p. 337.

HAUNTS AND HABITS. The Fork-tailed Flycatcher is a well-marked species that rarely straggles into the United States from the south. It is noticeable that the specimens so far recorded in this country have appeared along the seaboard, and most of them not far from the shore. Probably this indicates that they were blown here by severe storms which carried them to sea, possibly from the coasts of Mexico or the Antilles. It is significant that there is no record from the interior of the country, though the bird inhabits a large part of Mexico. Its habits are similar to those of the flycatchers, but Sclater and Hudson note one departure from the usual habits of flycatchers as follows : "They are not gregarious, but once every day, just before the sun sets, all the birds living near together rise to the tops of the trees, calling to one another with loud, excited chirps, and then mount upward like rockets to a great height in the air ; then, after whirling about for a few moments, they precipitate themselves downward with the greatest violence, opening and shutting their tails during their wild zigzag flight, and uttering a succession of sharp, grinding notes. After this curious performance they separate in pairs, and, perching on the tree-tops, each couple utters together its rattling castanet notes, after which the company breaks up." [1]

Muscivora forficáta (GMELIN). Scissor-tailed Flycatcher.

Other name: SWALLOW-TAILED FLYCATCHER.

DESCRIPTION. — Bill decidedly shorter than head, moderately broad at base ; a typical flycatcher with long wings and an exceedingly long and very deeply forked tail, *much longer than wing;* first outer primary much attenuated and narrow for about .75 to .95 in. *Adult male:* Above generally light gray, head paler, with a concealed central patch of orange-red in center of crown ;

back and scapulars suffused with a pinkish tinge (sometimes tinged yellowish) ; wings blackish, and tips of wing-coverts and secondaries white or whitish ; middle tail-feathers black or blackish, margined terminally with pale grayish-brown, three outer ones on each side white, usually tinged salmon-pink, their ends black for a considerable part of their length ; upper part of sides of head variable, from pale gray, some dusky in front of eye and on ear-coverts, to paler gray with very little dusky ; lower part of sides of head and under plumage generally white, shading into very pale gray on breast and into salmon on sides, flanks and under tail-coverts ; a paler, more pinkish tint on wing linings ; axillars and patch on under wing-coverts orange red to scarlet ; inner webs of wing-feathers broadly edged with pinkish-white ; bill dark horn-brown or blackish ; iris brown ; legs and feet dark brown ; claws black. *Adult female:* Similar to adult male, but tail shorter, crown-patch obsolete, sometimes wanting, and bright colors generally duller. *Young in first winter plumage:* Similar to adult female but crown-patch always wanting, most of gray more brownish or drab-gray, less orange under wings, and belly and under tail-coverts largely creamy-buff. *Young in juvenal plumage:* Similar to first winter plumage, but

SCISSOR-TAILED FLY-
CATCHER

wings slightly lighter ; upper plumage dusky grayish-brown with lighter feather-margins and tips ; tail blackish-brown with narrow pale edges and tips ; below chiefly grayish-white.

MEASUREMENTS. — Length 11.50 to 15.00 in. ; spread 14.20 to 15.50 ; folded wing 4.35 to 5.15 ; tail 6.50 to 12.00 (forked 5.00 to 7.00 in male) ; bill .55 to .70 ; tarsus .68 to .72. Female smaller than male.

[1] Argentine Ornithology, Vol. I, 1888, pp. 160, 161.

MOLTS. — Probably the molts of this species are similar to those of the Fork-tailed Flycatcher, but not enough molting specimens available to determine this.

FIELD MARKS. — Size near Kingbird, but unmistakable because of extremely long, forked tail, which in flight opens and shuts like a pair of scissors; light gray above, white below; wings dark with white feather-edges; wing linings and sides pink with a patch of bright orange-red or scarlet under wing; very graceful in air.

VOICE. — A series of twittering notes, sounding like *psee psee;* in play or anger a harsh *thish-thish* (C. Bendire).

BREEDING. — In open country or more rarely open woods; in neighborhood of farm or ranch buildings in prairie districts, wherever there are trees. *Nest:* Built of small twigs and weed-stems, sometimes unlined, often lined with cotton, wool, hair or a few feathers; sometimes also rags and twine; about 6 inches by 3 and 2 in depth (outside measurements); built from 4 to 20 feet up in deciduous tree, on limb or in fork of limb. *Eggs:* 3 to 5; .80 to .94 by .61 to .72 in.; usually resemble those of Kingbird, but smaller and rarely unspotted; some, however, are rather finely freckled with brown; figured in Bendire's "Life Histories of North American Birds", Vol. II, Plate I, Figs. 12 and 13. *Dates:* April 19 to July 6, Texas. *Incubation:* Period about 12 days (Bendire); 12 to 13 days (Burns); by female. One brood yearly; probably two in some cases.

RANGE. — Chiefly parts of central southern United States (east of Rocky Mountains), Mexico and Central America. Breeds from southeastern Nebraska, southern Kansas, central western Missouri, western Arkansas and western Louisiana through Oklahoma to southern Texas, southeastern New Mexico and northern Tamaulipas; in winter regularly from southern Mexico to Panama. Accidental or casual northward and eastward to Mackenzie River Valley, southern Manitoba (northern Manitoba, York Factory in summer), Wisconsin, Colorado, Quebec, Ohio, Vermont, New Brunswick, Massachusetts, Connecticut, New Jersey, Maryland, Virginia, south to Florida.

DISTRIBUTION IN NEW ENGLAND. — Accidental summer visitor to Massachusetts and Connecticut; Records: A doubtful record for *Vermont,* viz. — St. Johnsbury, 1884, bird shot by C. W. Graham,[1] and said to have been sent to Dartmouth College Museum, though not there now.[2] *Massachusetts:* Plymouth, May, 1918, bird seen and reported by Mrs. Catherine Morton;[3] Duxbury, July, 1918 (Same bird?) *Connecticut:* Wauregan, about April 27, 1876, bird shot by C. N. Carpenter.[4]

HAUNTS AND HABITS. The Scissor-tailed Flycatcher has a longer tail than any other bird of its size that visits North America except the Fork-tailed Flycatcher. In the air it is one of the most graceful and attractive of birds, flying with extreme lightness and turning with the greatest ease. Rising from the top of some tall tree it flutters and floats through the air and returns to its perch, or it flies easily along low over the grass apparently searching for insects. At other times it rises very high and circles about as if in play. Its notes resemble those of the Kingbird, and it seems as bold and fearless as the latter in attacking birds of prey, often alighting upon their backs and pecking them fiercely. The Scissor-tail is a great wanderer, and may be found flying over almost any region except a very mountainous country. Cultivated land, prairie and woodland are all visited, though it seems to prefer the more open lands. It is a mere straggler

---

[1] Random Notes, Natural History, Vol. I, No. 8, 1884, p. 3.

[2] Brewster, Wm.: Editor, Minot's Land and Game Birds of New England, 1895, pp. 475–476.

[3] Batchelder, Miss Minnie K.: *in litt.*

[4] Purdie, H. A.: Bulletin Nuttall Ornithological Club, Vol. II, 1877, p. 21; and Merriam, C. Hart: Birds of Connecticut, 1877, p. 50.

PLATE 55

PLATE 55

CRESTED FLYCATCHER
Page 336

OLIVE–SIDED FLYCATCHER
Page 344

ADULT

ADULT

KINGBIRD
Page 327

ADULT

ARKANSAS KINGBIRD
Page 333

ADULT

All about one-half scale.

Louis Agassiz Fuertes

in the north and east. About ninety per cent of the food of the Scissor-tail consists of insects. The vegetal food is chiefly small wild berries or other fruit and a few seeds.

ECONOMIC STATUS. As this bird feeds very heavily on grasshoppers and crickets, it is undoubtedly of considerable economic importance where it is common. In the north and east it is too rare to be of any service to mankind.

Tyránnus tyrannus (LINNÆUS). Kingbird.

Other names: BEE-BIRD; BEE-MARTIN.

Plate 55.

DESCRIPTION. — Bill about half length of head; wings long; only two outer primaries evidently emarginated in adult; tail ample, but not very long, nearly even although slightly rounded at each side. *Adult male:* Blackish-slate above, still darker or blackish on top and sides of head; rather large, concealed, central patch, varying from orange to scarlet in center of crown; feathers of lower rump more or less margined pale gray or grayish-white around ends; upper tail-coverts black, margined white; tail black, tipped (abruptly and rather broadly) white which runs up a little on outer edges of lateral feathers, especially outer one; wings darker than back; middle and greater coverts, secondaries and tertials edged white; primaries and their coverts more narrowly edged pale gray; lower plumage, from cheeks and chin downward, white; upper breast shaded gray, its sides distinctly gray; under wing-coverts largely dark, variable, and in most cases whitish on margins, but usually dark centrally; bill black, slightly brownish at base below; iris brown; legs and feet brownish or grayish-black. *Adult female:* Similar to male, but orange-red crown-patch smaller, and tips of longest primaries not so much emarginated. *Young in first winter plumage:* Similar to adults, but crown-patch (if any) paler, more yellow and smaller. *Young in juvenal plumage:* Similar to adults, but no orange-red crown-patch; dark brown rather than slaty above; top of head usually little, if any, darker than back; tail black, white at tip narrower than in adult, and sometimes partly obscured by tinge of brown or dusky especially on outer feathers; *first two primaries not emarginated.*

MEASUREMENTS. — Length 8.40 to 9.00 in.; spread 14.00 to 15.00; folded wing 4.45 to 4.75; tail 3.40 to 3.75; bill .75 to .87; tarsus .60 to .70; female averaging about as large as male.

MOLTS. — Apparently most young birds are still in juvenal plumage when they leave New England for the tropics, though some begin a molt of body feathers in August or September; in the spring when they return they are as adults; beginning of postjuvenal molt into first winter plumage is indicated in a few birds taken in late August; adults have a complete postnuptial molt, beginning in August or September, and probably partial prenuptial molt completed in March or April.

FIELD MARKS. — Size about that of Catbird; a dark slaty bird with blackish head, two narrow, white wing-bars, black white-tipped tail and white below with a tinge of gray in breast.

VOICE. — A shrill twittering *"kipper-kipper"* (R. Hoffmann); shrill twitters often resembling those of swallows, the syllable *king* commonly recurs amongst them (Minot); *Twip-ip-ip-ip* (C. Bendire); *Tizic tizic* and *tsee tsee tsee tsee* (W. L. Dawson); "loud excited *chic-chews* often repeated," a "harsh *chew-whe, chick-ak*" (O. W. Knight); also a rather squeaky attempt at flight-song.

BREEDING. — In open and cultivated lands, about shores of lakes and rivers or the sea, and about bushy borders of meadows and marshes. *Nest:* A ragged structure outside but well made within; placed in an apple or other tree (rarely in a pine), in a bush or on stump, fence post, eaves-trough, fence rail, bridge, or other structure, from 3 to 20 ft. high; once 100 ft. on arm of church-cross in Woodsville, N. H., the encircling wooden wreath making its roof; often by a roadside, river or meadow (one nest built on ground. Caroline Jones, Bennington, Vermont, *in litt.*), built of such material as twigs, rootlets, weeds, twine, hair, etc., lined with grass, hair or wool, plant-down, moss, catkins, etc. *Eggs:* 3 usually, 5 rarely, commonly 3 or 4; .82 to 1.06 by .67 to .76 in.; marked with spots ranging from few to many, generally heaviest toward large end, varying from chestnut-brown to purplish-brown, also some lilac or purple; figured in Bendire's "Life Histories of North American Birds," Vol. II, Plate I, Figs. 14 and 15. *Dates:* April 25 to May 10, Florida; May 30 to July 4 (July 17), Massachusetts. *Incubation:* Period 12 to 16 days (various authors); usually or chiefly by female, male sometimes assists. One brood yearly, possibly sometimes two.

RANGE. — North and South America. Breeds from southern Mackenzie, central Manitoba, northern Ontario, southern Quebec and Nova Scotia south to southern Oregon, central Nevada, northern New Mexico, central and southeastern Texas, and the Gulf Coast to southern Florida; south in winter from Costa Rica to southern Bolivia, Peru, Ecuador, Colombia and British Guiana; migrates regularly through Mexico and Central America; casual migrant to the Bermudas, the Bahamas, Cuba, Swan Island and possibly other islands of the West Indian group; accidental in Greenland and casual in California.

DISTRIBUTION IN NEW ENGLAND. — Common migrant and summer resident; only locally distributed in woods, where breeding mostly about edges, or along shores of ponds, lakes and rivers.

SEASON IN MASSACHUSETTS. — (April 15, 19, 21) May 3 to September 28 (October 16 and 20).*

HAUNTS AND HABITS. Some of the American Indians knew this bird as the "little chief," but the English settlers, fleeing from tyranny at home, called him the King Bird.† The naturalists dubbed him the Tyrant Flycatcher, but the first name stuck. Nevertheless, the despotic disposition which the bird and some of its congeners exhibit to both greater and lesser fowls has induced ornithologists to name this great American group of birds *Tyrannidæ* or Tyrant Flycatchers. The Kingbird is typical of this group. Savage and fearless he assails any bird that comes in his way or interferes with his own welfare or that of his neighbors. Hawks, crows, owls, vultures and even eagles feel the weight of his displeasure; about the only birds which he cannot drive away from the vicinity of his domicile are the Hummingbird and the Duck Hawk.‡ Occasionally a militant Baltimore Oriole with its keen-pointed beak will do battle with the Kingbird. The Catbird sometimes disputes his sovereignty, while the "English" Sparrow has been known to defeat the Kingbird by force of numbers, but most of the feathered race deem it wiser to leave when the Kingbird hovers above them.

While the female is sitting on the nest, the male stands guard on a tree-top to drive away intruders. He rarely, if ever, attempts to strike a large bird on the ground or on a perch. Therefore, if a crafty Crow slips into a tree unseen by the Kingbird and rifles a nest of its contents, the black robber is safe until he flies; then the avenger strikes. The little tyrant mounts above him in the air and chases him away. Often the Kingbird strikes the Crow, and sometimes even rides on his back while dealing out summary punishment with pointed bill. The little bird is valiant in defense of its young, and may attack a cat or even a birds'-nesting boy if he climbs the nest tree. I once saw a Kingbird

---

* Two Kingbirds were seen September 15, 1910, at Cape Sable Island (Nova Scotia), by Mr. Farley — a late date for Nova Scotia.

† Among the people of Mashpee, one of the last two Indian villages in Massachusetts, it is known as the King Priest, a name which bears little resemblance to little chief, but has a somewhat similar meaning.

‡ There is a story of a Cooper's Hawk driven away by a Kingbird. But when the hawk reached the shelter of a wood, he turned before entering, seized his pursuer in his claws and flew off with him.

in such a case strike a boy on the head, and often a boy has thrown up his hat under or near a Kingbird's nest to see the bird attack it.

The Kingbird ordinarily does not trouble other inoffensive small birds, unless they come too near his nest. Occasionally, when nest-building, however, the bird is seen to tear down the nest of the Chipping Sparrow, Chebec or some other small bird and to use the material thus purloined in building its own nest. The late Ned Dearborn well describes a common habit of the Kingbird as follows: "The nervous irritability, characteristic of all our flycatchers, is most highly developed in this species. At times it is so pent up that the bird becomes a veritable fury, and dashes upward toward the clouds, crying fiercely, and ever and anon reaching a frenzied climax, when its cry is prolonged into a kind of shriek, and its flight a zigzag of blind rage. These exhibitions are frequently given in the teeth of the premonitory gust before a thunderstorm, as if in defiance of the very elements." [1] The flight of the Kingbird ordinarily seems fluttering and desultory with short vibrations of wings not fully spread, but when he pursues a hawk or a crow he shows speed enough to overtake the enemy time after time.

When winter has passed, the Kingbirds move up from Central and South America and usually begin to arrive in southern New England about May 10. There are earlier stragglers, but the very few that reach the coast of Massachusetts in early April probably were blown off shore in the south and carried north by some cyclonic storm. Kingbirds evidently are fond of water. They often build their nests in low bushes on a river shore or in the water and they may be seen flycatching along the ocean beach and nesting among the sand dunes, where fresh water is scarce. They bathe either by standing in shallow water and then dipping and fluttering or by flying down to the surface of the water to dip and rise again. As soon as the females arrive, the males begin their courtship, which is carried on largely in the air, where the male can best exhibit his beauties with spread wings and tail, while he seeks the company of the chosen one, fluttering and sailing, rising and falling in an effort to charm her. At this season the males are very pugnacious and some terrific battles are fought.

When union is consummated both sexes engage in the construction of the nest and the care of the young. If the first nest is destroyed they usually rebuild near by. They now become doubly vigilant and truculent and woe betide the bird that in any way interferes with their domestic arrangements, though they may even allow inoffensive small species to nest in the same tree. In August, the young having been reared, the return flight to the south begins, but some birds, breeding later perhaps than the majority, remain with us until about the middle of September, when they move slowly south. Any birds seen later than September are mere accidental stragglers.

The Kingbird seems to prefer insects to all other food, and sometimes seeks them in strange situations for a flycatcher. Mr. Wendell P. Smith writes from Wells River, Vermont, that while harrowing two acres of land May 26, 1924, he counted ten Kingbirds on the piece, feeding on the ground, as well as catching insects close to the

---

[1] Dearborn, Ned: Birds of Durham and Vicinity, 1903, p. 59.

ground, but in moving over the ground in such cases they use their wings in preference to their feet. Following a great fire in the woods at Monument Beach on Buzzards Bay, July 16, 1909, where a considerable tract of ground was burned over, a Kingbird which was feeding her young, was seen to fly close up to a brisk back-fire, and catch insects which seemed to be very abundant there, for she made trips back and forth at one minute intervals. Mr. H. L. Taylor writes from Jamestown, Rhode Island, that he saw a Kingbird flutter up against his window. When he went to the window, the bird flew into a small bush about five feet away and watched a moth inside the window. Mr. Taylor caught the moth, opened the window and tossed it out. The Kingbird had it, he says, "before it had gone three feet," ate it and came back for more. Mr. Taylor put another moth in the window, the bird came again, and the whole performance was repeated. The following is quoted from one of my former works:

"The Kingbird, although primarily a feeder on flying insects, can adapt itself to the pursuit of other food. In flying about it often takes insects by skimming and fluttering over water, or by picking them from the grass or trees. After the severe rain-storm of June, 1903, when the air was swept clear of all flying insects by torrents of rain, Mr. Outram Bangs saw Kingbirds picking up from the ground dead or dying insects.

"They sometimes alight on plowed lands, and pick up grubs and myriapods; they will also eat wild berries and seeds. Very large beetles are taken, such as May beetles and *Cetonias*, as well as some of the beneficial tiger beetles and ground beetles. Weevils of both grain and fruit, click beetles, grasshoppers and crickets, wasps, wild bees, ants, and flies are prominent among the food materials of this bird. Among the flies taken are house flies and several species that trouble cattle; but smaller insects, like mosquitoes, gnats and midgets, are not ignored. Leaf hoppers and many other bugs are taken; and a great variety of caterpillars, mostly of the hairless species, are eaten or fed to the young.* This bird is destructive to moths of many kinds, among them the gipsy moth. In two and one-half hours seven of these birds were seen to take seventy-nine male and twenty-four female gipsy moths, and they killed in that time a great many more that could not be positively identified.

"The Kingbird, therefore, is particularly beneficial about the garden and orchard, for it eats very little, if any, cultivated fruit. The only bad habit attributed to this bird is that of killing honey bees, and even while catching bees it seems about as likely to do good as harm. Professor Beal states that a bee raiser in Iowa, having good reason to believe that the Kingbirds were feeding upon his bees, shot a number near his hives, but an expert entomologist could find no trace of bees in their stomachs. The investigations of the Department of Agriculture seem to indicate that the Kingbird does not ordinarily reduce the aggregate number of working bees. Only fourteen out of two hundred and eighty-one stomachs examined contained any remains of honey bees. There were but fifty bees found, forty of which were drones, only four were positively identified as workers, and six were so much broken as to render the distinguishing of sex impossible. Pro-

---

* Caterpillars are picked from the trees or taken in the air as they hang suspended by their silky threads.

fessor Beal finds that the Kingbird feeds on robber flies, — insects which prey largely on other insects, especially honey bees. He considered nineteen robber flies contained in the Kingbirds' stomachs to be more than an equivalent for the working bees found; and the destruction of drones by Kingbirds is a benefit. On the whole, it seems probable that, while the Kingbirds eat some bees, they confine their bee-eating mainly to the drones, and also protect the bees by killing the moths and flies that prey upon them." [1]

In an excellent bulletin of the Biological Survey written by Prof. Beal since the above quotation was penned, he gives a summary of the food found in 665 stomachs of these birds, taken mainly in the months when the bees are active. Honey bees were found in only 22 stomachs and the total number of bees found was 61, of which 51 were drones, 8 workers and 2 not determined. Robber flies which kill bees were found in 19 stomachs, 26 flies all told. Dr. Riley states that one species of robber fly has been seen to kill 141 honey bees in a single day.[2]

ECONOMIC STATUS. In many ways the Kingbird is an ally of the farmer. When it builds a nest near the poultry-yard, it drives the hawks and crows away from the chickens. In this manner also it protects other insect-eating birds, their nests, eggs and young. In its feeding habits it is mainly beneficial, though it eats some small fruit and some bees, but nearly ninety per cent of its food consists of insects, mostly injurious. Therefore, it well deserves protection.

Tyrannus dominicénsis (GMELIN). Gray Kingbird.

DESCRIPTION. — Similar to Kingbird in form, but bill much larger, longer, wider and heavier; much paler and grayer above. *Adult male:* Above slightly smoky gray with darker shaft-streaks on top of head, and a large concealed patch of orange-red on crown; tips of longer primaries attenuated; tail dark grayish-brown, the feathers very narrowly edged pale brownish-gray or whitish; wings deep grayish-brown, primaries and primary-coverts darker, wing-coverts and secondaries edged rather broadly pale gray or whitish, and primaries very narrowly so edged; upper parts of sides of head mixed grayish and dusky; ear-coverts dusky or blackish; lower jaw and lower plumage white, shaded with pale gray in middle of breast, deepening on sides and flanks; under tail-coverts sometimes tinged yellowish; axillars and under wing-coverts tinged yellowish or pale primrose-yellow; bill black; iris brown; legs and feet brownish-black. *Adult female:* Similar, but tips of longer primaries not so attenuated as in male. *Young in juvenal plumage:* Similar to adults, but lighter and more brownish above with rufous edgings on wing-coverts, rump, upper tail-coverts and tail, crown-patch wanting and tips of primaries not emarginated or attenuated; no orange crown-patch.

GRAY KINGBIRD

MEASUREMENTS. — Length 9.25 to 9.80 in.; spread 14.55 to 16.10; folded wing 3.80 to 5.06; tail 3.40 to 4.25; bill 1.04 to 1.45; tarsus .74 to .80.

[1] Useful Birds and Their Protection, 1907, pp. 238–239.
[2] Beal, F. E. L.: U. S. Department of Agriculture, Biological Survey, Bulletin No. 44, 1912, pp. 11–19.

MOLTS. — Juvenal plumage acquired in the nestling by complete postnatal molt; during first winter young birds apparently molt completely again, as in spring they seem to be as adult. Adults have complete postnuptial molt in autumn, and probably a partial prenuptial molt about the head in spring, but not enough molting material available to confirm this.

FIELD MARKS. — Similar in size and shape to Kingbird, but somewhat larger, bill much longer and larger, and upper plumage much lighter and grayer; in flight under wing-coverts show yellow, or yellowish, where those of Kingbird show white.

VOICE. — "A ceaseless shriek" being a repetition of three notes like pe-cheer-y (R. Hill).

BREEDING. — In or near woodland. *Nest:* Loosely built in tree or bush, of twigs and rootlets, lined with finer similar material. *Eggs:* 3 or 4; .89 to 1.09 by .69 to .76 in.; elliptical ovate or elongate ovate; cream to pinkish or flesh color, spotted with various shades of brown, purple and lavender; illustrated in Bendire's "Life Histories of North American Birds," Vol. II, Plate II, Figs. 3 and 4.

RANGE. — Parts of tropical and subtropical North America, West Indies, central and northern South America. Breeds from Georgia and Florida (southeastern South Carolina casually) through Bahamas and West Indies to Colombia and Venezuela; casual in migration in Central America from Yucatan to Panama, and in the Bermuda Islands; in winter from Haiti, Porto Rico and Jamaica southward. Accidental in New Jersey, Massachusetts, New York and British Columbia.

DISTRIBUTION IN NEW ENGLAND. — Accidental visitor from the south. One record — *Massachusetts:* Lynn, immature bird taken October [23], 1869, by C. I. Goodale.[1]

HAUNTS AND HABITS. The Gray Kingbird is a mere straggler in New England. It has been reported more than once in Massachusetts, but the record given above appears to be the only one substantiated by a specimen taken in the state. I am not sure that I have seen the bird alive even in the south, although it summers in Florida. Mr. C. J. Maynard, who has had excellent opportunities to observe the species in Florida, says of it: "There is a similarity in the flight of the Gray King Bird and that of the common King Bird, but the former may be at once recognized by their heavier movements, and they are much less agile. The northern species are noisy birds but in this respect they are excelled by the Gray King Birds which are constantly chattering. They not only utter their cries while flying, but will also give their shrill notes while sitting, raising their wings while so doing, very much after the manner of the Red-winged Blackbirds." [2] Mr. Richard Hill describing the habits of the species in Jamaica is quoted by Brewer substantially as follows: "In feeding, just before sunset, they usually sit eight or ten in a row, on some exposed twig, darting from it in pursuit of their prey, and returning to it to devour whatever they have caught. They are rapid in their movements, ever constantly and hurriedly changing their positions in flight. As they fly they are able to check their speed suddenly, and to turn at the smallest imaginable angle. At times they move with motionless wings from one tree to another. When one descends to pick up an insect from the surface of the water, it has the appearance of tumbling, and, in rising again, ascends with a singular motion of the wings, as if hurled into the air and endeavoring to recover itself. This Flycatcher is also charged by Mr. Hill with seizing upon the Hummingbirds as they hover over the blossoms in the garden, killing and devouring them." [3]

[1] Allen, J. A.: American Naturalist, Vol. III, 1870, p. 645.
[2] Maynard, C. J.: Birds of Eastern North America, 1896, p. 407.
[3] Baird, Brewer and Ridgway, History of North American Birds, Land Birds, 1874, Vol. II, pp. 321, 322.

Tyrannus verticális SAY. Arkansas Kingbird.

Other name: WESTERN KINGBIRD.

Plate 55.

DESCRIPTION. — Similar in shape to Kingbird but larger and very much lighter above. *Adult male:* Ends of several outer primaries much emarginated; top of head and back of neck gray with a reddish-orange or orange-red patch in center of crown; back, scapulars and upper rump yellowish-gray or tending to olive; lower rump grayish with dark feather-centers; upper tail-coverts mainly black or blackish; tail black, outer web and shaft of outer tail-feathers white or whitish, sometimes black toward tip; wings deep or dusky grayish-brown, all the feathers edged paler or grayish; sides of head to below eyes and ear-coverts gray, darker than crown, with a faint dusky stripe through eye; sides of lower jaw, chin and upper throat white (often slightly grayish) deepening into pale gray on upper breast; rest of under plumage chiefly canary yellow, becoming paler on under tail-coverts and yellowish-olive on sides and flanks and on sides of upper breast; wing linings and axillars largely pale yellowish; bill black or brownish-black, slightly lighter at base below; iris brown; legs and feet brownish-black. *Adult female:* Similar to male, but tips of primaries not so much emarginated and crown-patch usually smaller. *Young in juvenal plumage:* Similar to adult, but without orange crown-patch, gray of head browner, feathers of lower rump margined at ends with light greenish-brown or buffy-brown, light edges of wing-coverts broader and yellow, lower plumage paler, and first primary not emarginated.

MEASUREMENTS. — Length 8.00 to 9.50 in.; spread 15.20 to 16.50; folded wing 4.70 to 5.25; tail 3.60 to 4.00; bill .75 to .89; tarsus .70 to .75; female rather smaller than male.

MOLTS. — Juvenal plumage acquired by complete postnatal molt beginning in nest; during autumn a molt, possibly complete, takes place and young bird apparently becomes as adult in its first winter plumage; adults have complete postnuptial molt beginning in August or September and partial prenuptial molt probably in spring — not sufficient molting specimens to furnish desired data.

FIELD MARKS. — Larger and much lighter above than Kingbird; head gray, tail black without white tip of Kingbird but outer webs of outer tail-feather on each side white; breast gray and belly yellow.

VOICE. — Similar to notes of Kingbird but louder and harsher (E. Coues); a low warbling twitter; shrill metallic-sounding notes (C. Bendire); said also to utter peculiar wailing sounds at night; more noisy even than Kingbird.

BREEDING. — Similar to that of Kingbird. *Nest:* Like that of Kingbird but often placed near trunk of tree, rarely on ledge, often on crossbar of telegraph pole where trees are scarce or on fence or building; varies greatly in outer dimensions, but usually larger and of softer material than that of Kingbird. *Eggs:* 3 to 5; similar to those of Kingbird, but averaging slightly smaller; figured in Bendire's "Life Histories of North American Birds," Vol. II, Plate I, Figs. 16 and 17. *Dates:* From May 15 in south to July 15 in north. *Incubation:* Period 12 to 13 days; by both sexes. One brood yearly, probably sometimes two.

RANGE. — Western United States and contiguous parts of Canada and Mexico to Central America. Breeds mainly in Austral zones from southern British Columbia, southern Alberta, southern Saskatchewan, southern Manitoba, and western Minnesota south to northern Lower California, Chihuahua, Mexico, and east to western Iowa, central Kansas, central Oklahoma, and west central Texas; in winter from Sonora, northern Mexico, through western Mexico to Guatemala; east in migration to southeastern Nebraska; casual or accidental in Missouri, Illinois, Wisconsin, Maine, Massachusetts, New York, New Jersey, Maryland and Florida.

DISTRIBUTION IN NEW ENGLAND. — Accidental visitor. Records: *Maine:* Elliot, October, 1864, immature bird shot by George E. Brown;[1] Hallowell, November 12, 1920 — January 15, 1921, seen by

---

[1] Purdie, H. A.: Bulletin Nuttall Ornithological Club, Vol. I, 1876, p. 73.

Mrs. C. W. Alexander and reported by Carrie E. Miller;[1] Kittery Point, August 25, 1925, bird seen;[2] Saco, December 6, 1925, bird seen;[3] Woolwich, November 23, 1925, immature male shot.[4] *Massachusetts:* Chatham (Monomoy), October 20, 1912, immature male taken by F. H. Kennard and recorded by him, now in collection of Boston Society of Natural History.[5] Falmouth, November 10, 1918, bird taken by Dr. L. C. Jones, now in mounted collection of Boston Society of Natural History.[6] Chatham, November 29, 1919, female taken by A. C. Bent,[7] now in Bent collection at the Museum of Comparative Zoölogy at Cambridge. Barnstable (Marston's Mills), February 9, 1920, immature female, long dead, found on snow by D. L. Garrison.[8] Ipswich, September 19, 1920, seen and recorded by Dr. C. W. Townsend.[9] Marblehead, November 20, 1920, bird seen and recorded by Charles B. Floyd.[10] Marshfield, October 30, 1921, two immature males taken by Joseph A. Hagar, now in collection of Boston Society of Natural History.[11] Edgartown, November 12 and 13, 1921, two birds seen and recorded by Francis A. Foster.[12] Edgartown, November 13 and 16, 1921, bird seen and recorded by Mrs. Mona W. Worden.[13] Mattapoisett, December 7, 1921, bird seen and recorded by J. E. Norton Shaw.[14] Plymouth, December 15, 1921, recorded by Miss Minnie K. Bachelder.[15] West Manchester, September 3, 1922, bird seen and recorded by Miss E. D. Boardman.[16] Cambridge, November 21, 1922, bird seen and recorded by Osborne Earle.[17] Scituate, November 10, 1923, bird seen by H. S. Shaw, Jr.[18] *Rhode Island:* Watch Hill, September 24, 1913, bird seen and recorded by Ludlow Griscom.[19] *Connecticut:* Meriden, November 4, 1921, bird seen and recorded by Lester W. Smith.[20]

SEASON IN MASSACHUSETTS. — September 2 to December 15.

HAUNTS AND HABITS. The Arkansas Kingbird has a commanding personality. It differs little in habits from the common Kingbird. It is quite as fearless and audacious, is very pugnacious in the breeding season, and the males have frequent battles among themselves. It frequents the more open country, as the Kingbird does. It is a conspicuous bird, takes a commanding perch and seems to think it necessary to twitter and screech whenever it does anything. In Massachusetts the bird has been found always near the sea-shore and only in autumn or winter.

ECONOMIC STATUS. In Farmer's Bulletin, No. 506, by Professor F. E. L. Beal and Mr. W. L. McAtee, an analysis of the contents of 109 stomachs of the Arkansas Flycatcher is given. The food is there shown to be composed of insects, near 90 per cent,

---

[1] Auk, Vol. XXXVIII, 1921, p. 603.
[2] Townsend, Charles W.: Auk, Vol. XLIII, 1926, p. 99.
[3] Abbott, Sarah Rideout: Maine Naturalist, Vol. V, 1926, p. 166.
[4] Haven, Herbert M. W.: Auk, Vol. XLIII, 1926, p. 371.
[5] Auk, Vol. XXX, 1913, p. 112.
[6] Jones, L. C.: *in litt.*
[7] Bent, A. C.: *in litt.*
[8] Townsend, C. W.: Auk, Vol. XXXVIII, 1921, p. 114.
[9] Auk, Vol. XXXVIII, 1921, p. 113.
[10] Auk, Vol. XXXVIII, 1921, p. 114.
[11] Hagar, Joseph A.: *in litt.* and Auk, Vol. XXXIX, 1922, p. 418.
[12] Foster, Francis A.: *in litt.* and Auk, Vol. XXXIX, 1922, pp. 417, 418.
[13] Worden, Mrs. M. W.: *in litt.*
[14] Shaw, J. E. N.: *in litt.*
[15] Bachelder, Miss M. K.: *in litt.*
[16] Boardman, Miss E. D.: *in litt.*
[17] Earle, Osborne: *in litt.*
[18] Shaw, H. S. Jr.: *in litt.*
[19] Auk, Vol. XXXI, 1914, p. 248.
[20] Auk, Vol. XXXIX, 1922, pp. 270, 271.

and the rest chiefly wild fruit and seeds. The amount of beneficial insects is so small and that of pests so large that the bird must be regarded as beneficial. Professor Beal, who in another bulletin gave an exhaustive account of the food of this species, concluded that: "On the whole, it appears that the Arkansas Kingbird is one of the most useful birds in the region where it is found." [1]

Tyrannus melanchólicus satrápa (CABANIS AND HEINE). **Lichtenstein's Kingbird.**

DESCRIPTION. — A typical *Tyrannus* with tips of longer primaries much attenuated. *Adult male:* Top of head and hind neck gray, a longitudinal, reddish-orange crown-patch; back, scapulars and rump gray and yellowish-olive-green mixed (in some specimens these parts mostly gray, in others chiefly green); upper tail-coverts darker, the feathers very narrowly margined paler; tail dusky gray-brown, its feathers margined paler at ends, and their outer webs very narrowly edged pale olive, paling to near white on outer feathers; wings dusky grayish-brown, posterior lesser coverts broadly edged grayish, greater coverts and secondaries edged paler, and sometimes with yellowish-olive (light edges broadest on secondaries), primary coverts and primaries with narrow light edges; sides of head gray, darkening toward base of bill and lightening below, where it fades into white or whitish on chin and throat; lower throat slightly tinged gray; upper breast yellowish-olive, deepening at sides; rest of under plumage near canary yellow paling on under tail-coverts; axillars and wing linings paler yellow; inner webs of flight-feathers edged yellowish-white for part of their length; bill black or blackish, sometimes more brownish at base below; iris brown; legs and feet black or blackish. *Adult female:* Similar to male, but crown-patch usually smaller, and tips of longer primaries less attenuated. *Young:* Like adults, but lacking crown-patch; upper plumage duller and browner, wing-coverts and tail-feathers conspicuously margined pale cinnamon or buffy, and lower plumage usually paler.

MEASUREMENTS. — (One specimen). Folded wing 4.75 in.; tail 4.00; bill .75; tarsus .70.

MOLTS. — Only one (apparently) molting specimen examined; had lost two outer tail-feathers which were being replaced, May 21.

FIELD MARKS. — When seen from below resembles Crested Flycatcher, but bill larger and bird much brighter yellow below; has fluttering flight like other kingbirds.

VOICE. — "A high-pitched trilling call"; a staccato cry like those of other kingbirds (A. Wetmore).

BREEDING. — Nest and eggs much like those of our own Kingbird but nest more flimsy.

RANGE. — Western and southern Mexico from Sinaloa and Vera Cruz through Central America and south to Colombia and Lower Amazon Valley, also to Tobago and Trinidad; accidental in Maine, Grenada, and probably in Cuba.

DISTRIBUTION IN NEW ENGLAND. — Accidental visitor from the tropics. Records: *Maine:* Scarborough, a young male taken October 31, 1915, by George Oliver, presented by him to the Portland Society of Natural History and recorded by A. H. Norton. Mr. Norton calls attention to the fact that two very intense tropical cyclones had visited the United States previously, one in August and the other in September, 1915. [2]

HAUNTS AND HABITS. This occurrence of this tropical species in Maine is entirely accidental. It forms our only record for the United States. Its habits are similar to those of other flycatchers of the genus. Its food according to an examination of the stomach of the Maine specimen is such as any flycatcher might take.

---

[1] U. S. Department of Agriculture, Biological Survey, Bulletin No. 44, 1912, p. 22.
[2] Auk, Vol. XXXIII, 1916, pp. 382–383.

Myiárchus crinítus (Linnæus).   Crested Flycatcher.

Other names: GREAT CRESTED FLYCATCHER; WHEEP.

Plate 55.

DESCRIPTION. — Similar to Kingbird in shape, but larger, rather more slender; bill nearly as long as head, and head somewhat crested; wings rounded, second primary longest. *Adults (sexes alike):* Above olive or brownish-olive, usually a little more brownish on top of head, where center of each feather is darker; middle pair of tail-feathers and outer webs of others with dusky brownish-olive or yellowish edges; outer web of first outer tail-feather sometimes margined whitish, and inner webs of all but middle pair chestnut or "cinnamon rufous"; wings dusky grayish-brown, coverts and secondaries margined with buffy, these margins broader at ends of greater and middle coverts (where they form two light bars across wing), and broader and lighter on tertials; primaries tinged on edges of both webs with chestnut, cinnamon-rufous or cinnamon-buff; sides of head gray, tinged olive on ear-coverts; chin, throat and most of breast gray, paling slightly on chin and throat; elsewhere below light yellow, passing into pale yellowish-olive on sides and flanks, and into pale yellow on axillars and wing linings; bill deep to dark horn-brown, paling at base below; iris brown; legs and feet vary from dusky-brown to bluish-black. *Young in first winter plumage:* Practically indistinguishable from that of adults. *Young in juvenal plumage (sexes alike):* Similar to adults but darker above, bars on wing less clearly defined, a tinge of rusty on upper tail-coverts, rusty edgings on tail-feathers, middle and greater wing-coverts and primaries.

MEASUREMENTS. — Length 8.00 to 9.20 in.; spread 12.80 to 14.00; folded wing 3.80 to 4.40; tail 3.44 to 3.80; bill .80 to .98; tarsus .82 to .92. Female smaller than male.

MOLTS. — Complete postnatal molt of nestling, following natal down, produces juvenal plumage; in autumn a postjuvenal molt gives bird first winter plumage which, apparently, is as adult; adults have complete autumnal molt and incomplete prenuptial molt in late winter or early spring.

FIELD MARKS. — Somewhat larger than Kingbird with much longer bill; head somewhat more crested; olive above with darker wings, crossed by two yellowish or whitish bars; throat and upper breast gray or ashy; yellow elsewhere below.

VOICE. — Alarm note an unmusical and unearthly *wheep* (George Gladden); also rendered *queep, week, wheek, freight etc.* by other authors; this is an alarm note, frequently repeated; a harsh squeak like "*païp, païp, payŭp paywip*" (Nuttall); "a series of somewhat shrill whistles often followed by a harsh chatter," and a call nearly resembling one call of Bob-white (C. J. Maynard); most commonly a clear whistle *e-whuit-huit*, or *wit-whit, wit-whit*, repeated five or six times in a somewhat lower key, "varied also to *whuir, whuree* or *puree*" (C. Bendire); *wheeoo* (W. L. Dawson); besides its characteristic well-known, loud, brusque whistle "*queep*," it has a very different loud note, uttered in succession like "*queer-queer-queer-queer*", also some lower notes (J. A. Farley).

BREEDING. — Usually in orchards or woods, in wooded bottomlands bordering streams, etc. *Nest:* Usually in natural hollow of trunk or branch of apple, pear or forest tree, or in hollow fence-post or rail, in a nesting box, in deserted hole of woodpecker or sometimes in some nook about or in a vacant building, in a stovepipe, or in a heap of logs or lumber; from 5 to 60 feet high; built of trash, moss, twigs, hair, leaves, grass, fur, feathers, etc., the finer material used for lining; usually one or more cast skins of a snake, incorporated somewhere in the mass or outside it.* *Eggs:* 3 to 8; .85 to 1.00 by .60 to .70 in.; mostly ovate or short ovate; creamy to pinkish or reddish-buff with black lines and scratches of brown, purple and lavender (more or less like pen scratches), irregularly placed over the surface; shell slightly glossy; figured in Bendire's "Life Histories of North American Birds," Vol. II, Plate II, Figs. 8 and 9. *Dates:* May 27 to June 13, Connecticut; June 11 to 28, Maine. *Incubation:* Period 14 days (O. W. Knight); about 15 days (C. Bendire); by both sexes. Usually one brood yearly, may raise two rarely in the south.

---

* Sometimes snakes' skins of various sizes make up almost the entire nest. (Journal Maine Ornithological Society, Vol. VI, 1904, p. 67).

RANGE. — Eastern North America and northern South America. Breeds from northern edge of Transition Zone in southern Manitoba, northern Michigan, southern Ontario, southern Quebec and New Brunswick south to southern Texas, the Gulf coast and southern Florida; west to eastern Nebraska, central Kansas, central Oklahoma and west central Texas; in winter from southern Florida and eastern Mexico south to Cuba (casually), Panama and northern and southwestern Colombia.

DISTRIBUTION IN NEW ENGLAND. — *Maine:* Common to rare migrant and summer resident in southern parts, becoming extremely rare in northern half. *New Hampshire:* Uncommon migrant and summer resident north to valleys of White Mountains; rare farther north and absent on high elevations. *Vermont:* Common to uncommon migrant and common summer resident, chiefly in farming country; wanting on higher elevations. *Massachusetts:* Uncommon to rare migrant and generally uncommon to rare local summer resident. *Rhode Island:* Uncommon migrant and summer resident. *Connecticut:* Not uncommon migrant and locally common summer resident.

SEASON IN MASSACHUSETTS. — (April 19) May 1 to September 29 (October 12 and 15).

HAUNTS AND HABITS. The Crested Flycatcher normally is a dweller in the forest. In New England, however, most of the ancient forest trees with hollow trunks and branches have fallen before the axe of the woodsman, and now this bird finds nesting places in the cavities of many old orchard trees. For this reason chiefly, perhaps, it is found largely to-day in open farming country, and especially in neglected orchards near woodland, but the woods were its first love, and often to-day it may be seen perched near the top of some tall forest tree from which it darts forth in pursuit of its insect prey. It is a prominent bird, for it is the largest and in some ways the handsomest of our flycatchers; it often occupies a conspicuous perch, and its notes are so loud as to compel attention. Its battles in the air are fierce and noisy and it is inclined to bully other birds. It is quick, however, to rush to the defense of feathered neighbors in distress, for on several occasions when I have concealed myself in the woods or underbrush and imitated the cry of a bird in pain or distress this flycatcher has dashed almost into my face before it discovered its mistake. So far as I have been able to observe, this species is solitary, and in New England a lone bird or a single pair keeps guard over a considerable domain. I have not known two pairs to nest within half a mile of one another, though they may be distributed more numerously where the species is common.

During the month of April and the early part of May this species migrates northward, flying mostly by day and feeding as it goes. Courtship usually begins here during the latter part of May, when, if two rival males aspire to the favors of one female, a fierce battle ensues which results in one or both combatants losing more or less feathers. When the pair is finally united a search begins for a suitable cavity, and if one cannot be found in some tree, almost any kind of a nook may be selected, even a bird house or nesting box. Receptacles for nesting seem to be used without regard to their shape, situation or height from the ground, if only the interior is large enough for the bulky nest and the entrance of sufficient size to admit the birds. Being an active and industrious fowl it may occasionally choose some large, deep cavity when in want of a better place, and fill much of the superfluous space with a mass of rubbish built high, as a foundation to its domicile; or if the hole is too deep for it to fill laboriously, it may block the cavity with sticks and rubbish placed crosswise, and then build its nest on the platform thus prepared.

Many attempts have been made to account for its almost universal habit of adding a cast-off snake skin to the nest.   Some believe that this is placed there for the purpose of frightening predatory animals away,* but it is often so bestowed as to be invisible from the entrance and it is hardly possible that a dried skin would frighten any animal, unless indeed the scent of the snake still lingers about it.   Dawson tells us that in one nest where there was no snake skin there was a piece of tough tissue paper which "rustled ominously when the hand was inserted.   The secret was out," he says; "it is the rustle of the snake-skin which either delights the bird, or to which it trusts for giving warning of an enemy's approach during the owner's absence, — a sort of burglar alarm as it were."   This, however, is mere conjecture.   Neltje Blanchan (Mrs. Doubleday) even went so far as to suggest that the crests of the young birds might be accounted for by their early fright at discovering a snake skin in the nest, which clever conceit no one would be so simple as to take seriously.   Both sexes engage in nest building, and when a large cavity requires filling or when the building is interrupted by stormy weather, two weeks may elapse before the nest is complete.   Allowing two weeks for incubation and two more for the young to reach the flight stage, the young would rarely appear on the wing in New England until about the first week in July.   The parents feed them with insects and defend them with great fury against their numerous enemies.   In attacking an intruder their swift flight and power of quick turning come into play and are used to great advantage in avoiding retaliation.

This bird has favorite perches near the tops of tall trees which it is likely to occupy at about the same hour, day after day.   The food of the Crested Flycatcher consists, according to the late Professor Beal, of 93.7 per cent animal matter and 6.3 per cent vegetal, of which the former quantity is chiefly insects.   Among the insects taken are sawflies, horseflies, stinkbugs, May beetles, strawberry weevils, cotton-boll weevils, cicadas, leaf hoppers, grasshoppers, crickets, katydids and great numbers of caterpillars and moths. The vegetal food consists largely of wild fruit.

ECONOMIC STATUS.   This bird is believed to be one of the most useful flycatchers where it is common, though it may now and then take a few bees.   Professor Beal, however, found but one honey bee in examining 265 stomachs.   In many New England localities it is too uncommon or rare to be reckoned with.

Sayórnis phœbe (LATHAM).   Phœbe.

Other names: BARN *or* BRIDGE PEWEE; PHŒBE BIRD.

Plate 56.

DESCRIPTION. — Bill slender, not half as long as head; wings rather long and pointed; tail nearly as long as wing, very slightly forked, its outer tips somewhat rounded on each side; a typical flycatcher. *Adults in nuptial plumage* (*sexes alike*): Above chiefly grayish-olive, paling somewhat toward tail; top

*See Frank Bolles on "Snake Skins in the Nests of Myiarchus crinitus" (Auk, Vol. VII, 1890, p. 288).

PLATE 56

PLATE 56

WOOD PEWEE
Page 347

PHŒBE
Page 338

ADULT

ADULT

LEAST FLYCATCHER
Page 358

ADULT

ACADIAN FLYCATCHER
Page 352

ALDER FLYCATCH
Page 354

ADULT

ADULT

YELLOW–BELLIED FLYCATCHER
Page 350

ADULT

All about one-half scale.

Louis Agassiz Fuertes

and sides of head and back of neck considerably darker (dark sooty-brown); wings and tail darker than back, outer webs light grayish-olive at edges; outer webs of secondaries and tertials, end-margins of greater and middle secondaries and edge of outer web of outer tail-feathers much lighter than the rest, the latter olive-whitish; a little dull white usually shows before eye and on lower eyelid; below, chiefly dull yellowish-white; worn specimens or those that have been in burnt woods often more or less gray or dusky below; throat sometimes shows a little grayish intermixed; sides of breast light grayish-olive; wing linings and axillars yellow or yellowish with a little cast of grayish and some dusky, grayish feather-centers near margin of wing; bill black or blackish, becoming a little lighter or more brownish below; iris brown; legs and feet black. *Adults in winter plumage (autumn):* Similar to spring adults but more decidedly olive; edges of all wing-feathers more yellowish, and whitish below replaced by yellow or yellowish. *Young in first winter plumage (sexes alike):* Similar to autumnal adults. *Young in juvenal plumage:* Similar to autumnal adults, but browner olive above; middle and greater wing-coverts tipped cinnamon or buffy, forming two conspicuous wing-bars; tail also slightly tipped same, and upper tail-coverts tinged cinnamon.

MEASUREMENTS. — Length 6.25 to 7.25 in.; spread 10.52 to 11.25; folded wing 3.10 to 3.55; tail 2.78 to 3.50; bill .63 to .74; tarsus .66 to .72; female smaller than male.

MOLTS. — Juvenal plumage succeeds natal down by complete molt; in August partial molt begins (flight-feathers and tail not molted), and in first winter plumage young bird is practically as adult; adult apparently molts but once a year — in August and September.

FIELD MARKS. — Adults near Bluebird size; in spring grayish olive-brown, head much darker; *no conspicuous wing-bars* such as are prominent in Wood Pewee and other small flycatchers and whitish below more grayish on throat and breast; sides dark like back; adults and young in fall, yellow or yellowish below; young then show distinct cinnamon wing-bars; bird commonly jets its tail with sidewise sweep; bill is dark below instead of light as in Wood Pewee; head is darker above than in latter.

VOICE. — Common note a jerky *fébe* occasionally alternating it with *fébrizzy;* "*see-whee* with the accent on the last syllable"; in the breeding season a low twittering warble; alarm note *tchak-tchak* (C. Bendire); also a sharp *chip;* attempt at flight-song, *chick-a-de chick-a-de-phee-fweé-phee-bwe-phee-bwe* (W. C. Wheeler); *previt-previt* repeated incessantly and "at last, rising on the last syllable," "*preVEE* as if insisting on that with peculiar emphasis" (Thoreau).

BREEDING. — In forests or farming country, anywhere where its favorite nesting sites may be found, except in thickly settled places, as cities. *Nest:* On face of bank or cliff, on upturned roots of fallen tree or in cave or even over a house door; but usually under ample shelter such as is offered by overhanging bank, a cave, bridge, culvert, or the eaves or roof of some outbuilding or veranda, and on or against some firm support, such as rock, root, ledge or beam; when placed on top of beam or post it often is nearly circular, but when set against a wall it is more nearly the shape of half a shallow cup; built largely of mud, covered mostly with moss with often a few dead leaves or a little fern down, and lined with fine roots, grasses, feathers, dry moss, etc.; neat and compact.* *Eggs:* 3 to 8; commonly 4 or 5; .66 to .80 by .50 to .60 in.; usually ovate; unspotted white, or more rarely with a few scattered reddish-brown or blackish spots; figured in Bendire's "Life Histories of North American Birds," Vol. II, Plate I, Fig. 28. *Dates:* April 27 to August 15, Massachusetts. *Incubation:* Period 12 to 16 days (authors), probably usually 14; by one or both sexes. Two broods yearly, sometimes three, when there is a long, hot summer.

RANGE. — Eastern North America chiefly, north to about the northern border of the Canadian Zone, and Mexico. Breeds from southern Mackenzie, northeastern Alberta, central Saskatchewan, central Manitoba, central Ontario, southern Quebec, New Brunswick, Prince Edward Island and Nova Scotia south to northeastern New Mexico, central Texas, the highlands of northern Arkansas, northern Mississippi, northern Alabama, northern South Carolina, and central North Carolina; in winter casually

* The bird has been seen to light on the back of a horse or a cow and help itself to hairs for a nest-lining (Bird-Lore, Vol. XXVI, 1924, p. 177).

from Massachusetts, Connecticut, Pennsylvania and New Jersey, and regularly from Arkansas, Tennessee, and southern Virginia south to Florida, the Gulf coast, eastern and southern Mexico; casual west to eastern Wyoming, and eastern Colorado; accidental in southern California and Cuba.

DISTRIBUTION IN NEW ENGLAND. — Common migrant and summer resident, except at higher elevations of northern Maine and northern New Hampshire; casual in winter in southern parts; there are scattering winter records for Massachusetts and Connecticut and one for Milford, New Hampshire, February 13, 1919, and another for Bennington, Vermont, February 1, 1922.

SEASON IN MASSACHUSETTS. — (February 7 to 24) March 12 to October 26 (November 15, winter).

HAUNTS AND HABITS.   Phœbe is an early bird.   The chill and blustering winds of March still sweep over fields of frozen snow, when this little feathered wanderer comes from its winter sojourn in more southern lands to its favorite home in the north.   Soon its familiar note is heard about the barn, in the orchard or along the rushing stream. Now and then one of these early birds may be seen darting out from its perch in a March snow-storm, apparently catching insects, but Mr. C. J. Maynard tells me that he saw one thus snapping up the whirling snowflakes, which may have been one of its ways of securing water.   Phœbe is early also in another sense.   In the dusk of morning before the break of day, while Screech Owls and Whip-poor-wills are still abroad, Phœbe flits silently from mountain cliff, overhanging bank or some other sheltered retreat where she has passed the night and soon her voice may be heard along the river, greeting the first signs of the coming day.   She seems to be endowed like the night birds with vision that can pierce the gloom of dusk in shadowy places and so mark down the fluttering insects of the night before they have retired to their daylight retreats.   Phœbe seeks the waterside because many insects develop early there, and though the little bird can eke out a precarious existence before the insects develop, they are her favorite food.   In chill April for instance, while the days still remain cool and the nights frosty, Phœbe lives commonly in the woods, flycatching over pools of standing stagnant water, where numerous flying insects flutter when the sun shines.   Another reason for the preference for a home near water is that Phœbe is a great bather and often may be seen flying over the water, plunging in her breast and wing-tips, and afterward shaking the shining drops from her feathers.   The bird also frequently alights in shallow water and bathes by dipping and fluttering in the manner of most perching birds.

Phœbe's choice of a home, however, is not decided so much by proximity to water as by available nesting sites.   She will go far from water to build her nest on a mountain cliff or in some isolated cave in the rocks; but along the many streams of New England, high banks and many bridges furnish her such sites as she most desires for her little dwelling, and along the streams too she can find the mud and moss which go into the construction of the small compact nursery in which the young are cared for and fed.

Every farmer's boy knows where the "Phœbe bird" nests, and such favorite nesting sites are revisited by the birds year after year.   A pair once built a long string of nests in succeeding years over a doorway; sometimes they use the same nest for several years, building it up by successive stories.   Another Phœbe, observed by Mr. A. C. Bagg, of Holyoke, built two nests, laying two eggs in each, and divided her time between the two ; but this bird must have been subnormal to say the least ; sometimes the nest in which the first brood is reared is repaired and used again during the same season.   Often, however, a new nest is built for the second brood in a different situation ; sometimes several nests are built in the same season.   One reason for this is that the fondness which Phœbe exhibits for poultry houses and her habit of lining her nest with hen feathers tend to infest the little family with those tiny red mites, so abundant where poultry are kept.   These and bird lice are sometimes so numerous in the nest of the Phœbe that the young succumb to their attacks.   A thorough dusting of the nest with insect powder will dispose of most of these pests.

I have spoken of the Phœbe in the feminine gender, as the female alone is believed to be the builder of the nest, but in some cases both birds have been seen at work upon it. Mrs. R. L. Champlin informs me that on April 20, 1926, she watched, from a window about four feet away, a pair, then beginning a nest in a garage.   In the afternoon of that day they abandoned that site, and the next morning started a new domicile under the eaves of a small building.   After two hours at this they began again in another corner of the building where they finally decided to stay, but if anyone outside approached, they flew to the other nest and began working on that.   Where Phœbes have become accustomed to breeding in a certain building and find it closed on their return from the south, they sometimes succeed in entering through a broken window, a woodpecker hole or a large knot hole.   Mr. William B. Olney of Seekonk, Massachusetts, has an old building in which a pair of these birds breed.   Early in the season for two or three years a Phœbe came and alighted on the clothes-line near the cellar door and called until some one opened the door, when the bird went in and built a new nest or repaired the old one.

The Phœbe nests early and thus lives up to its reputation as an early bird ; it sometimes chooses strange situations for its nest.   Occasionally one is plastered on a perpendicular wall, but the birds prefer some sort of shelf, as a beam, to support it.   One pair built a nest in an old tin colander hung on the wall of a barn, another was placed in an old coffee pot hanging on a nail in a deserted cabin, and more than once I have seen a Phœbe's nest in an uncovered cigar box nailed up on a cottage wall under the veranda roof.   Another pair built in a well, five feet below the surface.   They reached the nest by passing through a knot hole in the platform that covered the well.   Another pair built in an air shaft of a coal mine.   Individual Phœbes, which have become accustomed to man and his works, often seem very fearless in their choice of a nesting site.   Bridges over which heavy teams and cars pass daily, railroad culverts over which roll many heavy trains every twenty-four hours, farmhouse sheds and barns where people and animals often pass are chosen.   Mr. Franklin P. Cook writes from Lawrenceville, New Jersey, that he found a nest of this species inside a field telephone box on a rifle range near there.   The banging of long-range rifles and the whistling of the bullets passing by did not seem to disturb the birds in the least.   Mr. Aretas A. Saunders of Fairfield, Connecticut, tells me of a Phœbe's nest in a quarry where blasting was going on about fifteen feet away. Blasting was continued daily after the middle of April, 1922, yet the bird brought out her first brood safely, relined the nest and on June 27 was sitting on five eggs. When the men fired a blast they placed a board in front of the nest to protect it.* The Phœbe's first brood often requires six or seven weeks, or even more, from the beginning of the nest until the young have flown; but when the same nest is used for the second brood, a month is ample time, as this brood is reared in warm weather, when food is plentiful and storms usually are few. Mr. Franklin P. Campbell informs me that a brood left a nest under his veranda in July, just eleven days from the date of the hatch. Both birds often take part in incubation and in feeding the young, and within one or two days after the first brood leaves the nest, the female begins another or starts repairs on the old nest, while the male cares for the first brood.

The Phœbe takes its prey, like other flycatchers, by watching from some prominent perch and darting out at passing insects which it captures mostly in the air, but it also gets more or less food from the ground, especially when the young are being fed. Its tail seems to be very loosely hung and bobs up and down or sweeps sidewise very frequently. It seems a fearless bird, for it often nests in plain sight on cliffs, frequented by the powerful Duck Hawk, but I have noticed that in such a case it seldom flies out far from the cliffs into the open, and that in passing down to its nest from the top of the crag it shoots down like a plummet, close to the rock, and exposes itself as little as possible. Not many feathers of the Phœbe are found around the Duck Hawk's nesting place although the hawk gets one rarely. Phoebes let the Duck Hawk severely alone, but sometimes, like the Kingbird, chase other hawks or crows. They usually live at peace with the smaller birds, except when two rival males contend for the favors of the same female, when a spirited contest ensues.

During his mating days the male may be seen, at times, fluttering about ecstatically in a circle and pouring forth what no doubt passes for a flight-song with his indulgent mate. Sometimes the bird rises high repeating his usual notes with some twittering variations, but it can hardly be called a musical triumph. Often this is an early morning performance.

The young are fed almost entirely on insects, which constitute by far the greater part of the food of the adults. Among the many pests that this bird eats are houseflies, mosquitoes, cankerworms, codling moths, gipsy moths, brown-tail moths and vast numbers of other destructive moths, curculios, cottonboll weevils, strawberry weevils, cornleaf beetles, snap beetles, elm leaf beetles, cucumber-beetles, ants, grasshoppers, locusts and ticks, and it takes flies from the backs of cattle; also hairy caterpillars, which it takes on pendant leaves or as they hang by their threads. In studying the food of the Phœbe one wonders how such an insectivorous bird can exist in New England in February and March and how it can withstand the storms of this period. During severe snow storms this bird betakes itself to some shelter such as a shed, a barn cellar or a poultry

---

*Perhaps the most unusual site was on a brace under the guards of the steam ferry-boat that ran between Middletown and Portland, Connecticut (Ornithologist and Oölogist, Vol. VII, 1882, p. 183).

house. I have seen it in February on the ground with Field Sparrows apparently picking up small seeds. In late winter and early spring the bird subsists more or less on seeds and wild berries, and such material makes up about 11 per cent of its food for the year, but it prefers animal food and especially insects. In Bulletin No. 44 of the Biological Survey, Professor Beal gives a full account of the food found in the stomachs of 370 Phœbes. He found that the bird destroyed some useful parasitic insects and that it sometimes ate honey bees. Mr. A. W. Higgins informs me that he saw one on September 25, 1924, eating Kaffir corn from the ground.

ECONOMIC STATUS. The fruit that the Phœbe eats is so small in quantity as to be negligible. Its only known harmful trait is the occasional destruction of a few fish fry. It well deserves all the protection it usually receives at the hands of man. Professor Beal concludes his summary with the remark that the bird pays ample rent for its accommodations.

Sayornis sáyus (BONAPARTE). Say's Phœbe.

DESCRIPTION. — Similar in shape to Phœbe but larger and *tail much shorter than wing and brownish-black*, edges of greater and lesser wing-coverts, secondaries and outer edge of outer primary are dull white; more grayish-brown than olive-brown above, including sides of head which pass gradually into pale buffy-brownish-gray of chin and throat; upper breast and sides somewhat darker than chin and throat and usually more buffy in center than on sides; *rest of lower plumage cinnamon-buff*, except wing linings and axillars which are lighter buff; bill black; iris brown; legs and feet black. *Young in juvenal plumage:* Similar to adults, but browner above with two distinct narrow cinnamon or buffy wing-bars, formed of light tips of greater and middle coverts.

MEASUREMENTS. — Length 7.50 to 8.05 in.; spread 12.50 to 13.25; folded wing 3.90 to 4.25; tail 3.35 to 3.75; bill .65 to .80; tarsus about .90; female smaller than male.

MOLTS. — Molts probably like those of Phœbe, but not sufficient molting material available to determine this.

FIELD MARKS. — Size larger than Phœbe, smaller than Kingbird; distinguished by black tail, pale, grayish, faded appearance of back, whitish bars on wing and cinnamon-buff under-body, very active and restless.

VOICE. — A pathetic and plaintive *phee-ur* always given with a twitch of the tail (C. Bendire); not so vigorous a note as that of Phœbe, and a little tremulous; also like Phœbe a twittering attempt at song in the mating season.

BREEDING. — Seldom in forests but often in open country far from water. *Nest:* In similar locations to those of Phœbe, on cliffs, buildings, bridges, etc.; built of materials similar to those used by Phœbe, except that mud is seldom used, and that hair or wool are commonly utilized in lining. *Eggs:* Like those of Phœbe, usually a little larger; figured in Bendire's "Life Histories of North American Birds," Vol. II, Plate I, Fig. 29. *Dates:* Early March to late May, New Mexico; May 21 to June 3, Montana; July 1, Utah. *Incubation:* Period about 12 days (Bendire). Two broods yearly; in some cases possibly three.

RANGE. — Western North America and Mexico. Breeds from central Alaska, northwestern Mackenzie, northeastern Alberta, central Saskatchewan and central North Dakota south to northern Lower California, northern Sonora, northern Durango, southern New Mexico, and western Texas and east to the edge of the Great Plains in northwestern Oklahoma, central Kansas, and central Nebraska; casually east to western Iowa; south in winter from northern California, southern Arizona, southern New Mexico and central Texas to southern Lower California and southern Mexico. Accidental in migration in Wisconsin, Missouri, Michigan, Illinois, Massachusetts, Connecticut and Quebec.

DISTRIBUTION IN NEW ENGLAND. — Accidental visitor in Massachusetts and Connecticut. Records: *Massachusetts:* North Truro, September 30, 1889, adult male taken by Gerrit S. Miller, Jr.[1] *Connecticut:* Gaylordsville, December 15, 1916, adult female shot and in collection of Dr. H. B. Bishop.[2]

HAUNTS AND HABITS. Say's Phœbe is a large pale Phœbe of the arid regions on the great plains of western North America. It much resembles the eastern Phœbe in appearance and habits, but unlike that well-known bird, it frequents mostly open unforested lands often far from water. Its habits are similar to those of the Phœbe, but it is even more active. It is a mere straggler to New England.

ECONOMIC STATUS. See page 323.

Nuttallórnis boreális (SWAINSON). Olive-sided Flycatcher.

Other names: THREE-DEER; PITCH-PINE FLYCATCHER

Plate 55.

DESCRIPTION. — Bill much larger than that of Wood Pewee; head large; wings exceeding tail by about half its length; tail only very slightly forked; tarsi very short. *Adults (sexes alike):* Above chiefly slaty olive-brownish or dark smoke-gray; feathers on top of head darker centrally; wings and tail dusky-blackish; wing-coverts edged and tipped grayish; secondaries edged lighter than wing-coverts and tertials edged and tipped whitish; conspicuous white or yellowish-white tuft of feathers on each side of rump (often concealed under wings); below chiefly white in center (often tinged pale yellow) from chin to tail, becoming brownish-gray on either side, slightly tinged with olive; under tail-coverts with V-shaped markings of same; axillars and wing linings brownish-gray, the feathers edged paler; bill black above, brownish below, dusky toward tip; iris brown; legs and feet brownish-black. *Young in juvenal plumage:* Similar to adults but tips of wing-coverts buffy or rusty.

MEASUREMENTS. — Length 7.10 to 8.00 in.; spread 12.25 to 13.50; folded wing 3.80 to 4.50; tail 2.74 to 3.05; bill .72 to .82; tarsus .55 to .68; female smaller than male.

MOLTS. — Juvenal plumage follows natal down by complete postnatal molt; late postjuvenal molt begins in September (Dwight); this molt probably complete, after which young become as adults; adults have one complete (postnuptial) molt beginning in August.

FIELD MARKS. — Size slightly larger than Bluebird, but smaller than Kingbird, with relatively shorter tail; bill and head rather large; body robust; dark olive-gray and brownish above, dark brownish-gray on sides with a whitish stripe from chin down middle of breast and belly to tail-coverts. Two white tufts often show, one on each side of rump above wing (shown in plate 55).

VOICE. — A two-syllabled call supposed to resemble the words *three-deer* or *three cheers*, or a three syllabled call *"tuck three beers"* (Hoyes Lloyd); a low *chuck*, audible when near, followed by the louder *whit whew* (A. R. Whiting); *pi-pee* or *pip, pi-pee* (Ralph Hoffmann); alarm note *puip puip puip* (C. Bendire); a monotonous note like *till-till-till* or *pe-pe-pe* (Thoreau); besides the loud *quip-peer-peer*, *borealis* has minor notes which, while not loud, may be heard at some distance — like *pit-pit-pit*, resembling very much similar notes of the Yellowleg; both sexes utter these little *pits* or *quips* (usually three in succession) and other conversational twitters; these conversational *pits*, etc., indicate a nesting pair, while the loud *quip peer-peer* may indicate only a lone male. The female (who may be alone) twitters as she hurries back and forth with twigs for the nest; besides these *pits* or *quips* there are other still fainter notes — very soft and short — uttered often when the nest is building (J. A. Farley).

BREEDING. — Usually in open woods near some clearing where part of the timber has been cut (often near water) where some tall dead tree serves as its watch tower. *Nest:* Commonly saddled in small

---

[1] Auk, Vol. VII, 1890, p. 228.

[2] Auk, Vol. XXXVIII, 1921, p. 586.

FIG. 58. — NEST AND EGGS OF WOOD PEWEE

Page 348

FIG. 59. — OLIVE-SIDED FLYCATCHER AND NEST

Page 344

crotch on rather horizontal branch of spruce or other coniferous tree; rarely in an orchard; from 10 to 50 feet from ground; rather small for bird of such size, and quite shallow, built of fine rootlets, small twigs and *usnea* and lined with moss and rootlets; a mossy saucer, usually set among a mass of fine twigs projecting from the limb on which it rests; thus difficult to see from beneath. *Eggs:* 3, rarely 4; .80 to .92 by .60 to .68 in.; ovate; from cream to pinkish, spotted and blotched with shades of chestnut, purple and lavender, usually wreathed about large end; much like those of Wood Pewee, but larger; figured in Bendire's "Life Histories of North American Birds," Vol. II, Plate II, Figs. 15 and 16. *Dates:* May 27, Kansas; June 5 to about July 1, New England. *Incubation:* Period about 14 days (Bendire). One brood yearly.

RANGE. — North America, Central America and south to central South America. Breeds chiefly in Canadian and Transition zones, in coniferous forests from central Alaska, southern Mackenzie, central Manitoba, northern Ontario, southern Quebec, and Newfoundland south to southern California, northern Lower California, Arizona, New Mexico and central western Texas; also formerly to Kansas (casually) and now sparingly to South Dakota, northern Minnesota, central Wisconsin, central Michigan, southern Ontario, northwestern Pennsylvania, New York and Massachusetts, and south in mountains to eastern Tennessee and southwestern North Carolina. Migrates through mountains of Mexico and Central America. Winters from Costa Rica, casually southern Mexico, south to Peru, western Ecuador and Colombia; accidental in southern Greenland, and Bermuda Islands.

DISTRIBUTION IN NEW ENGLAND. — *Maine:* Uncommon migrant and more or less common local summer resident. *New Hampshire:* Uncommon migrant and occasional local summer resident, more or less common northward. *Vermont:* Uncommon migrant and summer resident, chiefly in elevated regions. *Massachusetts:* Uncommon to rare migrant and rather uncommon summer resident west of the Connecticut River; rare and local elsewhere; formerly more common. *Rhode Island:* Rare migrant.

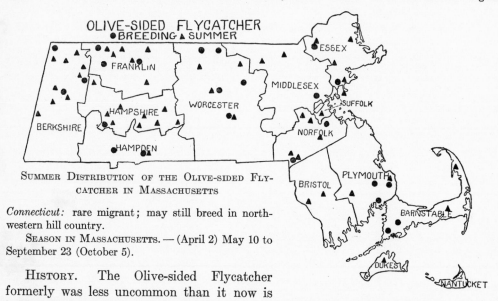

SUMMER DISTRIBUTION OF THE OLIVE-SIDED FLY-
CATCHER IN MASSACHUSETTS

Connecticut: rare migrant; may still breed in north-western hill country.

SEASON IN MASSACHUSETTS. — (April 2) May 10 to September 23 (October 5).

HISTORY. The Olive-sided Flycatcher formerly was less uncommon than it now is in New England, south at least to Massachusetts and through most of that state. Nuttall (1832) observed the species breeding in Cambridge; Samuels (1870) found it not very common in New England and tells of two nests found in West Roxbury and one in Dorchester (both now parts of Boston) within two years; Minot (1876) regarded it as "neither rare nor common" in Massachusetts; Brewster found three pairs of these birds and two nests at Mt. Auburn, Cambridge, in 1867, where Nuttall first reported the discovery of a nest found in 1830. Brewster says also (1895) that the bird "used to breed sparingly but regularly within twenty miles of Boston, to the north and west but during the past ten or fifteen years it has nearly if not quite deserted this region." In the '70s I found it breeding very sparingly about Worcester and in northern Worcester County. Within the last ten years it has bred at Wareham, Carver, Plymouth and Falmouth, and undoubtedly does so still, as well as in other towns in lower Plymouth County. Brewster declared (1895) that it still nested on Cape Cod in considerable numbers. To-day, it breeds regularly in the mountainous country west of the Connecticut River and in the Berkshire hills, but even there the species is uncommon or rare. In northern New England its status now seems to be about the same as in western Massachusetts, except in Maine, where it ranges from rather common to rare, according to locality. No reason for the decrease of the species in New England has been advanced, though Brewster considered it probable that at one time it overflowed into Massachusetts from its normal range to which it has since receded; but like the Hermit Thrush, the Olive-sided Flycatcher breeds too often in the Alleghanian Faunal Area to be regarded as a typical Canadian form.

HAUNTS AND HABITS. — The Olive-sided Flycatcher is a forest recluse. Normally it lives and breeds about unfrequented swamps, lonely mountain lakes and ponds or mountain streams, where coniferous forests grow. It is by no means confined to the mountains, however, and may even breed on lowlands near the sea, but in such cases it nests near water or wet lands. It seems fond of the spruce in the northern part of its range, and in the southern part seems to prefer pitch pine. Formerly in eastern Massachusetts it bred in orchards and open groves and in old fields grown up to red cedars (Virginia junipers), but this was a departure from its usual habits. It seems to prefer some lone swamp or lake, where fire or flood has killed some trees, or where the settler has girdled them, and left them standing bleak and bare to be used by the bird as watch towers on which it sits very erect and from the tall tops of which it shoots straight up into the air and then stoops hawk-like or else darts off most gracefully at varying angles in pursuit of its insect prey. Our recluse is pugnacious; his mate is company enough, and he defends an exclusive territory against any interloping male of the same species. When another male appears the two often battle in the air until both are completely exhausted.

The Olive-sided Flycatcher usually arrives in May and always alone. During the period of migration one may appear anywhere, usually perched in or near the top of some tree on the edge of the woods or in the orchard, silent and watchful, except that on its breeding grounds its loud cries frequently are heard. The shallow nest is placed well out on some rather slender limb, often high from the ground in a coniferous tree where it is difficult to reach. "Imagine, if you can, lying upon one end of a bright green limb, a shallow saucer of light green Spanish (*usnea*) moss, the outer edges fading off into delicate tracing against the darker and richer green and reposing in the center depression three rich, creamy eggs, whose bright spots were fairly brilliant in the dazzling sunshine; all this with a dense background of the richest green, for looking down as we were, nothing beyond the foliage could be seen. It was a sight I shall never forget." [1]

The birds are very brave in defense of their eggs or young. As the climber nears the nest, they become miniature furies, darting close to one's head and snapping their bills like owls, but behaving far more bravely than most birds of prey. In August when the young are strong on the wing, both old and young start on their long journey to South America.

The food of this flycatcher consists almost entirely of flying insects, chiefly hymenoptera. According to Professor Beal the bird is a typical flycatcher. Only three per cent of its food consists of fruit, but in addition to the injurious insects that it eats, it takes many ground beetles, a few parasitic hymenoptera and a larger proportion of bees than does the Kingbird, and it does not select the drones but takes workers also.

ECONOMIC STATUS. Were this bird at all numerous in cultivated lands, it might become destructive to honey bees; otherwise, it is of no great economic importance.

Myióchanes vírens (LINNÆUS). Wood Pewee.

Other names: PEWEE; DEAD-LIMB BIRD.

Plate 56.

DESCRIPTION. — Bill small and rather slender. Bird much less robust than Olive-sided Flycatcher, with tail relatively longer and slightly but distinctly forked, and no conspicuous white tufts on sides of rump. *Adults (sexes alike):* Above, chiefly olive or brownish-gray, darkening on top of head where feathers are darker centrally; tail deep grayish-brown; wings dusky, pale gray tips of middle and greater wing-coverts forming two dull white wing-bars; secondaries also with pale edges which become broader on tertials; sides of neck usually lighter than back; chin and throat whitish or yellowish-white; sides of upper breast and sides of body pale grayish-olive; rest of lower plumage yellowish-white or very pale yellow; wing linings and axillars like sides of body, but feathers with yellowish margins; bill brownish-black above, *whitish or pale yellowish below, brownish at tip;* iris deep brown; legs and feet brownish-black. *Young in juvenal plumage:* Much like adults, but wing-coverts sharply tipped buff, forming two distinct wing-bars; feather-tips of most of upper plumage light buffy-brown; olive on sides of breast usually more distinctly defined against yellow of other under plumage.

MEASUREMENTS. — Length 6.00 to 6.75 in.; spread 9.75 to 11.00; folded wing 3.15 to 3.55; tail 2.50 to 3.00; bill .60 to .72; tarsus .45 to .56. Female smaller than male.

MOLTS. — Juvenal plumage follows natal down by complete postnatal molt; first winter plumage produced by partial molt beginning in late August or September, young bird then becoming practically as winter adult; both old and young acquire spring plumage by fading and wear, under which the lower plumage and the yellowish wing-edgings become whiter; adults have one complete molt annually — the postnuptial — beginning in late August or September.

FIELD MARKS. — Size near that of Song Sparrow; somewhat smaller than Phœbe, but larger than the small flycatchers of the genus *Empidonax;* a rather dark olive or brownish-gray bird above, with *two white wing-bars;* breast narrowly whitish or yellowish, washed on sides with grayish-olive; distin-

---

[1] Noble, Frank T.: Journal of the Maine Ornithological Society, Vol. IV, 1902, p. 51.

guished from Phœbe at once by its distinct white (buff in the young bird) wing-bars; seldom, if ever, flirts its tail in the loose or sidewise manner of Phœbe; not so restless as Phœbe; often sits nearly motionless and upright for a time with now and then a quivering of the wings, occasionally uttering the note which gave it its name; *bill whitish or pale yellowish below* where Phœbe is darker; it is longer and relatively more slender than any of the smaller flycatchers of New England.

VOICE. — A drawled, plaintive, sighing *peé-we* or *peé-a-wéé, pe-éér*, also a low *chip* which sometimes prefaces the *pee-a-wee*, and about the nest a *chitter* or *chipper;* male in breeding season, a low twittering warble (C. Bendire); occasionally makes a rather creditable attempt at song in spring; has a short song-flight in autumn.

BREEDING. — Usually in woodland; more rarely in orchards or shade trees near edges of woods. *Nest:* Built on nearly horizontal branch from 6 to 50 feet up; a beautiful dainty saucer-shaped structure of little depth, of bark, rootlets, plant fibers, etc., lined with plant down, wool, horsehair or similar but finer materials of the same sort as those of which the nest is composed and covered outside with bits of tree lichens, so that from below it appears like a knot or excrescence on the limb; or of another type (usually in a pine), a bunch of lichens in plain sight, but concealed by its resemblance to other bunches of lichens on lower limbs. *Eggs:* 2 to 4; usually 3; .65 to .79 by .50 to .56 in.; ovate to short or rounded ovate; milk-white to cream, marked in irregular ring around large end with spots, blotches and small specks of various browns, heliotrope, purple and lavender; rarely much marked at small end; figured in Bendire's "Life Histories of North American Birds," Vol. II, Plate II, Figs. 18 and 19. *Dates:* June 5 to 20, Virginia; June 10 to July 25, Massachusetts. *Incubation:* Period about 12 days (Bendire); 13 days (O. W. Knight); 12 to 13 days (Burns); chiefly or wholly by female. One brood yearly, possibly sometimes two in southern New England; a second brood of two young in South Carolina (A. T. Wayne).

RANGE. — Eastern Northern America (north to southern Canada), and south to central South America. Breeds from southern Manitoba, southern Ontario, southern Quebec, New Brunswick, Prince Edward Island and Nova Scotia south to southern Texas, the Gulf states and central Florida, west to the edge of the Great Plains in central North Dakota, central Nebraska and central Texas, migrates through eastern Mexico; winters from Nicaragua (probably southeastern Mexico) through Central America to Peru, Ecuador and Colombia; casual migrant in Cuba, Bermuda Islands and eastern Colorado.

DISTRIBUTION IN NEW ENGLAND. — Common migrant and common summer resident except on the higher elevations of northern New England.

SEASON IN MASSACHUSETTS. — May 5 to September 26 (October 1).

HAUNTS AND HABITS. "When the tide of spring migration is at its height, and the early morning woods are bursting with melody, a pensive stranger, clad in soberest olive, takes his place on some well shaded limb and remarks, *pe-a-wee*, in a plaintive voice and with a curious rising inflection at the end. Unlike his cousin, the Phœbe, who came too early in March, and who felt aggrieved at the lingering frosts, the Wood Pewee has nothing that he may rightly complain of. The trees are wreathed in their tenderest greens; the fresh blossoms opening to the waving breeze, are exhaling their choicest odors; the air hums with teeming insect life. But the Wood Pewee takes only a languid interest in all these matters. His memory is haunted by an unforgotten sorrow, some tragedy of the ancestral youth, and he sits alone, apart, saying ever and anon as his heart is freshly stirred, *pé-a-wee, pé-a-wee.*" Thus William L. Dawson [1] aptly characterizes the Pewee and its pensive lay.

The sad or dreamy nature of its call, however, is in harmony with its environment among the whispering trees. Its plaintive tone is deceptive, for the Pewee evidently is a

[1] Birds of Ohio, Vol. I, 1903, pp. 320–321.

happy bird.   Dallas Lore Sharp says that "not much can be said of the Flycatcher family except that it is useful — a kind of virtue that gets its chief reward in heaven." . . . "a duck" he says "seems to know that it cannot sing.   A flycatcher knows nothing of its shortcomings.   He believes he can sing and in time he will prove it."

It is true that, as a family, flycatchers are not singing birds, but the Wood Pewee comes nearer to being a song bird than any other flycatcher with which I am well acquainted.   It has the sweetest and most pleasing voice of them all.   In spring and early summer the male often attempts at early morning and occasionally at evening a song of some length which is really quite a creditable effort for a flycatcher.   The bird seems to show little of the irritability and pugnacity that renders most of our flycatchers quarrelsome and even tyrannical.   When on the lookout for its prey it does not take up a position at the top of a tree, like some of the other members of the family, but sits upright on some dead limb in the cool shades of the forest where light and shadow fleck the leafy ground, and from this perch sallies forth from time to time in pursuit of ill-fated insects, which with snapping bill it captures unerringly.   Like the Phœbe the Pewee is abroad even before daylight, and seems to be able to pursue and capture its winged victims before it is light enough within the woods for the human eye to perceive the little bird.   In New England, where woodlands are numerous, the Wood Pewee breeds mostly within their shades, although it occasionally nests in an orchard tree near the woods; in other more open parts of the country its nest is not infrequently to be seen in orchard and shade trees.   Usually it is saddled on a dead limb at no great distance from the ground, but in South Carolina, according to Arthur T. Wayne, it sometimes builds at a height of ninety feet.   The young are tended and fed by both parents, and normally leave the nest in about 18 days.   The adults are devoted to their offspring and have been known to defend them courageously by darting at a man's head, though they are not brave enough actually to attack a human being.   They feed the young for quite a long time after the fledglings have left the nest, and while they still continue to call on their parents with a mouse-like squeak.   Mr. W. E. Snyder relates that where a pair of Kingbirds disappeared, leaving their fledged young, a lone Wood Pewee fed the orphans for ten days until they also left the neighborhood.[1]

Professor F. E. L. Beal of the Biological Survey, reporting on the contents of 359 stomachs of the Wood Pewee, finds that its animal food (chiefly small insects) makes up 98.97 per cent of the nutriment for the year, the vegetal food consisting of a small quantity of berries and seeds.   Beetles, including destructive weevils, curculios and borers, also flies, moths, caterpillars, grasshoppers, crickets and bugs are eaten in greater or less quantities.   The bird takes a larger percentage of hymenopterous parasites (useful insects) than some of the other flycatchers, and also occasionally catches small trout from ponds in fish hatcheries.

ECONOMIC STATUS.   In summarizing the evidence for and against this bird, Beal says that it does far more good than harm.

---

[1] Auk, Vol. XXX, 1913, p. 273.

Empídonax flavivéntris (W. M. & S. F. Baird). Yellow-bellied Flycatcher.

Plate 56.

DESCRIPTION. — A typical, small flycatcher with large subcrested head, bill rather broad at base, wings ample, and tail slightly forked, 1st primary usually equal to 6th. *Adults (sexes alike):* Above, olive-green or greenish-olive; tail rather dark grayish-brown, each feather narrowly olive on outer edge of outer web; wings dusky or blackish, lightening somewhat on primaries; middle and greater wing-coverts broadly tipped pale olive-yellow forming two conspicuous wing-bars, secondaries edged narrowly with same, except basally, tertials more broadly edged with same; a conspicuous eye-ring and lower plumage pale yellow, passing into light yellowish-olive on upper breast and sides of breast; axillars and wing linings also yellow, outermost under wing-coverts with dark grayish centers; bill black above, pale yellow below; iris brown; legs and feet dusky-brown to blackish. *Young in juvenal plumage:* Similar to adults but slightly duller above; throat less yellow and wing-bars buffy or brownish yellow; "bill black; the under mandible flesh; feet dusky flesh-color" (J. Dwight).

MEASUREMENTS. — Length 5.10 to 5.80 in.; spread 7.90 to 8.70; folded wing 2.60 to 2.80; tail 2.00 to 2.30; bill .48 to .52; tarsus .64 to .70. Female smaller than male.

MOLTS. — Young birds acquire juvenal plumage after natal down by complete postnatal molt in the nest; first winter plumage is produced by postjuvenal molt; not sufficient material available to determine whether this is complete; by fading and wear (probably) young appear as adults on returning north in spring; adults have one complete postnuptial molt after leaving New England; this shows a deeper yellow than spring plumage which may be partially acquired by molt in winter in the south, but material available is insufficient to determine this.

FIELD MARKS. — Near Chipping Sparrow size, head larger; olive green above and *more decidedly yellow below* than any other small flycatcher of eastern North America; has an olive shade across breast and yellow eye-ring; should be unmistakable in spring as it is then the *only small flycatcher that is distinctly yellow below, including the throat;* our other small flycatchers have the throat white or whitish; Acadian Flycatcher is only *yellowish* below; in autumn when others are yellowish below, identification is more difficult.

VOICE. — "A soft whistling '*queep*' or '*seek*'" (O. W. Knight); a low plaintive *peeh-peh pee-a pee-wick* or *ti-pee-a* (E. H. Eaton); alarm note *turri turri* (C. Bendire); on its breeding grounds a song is attempted with very indifferent success, given by Dr. Hoy as *pea-wāyk-pea-wāyk* several times repeated; it is soft and "not unpleasant"; "its 'song' sounds like *killic* given 'very gravely'; its low short note is like *pea* or *t'wee* or *too-wee*, often repeated a good many times in succession" (J. A. Farley).

BREEDING. — Commonly in and about secluded mossy swamps, wooded with coniferous trees. *Nest:* Sunk in sphagnum or other moss (often wet), on ground, bank of stream, stump, upturned tree roots or rock near ground; built of fine rootlets, fine grasses, mosses, etc., and cunningly hidden (Fig. 60). *Eggs:* Commonly 4, rarely 5; .64 to .70 by .50 to .52 in.; ovate; white or creamy white, spotted or very finely dotted with "cinnamon-rufous to walnut brown" and occasionally a speck or two of purplish; markings usually thickest near large end; figured in Bendire's "Life Histories of North American Birds," Vol. II, Plate II, Fig. 23. *Dates:* June 8 to 17, New York; June 14 to 27, Maine. *Incubation:* 12 to 14 days. One brood yearly.

RANGE. — Eastern North America, eastern Mexico and Central America. Breeds from northwestern British Columbia, southern Mackenzie, central Manitoba, southern Ontario, central Quebec and Newfoundland south to central Alberta, east central North Dakota, Minnesota, northern Iowa (casually), southern Wisconsin, northern Indiana, southern New York, and central New England and in mountains to Pennsylvania; west in migration to Nebraska, Oklahoma, and central Texas; south in migration through northeastern Mexico, and southeastern United States to Florida and Gulf coast; winters in central Mexico and Central America to Panama; accidental in Greenland.

DISTRIBUTION IN NEW ENGLAND. — *Maine:* Rather uncommon migrant; common to rare summer resident in northern and eastern parts in Canadian Zone. *New Hampshire:* Rather uncommon migrant, but rather common summer resident from White Mountains (to above 3000 feet) north, and very local south to Mt. Monadnock. *Vermont:* Rather uncommon migrant and uncommon local summer resident, often in mountain bogs. *Massachusetts:* Uncommon migrant; may have bred on Mt. Greylock; no definite breeding record. *Rhode Island:* Rare migrant. *Connecticut:* Uncommon migrant.

SEASON IN MASSACHUSETTS. — May 15 to June 10 (June 15); August 25 to September 25 (November 29, December 6).

HAUNTS AND HABITS. "To see this little Flycatcher at his best, one must seek the northern evergreen forest, where, far from human habitations, its mournful notes blend with the murmur of some icy brook tumbling over mossy stones or gushing beneath the still mossier decayed logs that threaten to bar its way. Where all is green and dark and cool, in some glen overarched by crowding spruces and firs, birches and maples, there it is we find him, and in the beds of damp moss he skilfully conceals his nest. He sits erect on some low twig, and, like other Flycatchers, the snap of his bill tells of a sally after his winged prey. He glides quietly away when approached, and his occasional note of complaint may be heard as long as one remains in his vicinity. During the migration this species is silent, and its several distinctive notes are not available for its identification, and the same thing may be said of our other small Flycatchers. Great similarity in plumage exists between them all, and without the bird in hand, identifications are at best questionable.

"The song is more suggestive of a sneeze on the bird's part than of any other sound with which it may be compared. It is an abrupt *psĕ-ĕk*, almost in one explosive syllable, harsh like the deeper tones of a House Wren, and less musical than the similar but longer songs of the Alder or the Acadian Flycatcher. It is hardly surprising that the birds sing very little when we see with what a convulsive jerk of the head the notes are produced. Its plaintive call is far more melodious — a soft, mournful whistle consisting of two notes, the second higher pitched and prolonged, with rising inflection, resembling in a measure *chū-ē-ē'-p*." [1] The flycatchers of the genus Empidonax are thus dubbed the kings or rulers of gnats, or at least that is what the Greek name signifies, but they are really destroyers of the gnat tribes. The one now under consideration seems to seek out places infested by many mosquitoes, and seems to delight in reducing the number of these pests. According to my experience the Yellow-bellied Flycatcher is always, even in migration, a bird of wet or swampy woods, particularly amid rather low undergrowth, along streams or about borders of swamps. In the northern wilderness it breeds in sphagnum bogs among coniferous forests. There in the moist, gloomy, insect-infested morass the little bird is happy, well fed and perfectly at home. More or less silent in migration, it becomes quite loquacious in its summer home, accompanying its frequent remarks with fluttering wings and a quick jetting of its rather brief, caudal appendage. It is recorded above as an uncommon migrant in Massachusetts, but in some years it is either

---

[1] Thus writes that keen observer Dr. Jonathan Dwight, Jr. in Chapman's Handbook of Birds of Eastern North America, 1914, pp. 344, 345.

much more common or more widely distributed than in others. Usually its principal spring migration comes late in May, and in some backward seasons the flight continues well into June. Thus the bird's greatest numbers appear at a time when it can easily hide amid the umbrageous thickets of its chosen retreats, for the well or fully developed leaves and the swarming mosquitoes in its haunts render calm and uninterrupted observation difficult. The bird itself is secretive and quiet and has no trouble in keeping out of sight. Also its return migration is at its height while the trees are still in full leaf in August and before most people begin to watch for returning wood birds. Thus the bird very often escapes observation by all except keen and expert bird watchers and collectors.

The Yellow-bellied Flycatcher is a great ant-eater, as flying ants make up a considerable proportion of its food. Apparently it eats very few useful insects and it takes many harmful beetles, moths and caterpillars and some garden and orchard pests.

ECONOMIC STATUS. The retiring habits of this bird deter it from any important service to agriculture. Its economic value lies chiefly in such control as it may exercise over forest pests.

Empidonax viréscens (VIEILLOT). Acadian Flycatcher.

Other name: GREEN-CRESTED FLYCATCHER.

Plate 56.

DESCRIPTION. — Similar in shape to Yellow-bellied Flycatcher but a little larger and bill broader; 2d and 3d primaries longest and nearly equal, 4th noticeably shorter, 1st about equal to 5th, much longer than 6th. *Adults (sexes alike):* Above rather dark, grayish olive-green, varying somewhat with the season, but usually lighter than the Yellow-bellied Flycatcher; tail grayish-brown, passing into the color of back on outer edge of each outer web; wings darker or dusky; middle and greater wing-coverts tipped rather widely with very pale buff or olive-buff forming two rather wide, conspicuous wing-bars; secondaries and tertials edged (except basally) with same; a dull white or yellowish-white eye-ring; sides of neck and sides of head like back, becoming grayish before eye, and fading into yellowish-white or tawny-white on chin and throat, which tint extends over rest of lower plumage, becoming more yellowish on breast and posteriorly and passing there into a light primrose or pale sulphur-yellow tint, that also tinges a shade on sides (which are otherwise like the color of back) and becomes again light primrose or pale sulphur-yellow on wing linings and axillars; yellow tints stronger in autumn than in spring; bill light brown to blackish-brown above, light brown to pinkish below; iris brown; legs and feet dark gray or blackish. *Young in juvenal plumage:* Similar to autumnal adults, but feathers of upper plumage usually more or less *tipped pale buffy* often giving the back a slightly barred appearance (the only species of the genus so marked), and wing-bars buff or creamy-buff. "Bill black, the lower mandible pinkish buff. Feet sepia, nearly black when older" (J. Dwight).

MEASUREMENTS. — Length 5.60 to 6.25 in.; spread 8.90 to 9.50; folded wing 2.65 to 3.15; tail 2.14 to 2.60; bill .50 to .63; tarsus .50 to .61. Female smaller than male.

MOLTS. — Postnatal molt of nestling follows natal down and produces juvenal plumage; "first winter plumage acquired, apparently, by an incomplete postjuvenal molt" (J. Dwight), but as these birds pass south before molting and molting specimens are not available I have seen no evidence of this; on the return of young in spring they are as adults; adults are supposed to have but one complete molt (postnuptial), which takes place in their winter quarters; specimen taken February 19 in Colombia shows signs of molt on throat.

FIG. 60. — NEST OF YELLOW-BELLIED FLYCATCHER
Page 350

FIG. 61. — YOUNG OF YELLOW-BELLIED FLYCATCHER
Page 350

FIELD MARKS. — Difficult to distinguish in the field from Alder Flycatcher; appears dark grayish above, but the green tinge appears in strong light; pale under plumage has sulphur-yellow tinge with a shade of grayish or greenish on upper breast; *two wing-bars buff or pale buffy-whitish;* yellow below resembling that of Yellow-bellied Flycatcher, but paler and *throat white* or whitish while that of the latter is yellow. Old and young Acadian Flycatchers are quite yellow below in autumn.

VOICE. — A very silent bird when seen in southern New England; common note on breeding grounds a single *spee* or *peet,* repeated at short intervals and accompanied by a rapid twitching of tail; a more peculiar note is a louder *pee-e-yúk;* bird seems to articulate this with difficulty with bill pointed upward and wings trembling like a fledgling begging for food (F. M. Chapman); a quick, sharp, emphatic *whut-ur-see* (N. S. Goss). Bendire writes the call note *queep* and the attempt at song *wick-up* and another call like *whoty-whoty;* its common note resembles very closely the *rhi-bee* of the Alder Flycatcher (J. A. Farley).

BREEDING. — In well-watered woodlands or thickets. *Nest:* On low, rather horizontal or drooping branch, usually toward the end and surrounded by twigs or small branches; from 4 to 20 feet high; not as neat, deep or well-built as those of other small flycatchers, with little lining and thin bottom, often partly suspended from twigs that surround it; composed of rootlets, grasses, mosses, weed stems or similar material, usually decorated with catkins from some tree, and sometimes with blossoms; structure often resembles a bunch of "drift" left in the crotch of a low branch by the high water of the stream which it so often overhangs. *Eggs:* 2 to 4; .66 to .79 by .50 to .59 in.; ovate to elliptical ovate; pale cream to buffy, very sparingly spotted and specked with dark brown to light reddish-brown, markings usually thickest about large end; figured in Bendire's "Life Histories of North American Birds," Vol. II, Plate II, Figs. 26, 27. *Dates:* May 15 to 30, South Carolina; May 29 to July 9, Middle States. *Incubation:* Period about 12 days. Probably but one brood yearly.

RANGE. — Eastern United States and extreme southeastern Canada south to northern South America. Breeds to the upper limit of the Carolinian Zone from northeastern Nebraska, Iowa, northern Illinois, southern Michigan, southeastern Ontario, central New York and casually or accidentally southern Vermont and Massachusetts west to central Kansas, eastern Oklahoma and central Texas and south to southeastern Texas, Gulf states and northern Florida; south in migration to the Bahamas (casually), Cuba (occasionally), and through eastern Mexico and Central America. Winters from western Ecuador to Colombia.

DISTRIBUTION IN NEW ENGLAND. — Casual or accidental migrant and rare local summer resident in southern New England. Records: *Vermont:* Rare or casual migrant and casual summer resident in southern part; breeding record, Bennington, July 14, 1904; nest with young found by Dr. Lucretius H. Ross.[1] *Massachusetts:* Casual migrant and summer resident; breeding record, Hyde Park, June 1888, nest and three eggs taken by Frederick W. Hill; this set and one of the parent birds went to the Brewster collection;[2] specimen now in collection of Museum of Comparative Zoölogy. *Connecticut:* Rare migrant and rare local summer resident, chiefly near coast. Breeding records: spring, 1875, Stamford, nest with five eggs (Hoyt); June 25, 1893, Greenwich, nest with three young (Voorhees); June 2, 1894, Stamford, nest with three eggs (Rowell); May 20, 1903, Danbury, one pair, believed to be breeding, collected (Hamlin); June 2, 1906, Stamford, two nests with three eggs each, two other pairs of breeding birds, six old nests found (Porter);[3] Stamford, June 7, 1906, nest with three eggs.[4]

SEASON IN MASSACHUSETTS. — Reported from mid-May to early September.

HAUNTS AND HABITS. Owing to the close resemblance borne by the Acadian Flycatcher to the Alder Flycatcher or even to the Least Flycatcher, especially in the autumn,

---

[1] Vermont Bird Club, Bulletin No. I, 1906, p. 18.

[2] Ornithologist and Oölogist, Vol. XIII, 1888, p. 160; and Brewster, William, Editor, 2d edition Minot's Land and Game Birds, 1895, p. 300.

[3] Sage, Bishop & Bliss, The Birds of Connecticut, 1913, p. 104.

[4] Porter, Louis N.: Auk, Vol. XXIV, 1907, p. 99.

it is difficult to get accurate information regarding its distribution, status or habits in southern New England. I have received within the last ten years a considerable number of reports of this species from various parts of New England, but as both this and the Alder Flycatcher are mostly silent in migration, and as both appear so much alike in the field that only those who have known both species for years are capable of surely distinguishing them, I have concluded to discard all sight records and depend entirely on specimens collected and identified by competent persons. Such specimens are remarkably few in New England and although the bird has been *reported* from New Hampshire and Maine, I have seen no specimen actually taken in those states. The Acadian Flycatcher is first of all a bird of the wilderness, nesting in the deep woods, in a well watered country, either in swamps or on dryer lands. It does not sit on the top of tall trees as does the Olive-sided Flycatcher, nor is it as often found in low shrubbery as is the Alder Flycatcher. It loves the shady woods and usually takes its stand on a rather low limb to watch for its prey. It is a bird of the lower and more open spaces of the woodland, but occasionally builds its nest on some low limb by a roadside. I have seen it nesting only on Long Island, New York, and am not aware that I have ever seen it alive in New England. Still the bird may be easily overlooked and may be less rare than the paucity of our present information would indicate. Even in the southern states in localities where it is the commonest of flycatchers, it is often passed by unnoticed, as it is rather shy and usually keeps well within the shadows of the trees.

From southern Illinois and West Virginia southward it is a very common bird. Like most of the flycatchers it is somewhat arrogant and pugnacious.

The food of this flycatcher is similar to that of other woodland species as itemized by Professor Beal in Biological Survey Bulletin No. 44. Animal food makes up 97.05 per cent of the whole, mostly insects, of which it takes multitudes. Beetles, particularly weevils, ants, bees and wasps form the largest item or 39.93 per cent. As the bird is a forest haunter most of the bees are believed to be of wild stock. Bugs, moths, flies, spiders, tree crickets and many other forest insects are taken, but comparatively few useful parasitic insects.

Economic Status. Professor Beal concludes that the Acadian Flycatcher is one of those birds whose function is to help keep down the great flood of insect life to a level "compatible with the best interests of other forms of life."

Empidonax traílli alnórum Brewster. Alder Flycatcher.

Other name: Traill's flycatcher.*

Plate 56.

Description. — Similar to Acadian Flycatcher, but differing from it somewhat in dimensions and coloration; 3rd primary longest, second hardly shorter than 3rd, 1st shorter than 5th; tail nearly even or slightly rounded at end, its feathers rather broad and pointed, while those of Least Flycatcher are narrower and more rounded at ends, and the tail more forked; plumage more silky than in the Least Flycatcher, rump

---

* This name is now given to the western race of the species.

same color as back, and eye-ring narrow and rather yellow; also differing from the western race, *E. trailli trailli* in being of richer and more olivaceous color above, wing-bars yellower (or paler when faded), bill decidedly smaller and legs a little shorter. *Adults (sexes alike):* Greenish-olive above, somewhat variable (sometimes tinged with grayish-brown or brownish-gray), graying on top of head and back of neck; feather-centers on top of head darker; tail deep grayish-brown, passing into olive on edges of outer webs, outer web of outer tail-feather paler, sometimes very pale, approaching whitish; wings darker grayish-brown than tail, with two pale olive-buff, pale buff, brownish-gray or even whitish wing-bars; secondaries and tertials edged (except basally) same; some whitish in front of eye and an eye-ring of same; rest of sides of head and sides of neck slightly paler and grayer than other upper plumage, fading into white or whitish of chin and throat; upper breast and sides of breast pale brownish-gray or olive-gray; sides paler and flanks still paler; rest of lower plumage tinged more or less with pale yellow, including axillars and wing linings, the latter having feathers with dark centers along edge of wing; bill dusky brown to brownish-black, or black above, very pale brownish below, with a pinkish or purplish tinge; iris brown; legs and feet blackish. *Young in juvenal plumage:* Similar to adults, but browner above and wing-bars buff or cinnamon-buff; "some specimens are wholly ashy everywhere below, without any yellow tinge"; "bill black, the lower mandible pinkish buff, feet sepia" (J. Dwight).

MEASUREMENTS. — Length 5.20 to 6.00 in.; spread 7.75 to 9.00; folded wing 2.50 to 3.30; tail 2.28 to 2.70; bill .55 to .68; tarsus .52 to .66. Female smaller than male.

MOLTS. — Complete postnatal molt in the nestling produces juvenal plumage; first winter plumage is perfected by partial postjuvenal molt, fading and wear take place and in first nuptial plumage young are as adults; adults have complete postnuptial molt in autumn after arrival in the south; a bird taken in Yucatan, April 5, appears to be molting about the throat.

FIELD MARKS. — Difficult to identify in the field except by its notes, and it is more or less silent in migration; size not appreciably different from that of other small flycatchers, though larger than next species; wing-bars usually pale buffy or brownish-gray and bird is usually with *browner tinge above* than our other small flycatchers.

VOICE. — The call note is variously described; *huip huip* (Bendire); a slightly querulous *pu* often repeated; a *pu-eé;* a low *pip, pep* or *peep,* a softly whispered whistle *pip-whee pip-whee* or *pip-whing,* the song note being variously rendered as *rhi-bheé* or *rhi-bheea,* as commonly heard, becoming *r-r-rhee* when within a few feet of the listener (J. A. Farley); *ease-we-up* (Knight); *e-zu-e-up* (Dwight); *wee-ze-up* (F. H. Allen); *greadeal* or *krateel* (W. DeWitt Miller); *ke-wick* (C. J. Maynard); *qui-deé* (R. Hoffmann); *che-beé-u* (Minot); alarm note somewhat like *whuish-whuish* (Bendire); *ca-weet* (F. H. Allen).

BREEDING. — In wet, swampy or marshy lands, in thickets, usually in or near alders, and in wet bushy meadows thickly grown up with wild roses, sweet gale, skunk cabbage, and tall meadow grass, often in hummocks bordering streams or small bodies of water. *Nest:* In small bush (often in wild rose bush) about 2 to 4 feet from ground (seldom 6 feet or more); frequently in a thicket of small bushes, ferns, etc.; in upright crotch and supported by or partially suspended from and among shoots and twigs; a compact but not neat structure of shreds and bark, grasses, vegetable fiber, weed stalks, etc., often "stringing" down, lined with fine grasses and occasionally a little hair or plant down. *Eggs:* 2 to 4, usually 3; .68 to .78 by .50 to .55 in.; mostly ovate; pinkish-buff or creamy-white to white with spots of different shades of brown, chiefly near large end, sometimes wreathed about it, also some sparsely distributed specks of blackish-brown; egg of Traill's Flycatcher figured in Bendire's "Life Histories of North American Birds," Vol. II, Plate II, Fig. 30. *Dates:* June 19 to July 3, Massachusetts. *Incubation:* Period about 12 days. One brood yearly.

RANGE. — Most of northern and eastern North America, Mexico and Central America. Breeds from Yukon Valley in Alaska, Yukon, northwestern Mackenzie, northern Manitoba, northern Ontario, central Quebec and Newfoundland south to central southern British Columbia, northwestern and southeastern Montana, northeastern Colorado, southern South Dakota, central Arkansas, southern Kentucky, western Maryland, northern New Jersey (casually), Connecticut and Massachusetts, and west to western and southeastern Alaska and western British Columbia; migrates southward through southern states and southeastern Mexico, and west to central Colorado, western Texas and Oaxaca; winters from Yucatan and Nicaragua to Ecuador; accidental in Bermuda.

DISTRIBUTION IN NEW ENGLAND. — *Maine:* Common migrant and common to rare local summer resident. *New Hampshire:* Common migrant and common to rare local summer resident below 2000 feet; less common summer resident in southern part. *Vermont:* Common migrant and common local summer resident. *Massachusetts:* Common migrant; common local summer resident in hill country west of Connecticut River; rare summer resident in eastern part of state; rare or wanting in summer in southeastern section. *Connecticut:* Common migrant in western part and rare local breeder in north-western section.

SEASON IN MASSACHUSETTS. — May 14 to August 25 (September 6).

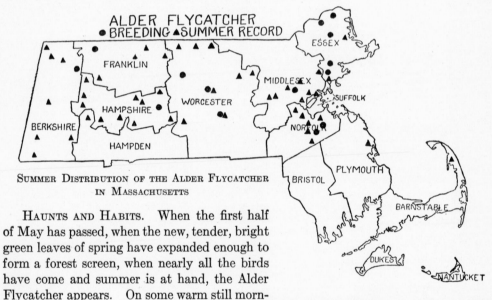

SUMMER DISTRIBUTION OF THE ALDER FLYCATCHER
IN MASSACHUSETTS

HAUNTS AND HABITS. When the first half of May has passed, when the new, tender, bright green leaves of spring have expanded enough to form a forest screen, when nearly all the birds have come and summer is at hand, the Alder Flycatcher appears. On some warm still morning in the waning of the Maytime the bird watcher notes here and there in the edge of the woods, on a pasture fence, in a small tree by the bog or even in the orchard, a small flycatcher usually on a rather low perch, sitting quite erect, silent and watchful, occasionally dashing out in pursuit of a flying insect or flitting from one point of vantage to another. This is the Alder Flycatcher in migration — quiet, watchful and discreet. Unlike the Chebec it rarely appears until summer is at hand and if the season is late, its migration is delayed and may continue in southern New England until the 10th or 12th of June.

This bird breeds less rarely in Massachusetts than published records would indicate. It resembles the Chebec so closely and comes so late that it is likely to be overlooked, as on its breeding grounds it is inclined to keep much under cover of the foliage. It breeds in wet, bushy meadows, flies rather low and is very inconspicuous, and as its autumnal

FIG. 62. — ALDER FLYCATCHER'S NEST AND YOUNG

Page 355

FIG. 63. — PRAIRIE HORNED LARK, NEST AND YOUNG

Page 365

migration takes place mostly in August, when few people observe fall migrants, it is rarely noted. No sooner are its young able to fly well and feed themselves than both old and young begin to depart for the south. The Alder Flycatcher is not, as its name seems to imply, confined to alders. It usually nests near but not on them, and may be found about them as they grow along the water-courses and the swampy borders of the more open bushy marshes and meadows in which it breeds, but in migration it may be found almost anywhere, even in city parks. Mr. J. A. Farley, who has made a special study of the nesting of the species in Massachusetts, writes as follows regarding its breeding habits:

"The Alder Flycatcher arrives in eastern Massachusetts about May 20. By the thirtieth of the month it has always reappeared on its breeding grounds. These are bushy meadows grown (or growing) up more or less thickly with alders. The lower growth in such places consists of wild roses (*Rosa*), sweet gale (*Myrica gale L.*), and other swamp shrubbery, together with the usual mixed meadow herbage. Mingled with the alders will be young swamp maples and birches and oftentimes scattering white cedars. The whole forms a thick, at times almost choked, expanse of meadow growth. The wild roses in which the Flycatcher is so fond of nesting seem to be almost as much an essential in its summer home as the alders themselves. The bird builds its nest year after year in the same favorite spot which may be of quite limited area. In a small meadow in the town of Lynnfield, where five years elapsed between the taking of two nests (June 16, 1895, and June 27, 1900), I recall that the second nest was placed in almost identically the same spot as the first. Two other nests (of other seasons) I also found in the same area, which was less than an acre in extent.

"The erroneous idea* that the Alder Flycatcher is a very shy bird appears to obtain. This is due to the fact that its feeding-habits rather than any inherent shyness cause it to hug closely its favorite alders and other coverts. Besides keeping quite habitually within copse or thicket, with the general scope of its activity circumscribed by at least their outer fringes, it does not as a rule perch or fly high. The thick foliage of June and July aid materially in its concealment, so that it is not always easy to get even a momentary glimpse of the bird which may be calling and flying about within a few yards. The exceptions to the general rule that the Alder Flycatcher is *par excellence* a bird of copse and undergrowth are the little creature's infrequent short flights out into the open, and its brief visits to some favorite vantage-point above the line of foliage, for the deliverance of its harsh cry. But the emphatic preachment of the small protagonist of the alders is quite as apt to be heard while the performer is perched unseen within his thicket and but a few feet from the ground. It should be further noted that the Alder Flycatcher is most in evidence during the days following its arrival from the South, and before the breeding season is well advanced. In May and June one may be now and then seen flying about freely from tree-top to tree-top in its home meadow. The Alder Flycatcher in eastern Massachusetts is no shyer than most other small birds. It is scarcely shyer than the

---

* This, in spite of the fact that long ago the species was reported by Mr. Brewster to be "retiring but not shy." (Hist. North American Birds, Vol. II, 1874, p. 371.)

Least Flycatcher, although a more restless bird than its orchard-loving cousin. The Alder Flycatcher does not hesitate to fly about from one bosky clump to another in its meadow. But when arrived at the concealing growth, it may remain a long time therein before venturing forth again. . . .

"In the matter of its behaviour at the nest the Alder Flycatcher, in contrast to its general habits, may be fairly considered shy. It is not a close sitter. I have tried repeatedly to catch the female on her eggs but never but once succeeded in so doing. In this exceptional case the bird undoubtedly trusted to the effective concealment of the nest by the very thick clump of wild roses in which it was placed. I stood for several seconds beside this unseen nest before the bird flew. After being flushed the female flycatcher is chary about showing herself in the neighborhood of the nest. So, too, the male. The low *pep* of protest somewhere near will be often the only evidence of the Flycatchers' connection with their nest."[1]

In analyzing the food of the species to which this bird belongs Professor Beal examined the contents of 135 stomachs. He found that Hymenoptera composed 41.39 per cent of the food contained therein, and a comparison of the number of each species eaten shows that the bird destroys a rather large number of useful parasitic insects. Otherwise its food is much like that of other flycatchers, except that it eats comparatively few crop-pests, among them grasshoppers and chinch bugs. Its vegetal food consists chiefly of wild berries.

ECONOMIC STATUS. This bird apparently does no direct harm to agriculture. Professor Beal says that the bird's function in nature "is to assist in keeping insects down to such a level of abundance as consists with the best interests of both plants and insects."[2]

Empidonax mínimus (W. M. & S. F. BAIRD). Least Flycatcher.

Other name: CHEBEC.

Plate 56.

DESCRIPTION. — *Adults (sexes alike):* Similar to Alder Flycatcher (see page 354), but smaller; eye-ring *wider and whiter*, more whitish in front of eye, wing-bars and other wing-markings very pale brownish-gray or ashy-whitish and *tail slightly forked*; much whiter in general below than either Alder or Acadian Flycatcher; some specimens, however, are yellowish below in autumn, and some spring birds have a yellowish tinge below. *Young in juvenal plumage:* Similar to adults, but wing-markings dull buff, and gray of upper breast and sides more brownish.

MEASUREMENTS. — Length 5.00 to 5.75 in.; spread 7.54 to 8.50; folded wing 2.20 to 2.80; tail 2.10 to 2.50; bill .48 to .60; tarsus .63 to .65; female smaller than male.

MOLTS. — Juvenal plumage acquired by complete postnatal molt in the nest; first winter plumage is produced by postjuvenal (possibly complete) molt during or after autumnal migration; when young return in spring they are as adults. Adults molt completely after they leave the north in autumnal migration.

FIELD MARKS. — Smallest New England Flycatcher; size of Chipping Sparrow or smaller; olive-green above, tinged brownish; prominent eye-ring and wing-bars very pale or whitish.

---

[1] Farley, J. A.: Auk, Vol. XVIII, 1901, pp. 348, 349, 354.   [2] Biological Survey, Bulletin No. 44, 1912, p. 63.

VOICE. — Call note *whit;* usual note *se-bíc* (Hoffmann); also a flight-song (?) a "twittering warble" in which both notes may be prominently repeated many times; sometimes *chebêc-tree-treo, chebêc-trreee-cheu* (E. A. Samuels); also "querulous exclamations (*wheu, wheu, wheu*) more or less guttural and subdued" (Minot).

BREEDING. — In open woods or wherever trees are separated by slight spaces; usually in or about cultivated lands, in orchards and shade trees, or in the edges of woods or swamps not thickly wooded. *Nest:* A rather neat, compact structure, usually in an upright fork from 8 to 40 feet up, but commonly low, sometimes (but rarely) high in a *white pine;* built of shreds of bark, plant fibers, grass, spider web, cocoons, etc., lined with finer similar materials and plant down and sometimes with hair or feathers also. *Eggs:* 3 to 6, usually 3 or 4; .60 to .67 by .45 to .51 in.; short or rounded ovate; white or creamy white, very rarely dotted faintly with reddish-brown; figured in Bendire's "Life Histories of North American Birds," Vol. II, Plate II, Fig. 31. *Dates:* May 25 to June 10, Virginia; June 10, New York; May 20 to late July, New England. *Incubation:* Period 14 days (A. A. Saunders); 12 days (O. W. Knight); by both sexes. One brood yearly, perhaps two rarely.

RANGE. — Central and eastern North America, west to the Rockies, eastern Mexico, Central America and central South America. Breeds in Canadian and Transition zones from west central Mackenzie, northern Alberta, central Manitoba, northern Ontario, southern Quebec and Cape Breton Island south to western Oklahoma and (possibly) west central and northeastern Texas, central Nebraska, central Iowa, Illinois, Indiana, Ohio, Pennsylvania and New Jersey, and in mountains to western North Carolina and eastern Tennessee, and west to Alberta, western Montana, and Wyoming; winters from northeastern and central western Mexico to Central America, Colombia, and northern Peru; accidental on Grand Cayman, an island south of Cuba.

DISTRIBUTION IN NEW ENGLAND. — Common migrant and summer resident, except in deep forests; in White Mountains and elsewhere at altitudes below 2000 feet.

SEASON IN MASSACHUSETTS. — (April 13) April 22 to September 21, (October 2, 10, 15 and 16. November 20).

HAUNTS AND HABITS. The Least Flycatcher or Chebec may be characterized by superlatives. It is the smallest, earliest, tamest, smartest, bravest, noisiest and most prominent member of its genus in New England, and many ladies will agree that it is the dearest. A flight of Chebecs was reported about Pittsfield, Massachusetts, on March 31, 1920, but this seems hardly credible. However, the bird arrives in spring before the other small flycatchers. A few individuals are here ere the end of April, and when a thousand orchards burgeon with the bloom of spring, when the first misty green begins to screen the woodlands, a host of these little feathered warriors spreads over New England. At first, in migration, they are rather silent and appear wherever open spaces among the trees or along the edges of thickets give them fly-room. At this time they may be mistaken for the Alder Flycatcher, as they may frequent alders along a brook and may even appear among the tall bushes at the edges of meadows. Later, when the females come, the males are the most vociferous and pugnacious of their kind, and nearly every orchard resounds with their cries. Although usually their relations with other birds are amicable, they fight fiercely among themselves in the mating season. When rival males meet, the issue is decided at once by combat. The loud unmusical *chebéc* is uttered with the utmost vim and vigor, accompanied by an upward jerk of the head and a flirt of the tail, as if to call attention to the little bird's superior musical abilities, while some of his softer notes are given with a characteristic trembling of the wings, as if he were rendering ecstatic melodies. His emphatic call is sometimes repeated almost incessantly by the male, who stands guard over the nest while the female is incubating. The male has a so-called flight song which consists of a jumble of notes uttered in a kind of ecstasy while he flutters about in a circle. The nest building is an interesting operation. Mr. A. A. Cross, who watched a female at this work, sent me a letter from which I append the following graphic description:

"It so chanced that in June, 1916, following a shower which had thoroughly dampened vegetation, I stepped from a clump of small pines facing an alder run. My eyes almost instantly focused upon the nest of a Least Flycatcher. About one half of the upper edge seemed literally torn to pieces, the frayed fragments projecting in all directions. The work of some robber, I thought. Such was not the case, for presently the owner appeared with her beak full of building material which, a piece at a time, she thrust into the edge of the nest, leaving the loose ends free. Watching her, I noted that she was gathering the inner bark from the dead and broken stems of last year's goldenrod. She made many trips, working rapidly, and disposing of the material as in the first case. In about 20 minutes she had finished, causing the edge of the nest to look like a miniature hedge. She then settled herself solidly in the nest, hooked her head over the edge and pivoting on her legs ironed out the rough brim with her throat, putting considerable energy into the work and working first one way and then the other. In this manner she was able to take in about one-third of the circumference of the nest before changing her position. Then readjusting herself, she continued the process until the nest was finished. This was the last step in the building of the nest, the following morning it contained one egg. Had the material used not been rendered pliable by the rain it would not have stayed in place readily."

The building of the nest usually occupies from six to eight days. The eggs are laid daily and occasionally two in one day. Incubation takes about two weeks, and the young remain in the nest nearly two weeks. About six weeks are thus required for the first brood, and it is very doubtful if a second is ever reared in New England, though that may happen in the Middle States. The parents are very devoted to their young, and are exceedingly brave and active in their defense. Squirrels and other small animals that approach too near the nest are attacked and driven off, but the Crow can rob the nest with impunity. The following notes from Mr. F. H. Mosher show how this bird will defend its rights against larger birds: "May 15, 1899. — A pair of Least Flycatchers had just begun their nest in an apple tree by placing some bunches of cottony material and a few strings and straws. A female Oriole, happening along, appropriated the string for her own use, and carried it away. The Flycatchers came soon after, and were very much disturbed on finding the nest materials scattered, and had quite a talk over it. In a few moments the Oriole came back for more string, when both Flycatchers flew at her and snapped their bills savagely in her face. The Oriole did not seem to mind them much, and kept on going toward the nest. When the Flycatchers found they could not scare her in this way, they both attacked her fiercely, and pulled out quite a number of feathers, keeping up a steady scold. The Oriole attempted to retaliate, but when she attacked one of the Flycatchers the other struck her from the other side, and several times she was knocked completely off the branch. Finally she beat a precipitate retreat, one of the Flycatchers chasing her out of sight." [1]   Mr. Arthur J. Parker sends me the following which exhibits the belligerent disposition of the bird when annoyed by swarming caterpillars: "June 14, working in my garden, heard a sustained and repeated noise of bill snapping; knew it to be a particular Chebec with nest in apple tree near by. The angry sounds kept up, so frequently repeated that I thought there must be something more than ordinarily annoying to the Chebec. Went close and this is what I saw. The Chebec was doing many times what he must have been doing for sometime previously. The bird flew into the apple tree containing its nest, and chattered its bill belligerently as it approached. Then it seized a large gipsy caterpillar (sometimes more than one) and carried it out of the tree and perched on the branch of a tree at a distance of about 20 feet and there dropped its victim (crippled I imagine), and at once repeated the performance, threatening sounds and all. The tree was swarming with the large caterpillars."

The Chebec, unlike the other small flycatchers of its genus, has gradually become accustomed to man and his works and prefers his neighborhood to more retired localities. While orchard and shade trees are its favorite breeding places, it may be found nesting in village and city streets. Stakes, bean poles, dead limbs in orchards, clothes-lines and the poles which uphold them are favorite perches for this little bird, from which it marks down flies, moths and other small winged game, which it pursues and captures with snapping bill, returning to its perch to devour them.

The Chebec feeds chiefly on insects, most of which it gets on the wing, but it takes some from plants and trees, and may even go to the ground for them in case of necessity. As it comes in close contact with agriculture it takes many farm pests, such as cotton-boll weevils, squash beetles, cucumber beetles, clover weevils, plum curculios, ants, moths (including gipsy moths), caterpillars (including cutworms), bark beetles and the fly of the railroad worm.

ECONOMIC STATUS. The Chebec destroys a comparatively small number of useful beetles and a greater number of parasitic insects. It takes no grain, however, and practically no fruit, does no direct harm to agriculture and destroys a number of first class farm pests. Apparently the injury done is slight compared to the good.

SUBORDER OSCINES. SONG BIRDS.

Number of species in North America 299; in Massachusetts 133.

Birds of this group have in the syrinx a highly complex and effective musical apparatus. They are all song birds or capable of producing musical sounds. Each side of the tarsus is covered with a horny plate (except in Larks, Thrashers and some of the

---

[1] Useful Birds and their Protection, 1913, p. 230.

Wrens), the two meeting in a ridge behind.   They have ten primaries, the first never the longest but short or "spurious," or almost wanting, leaving only nine apparent.

FAMILY **ALAUDIDÆ**.   LARKS.

Number of species in North America 2; in Massachusetts 1.

The larks comprise a group of birds mostly confined to the Old World, and distinguished by the terrestrial character of their feet which are formed more for walking than for perching.   Larks have a very long, straight hind claw (the "larkspur") — a distinction which they share with very few other birds.   Although they have the vocal apparatus of song birds, they are exceptional *Oscines* as some of them have apparently but nine primaries, the outer one being undeveloped, and the tarsus is scaled behind.   These birds should not be confused with Titlarks or Meadowlarks; the former, having the long, straight hind claws, is classed with *Motacillidæ*, while the Meadowlarks belong with *Icteridæ*.

ECONOMIC STATUS.   Larks are regarded as useful birds, though they eat more or less grain.

FOOT OF LARK, SHOW-
ING LONG HIND
CLAW

NOTE.   The European Skylark, *Alauda arvensis*, has been introduced several times in the United States, but has failed to establish itself.   In 1887 a few apparently bred on Long Island and the species has been reported in southern New England.   If it has ever appeared here it is now apparently extirpated.

Otócoris alpéstris alpestris (LINNÆUS).   Horned Lark.

Other names: SHORE LARK; SNOW LARK.

Plate 57.

DESCRIPTION. — Bill narrow, pointed, much shorter than head; head with peculiar feathers on each side similar to the "ears" or "horns" of some owls and capable of slight erection; only nine primaries apparent; hind claw nearly straight, longer than hind toe; wings long and pointed, secondaries and tertials especially long; tail nearly even at end.   *Adult male in breeding plumage:* Above, chiefly light brownish, everywhere streaked with grayish-brown, becoming dusky at feather-centers; scapulars, back, rump and sides of neck more or less tinged vinaceous; tail mostly black; central tail-coverts nearly as long as tail (partly concealing tail when closed), colored like back; middle tail-feathers chiefly same, two outer pairs edged white, except basally; wings deep grayish-brown with paler feather-edges, outer edge of outer primary white; patch across upper forehead and about half of fore crown black which also extends from this patch to ends of "horns"; lower forehead, sides of head, chin and throat chiefly yellow, varying more or less from primrose or light straw to yellowish-white, and usually deeper on chin and throat; black patch running from base of upper mandible under eye, broadening behind eye and passing down below ear coverts on sides of throat, and a broad black subcrescentic patch across lower throat and upper breast; elsewhere below white; sides and flanks streaked with "dull vinaceous or vinaceous cinnamon and dusky."   *Adult male in winter plumage:* Similar to adult male in breeding plumage, but black markings of head, especially that across its top, more or less obscured, yellow about head deeper, white of breast spotted or streaked with pale grayish-brown, dusky feather-centers of upper plumage less distinct

PLATE 57

PLATE 57

HORNED LARK
Page 362

ADULT MALE

ADULT FEMALE

PRAIRIE HORNED LARK
Page 365

ADULT MALE

ADULT FEMALE

YOUNG IN FIRST WINTER PLUMAGE

and middle wing-coverts edged whitish. *Adult female in breeding plumage:* Similar to breeding male, but smaller and duller and without black patch on top of head (many have some slight touches of black or blackish there); black patch on side of head smaller and duller or dusky and more or less obscured by whitish or yellowish-white feather-tips; black throat-patch also smaller, and yellow of head and throat paler and duller; also less vinaceous above. *Adult female in winter plumage:* Similar to breeding plumage, but slightly grayer above, somewhat marked on breast, and sides and flanks more distinctly streaked; yellows deeper than in summer, and black markings about head even more obscured than in male. *Young in first winter plumage:* Similar to winter female. *Young in juvenal plumage:* Top of head blackish, speckled with brownish-white; elsewhere above brownish and dusky, each feather tipped with spot of yellowish-white; scapulars brown, each with cross spot of black near end; stripe above eye and spot below it pale yellow; side of head otherwise dusky, sprinkled with whitish; chin and throat pale or dull yellow, this color extending up a little on sides of neck; upper breast pale brownish-buffy with rows of dusky spots; elsewhere below yellowish or yellowish-white; bill mainly bluish-black, below basally light bluish-gray; iris dark brown; legs and feet black.

MEASUREMENTS. — Length 6.75 to 8.00 in.; spread 12.25 to 14.00; folded wing 3.95 to 4.60; tail 2.50 to 3.10; bill .47 to .62; tarsus .80 to .90. Female smaller than male.

MOLTS. — Complete postnatal molt disposes of nestling down and produces juvenal plumage; partial or possibly complete postjuvenal molt in autumn produces first winter plumage which is practically as winter adult, and first nuptial plumage (as adult) acquired by wear without spring molt; adults have but one (complete autumnal) molt, and nuptial plumage acquired by wear.

FIELD MARKS. — Size, slightly larger than Bluebird. *Adult male:* Brown above and on sides, with a rich vinaceous tinge; whole face and throat yellow to pale yellow with three prominent black marks, (1) across top of forehead (usually obscured in winter), (2) on side of head running down back of and below eye and (3) subcrescent across lower throat; horns also more or less black, but not usually noticeable in the field. *Female and young:* Similar but duller, yellow less bright, little or no black across top of forehead and other black marks about head obscured by brownish or whitish; striped on breast; ordinary flight rather low, in prolonged undulations; walks, does not hop. "As the birds fly overhead the black tail with white corners . . . contrasts sharply with the white belly" (C. W. Townsend). See Field Marks under Prairie Horned Lark (page 365). Horned Lark is confused sometimes with Pipit but should not be, as Pipit has no heavy black marks about head and has more white in tail.

VOICE. — A low, rather long and sibilant, chirp or whistle like *tweet* (very like similar note of Pipit, but readily distinguished from the notes of Snow Buntings with which it often is associated); also a short flight-song on its breeding grounds, sometimes given on the ground; a peculiar note heard in Labrador *zzurrit* often preceded by *whit-zzurrit* (Townsend and Allen).

BREEDING. — On grassy, barren or mossy lands or islands near or not far from sea-coast. *Nest:* A deep cup sunk in ground or moss, and hidden by surrounding mosses, built of fine, dry grass, lined with plant down and feathers. *Eggs:* 4 or 5; .90 to .95 by .65 to .75 in.; light drab or grayish; rather uniformly spotted with various shades of brown. *Dates:* May 31 to July 17, Labrador. *Incubation:* Largely if not wholly by female; no other data.

RANGE. — Eastern North America. Breeds chiefly in the Arctic zone from Hudson Strait south to southern end of James Bay, south central Quebec, southern Labrador and southern Newfoundland. In winter west and south to Manitoba and Nebraska, Missouri, and South Carolina, and casually to Louisiana, Georgia and Bermuda. Accidental in Greenland.

NOTE. The Horned Lark *Otocoris alpestris* as a species ranges over North America, northern South America, Europe, Asia and northern Africa. It has been separated into many races.

DISTRIBUTION IN NEW ENGLAND. — Common migrant and rather less common winter resident, most common coastwise.

SEASON IN MASSACHUSETTS. — September 27 to April 19 (May 27).

HAUNTS AND HABITS.　Along the winter beaches the Shore Lark runs.　Where restless rolling surf has piled up blocks and cakes of ice and hardened snow, in open spots where the snow has melted, or on the bare and open sands left by the receding tide, the larks in merry companies industriously seek their sustenance.　Their tracks may be seen almost anywhere along the beaches of New England in the fall and winter months, and in migration they sometimes penetrate far into the interior.　Dr. Charles W. Townsend gives the following excellent description of the habits of the species along our coast:

"The old term, Shore Lark, is a most appropriate name for this bird, as it is generally seen near the shore.　Here it is equally at home on the beach, among the dunes, and in the salt marshes, as well as on the hills and in the cultivated fields.　It occurs in small or large flocks, sometimes to the number of two hundred.　It is found alone or associated with Snow Buntings and occasionally with Longspurs.

"The Horned Lark is a swift walker, and, considering its short legs, takes long strides. It picks at the grass-stalks from the ground, never alighting on them as do the Snow Buntings and Longspurs.　It sometimes flies up from the ground, seizing the seeds on the tall grass or weed-stalks, at the same time shaking many off onto the ground, which it picks up before flying up to repeat the process.　Horned Larks are frequently found in roads picking at the horse-droppings, especially when much snow has covered the grasses and weeds.　They also come into the farm-yards for scraps of food.

"Although a ground bird, the Horned Lark occasionally alights on the extended roots of old tree stumps two or three feet from the ground and on stone walls.　I have never seen it in trees.　It is a persistent fighter or extremely playful, whichever you will, and is constantly engaged in chasing its fellows.　I have seen two face each other for a moment, with heads down like fighting cocks, the next instant twisting and turning in the air, one in hot pursuit of the other.　When in flocks with the other winter birds, they more frequently chase them, especially the smaller Longspurs.　I have also seen them chase Snow Buntings, and often Ipswich Sparrows that were feeding with them, and once, what appeared to be a Prairie Horned Lark.

"Horned Larks fly in scattered flocks with an undulating motion.　Their flight is often at a considerable height from the ground, and their call notes appear to come from out of the depths of the sky.　These notes may be written *tssswee it, tsswt,* the sibilant being marked.　At times the notes are almost trilled.　They are emitted as the birds fly and occasionally from the ground." [1]

Dr. Townsend describes correctly (above) the Horned Larks' manner of feeding. They are hardy birds.　In midwinter they take snow baths.　When the snow is crusted they may be seen feeding at times with Snow Buntings, while both species are exposed to the freezing wind.　Sometimes as the little birds hop up to peck seeds from the weeds they are blown sidewise along the smooth surface before they can recover their footing and again face the gale.

The food of American Horned Larks has been quite exhaustively investigated at the

---

[1] Birds of Essex County, Massachusetts, 1905, pp. 233–234.

Biological Survey, and Mr. W. L. McAtee in Bulletin No. 23 of the Survey has reported upon the examination of 1154 stomachs of the various races. The food materials vary but little in the several forms, except where, as in the case of California, seasons, climate and vegetation differ considerably from the same conditions in New England. Animal matter forms 20.6 per cent of the food for the year and vegetal matter 79.4 per cent. The animal food is chiefly insects including such pests as weevils, May beetles, leaf beetles, grasshoppers and caterpillars. The vegetal food consists of the seeds of weeds and grasses, grain and fruit. Outside of southern California where the percentage of wheat is high in the stomach contents, all grains form but 12.2 per cent of the food for the year. Fruit remains in the stomachs were insignificant and consisted only of seeds. Insects formed 26.6 per cent of all the food material, and of the vegetal food weed seeds formed 79.4 per cent.

ECONOMIC STATUS. See page 362.

Otocoris alpestris praticola HENSHAW. Prairie Horned Lark.

Plate 57.

DESCRIPTION. — *Adult male and female:* Similar to Horned Lark in all plumages (see page 362), but smaller and nape, lesser wing-coverts and scapulars, though tinged with vinaceous, not so dark, back more gray, yellow of throat paler or even white and *broad white or whitish stripe over eye. Note:* Some are much more yellowish about the head than described above. Miss Elizabeth Dickens notes that the male of a pair which has nested for several years not far from her door on Block Island (if it is the same bird all the time) grows a shade whiter about the throat every year. *Young in first winter plumage:* Similar to adult female. *Young in juvenal plumage:* Similar to young of Horned Lark, but *much darker;* above sooty-brown or sooty-blackish with small triangular dots and bars of yellowish or whitish; upper breast heavily spotted or clouded with dusky; light edges of wing-coverts and flight-feathers more prominent than in adults.

MEASUREMENTS. — Length 6.90 to 7.40 in.; spread 12.25 to 13.25; folded wing 3.75 to 4.20; tail 2.40 to 2.60; bill .47 to .60; tarsus .80 to .83. Female smaller than male.

MOLTS. — Apparently in all respects similar to molts of Horned Lark (see page 363).

FIELD MARKS. — Similar to Horned Lark but paler and not so vinaceous above; throat paler or whitish and *line over eye white;* adults easily determined in the field if typical specimens are seen, but individuals of the two races sometimes so closely resemble each other as to be indistinguishable in the field; usually seen on ground where like Horned Lark it *walks* or runs.

VOICE. — Similar to that of Horned Lark; a common utterance *seet-te-sweet;* a musical alarm note *pee-u-wee* or *pee*, followed after a pause by *pee-u-weé*, often shortened to *pee-u* given in the nesting season (L. McI. Terrill); also a flight-song somewhat similar to that of Horned Lark, and like that also sometimes given from some slight elevation of the ground.

BREEDING. — In New England usually about upland pastures where the grazing of cattle keeps the grass short, or on golf links. *Nest:* Beside a rock, piece of wood, clod or tuft of grass, rarely in a cultivated field; built of grass and often lined with thistle-down and a few feathers; similar to that of Horned Lark; usually sunk in ground (for the first brood at least) and woven solidly so as to withstand the fierce March winds; second nest, on the contrary, loosely constructed.[1] *Eggs:* 3 to 5; * .72 to .96 by .57 to .66 in.; similar to eggs of Horned Lark but somewhat smaller and usually a trifle lighter in color; figured

---

[1] Auk, Vol. XXVII, 1910, p. 26.   * A report of 8 in one set (Bird-Lore, Vol. XXII, 1920, p. 85).

in Bendire's "Life Histories of North American Birds," Vol. II, Plate V, Fig. 25. *Dates:* From February 23, Wisconsin, to July 16, Massachusetts. *Incubation:* Period 12 days (H. O. Green); 11 days (L. McI. Terrill); 14 days (A. W. Butler). By both sexes, but chiefly by female; two or three broods yearly, possibly sometimes four.

RANGE. — Western United States and southeastern Canada. Breeds chiefly in Transition and Canadian life-zones, in northeastern United States and southeastern Canada from southern Manitoba, central Ontario, and southwestern Quebec south to eastern Oklahoma, Arkansas, Missouri, southern Illinois, southern Indiana, Ohio, West Virginia, eastern Pennsylvania, southeastern New York and possibly New Jersey, and west to eastern North Dakota, eastern Nebraska and eastern Kansas; in winter south to Texas, northern Louisiana, central Alabama, central Georgia and southern Florida. Casually to Colorado and Arizona.

DISTRIBUTION IN NEW ENGLAND. — *Maine:* Rather uncommon migrant and local summer resident in open country; casual in winter. *New Hampshire:* Uncommon to rare migrant and uncommon or occasional summer resident, though sometimes not uncommon locally in White Mountain region and north of same. *Vermont:* Uncommon migrant and local summer resident; rare in winter. *Massachusetts:* Uncommon to common migrant and occasional or rare local summer resident becoming yearly less rare; occasional in winter, particularly coastwise.* *Rhode Island:* Rare migrant but not uncommon local summer resident in a few localities; uncommon and local in winter. *Connecticut:* Uncommon

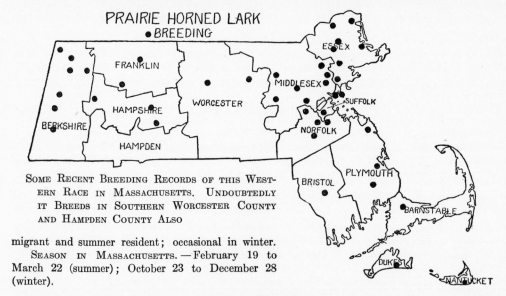

SOME RECENT BREEDING RECORDS OF THIS WESTERN RACE IN MASSACHUSETTS. UNDOUBTEDLY IT BREEDS IN SOUTHERN WORCESTER COUNTY AND HAMPDEN COUNTY ALSO

migrant and summer resident; occasional in winter.

SEASON IN MASSACHUSETTS. — February 19 to March 22 (summer); October 23 to December 28 (winter).

HISTORY. Professor Walter B. Barrows has placed on record his opinion of the eastern movement of the Prairie Horned Lark in the following words: "It has been generally supposed that this bird was extending its range toward the east; that formerly it was restricted to the Mississippi Valley, but that since 1860 it had overspread the eastern states, even reaching eastern Massachusetts in 1903. It seems doubtful whether this is really the case. It is conceivable that the species has always occurred in small numbers

* A flock of 25 passed the winter of 1898 in Longmeadow, Massachusetts (Robert O. Morris: Auk, Vol. XVI, 1899, p. 85).

throughout the northeastern states, but that it has passed unnoticed until recent years, when the increase in the number of collectors and the more general publication of field notes have called attention to its presence." [1] I cannot agree with this view, as the eastward movement of the Prairie Horned Lark seems to be a fact; it is not a mere supposition. To-day this bird breeds locally in open lands throughout the New England States though not commonly. Had it done so in the 60s, 70s or 80s of the last century, keen collectors like C. Hart Merriam, A. K. Fisher, John H. Sage, William Brewster, Henry Henshaw and Henry A. Purdie, must have found it; but thus far the only record that I have seen of the Horned Lark in New England in the breeding season during this period is that of Brewster, whose statement follows:

"There is a general impression that it has extended its breeding range into New England, from New York and regions further to the westward, within the past twenty-five or thirty years. I suspect, however, that it has been a summer resident of Massachusetts during a somewhat longer period, for on July 5, 1869, I saw at Concord a pair of birds which were certainly Horned Larks of some kind and which, in the light of our present knowledge, it is fair to assume must have belonged to the form *praticola*. They were flying about over some sandy fields admirably adapted for breeding grounds and, indeed, closely similar to summer haunts of the Prairie Horned Lark that I have visited in New York state and elsewhere." [2] Had it been breeding about Worcester in the 70s, I cannot see how it could have been missed by either my friends William S. Perry and John A. Farley or by myself, as we covered most of the ground about the city in which the bird could breed and probably located every breeding species. The above paragraph from Brewster seems to be the only evidence on which Professor Barrows could rely to support his contention, and it is quite possible that a few pairs of Prairie Horned Larks were then in this region; but it seems improbable that they could have been distributed over it in the breeding season as they are to-day without being seen, taken and recorded many times. There are many indications of an extension of the breeding range of this race during the last 70 years from the Middle West to the Atlantic Coast. Butler, writing of the bird in Indiana (1878), says: "They are evidently gradually extending their range as the country is brought more and more under cultivation." [3] He also quotes Prof. B. W. Evermann to the effect that the bird was very rare in Carrol County, Indiana, in 1879, but by 1886 it was a common resident. Dawson (1903) giving the range of the bird in Ohio says: "Evidently increasing in numbers and distribution." Bendire (1895) says: "Within the last thirty years the Prairie Horned Lark has extended its breeding range very materially to the eastward, and in certain localities, notably in the southwestern parts of the Adirondack region, especially in Herkimer County, New York, where this bird was practically unknown twenty years ago, it is now a fairly common summer resident, and small companies may be found in every abandoned old clearing along the numerous

[1] Michigan Bird Life, 1912, p. 409.

[2] Birds of the Cambridge Region, 1906, p. 234.

[3] Butler, A. W.: Birds of Indiana, in 22d report of the Department of Geology and Natural Resources of Indiana, 1917, p. 875.

water courses in this otherwise heavily timbered region." [1] Eaton says of the bird in New York:

In New York State the history of this species has been exceedingly interesting. While many of our valuable song and insectivorous birds have been diminishing in numbers, this species has gradually increased year after year, until at the present time it inhabits the greater portion of this State as a summer resident. A perusal of the records before me indicates that in 1876 this species was found breeding in central and western New York. At Canandaigua by Mr. Howey (see N. O. C. Bulletin No. 3, p. 40); at Rochester by Mr. Jones (*ibid.*, p. 189); at Lowville by Doctor Merriam (*ibid.*, p. 53); in 1877 Mr. Rathbun found it breeding at Auburn; in 1881 Mr. Park found it breeding at Green Island near Troy. In 1884 it was found breeding first in Niagara County by Davison and in 1885 at Virgil (see "Forest and Stream," Vol. XXII, p. 144). In 1886 a female was taken at Long Island City on July 31 (see Dutcher, Auk, Vol. V, p. 181). In 1900 Mr. Lispenard S. Horton found it breeding at Gretna, and in 1899 Mr. Pember at Granville, Washington County. In 1905 the author found it on June 16 feeding its fledglings at Elizabethtown in Essex County. It is evident by a perusal of these records and many others, that there has been a great increase in the abundance of this species on the grasslands of New York and also of the surrounding states, until at the present time it has invaded not only the eastern part of New York, but Connecticut, Massachusetts, Vermont and other New England states. This species having originally been confined to the prairie region has now found conditions favorable to its habitation in the eastern states and has gradually been spreading year after year till now we must call it one of the common birds of the open field. [2] Turning now to West Virginia we find the following by State Ornithologist Brooks (1908): "A newcomer into West Virginia within the past ten years, this bird has extended its range into nearly all parts of our state. Now breeds in many of our counties." [3] His successor in office, Mr. I. H. Johnson, corroborated this statement in 1923.

Coming now to New England we find a statement from the pen of Dr. C. W. Townsend (1905): In the Auk [4] for January, 1904, he published some notes recording the extension of the breeding range of this subspecies to the eastern coast of Massachusetts, and these notes as quoted by him in his "Birds of Essex County" are given below:

"On August 9, 1903, at Ipswich, Mass., Mr. Ralph Hoffmann saw two adults of this species with a fully grown young bird. Two days later, on August 11, Mr. Thomas L. Bradlee shot, at the same place, two young birds, both females, and saw three other individuals. They were near a road in open fields not far from the sea. Again two days later, on August 13, I secured a young male of this species that was alone on the upper edge of Ipswich beach.

[1] Bendire, Charles: Life Histories of North American Birds, Vol. II, 1895, p. 334.

[2] Eaton, E. H.: Birds of New York, Part 2, 1914, pp. 203, 204.

[3] Brooks, Earl A.: Report of the West Virginia State Board of Agriculture for the quarter ending December 31, 1908. List of Birds found in West Virginia, 1909, p. 28.

[4] Townsend, C. W.: Auk, Vol. XXI, 1904, p. 81.

"The specimens secured by Mr. Bradlee were examined by Dr. J. Dwight, Jr., who stated in a letter to Mr. Bradlee that the birds 'were undoubtedly *praticola*,' and 'were in juvenal plumage, molting into first winter dress, only two or three primaries and a few rectrices remaining. In this condition this species (or any sparrow) does not and probably cannot migrate, so I have no doubt the birds were hatched near where they were found.'

"My own bird may have been from another brood, as although it was taken four days later, its plumage is more juvenal, being more spotted above, and having 9 juvenal rectrices and 4 juvenal primaries, against 5 rectrices and 3 primaries in Mr. Bradlee's birds. It was taken three miles from the first station.

"The Prairie Horned Lark has been seen at Ipswich before in the fall migrations, but this is the first time it has been found there in the breeding season. At last this enterprising bird in its progress eastward has reached the sea. Formerly a bird of the western prairies, it was recorded as breeding near Troy, N. Y., in 1881 (Park: Bull. N. O. C., Vol. VI, 1881, p. 177). Its first recorded breeding in New England was at Cornwall, Vt., in June, 1889 (C. H. Parkhill: O. & O., Vol. XIV, 1889, p. 87). In 1890 specimens were secured in the breeding season in Williamstown and North Adams, Mass., by Mr. Walter Faxon (Faxon: Auk, Vol. IX, 1892, p. 202), and a nest and eggs were found near Pittsfield by Mr. C. H. Buckingham July 10, 1892 (Brewster: Auk, Vol. XI, 1894, p. 326).

"In 1891 it was observed in June and July at Franconia, N. H. (Faxon: Auk, Vol. IX, 1892, p. 202). The foregoing records are from Faxon and Hoffmann on 'The Birds of Berkshire,' 1900, p. 138. They state that the bird is a 'rare summer resident at Williamstown, North Adams, Lanesboro, Pittsfield.'

"In 1899 the bird was found breeding as far east as Hubbardston in Worcester County, Mass., Mr. Frederick Cunningham, Jr., in July of that year 'finding a nest with eggs from which the young were safely reared' (Howe and Allen: 'The Birds of Mass.,' 1901, p. 81).

"Since then there have been several more records for New Hampshire as well as a number for its breeding in Maine. Dr. G. M. Allen[1] states that 'as far as at present known, therefore, the Prairie Horned Lark summers in New Hampshire in small numbers on the fallow and pasture lands to the west and north of the White Mountain Region.'

"In Maine there have been a number of breeding records for which I am indebted to Mr. J. Merton Swain. A pair was seen near Andover in that State on August 12th, 1899, by A. H. Norton.[2] On June 26th, 1900, Mr. Swain[3] heard the notes of Otocoris between Fairfield and Canaan, and three weeks later he saw a small flock and procured one adult female and two young. On April 23d, 1901, the same observer saw a pair building their nest near Fairfield, Maine. This pair laid four eggs.[4] The same year he saw a pair in Pittsfield and a pair near Hartland, and he states that several pairs have

[1] A list of the Birds of New Hampshire, 1903, p. 124 (Proc. Manchester Inst. Arts and Sci., Vol. IV, 1902).
[2] Norton, A. H.: Journal Maine Ornithological Society, Vol. II, p. 2, 1899.
[3] Swain, J. M.: Auk, Vol. XVII, p. 387, 1900.
[4] Swain, J. M.: Journal, Maine Ornithological Society, Vol. III, p. 30, 1901.

since nested along the Kennebec near Fairfield every year. He has also observed them breeding near Belgrade Lakes, Liberty, South China, Burnham, Unity and Livermore.[1] He also observed them nesting between Guilford and Sangerville, and near Farmington, and more lately near North Anson, Madison, Skowhegan and Norridgewock.

"Mr. Ora W. Knight writes me that Mr. Wallace Homer of Monson, Maine, found the Prairie Horned Lark nesting there in 1904, and that he himself found it at Bangor and Presque Isle under circumstances which indicated that it was breeding. It is evident that the Prairie Horned Lark has come to stay, and it will be an interesting addition to our avifauna.

"I have lately heard from several residents of Haverhill [Massachusetts] that a pair of Horned Larks, evidently *praticola* as I judge from a careful description written by Mr. Stanley D. Gray, has frequented some golf links on a hill near that city every summer since 1900. Mr. Gray writes under date of February 7th, 1904, that the bird 'is very tame at times, — have seen it in the center of a ring of people surrounding it at a distance of perhaps fifteen feet. Is less tame as the season advances. Have never seen it elsewhere than on Great Hill, Haverhill, where I have watched it for the past four years.'" [2]

It would be impossible in limited space to give the many records of the breeding of this bird in New England since 1905. It breeds now in nearly if not quite every county in Massachusetts and generally in unforested lands throughout the New England states.

We have traced its increase and dissemination from Indiana through Ohio and New York to New England. A probable reason for its extension eastward may be found in the fact that much of the prairie land in which it formerly bred has been settled and cultivated, and tree claims have been planted with trees, thus driving out the species from thousands of square miles in the aggregate (now wooded) in which it formerly bred. On the other hand a great region in Indiana, Ohio, New York and New England formerly heavily timbered has been more or less cleared, and the fields and pastures of the East offer suitable breeding places and a plentiful food supply for the species here. A bird which rears two or three broods each year is likely to occupy all suitable regions within its native life zones, and possibly the Prairie Horned Lark eventually may become a common bird in New England, where formerly it was unknown.

HAUNTS AND HABITS. This hardy bird is the first of all the song birds in vernal migration to push on toward the frozen north. Long before the Horned Larks leave us, even before the first Bluebirds appear, amid the lingering snows of February the bold and restless Prairie Horned Larks are on their way. They reach New York, Massachusetts, Vermont and southern Ontario usually during the first thaw in February, and it is quite possible that a few may remain all winter along the Massachusetts coast, as they do on Block Island. In nesting also they antedate all our other small birds. Many of these larks are mated by March first,* and most of the nests for the first brood are built before

---

[1] Swain, J. M.: Journal, Maine Ornithological Society, Vol. IV, 1904, p. 40.
[2] Birds of Essex County, 1905, pp. 235–237.
* Eggs have been found in Michigan in February (A. W. Butler).

the snow has entirely disappeared. They usually are located on the east or south side of some little rise of land where the sun has melted all the snow and the snow water has drained away. The nest is made beside some object or vegetation that will shelter it somewhat or render it inconspicuous. Sometimes a heavy snow-storm forces many of the birds to desert their unfinished nests or their incomplete sets of eggs, but if incubation has begun, so long as the bird can reach up and clear away the snow which covers her, just so long will she continue to impart warmth to the little speckled eggs. Thus, after a storm, nests have been discovered at the bottom of a deep little hole in the snow. When approached, the female ordinarily leaves the nest while the intruder is at some distance, and sneaks off quietly along the ground before she rises, but sometimes when the eggs are near hatching, and she is suddenly surprised while incubating, she may act like a crippled bird to deceive the enemy and entice him away. Commonly, however, neither bird exhibits much of that anxiety which often leads some birds to betray the situation of the nest.

My experience with this bird in the breeding season has been confined to two localities, one in Manitoba and the other in Massachusetts where I have not heard such extended flight-songs as are described elsewhere by others. After the young are hatched, the old birds manifest their anxiety by voice and action, but usually at a distance from the nest. Both parents assume the care of the young, but as soon as they are able to fly the female begins to prepare for a second brood, leaving the young chiefly if not entirely to the care of the male who faithfully feeds and guards them. If all goes well, two and even three broods may be safely reared. The song of this lark like that of the Skylark of Europe is not a remarkable performance (for, by the way, the vocal efforts of the latter will not compare as bird-music with the jingle of our Bobolink), but the flight that often accompanies the song is (as is the case with the Skylark) truly remarkable. How exhausting the effort that must be required of a small bird to rise both flying and singing up into the zenith beyond the range of human vision.

An extended description of the ordinary song and the song-flight is given by Bradford Torrey as follows:

"As for the quality and manner of the song, with all my listening and studying I could never hit upon a word with which to characterize it. The tone is dry, guttural, inexpressive; not exactly to be called harsh, perhaps, but certainly not in any true sense of the word musical. When we first heard it, in the distance (let the qualification be noted), the same thought came to both of us, — a Kingbird's formless, hurrying twitters. There is no rhythm, no melody, nothing to be called phrasing or modulation, — a mere jumble of 'splutterings and chipperings.' Every note is by itself, having to my ear no relation to anything before or after. The most striking and distinguishing characteristic of it all is the manner in which it commonly hurries to a conclusion — as if the clock were running down. . . . Sometimes — most frequently, perhaps — the strain was very brief; but at other times a bird would sit on a stone or a fence-post, or a ridgepole, and chatter almost continuously by the quarter-hour. Even then, however, this comical hurried phrase would come in at more or less regular intervals. I imagined that the larks looked upon it as the highest reach of their art and delivered it with special satisfaction. If they did, I could not blame them; to us it was by all odds the most interesting part of their very limited repertory.

"The most interesting part, I mean, of that which appealed to the ear; for, as will readily be imagined, the ear's part was really the much smaller half of the performance. The wonder of it all was not the music by itself (that was hardly better than an oddity, a thing of which one might soon have enough) but the music combined with the manner of its delivery, while the singer was climbing heavenward. For the bird is a true skylark. Like his more famous cousin, he does not disdain the humblest perch — a mere clod of earth answers his purpose; but his glory is to sing at heaven's gate.

"His method at such times was a surprise to me. He starts from the ground silently, with no appearance of lyrical excitement, and his flight at first is low, precisely as if he were going only to the next field. Soon, however, he begins to mount, beating the air with quick strokes and then shutting his wings against his sides and forcing himself upward. 'Diving upward' was the word I found myself using. Up he goes, — up, up, up, 'higher still and higher,' — till after awhile he breaks into voice. While singing he holds his wings motionless, stiffly outstretched, and his tail widely spread, as if he were doing his utmost to transform himself into a parachute — as no doubt he is. Then, the brief, hurried strain delivered, he beats the air again and makes another shoot heavenward. The whole display consists of an alternation of rests accompanied by song (you can always see the music, though it is often inaudible), and renewed upward pushes.

"In the course of his flight the bird covers a considerable field, since as a matter of course he cannot ascend vertically. He rises, perhaps, directly at your feet, but before he comes down, which may be in one minute or ten, he will have gone completely round you in a broad circle; so that, to follow him continuously (sometimes no easy matter, his altitude being so great and the light so dazzling), you will be compelled almost to put your neck out of joint. In our own case, we generally did not see him start, but were made aware of what was going on by hearing the notes overhead.

"One grand flight I did see from beginning to end, and it was wonderful, amazing, astounding. So I thought, at all events. There was no telling, of course, what altitude the bird reached, but it might have been miles, so far as the effect upon the beholder's emotions was concerned. It seemed as if the fellow never would be done. 'Higher still, and higher.' Again and again this line of Shelley came to my lips, as, after every bar of music, the bird pushed nearer and nearer to the sky. At last he came down; and this, my friend and I always agreed, was the most exciting moment of all. He closed his wings and literally shot to the ground head first, like an arrow. 'Wonderful' said I, 'wonderful!' And the other man said: 'If I could do that I would never do anything else.'" [1] The nesting cycle is very brief. One of my Canadian correspondents, Mr. L. McI. Terrill, gives one full breeding record as follows: "In this instance the entire opera-

[1] Torrey, Bradford: Footing it in Franconia, 1901, pp. 200–204.

tion, from the time the nest was commenced until the young had vacated, occupied twenty-five days, or possibly a little less. Three days were occupied in nest-construction, four in which to deposit the eggs, eleven (plus) for incubation, and seven to mature the young sufficiently to enable them to leave the nest." [1]

Some ornithologists believe that in some cases four broods are reared. This may be possible. "They sometimes nest in plowed fields. My father once noticed one of these birds in great distress, when harrowing. He went to see what was the trouble and found that a clod of earth had been turned over the nest by the harrow. The bird was putting its shoulder against the clod and pushing with all its little strength to move the clod." [2]

Larks are birds of the open country. They seek the treeless lands. I have never seen one in a tree, but now and then one may alight on a rock, a stone wall or stump or even a fence-post or rail. Seen in the fields and pastures they walk or run about or squat in the grass. If a hawk appears, they will disappear from sight (thanks to their protective coloration) until the danger is past. I have never seen one hop or jump along as the Robin does. In summer they are fond of dust-baths in the country roads, but I have never known one to bathe in water, though they may do so. As autumn comes on they live in a land of plenty as their grain crop, the abundant seeds of weeds and grasses, is ready for the gathering. They now renounce their family ties and assemble in loose flocks, sometimes with other races of the Horned Lark or with Snow Buntings, and forage over the land. As the frost begins to congeal the soil, and the snows of winter cover much of their food, they seek windswept, bare spots or weed patches or feed on undigested grain from horse droppings in the roads, but most of them drift southward, though sometimes in winter a few may be found with the Shore Larks along the coasts of southern New England.

ECONOMIC STATUS. To-day the Prairie Horned Lark is largely a bird of the farm. It lives and nests chiefly in pastures, grassy lands and cultivated fields. Its only injurious habit is grain eating and most of the grain taken is waste grain. It may do considerable damage where winter wheat is sown broadcast, especially if not immediately harrowed in, but where the grain is drilled in, the bird does it no appreciable injury. As a destroyer of insects (particularly cutworms), and weed seeds, it well deserves the protection that it receives under the laws of state and nation.

Otocoris alpestris hoÿti (BISHOP). Hoyt's Horned Lark.

DESCRIPTION. — Similar to Horned Lark, but grayer-brown above, except perhaps on back, throat paler yellow or yellowish and fore part of ear-region grayer. *Young:* Similar in color above to young of Horned Lark but stripe above eye dull buffy-white instead of pale yellow, and no yellow tinge below.

MEASUREMENTS. — Adult female (type specimen): Length 7.35 in.; folded wing 4.54; tail 3.01; bill (from nostril) .41; tarsus .89; measurements generally same as those of Horned Lark (L. B. Bishop). Female smaller than male.

---

[1] Terrill, L. McI.: Horned Larks in the Province of Quebec, from the Wilson Bulletin, Vol. XXIX, No. 100, September, 1917, p. 138. [2] Leonard, Wm. Jas.; Shoreham, Vermont, *in litt.*

MOLTS. — Apparently similar to those of Horned Lark.

FIELD MARKS. — The only possible field marks are given in the description above. It might be possible under best conditions to distinguish a typical specimen from Horned Lark in the field, but probably not from Prairie Horned Lark.

VOICE. — Similar to that of Horned Lark.

NEST AND EGGS. — Indistinguishable from those of Horned Lark.

RANGE. — Chiefly central North America. In summer from the lower Mackenzie Valley and Boothia Peninsula south to Lake Athabaska and northeastern Manitoba and east to west side of Hudson Bay. South in winter to Nevada, Utah, Kansas, Iowa, Michigan and Ohio. Casual west to British Columbia and east to New York, Connecticut, and (possibly) Massachusetts.

DISTRIBUTION IN NEW ENGLAND. — Casual or accidental migrant and winter visitor to Connecticut and possibly Massachusetts. *Connecticut:* Bridgeport, March 4, 1893, one male and one female taken, somewhat nearer this form than a true *alpestris* (Dr. E. H. Eames), in coll. of H. W. Beers; Stamford, February 17, 1894, male (L. H. Porter); Guilford, March 7, 1903, male taken from a flock of Horned Larks (L. B. Bishop); West Haven, January 24, 1905, male taken (A. Ganung), in coll. of L. B. Bishop; Guilford, November 3, 10, 1906, two taken (E. S. Woodruff).[1]

NOTE. Mr. C. J. Maynard and several other observers saw on Feb. 2, 1918, a pair of birds at Marblehead, Massachusetts, that were identified and reported as certainly of this race. They were very tame, allowing the observers to come within three yards or less, and the conditions for observation were excellent.[2] Ornithologists, however, are not likely to accept a first record for Massachusetts unless substantiated by the specimen.

HAUNTS AND HABITS. Hoyt's Horned Lark was described by Dr. L. B. Bishop in 1896 as a supposed new race. There is nothing to indicate that its haunts or habits differ appreciably from those of the Prairie Horned Lark which it closely resembles, except that it has a much more northern range which extends to the Arctic Ocean. As it has appeared a number of times in Connecticut, it is likely that in coming from the North it has passed through Massachusetts.

FAMILY **CORVIDÆ.** CROWS, JAYS, MAGPIES, ETC.

Number of species in North America 23; in Massachusetts 5.

This is a large family, and important in its relation to man. It is composed of birds of medium to rather large size. The first of the ten primaries is short, usually about half as long as the second, and several are more or less sinuated and quite narrow toward the tips. There are twelve tail-feathers. The tarsus is scaled in front and grooved on one or both sides. The bill is stout, frequently nearly the length of the head, tapering, usually rather acute and not distinctly notched nor hooked at the tip. The nostrils are covered thickly with tufts of bristly feathers as in the titmouses and there are bristles at the corners of the mouth. The tail is never forked, usually rounded. The family is nearly cosmopolitan, representatives being accounted for throughout the world, except in New Zealand, and some Polynesian Islands. Upwards of 200 species have been recognized. Though classed among singing birds and having a complicated singing

---

[1] Sage, Bishop and Bliss: The Birds of Connecticut, 1913, p. 106.
[2] Records of Walks and Talks with Nature, Vol. X, 1918, p. 26.

PLATE 58

PLATE 58

BLUE JAY
Page 375

Adults

CANADA JAY
Page 384

Adult

All about one-half scale.

Louis Agassiz Fuertes

apparatus, most of these birds do not sing, but some individuals (at least) utter pleasing sounds and some can imitate perfectly songs of other birds.

ECONOMIC STATUS. These birds undoubtedly function indispensably in the economy of nature and often some of them are extremely beneficial, but most of them are not regarded favorably by the agriculturist or the gamekeeper.

SUBFAMILY **GARRULINÆ**. MAGPIES AND JAYS.

Birds of this group have the wings short and rounded, the tail ample to long and also rounded, head frequently crested and colors usually bright, varied or strikingly contrasted. Generally the feet and bill are not so strong as in true crows, and the members of the group average smaller.

Cyanocítta cristáta cristata (LINNÆUS). **Blue Jay.**

Other names: JAY; JAYBIRD.

Plate 58.

DESCRIPTION. — Bill rather broad at base and nearly as long as head, which is prominently crested; nostrils covered by nasal tufts; wings somewhat rounded and tail considerably graduated. *Adult male:* Top of crested head, hind-neck, back, scapulars, rump, upper tail-coverts and all but greater upper wing-coverts, grayish-violet-blue; front of forehead sometimes paler or bluish-white; nasal tufts also paler or whitish; sides of head, chin and throat whitish or very pale bluish-gray, bordered posteriorly by a black collar which extends around back of head, passing behind and beneath crest, this collar becoming broadest and somewhat crescentic below throat; extreme front of forehead, small patch before eye, and very narrow line behind it also black; exposed parts of greater wing-coverts, secondaries, tertials and tail brilliant, dark azure-blue, barred black and all broadly tipped white, except middle pair of tail-feathers; white tips of tail-feathers increase in length toward the outer, where they occupy about one-fourth of feather; primaries azure-blue on outer webs, dusky on inner webs and at tips; breast, sides and flanks dull brownish-gray; belly and under tail-coverts white; wing linings dusky-blue; bill and feet black or blackish; iris brown. *Adult female:* Similar to adult male but slightly duller; crest usually shorter and black markings on wings and tail often not so wide and prominent. *Young in first winter plumage:* Resembles adult winter, but in birds examined the black markings on tail and wings are not so prominent as in most adults. *Young in juvenal plumage:* Similar to adults, but crest and tail shorter; upper plumage more gray than blue except wings and tail; wings chiefly blue, varied in imitation of adults; tail blue centrally barred black and with large white tips like adults.

MEASUREMENTS. — Length 11.00 to 12.50 in.; spread 15.70 to 17.50; folded wing 5.00 to 6.25; tail 5.05 to 6.00; bill 1.00 to 1.25; tarsus 1.20 to 1.45; weight (one specimen) 3 oz. (B. H. Warren). Female smaller than male.

MOLTS. — Juvenal plumage acquired in the nest by a postnatal molt, following gray down; first winter plumage produced by a postjuvenal molt of body plumage (July to September), difficult to distinguish from adult winter plumage, and worn until the next autumn; first breeding plumage, therefore, is acquired by wear; adults molt once a year (postnuptial, July to November) and are in most perfect plumage from late October to January, although breeding plumage is often very bright even if somewhat worn.

FIELD MARKS. — Size larger than Robin; unmistakable; the only New England bird of its size that has blue, black and white on both wings and tail, but sometimes mistaken for Bluebird by people unacquainted with birds.

VOICE. — Ordinary cry represented as *jāy jāy, djāy djāy, djáh djáh* or *dāh dāh;* a great variety of notes — a scream very like that of the Red-shouldered Hawk, a sound like a toy trumpet, and other notes rendered by different authors as *pa-ha, pa-ha, piuh-piuh, tink-tink, hash, hash, side-light, side-light, side-light, sid-lit, sid-lit, hilly-hilly-hilly, peedunkle, peedunkle, too-wheedle, too-wheedle, heeweeo-heweeo-heweeo, chillac-chillac-chillac, w-e-a-u-g-r, whēeo whēeo whēeo, keo-eyeo, we-hue,* etc.; these are but few of the Blue Jay's notes; also a harsh, rapid chatter, as rapid as a woodpecker's tattoo (Winsor M. Tyler); it chatters and gabbles softly for many minutes at a time, warbles at times, and imitates songs and calls of other birds; its sweetest common note is a pensive, bell-like call full of pathos, often heard in autumn woods.

BREEDING. — Usually in dense woods, preferring pine or other coniferous trees, but also in deciduous trees, and in shade trees or vines or even on houses in villages or in suburban parts of cities, rarely in barns or out-buildings in the country. *Nest:* In either coniferous or deciduous tree, in a crotch, on branches close to trunk or out toward end of branch, from 5 to 50 feet high, very rarely in a hollow tree; of sticks, twigs and rootlets, sometimes lined with strips of bark or feathers, leaves and grass; even mud is used on occasion. *Eggs:* 3 to 6; .99 to 1.20 by .79 to .90 in.; usually ovate; ground color varies much (sometimes on a single egg) from cream to olive-green, olive-buff, vinaceous buff, pea-green or even pale bluish-green or grayish-green, but usually olive or buffy, spotted and blotched irregularly with various browns and lavender or drab and sometimes with a few small spots of blackish also; figured in Bendire's "Life Histories of North American Birds," Vol. II, Plate V, Figs. 5, 6. *Dates:* April 25 to May 4, South Carolina; April 28 to June 18, Massachusetts. *Incubation:* Period 16 days (O. W. Knight); 15 to 17 days (Burns); by both sexes. One brood yearly, possibly sometimes two in the south.

RANGE. — Temperate eastern and central North America and north (west of Hudson Bay) to about latitude 58°. Breeds over most of its range, from northern Alberta, central Saskatchewan, central Manitoba, northern Ontario, southern Quebec and Newfoundland south to central northern Texas, central Missouri, central Indiana, central eastern Tennessee, northwestern North Carolina and Virginia and west to central Alberta, the Dakotas, western Nebraska, eastern Colorado, western Oklahoma and central northern Texas; casual in New Mexico and northern Manitoba (Fort Churchill); winters over all but extreme northern parts of its range, but migrates irregularly south to southern Illinois.

DISTRIBUTION IN NEW ENGLAND. — Common migrant and resident in all six states; most common in summer in northern sections and in winter along southern coastal region.

SEASON IN MASSACHUSETTS. — Permanent resident.

HAUNTS AND HABITS. The handsome, active Blue Jay is an engaging rascal. Where there are Blue Jays, there always is action and usually noise, for jays, like Crows, are fond of hearing their own voices. Often a great uproar in the woods may be traced to a dozen or more Blue Jays in the tree-tops, screaming as if in great terror or pain, and apparently for no earthly reason except to keep up the excitement which seems to be of the hair-raising kind, and to exercise their lungs; in autumn they seem to delight in gathering near some woodland dwelling, and "yawping" in a raucous chorus, apparently with no particular object in view, except to wake the sleepers; but let them find a Screech Owl dozing the day away close to the trunk of some tall pine — then we shall see real excitement! The woods ring again with the screaming chorus, and blue flashes to blue as the crested birds converge to the attack. In their excessive agitation the jays seem to lose their habitual caution, and it appears as if the mob would annihilate the despised and hated imp of darkness. Surely the poor little gray owl will be torn in shreds! But no! After half an hour of ceaseless clamor hardly a feather of the drowsy one is ruffled.

The onset of the blues consists mainly of fuss and feathers — bluff and bluster. Occasionally, however, the mob becomes so numerous and aggressive as to drive the owl out of the woods, but having thus rid themselves of his presence they do not follow far. The jays take good care to keep out of the owl's reach, for many a Screech Owl's nest is lined with the feathers of such as they.

Now and then the jays will attempt to badger a Sparrow Hawk, Red-shouldered Hawk or even a Sharp-shinned Hawk. With the latter, however, they are playing a dangerous game and they know it and always keep a line of retreat open where they can quickly plunge into some thicket, for if the hawk is either hungry or angry, he may rush suddenly upon one of the mocking crew and strike his victim down. The jay, now at bay, fights to the last gasp, but it avails him little, as the courage of his companions evaporates, and they fly, screaming, away to cover. Though the Blue Jay shows courage in defense of its young, it evidently prefers the rôle of a live coward to that of a dead hero and takes the very best of care of its own precious skin.

On the north shore of Lake Ontario a long cape called Point Pelee extends far out into the lake, and there great numbers of migrating birds assemble in autumn for their southward flight across the water. Many hawks follow them, and many small birds are killed by hawks on this Point. Taverner and Swales, who have spent considerable time on the Point during the fall migrations, tell how the jays avoided capture: "At times the jays seemed thoroughly to enjoy conditions and delighted to get in the middle of a safe thicket and ' jay ' their loudest. No sooner was the first note uttered than a hawk was on hand dodging around the retreat in the wildest fashion, while the jay within shrieked with well-feigned fear, but apparent delight. In fact the Blue Jay is a canny bird, and though the remains of other species were commonly met with, scattered over the ground around some little knoll or log, we recognized their blue plumage but once." [1]

" During the hawk flights of 1905 and 1906 they (Blue Jays) were much harassed by the Sharp-shins but, as they are perfectly able to take care of themselves and kept pretty close in the grapevine tangles, it is not probable that they suffered much, unless it was from the nervous strain of being continually on the outlook. But who ever saw a Blue Jay suffer from nervousness? In fact once within the shrubbery, they seemed to rather enjoy the situation, and from their safe retreats hurled joyous epithets at their baffled enemies." [2] The Blue Jay is regarded as a resident bird, wintering wherever it breeds; nevertheless it migrates more or less. Its migrations are of two kinds: (1) regular southward movements in autumn or winter from the more northern parts of its range and return movements in spring to its breeding places; (2) irregular movements in autumn or winter from those parts of its range where food is scarce to those where it is abundant. Migrations of the first class probably take place every autumn from the extreme northern parts of the range and extend to the middle states at least. Those of the second class usually occur from some region where beechnuts, chestnuts or acorns are not

[1] Taverner, P. A. and Swales, B. H.: Wilson Bulletin, Vol. XIX, 1907, p. 94.
[2] Taverner and Swales: *Ibid.*, No. 61, p. 142.

plentiful to some other region where some of them are abundant. Wherever beeches fruit in profusion, jays assemble in numbers in winter, becoming very scarce in other sections.   There are many records of Blue Jays traveling southward in autumn in flocks of from 50 to 100 more or less.   In southern New England the largest numbers usually pass from the 10th to the 25th of September.   These migrations take place in the daytime, but we get fewer observations of the spring flight than of the autumnal one, possibly because while jays usually flock in the fall in New England, they are seen in spring commonly singly or in pairs, and throughout most of the month of May doubtless work slowly northward day after day unnoticed.   In some years the autumnal migration in New England is not much noticed, in others it is quite marked in certain sections.   One of the regular migration routes is down the Connecticut Valley.   Eaton in New York[1] and Barrows in Michigan [2] report a much larger migration of Blue Jays in autumn and spring than our New England records indicate, though occasionally a migrating flock is seen here in May.   Mr. J. R. Mead, of Wichita, Kansas, says that many jays pass there regularly about the middle of September going southeast in long straggling flocks.[3]

Mr. E. A. Doolittle, of Plainsville, Ohio, recorded a flight on May 25, 1919, near the shore of Lake Erie but did not realize that he was witnessing a part of the spring migration.[4]

Many jays remain in New England all winter.   Some of these may be migrants from farther north, but others seem to be birds that nest here.   During the colder part of the year, many leave some of the higher and more exposed parts of the country and betake themselves to the valleys or to the more southern of New England's sea-coasts, where the cold is not so severe and the snow less often covers the ground.   Occasionally large flocks are seen in winter, apparently indicating local movement.   About two hundred were noted on an island in Lake Quinsigamond on a December day in 1904, and on January 19, 1921, the Reverend George E. Allen reported between forty-five and fifty birds in a scattered flock flying south over Plainfield, Massachusetts.   By the middle of April some jays have paired and a few have begun their nests.   Indeed they have been seen carrying sticks at much earlier dates.   This early desultory occupation may have given rise to the saying of the southern negro that "the jaybird carries sticks to the devil."

Although I have lived among Blue Jays and watched them much, I have never seen any special mating antics, but the Blue Jay is so prone to action of some peculiar kind whenever it opens its mouth to squall that special antics of the mating season may have been overlooked.   The males follow the females around, and now and then there is an ardent disagreement between two rival males, but that is all that I have noticed.   Usually a new nest is built each year, both birds working upon it, but rarely an old nest is slightly repaired and used.   When the stick-carrying begins, every stick that goes into the nest is tested with care.   The jay does not pick up dry sticks from the ground for the struc-

---

1 Eaton, E. H.: Birds of New York, Vol. II, 1914, p. 208.

2 Barrows, W. B.: Michigan Bird Life, 1912, p. 413.

3 Transactions Kansas Academy of Sciences, Vol. VI, 1897–1898, p. 217.

4 Auk, Vol. XXXVI, 1919, p. 572.

ture that is to hold its young, but breaks twigs and small branches from the tree; strong dead twigs are used and they even attempt to break green twigs which they seize with their bills in the tree-tops. Thus they secure a strong and lasting framework for the nest. When nesting in the woods, forest materials alone are used, but if near human habitations string, paper, cotton and other products of civilization may be interwoven with the woodland material. The nest finished, an egg is laid daily. Then the hitherto noisy and loquacious bird becomes silent and furtive. When coming to the nest he glides silently in among the lower branches and hops from limb to limb near to and around the trunk, watching on all sides, and thus, climbing a spiral stairway, reaches unobserved the nest on which his beloved partner sits waiting for him to bring the morsel which he politely tenders her. There must be considerable variation in the time of incubation as reliable observers have reported the period as from 14 to 17 days. Both sexes share in the duties of parenthood and both exhibit great bravery in defense of their young.

While the Robin often drives the jay from the vicinity of the Robin's nest, the jay attacks the Robin furiously when it approaches his own nest. The incubating bird is so devoted to her task that sometimes when her eggs are near hatching she will continue to cover them in the face of intrusion until actually lifted off the nest. At my farm in Wareham a pair of jays had fashioned their domicile on a pine tree, close to the farmhouse. One day one of my boys climbed the tree, took the mother off her eggs, stroked her and released her; she did not wait for him to leave but went right back and covered those eggs while he sat looking down upon her. Yet the Blue Jay is one of the most wary and cautious of birds. During a severe winter, when cold and snow were excessive, we succeeded in enticing many jays to come to a window to eat food that we provided for them there, but one cold morning one was caught in a trap set for a rat, and it was nearly two years from that day before we could induce another jay to come to that window. Nevertheless, devotion to their young not infrequently leads these ordinarily wary birds to throw aside all caution and attack human beings. There are cases on record where jays, nesting in towns, have struck passersby with wings, beak and claws when their callow young had fallen from the nest close to the street or on the sidewalk. Even shy jays of the woods have been known to attack the owner of a camp built directly under their nest. Mr. Charles J. Anderson told me of a cat that was tied to a tree to prevent it from killing birds, but it happened that a pair of Blue Jays had young in a nest concealed in that tree. When the cat attempted to climb the tree, both parent birds flew at him and drove him under a bush near by, where he cowered in fright. Mr. Anderson actually feared that the birds would "peck out his eyes." So much has been said about the cowardice of the Jay that it is as well to give the bird his just due. When caught in one of his thieving exploits by some righteously indignant bird, near his own size, he usually beats a hasty and inglorious retreat. He has even been seen in full flight from an oriole's nest with an angry male oriole within an inch of his tail. Nevertheless he will fight furiously for his own. I once watched a battle between a pair of Blue Jays and a red squirrel which started to climb their nest-tree. The birds kept to the air and struck with the force of flying missiles.

Back and forth, up and down they flashed, a bewildering zigzag maze of blue and black and white. The poor squirrel dodged one, only to become a fair mark for the other, until, forced to the ground, he fled incontinently.

Jays not only take good care of their young, but occasionally in winter or early spring one of these birds is seen to feed a companion. They are said to care for the aged and infirm. Mr. Frithof Kumlien tells of an old, worn, partially blind Blue Jay that was fed, tended and guarded by his companions, who never deserted him. They guided him to a spring where he bathed regularly, always with some of his companions close by. Mr. Kumlien approached the bird cautiously and caught it, thus assuring himself that it was old, worn and either partially or completely blind.[1] Maurice Thompson has said that the man who can look into a bird's nest, well set with tender-hued eggs, without feeling an inward smile, as if his soul were sweetly pleased, has lost something that is the chief ingredient of perfect sanity and simplicity. Even so! and does the sane man live who can look unmoved upon a nest filled with bright-eyed, alert, fledgling Blue Jays? Seen with the westering sun lowering to the far horizon, and throwing level rays between the dark plumed branches of their natal pine, they make a picture to be carried in the memory. The fluffy youngsters snuggle together in the nest for warmth, as the sun rays, sifted through branches stirred by the waning breeze, light up the picture and touch their pale gray crowns with the glories of the sunset. What a birthplace this! to be born in a nest swinging high in a noble pine and rocked by the winds from the four quarters of the world, to open wondering eyes to sky and sun, to know no roof but the overarching dome of heaven, no shelter but the mother's wing, to wax strong and fit and eager, and then, all at once, to leap forth upon the supporting air. A few days more and they will have mastered the art of flight, which man attempted vainly for centuries, and will give themselves unafraid to the varying currents of the air.

When the young have left the nest and learned to provide for themselves, the family roams through the woods, revelling in plenty that nature has provided for them; they are joined by others and it is a noisy rollicking crew. In the woods in September or October one may hear most of the notes that jays commonly utter, — from the clear clarion ring of the trumpet to the soft conversational chattering, meant only for the ears of their companions, and now they not infrequently imitate the soft "whisper songs" of smaller birds, for the Blue Jay as a mimic is second only to the Mockingbird, though most of his imitations are given in secret, and, apparently, are not meant for human ears. Let Dr. Hatch tell the story. He says: "The question of the jay's powers of mimicry of the notes of numerous other birds, has long been at rest with me, for I am an eye and an ear witness. His most wonderful, and most successful demonstrations have been in imitating very small birds like the Chickadee, Pewee, Winter Wren, several of the sparrows, and indeed almost every known species of the kind, whose combinations are not very long. It must be understood that these performances are invariably ' *en sutta voce*,' [sic] and audible to only those who are embraced in his auditorium by chances of fortuitous accident,

---

[1] Bendire, Charles: Life Histories of North American Birds, Vol. II, 1895, pp. 357–358.

which keeps the performer in blissful ignorance of his presence. My first opportunity transpired by my being placed in the covert of a fallen tree-top, to which the leaves were still clinging, before daylight in the morning to await a band of deer that were to be driven near there by a party of drivers acquainted with their 'runs.' I had been there nearly two hours in almost breathless silence, scarcely moving a muscle lest I might be discovered and while thus waiting numerous birds had been twittering and flying about the spot of my concealment ever since the daylight had come, amongst which were many Blue Jays. Now, any experienced hunter knows that if one of these irrepressible jays catches sight of him, his chances of a shot at a deer that is anywhere near him are gone for that time, and having just before received a preconcerted signal that some were approaching, my attention was centered upon a number of these birds but a little distance from me, ready to rob me of the fruits and considerations of my mutual sacrifices, when I saw and heard such a mimicry of many of the little birds before mentioned as no language can describe. Only one individual was engaged, and the notes which fell in showers like dewdrops, almost inaudible, were among the clearest, most delicate, sweet and melodious that ever found their way into a human ear. I was in an ecstasy of wonder and surprise and only sighed in silence that every lover of bird-song could not share my delight. I forgave him everything I had ever seen, heard, or surmised against him, and have never since harbored any but the kindest feelings toward him. If a diet upon canary brains and mockingbird's eyes can afford such inspiration, these songsters contribute as much in their deaths as in their lives, and the regally plumed Blue Jay should live forever. Since then I have his secret, and I have many times been his auditor undiscovered, and I have found that when undiscovered, he will prolong these solo performances considerably, constantly varying and modulating them in the most pleasing manner." [1]

My own experiences enable me to corroborate the good Doctor except in one particular. I am positive that the jay does not always imitate *sotto voce*, as on one occasion while concealed in the woods watching for deer (though without a rifle), I heard a full, loud, clear song of a Baltimore Oriole in the trees overhead. As it seemed a strange place for an Oriole at that season I scanned the tree-tops carefully and saw the singer — a Blue Jay. One day in October I heard and saw a jay imitate the mew of the Catbird, and on the same day in another wood, another jay sang the "whisper song" of the Catbird many times. Either bird would have deceived the most discriminating listener. I was deceived in both cases until I actually saw the performer. Mr. William C. Wheeler tells me that the Blue Jay seems to have even more ability to mimic than the Starling and that on March 11, 1925, one imitated clearly notes of the Baltimore Oriole, Goldfinch and Purple Finch and parts of the song of the Catbird and Brown Thrasher. The calls and songs were given in about three fourths of the full volume of the birds' voices imitated. It is still a question in my mind whether mimicry and ventriloquism are gifts shared by all Blue Jays or are practiced only by a select few. I have heard these birds much, when entirely concealed from them, and have rarely heard them imitate the songs of others,

---

[1] Hatch, P. L.: Notes on the Birds of Minnesota, 1892, pp. 263, 264.

though giving a great variety of soft notes peculiar to themselves. They imitate the cries of several hawks, reproducing them exactly. Dr. Jared P. Kirtland, of Cleveland, Ohio, had a colony of jays on his estate. During the day the poultry might be seen frequently running for hiding places while the turkey gobbler was searching the sky with upturned eye, alarmed by the mimic ventriloquial utterances of jays simulating the cries of hawks.[1] It is easy for jays to imitate some notes of hawks, for there is a similar quality in the strong, wild notes of both. Thoreau, writing of the jay in winter, says: "You hear the lisping tinkle of chickadees from time to time and the unrelenting steel-cold scream of a jay, unmelted, that never flows into a song, a sort of wintry trumpet, screaming cold; hard, tense, frozen music, like the winter sky itself. . . ." True, but in the winter woods it is a heartening sound of vigorous, wild nature, and the bird itself is a brilliant spectacle amid the bare limbs or on the white carpet of the snow. The most remarkable thing about the jay in winter is the ease with which it hides its azure beauty. Among bare and snowy limbs you see it fly, a most conspicuous, lovely object — its handsome wings and tail wide-spread — and then, as it alights, it disappears. It has merely slipped behind a limb which conceals its brilliant colors or has turned to face you behind a dead leaf or two and so becomes virtually invisible. Jays are such adepts at hiding that when the leaves are still on the trees they may be all about a person and yet escape observation. They may be circumvented, nevertheless, by the quiet sitter or by a person lying still on the ground. Their curiosity is then their undoing, and they will soon be heard conversing in very low tones, or they may approach and examine the intruder in silence. Curiosity often induces the jay, while keeping mostly concealed, to follow a man for a considerable distance through the woods; and a person concealed in shrubbery or thick trees may attract several of these birds by imitating a jay's cry of distress, as they seem to sympathize with the unfortunate.

The jay is a hardy bird, and as it commonly stores up food for winter, most individuals that winter in New England survive the most inclement seasons; but I have known a jay to perish of cold in a very severe winter though provided with food by human aid and finding shelter in a shed. The bird may have been weak or diseased although apparently it was not.

The jay seems to exhibit about as much intelligence as a Crow, and some of its behavior almost seems to indicate reasoning powers. Mr. Horace W. O'Connor says that he saw a Blue Jay with something white in its bill (probably bread or suet) alight on a limb about a rod from the window, thrust the substance into a hole in the rough bark, then drop to the ground, pick up a dead leaf, fly to the limb and place it carefully over the hole. The wind, however, blew the leaf away. The bird tried to catch it in the air and failed. Then it selected a much smaller leaf from the ground and rammed that into the hole, thus covering its find, and then packed the leaf down firmly with its beak.[2] Mr. J. N. Baskett says that he saw a Blue Jay lift its wing and rub pungent walnut leaves re-

[1] Baird, S. F., Brewer, T. M., and Ridgway, R.: A History of North American Birds, Land Birds, Vol. II, 1905, p. 276.
[2] My Friend the Jay. Unpopular Review, Vol. X, July–September, 1918, p. 39.

peatedly into the feathers beneath it.[1]   Miss Grace Ellicott, of Newcastle, Indiana, says that she saw a Blue Jay alight on an ant-hill and rapidly pick up a number of large ants which it tucked away under each wing until frightened away by a passer-by.[2]   Mr. W. L. McAtee suggests that the bird was taking advantage of the habit of ants to fasten their jaws into any object that presents itself.   In this manner the bird might carry them to its young, as the incident occurred in the nesting season.[3]   Unfortunately for the jay he has acquired an unsavory reputation among men, a part of which he deserves, if the killing of smaller birds can be considered a crime.   He has been seen to kill young pheasants and even chickens.   In winter he has been known to attack and kill birds as large as the Downy Woodpecker, but the Hairy Woodpecker seems able to defend itself against its larger antagonist.   There is a valid excuse, however, for the jay's so-called cannibalism, as it is his natural prerogative to eat the eggs and young of smaller birds or even the adults in case of necessity, if he can catch them.   His right to thus comport himself is quite as clear as that of the little birds to eat flies or caterpillars; moreover, from his point of view it is ethical for him to steal corn, for he is not supposed to know the grain is not his. It is only when judged by human standards that we find him lacking in virtue.

Many ornithologists regard the Blue Jay as a harmful species because it destroys the eggs and young of smaller birds, which they consider more useful than the Jay.   If we are guided by the conclusion of Professor F. E. L. Beal of the Biological Survey, however, who undoubtedly was in his day the greatest authority on the food of birds, we must concede the utility of the Jay.   Out of 292 stomachs examined only two showed remains of little birds.   Pieces of egg shell supposed to be from eggs of domestic fowls were found in eleven stomachs.   These were believed to have been broken shells picked up by the birds, which take mineral matter up to 14 per cent of the stomach contents including many discarded shells of hen's eggs.   No shells or other parts of birds' eggs were found. The principal food of these birds consisted of 24.3 per cent animal matter and 75.7 per cent vegetal.   Most of the animal matter was composed of insects with a few spiders, myriapods, snails and such small vertebrates as small fishes, small frogs, salamanders, mice and a very few small birds.   Among the insect pests eaten were May beetles, large numbers of fruit-eating beetles, grasshoppers, caterpillars and curculios.   Jays are known to eat many large, hairy caterpillars such as are not eaten in large numbers by many birds and often to kill wantonly many more than they eat, among them the tent, forest tent, gipsy, browntail and sphinx moth caterpillars; also to eat the eggs of insects, particularly those of the tent caterpillar moth.   More than 42 per cent of their food consists of nuts and acorns.   Chestnuts and beechnuts are favorites, corn makes up 17.9 per cent.   Jays eat a few cultivated cherries, but most of the fruit eaten by them is wild.

ECONOMIC STATUS.   Professor Beal says that the examination of 300 stomachs shows that the Blue Jay does far more good than harm.   We may not agree with that verdict, but there is a beneficial habit not yet considered.   Jays bury nuts and seeds in the ground,

---

[1] The Story of the Birds, 1897, p. 243.   [2] Guide to Nature, Vol. I, 1908, p. 168.
[3] Auk, Vol. XXXI, 1914, p. 405.

thus planting forests. They also regurgitate smaller seeds and so distribute them. As Barton says, in a few years they would replant all the cleared lands, and they are not known to distribute the seeds of poisonous plants.

Perisóreus canadénsis canadensis (LINNÆUS). Canada Jay.

Other names: WHISKEY JACK; WHISKEY JOHN; MOOSE-BIRD; GREASE-BIRD; MEAT-BIRD; CAMP ROBBER; MEAT HAWK.

Plate 58.

DESCRIPTION. — Bill rather short for a jay and broad at base; head without crest; plumage soft, thick and lax; folded wing and tail nearly equal in length, latter rounded. *Adults (male rather darker than female, otherwise, sexes alike):* Forepart and sides of head, including nasal tufts, forehead and fore-part of crown, sides of head up to ear-region, also chin and throat white which extends from throat almost around back of neck; top of head from forepart of crown to nape, narrow ring around eye (also back of neck) brownish-slate, black or blackish-slate, extending down on sides of head back of ear-region and more or less tinged gray on forepart of crown near white forehead; back, scapulars, lesser wing-coverts, rump and upper tail-coverts mouse-gray; wings and tail slaty-gray; primaries with slight bluish tinge, primaries and secondaries tinged strongly with bluish on outer web of each feather; middle and greater wing-coverts (sometimes), flight-feathers and tail (usually) slightly tipped white; below (except as de-scribed above), pale drab-gray, paler or white toward tail; iris brown; bill, legs and feet black. *Young in first winter plumage:* Virtually as adult, but white of forehead tinged more or less brownish. *Young in juvenal plumage:* Brownish or sooty slate-gray, darkening on top of head and upper parts of side head to dull black and lightening below toward tail; no white on forehead; feathers quite generally lighter toward bases and brownish at tips; wings above brown, secondaries and tertials with lead colored, outer edges, basal part of primaries the same, greater wing-coverts tipped grayish; tail slate-gray, tipped brownish-white.

MEASUREMENTS. — Length 10.70 to 12.10 in.; spread 16.00 to 17.50; folded wing 5.50 to 5.90; tail 5.30 to 6.30; bill .83 to .92; tarsus 1.30 to 1.36. Female smaller than male.

MOLTS. — Juvenal plumage acquired by complete postnatal molt of nestling; a partial postjuvenal molt of body plumage (June to August) produces first winter plumage, which is virtually as adult; juvenal wings and tail retained; first nuptial plumage is merely worn winter plumage; adults have but one molt — postnuptial (June to September) and complete.

FIELD MARKS. — Blue Jay size. *Adult:* Above, smoky-gray, lighter below, bill short for a jay, fore-head, head and throat white with a large, black patch on back of head; bird fluffed up, as it often is in winter, resembles a giant chickadee with partial black cap and white throat. When on the wing seems to float lightly in air with little exertion. *Young:* Brownish slate-gray or sooty-slate; head largely blackish.

VOICE. — A querulous *quee-ah, kuoo* or *whah* (O. W. Knight); harsh screams and low chattering notes somewhat similar to those of Blue Jay and many notes peculiar to itself; loud, clear wild *toots* (J. A. Farley); a disagreeable note similar to a scolding note of red squirrel (Harrison F. Lewis); a song in breeding season resembling that of catbird; "a harsh rattle," commonly given, a wide range of calls, all rich in tone; as one comes gliding to a perch near his mate, there is a series of rapid cries, a little grating, changing abruptly to a soft, high-pitched purring (J. B. DeMille).

BREEDING. — Mostly in northern coniferous forests, often in wooded swamps. *Nest:* Usually rather low and near trunk of coniferous tree, resting on branches; large for a Jay, neatly built of twigs, bark-strips, sphagnum and other moss and grass, with warm, soft lining of lichens or mosses and finally feathers of various birds. *Eggs:* 3 to 5, usually 4; 1.04 to 1.21 by .80 to .88 in.; long ovate to rounded ovate;

generally grayish, pale gray or pearl-gray, sometimes with yellowish tinge; speckled and spotted profusely with browns, slate and lavender or lilac, markings grouped into a circle around large end; figured in Bendire's "Life Histories of North American Birds," Vol. II, Plate III, Figs. 18 and 19. *Dates:* March 10 to April 10, central Canada; "March," Maine. *Incubation:* Period 16 to 18 days (Burns). One brood yearly.

RANGE. — Hudsonian and Canadian zones of northern North America, north to tree limit and west to eastern Alaska. Breeds from eastern Alaska, northern Mackenzie, northern Manitoba, northern Ontario and central Quebec south to southeastern British Columbia, southern Alberta, southeastern Saskatchewan, southern Manitoba, northern Minnesota, northern Michigan, southeastern Ontario, northern New York, northern Maine and New Brunswick; casual in Nebraska, southeastern Wisconsin, Pennsylvania and Massachusetts.

DISTRIBUTION IN NEW ENGLAND. — *Maine:* Uncommon to locally common resident in northern parts, from Lake Umbagog region to Washington County; elsewhere rare or casual. *New Hampshire:* Resident in northern part, and on higher elevations (above 3000 feet) where not always uncommon; in winter moves into valleys and slightly south. *Vermont:* Uncommon resident in northern part and on higher mountains; casual elsewhere. *Massachusetts:* Casual visitor chiefly in winter. Records: Newtonville, one seen at very close range in early summer, about 1874, by C. J. Maynard and recorded by him.[1] Salem, October 25, 1878, bird taken by Lorenzo A. Smith, now in Peabody Academy at Salem, recorded by William Brewster;[2] Woburn (wrongly recorded at first as from Arlington Heights), October 16, 1889, adult male taken by F. B. Winship, and first in collection of J. R. Mann and later in that of William Brewster;[3] Shutesbury, October 12, 1913, bird taken by E. Colfax Johnson and formerly in the collection of Massachusetts Commissioners on Fisheries and Game (identified by E. H. F.), specimen now lost; Mr. Johnson in his letter giving date of capture says that in December 1913 he saw two more about four miles from the spot where the first one was taken. West Stockbridge, March 1, 1918, bird seen twice feeding on barberries.[4] Newbury, October 30, 1921, bird seen at Golf Links.[5] Gardner, December 24, 1921, two birds seen at very close range by H. E. Rolfe.[6] Middleton (Hathorne, Danvers), February 15, 1922, bird seen by Seaver Macdonald; "seen repeatedly for over a month."[7] Quincy (Wollaston), March, 1922, wintering bird seen by A. J. Parker.[8] This or another wintered in the same locality during the winter of 1920–21 (E. H. F.).

SEASON IN MASSACHUSETTS. — October to May.

HAUNTS AND HABITS. The Canada Jay is an inhabitant of the northern wilderness where it consorts with the mighty moose. Its home is in boreal coniferous forests and swamps where civilized man seldom penetrates. In these wilds it shows little fear of mankind. It is only a straggler in Massachusetts where it soon learns to be somewhat more cautious. Its principal characteristic is its boldness. Probably most people who have camped in the forests of Maine or New Brunswick have experienced the attentions of this jay. It follows the hunter, and the sound of a gun attracts rather than repels it, as it has learned to associate that sound with meat. It trails after the trapper, and robs traps of their bait and even eats small animals caught in them. Camp is no more than

---

[1] The Birds of Florida, 1878, p. 168.
[2] Minot's Land and Game Birds of New England, 2d ed., 1895, pp. 474–475.
[3] Ornithologist and Oölogist, Vol. XIV, 1889, p. 176; and Brewster, William: Auk, Vol. VII, 1890, **p. 91.**
[4] Kniffen, Miss Lottie: *in litt.*
[5] Perkins, Mrs. H. W.: *in litt.*
[6] Rolfe, H. E.: *in litt.*
[7] Macdonald, Seaver: *in litt.*
[8] Parker, Arthur J.: Auk, Vol. XXXIX, 1922, pp. 418–419.

established when the Moose Birds "rally round" eager to snatch any bit of meat or other edible substance. In the winter, especially, when life in the north is hard, these birds will steal anything apparently edible and eat it, if possible, or carry it off to hide in some crevice of the trees. By this method of storing food they are enabled to sustain young in early spring before vegetation and animal life have developed, and their nests are made and the eggs laid while snow still lies deep in the woods, and when night temperatures often run below zero. Small articles like pieces of soap, plug tobacco and matches left lying about soon disappear from the camp, and sometimes other articles which could never by any possibility be of use to the birds go in the same way; any meat or fish left exposed in the open is soon carried off piecemeal by these Camp Robbers, as they are called. The name "Whiskey Jack" is said to have been derived from the Indian name of "Wiss-ka-chon" or "Wis-ka-tjon" which was corrupted by the whites to "Whiskey John" and then to "Whiskey Jack," but Professor F. G. Speck states in his "Myths and Folk-Lore of the Tiniskaming Algonquin and Timagami Ojibwa"[1] that the trickster-transformer *Wiskedjak*, meat bird, is the personified Canada Jay or "Whiskey Jack"; also he says in his "Bird-Lore of the Northern Indians" that among the Indians north of the St. Lawrence the name *Wiskedjak*, from which the English name "Whiskey-Jack" has been derived, is the common term applied to the Canada Jay [and its various races] from Labrador to the Rockies.[2] The bird is unlike other Jays in its extreme familiarity and its lack of fear of mankind. Around the camps of lumbermen, trappers and hunters the Camp Robbers soon become astonishingly tame. They learn to go into tents and even into buildings; they have dropped into canoes for food, while the occupants were paddling, and in winter have been known to feed from the hand. Even in Massachusetts in the hunting season where danger menaces the bird on every hand, it is not shy. Mr. H. E. Rolfe who saw two in Gardner in 1921 says that they came toward him and picked up grasshoppers near by; others have had no difficulty in approaching the birds.

Canada Jays usually travel in pairs or small parties of from three or four to ten, but stragglers into Massachusetts from time to time have been seen alone, and a few such have been taken by collectors.

The species (*Perisoreus canadensis*) is believed to be resident over most of its range, but there is some evidence to the effect that most of its members in the extreme northern part of the range move southward each winter. Mr. L. Turner writing of the country about southern Ungava Bay, says of the Labrador race: "After August it is very abundant until the next May, and is then very scarce until the following September." Major Mark Robinson, writing to me from Algonquin National Park, Ontario, near the southern part of the range of the Canada Jay, has reported movements there for several years in succession, and has seen large numbers in the winter. The movements of the species, however, are more or less irregular. It was reported from Massachusetts several times in 1921 and 1922; after that no reliable reports were received until 1927. In its choice

---

[1] Geological Survey of Canada, Memoirs 71, Anthropological, No. 9, 1915, p. 1.
[2] Public Lectures by the University of Pennsylvania Faculty, Vol. VII (1919–20), 1921, p. 365.

of food the Canada Jay is even more omnivorous than the Blue Jay. It attacks almost anything that seems edible, and in winter it is said at times to feed on the lichens that caribou eat. Probably it is fully as destructive to the eggs and young of other birds as is the Blue Jay. It subsists largely on insects in summer, and later on berries. There is no reasonable limit to its appetite. Any bird that will consume quantities of soap probably will take almost anything eatable. Indians say that it will eat moccasins and fur caps, but its food habits have never been the subject of exhaustive investigation.

ECONOMIC STATUS. Probably the Canada Jay is not of great economic importance, but Mr. William H. Moore found nearly 1000 eggs of the forest tent caterpillar in the stomach of one bird and asserts that in autumn the species feeds largely on locusts and beetles, and it also kills mice. Mr. Moore's verdict is that the bird is "highly beneficial." [1]

SUBFAMILY **CORVINÆ.** CROWS.

Number of species in North America 9; in Massachusetts 3.

The bill in this subfamily is strong and large, convex above and below. The wings are long and pointed, and when folded are much longer than the tail. The legs and feet are stout and fitted for walking. The plumage is somber as a rule and the sexes are alike with little seasonal change of plumage. The birds of this group are nearly omnivorous and are more or less gregarious.

Córvus córax principális RIDGWAY. **Northern Raven.**

Plate 59.

DESCRIPTION. — Bill large, long, stout, convex above and below; nostrils large and hidden by bristly feather-tufts, often more than half as long as bill; wings long, pointed and ample; tail slightly rounded; legs and feet stout and fitted for walking; feathers of throat somewhat long, very glossy and pointed, loosely hung and at times separated like a straggling beard. *Adults (sexes alike):* Black above and below with more or less metallic luster, chiefly purple and violet, sometimes with some greenish gloss on wings. *Young in first winter plumage:* Like adults but tail, wings and wing-coverts browner and more worn. *Young in juvenal plumage:* Similar to adults but smaller, feathers somewhat looser in texture and more brownish-black, and feathers of throat not noticeably longer or more separated than the rest; some greenish gloss on wings.

MEASUREMENTS. — Length 21.40 to 26.50 in.; spread 46.00 to 56.00; folded wing 15.50 to 18.00; tail 9.06 to 10.95; bill 2.80 to 3.25; tarsus 2.80 to 2.98. Female smaller than male.

MOLTS. — Juvenal plumage follows mouse-brown natal down, and develops mostly while nestling is still in nest. First winter plumage acquired by postjuvenal molt of body feathers and wing-coverts but not wings or tail which are retained until postnuptial molt; first breeding plumage is merely worn winter plumage; adults have complete postnuptial autumnal molt (July to October); worn breeding birds sometimes become quite brown on wings and tail.

FIELD MARKS. — Much larger than Crow, otherwise similar, but bill relatively longer; size, however, is deceptive at a distance unless among Crows, when size tells; then Raven appears nearly twice as large as Crow but the two not often seen together; the bearded throat is not usually noticeable in the field;

---

[1] Ottawa Naturalist, Vol. XVIII, 1904, pp. 143–144.

its flight often is hawk-like with more soaring and sailing than is the case with the Crow. When tail is spread (in flight) the middle feathers are noticeably longer than the outer. "The tail of a Crow when spread or partly spread is evenly and but very slightly rounded" (C. W. Townsend).

VOICE. — A rather hoarse prolonged *crauk* or *cronk;* ordinary call a loud *craak-craak*, sometimes a deep, grunting *koerr-koerr;* a clucking sound, a bell-like sound, also a variety of notes when undisturbed, one a metallic sounding *klunk* (C. Bendire); a hoarse *auk cr-a-u-u-uk* or *butty-wau* (O. W. Knight); a hoarse rolling *cr-r-r-cruk* (F. M. Chapman).

BREEDING. — Usually in forests or along the sea-coast. *Nest:* Near top of thick-topped coniferous tree, on some broken tree-top or on shelf of high cliff, commonly well sheltered by projecting rock above; built of sticks, lined with seaweed, grass, etc., or with strips of bark, hair or wool, etc. *Eggs:* 5 to 7; 1.65 to 1.95 by 1.30 to 1.40 in.; ovate to elongate ovate; pale pea-green to greenish-olive, spotted with browns, drab and grayish or lavender; illustrated in Bendire's "Life Histories of North American Birds," Vol. II, Plate IV, Fig. 3. *Dates:* April 9 to 14, Maine and New Brunswick; through May, northern Canada. *Incubation:* Period 20 to 21 days (Burns); by both sexes. One brood yearly.

RANGE. — Boreal North America chiefly, from northwestern Alaska, Banks Land and northern Greenland, to western Washington, northern Mackenzie, Arkansas, Tennessee, Alabama and northwestern South Carolina. Breeds over most of its range.

DISTRIBUTION IN NEW ENGLAND. — *Maine:* Uncommon resident, mainly coastwise. *New Hampshire:* Accidental winter visitor. *Vermont:* Rare winter visitor. *Massachusetts:* Accidental visitor. Records (from Howe and Allen's "Birds of Massachusetts," 1901, p. 87): Tyngsborough, prior to 1859, one taken;[1] Springfield, autumn of 1859, one taken by C. W. Bennett;[2] Dedham, two taken about 1859, one by Julius M. Lathrop, the other by Dr. H. F. Aten;[3] Williamstown, two taken, one "some time since," *i.e.* prior to 1877, and one with no data (both in Williams College collection);[4] Northampton, prior to 1901, one taken by E. O. Damon;[5] C. J. Maynard records a "nestling" received from Tyngsborough.[6] This specimen went to the Brewster collection, and later to the Museum of Comparative Zoölogy; an examination of the skin shows that it was not a nestling but was passing from juvenal to first winter plumage. Mr. Maynard says that he received it from W. Perham who took it at Tyngsborough. *Connecticut:* Records: West Haven, December 28, 1889, bird, "from its size, flight, and the marked emargination of its primaries, believed by L. B. Bishop to be a Raven, flew by him, about 125 yards away and 100 feet from the ground. As it uttered no sound, its identity is doubtful."[7] South Manchester, September 18, 1890, bird taken (O. J. Hagenaw).[8] Norwalk, May 25, 1919, bird seen by Clifford H. Pangburn and Aretas S. Saunders.[9]

SEASON IN MASSACHUSETTS. — Probably permanent resident formerly; now seen only in autumn or winter (if at all).

HISTORY. The Raven is the largest bird of the order *Passeres.* Dr. Newton, the eminent author of the Dictionary of Birds, regards it as "probably the most highly developed of all birds." It seems sad that such a bird, unique in this great group for size,

---

[1] Samuels [E. A.]: "Mass. Secy's Rep. Agric. 1859, p. 143" (Howe and Allen). This bird was presented by David and Daniel Parham (sic) and sent by them to the state collection at the State House. The record was published in the Seventh Annual Report of the Secretary of the Massachusetts Board of Agriculture for 1859 (published in 1860) and the bird is now in the state collection at the Massachusetts Agricultural College at Amherst.

[2] Allen, J. A.: Proceedings Essex Institute, Vol. IV, 1864, p. 75.

[3] Wakefield, J. R.: Birds of Dedham, 1891, p. 72.

[4] Tenney, Sanborn: American Naturalist, Vol. XI, 1877, p. 243; and Brewster, William: Auk, Vol. 1, 1884, p. 10.

[5] Morris, Robert O.: Birds of Springfield, 1901, p. 26.

[6] Birds of Eastern North America, 1881, p. 155.

[7] Sage, Bishop and Bliss: Birds of Connecticut, 1913, p. 107.

[8] Ornithologist and Oölogist, Vol. XV, 1890, p. 156.

[9] Auk, Vol. XXXVI, 1919, p. 572.

PLATE 59

PLATE 59

NORTHERN RAVEN
Page 387

Adult

FISH CROW
Page 402

Adult

CROW
Page 392

Adult

All about one-fourth scale.

Louis Agassiz Fuertes

power and sagacity should be doomed to disappear from the Commonwealth first established in the northern United States, but the bird is now vanishing if not already gone.

The Raven is a gargantuan Crow. It looks like a gigantic caricature of the Crow, with the Crow's features accentuated — a great, dour, somber, savage bird of evil repute. Dawson says that it "has been until lately, and from time immemorial, one of the most familiar objects within the ken of man. The Aryan herdsman complained to his fellows of the bird's depredations, while the Dorian fishermen of a later day regaled each other with stories of his sagacity, already centuries old." Our Raven is merely a geographical race of the ancient Raven of the Old World, and that bird of sinister appearance was regarded as a mysterious and semi-sacred being by peoples of the long ago. His ominous croakings were believed to be prophetic and to portend evil, while his almost preternatural sagacity was regarded either as an attribute of the divine or as derived directly from the Evil One. Various superstitions centered about his personality, and to-day some of the country people within the bird's range in North America still believe that its presence portends misfortune.

When the Pilgrim Fathers settled at Plymouth, the Raven must have been a common bird. William Wood writing in 1634 spoke of Ravens and Crows, and Josselyn (1674) asserted that the Raven was numerous then. But the bird soon became known as a killer of sickly sheep and new-born lambs, and the settlers waged a relentless warfare upon it, so that eventually it disappeared as a breeding bird from southern New England. It is said to have bred formerly on an inaccessible cliff on the side of Ragged Mountain in the town of Adams, Massachusetts, still called the "Raven Rocks" by farmers in the vicinity, and there are two birds in the Williams College Museum said to have been taken in Williamstown, and while the label of one says 1877, there is no record of the date of the other. Therefore, we have no absolute proof that the species ever bred within the limits of Massachusetts, though the young bird taken in Tyngsboro, Massachusetts, may have been reared there. So far as I am aware there is no record of a specimen taken in Massachusetts since the present century came in. Within the last eight years I have received letters from three different persons, each of whom believed that he had seen a Raven in winter within the state, but in each case the circumstances of the observation were such that I prefer not to record any of them, though it is quite possible that in one or more cases the belief was well founded. As the Raven still breeds no farther away than the coast of Maine, the probability is that other stragglers will be observed in Massachusetts, but it is a disappearing species.

HAUNTS AND HABITS. "When the thick, white fog hangs like a pall over the Magdalen Islands quite obscuring the surrounding water and causing the steep, conical, grass-covered hills near at hand to look like dim, greenish clouds suspended in mid air; when nothing is to be heard save the monotonous, never-ceasing sound of waves beating at the base of the high cliffs, and the east wind coming fresh from the ice-bergs which float in the mighty ocean not far away, is as chilly as a breath from the tomb; when all objects appear so distorted and unreal in the misty light, that one seems transported to another world; then a harsh croak is heard sounding out with such sudden distinctness as to be startling.

"One who is unaccustomed to the locality gazes about in amazement for there is not a living thing in sight, and the cry was so weird and coincided so perfectly with the gloomy surroundings as to suggest that it was of supernatural origin. Again the uncouth note is repeated but nearer, harsher and more real, and then the eye guided by the sound sees a black shape gliding through the mist. Then another appears and still another, followed by half a dozen more, while the air is filled with dismal croakings. One can by this time discern that the mysterious sounds are produced by Ravens which are returning from a predatory excursion to some neighboring island, for these black pirates take advantage of the obscuring fog in order to rob the nests of various sea-birds which breed near." So writes that ornithologist of great field experience, Mr. C. J. Maynard.[1] The Raven is an inhabitant of great forests and mighty cliffs. Its rugged form and hoarse, weird cries belong to the wilderness, far from the works of man, but the bird is so quick to take advantage of its opportunities, that where not molested it is even more bold than the Crow. It comes about the dwellings of Eskimos and Indians for food, and has even fed with domestic fowls near the white man's dwelling. It is peculiarly fitted, because of its size, strength, cunning and endurance, to survive where weaker birds cannot live. In case of need it is not in the least fastidious about its food. My friend, Capt. Donald Mac-Millan, tells me that it is the only bird, except perhaps the Snowy Owl, that is known to live through the long, dark winter in Northern Greenland, where if other food fails it can subsist on the ordure of the Eskimo dogs. Kumlien also found it resident at Cumberland Gulf on the west coast of Davis Strait. The Raven seems to take particular delight in teasing dogs, and is said sometimes to pick up stones or sticks and drop them on the unsuspecting canines. Major Bendire relates a story told by Mr. J. B. Bretherton showing how Ravens outwitted a dog. An Alaskan canine was earnestly endeavoring to consume a bone, when two Ravens alighted near him and sidled up toward his head until barely out of his reach, giving loud cries. Had the dog dropped the bone to catch one of the birds, perhaps the other might have seized the prize but the beast was not to be tricked in that way. Then a third Raven alighted on a fence and surveyed the situation. This bird soon flew down behind the dog, sneaked up and tweaked his tail so savagely that the brute turned to snap at the enemy in his rear. This gave one of the birds an opportunity to snatch the bone and make off. Mr. Joseph Mailliard of the California Academy of Sciences, tells of a similar strategy by means of which a Raven purloined a bone from a dog at Sitka, Alaska.[2]

Kumlien says that Ravens show great intelligence in capturing young seals. He saw one drop into the seal's hole in the ice thus cutting off its only means of escape. Then the second "attacked and brained the helpless victim." Some of these birds learn to steal the trapper's bait, but occasionally an incautious bird is trapped in the attempt.[3]

[1] Birds of Eastern North America, 1896, p. 452.

[2] The Gull, Monthly Bulletin of the Audubon Society of the Pacific, Vol. IX, No. 1, March, 1927.

[3] Nelson, E. W.: Report on the Natural History Collections made in Alaska (1877–81), 1887, p. 167.

There are many tales of the cunning of European Ravens. My only opportunities to watch the habits of the Northern Raven were on Vancouver Island off the Pacific coast and on the rocky forested islands and shores of Maine. In both regions the bird was extremely cautious. Along the Maine coast it usually nests in trees, while from Grand Manan northward it is far more likely to be found breeding on cliffs along the shore. Were it not for its strange notes this bird might be mistaken for a Crow, for it keeps at a distance from the observer. When seen with Crows it seems about twice as large as the ordinary Crow. Occasionally, however, an unusually large Crow appears among its companions and might be mistaken for a Raven.

The Raven has a habit of sailing and soaring, at times, high in the air, which I have never observed in the Crow. It seems to delight in sailing thus when a storm is breaking, and to enjoy the fury of the elements while it calmly breasts the gale. Nuttall asserts that the Raven has been seen in the midst of a thunder-storm with the electric fluid streaming from the end of his bill — a statement which may be doubted by the skeptic. Ordinarily its flight, though heavy, does not differ greatly from that of the more common Crow.

The Raven is said to feed its young largely by regurgitation, in the manner of the dove. It is extremely devoted to its callow offspring, and sometimes will risk its life in protecting them. It is said to attack even the eagle in their defense. The parents remain with their young throughout the entire summer and feed them for a long time after their charges have mastered the art of flight.

The Raven is indiscriminately voracious. Its food consists of anything edible, alive or dead, which it can catch, kill, disable or pick up; carrion, offal, garbage, filth, birds, mammals, reptiles, fishes; the lower forms of life found along the sea-shore, and particularly shell-fish, the shells of which it breaks by carrying them to a height and dropping them on rocks. It takes many insects and worms. It destroys many eggs and young of the larger birds. The large gulls band together to attack it when it encroaches on their breeding-grounds, but when these birds are driven from their nests by human intruders, Ravens are quick to take advantage of the opportunity to steal many eggs and hide them away for future food. I once visited an island off the Maine coast on which was a heronry of Great Blue Herons and Night Herons. Here the bones of many young Night Herons lay on the ground. As no Crows were seen on the island and no signs of predatory mammals, my companions attributed this destruction to a pair of Ravens which had young there. Ravens have been known to depopulate the nests in a heronry and compel the herons to seek quarters elsewhere. Regarding the vegetal food of the Raven — it can subsist on many kinds of fruit and grain, but it seems to prefer animal food.

ECONOMIC STATUS. In a farming community the Raven does much good by killing rats, mice and insect pests, and wherever unmolested it becomes a useful scavenger. On the other hand it is so destructive to young lambs and young chickens that the hand of every farmer and sheepman is against it. It is anathema to the gunner, for it eats rabbits and the eggs and young of ducks and other game birds. Though no thorough investigation of its food has been made in this country, it is regarded generally as inimical to man's interests.

Corvus brachyrhýnchos brachyrhynchos BREHM. Crow.

Plate 59.

DESCRIPTION. — Similar to Raven, but much smaller and without separated, long, pointed feathers on throat; feathers of back have dull tips which when held between eye and light give the back a slightly *scaled* appearance, not seen in the Fish Crow. *Adults (sexes alike):* Black from end of bill to tip of tail and claws, with much metallic gloss of violet on body; wings glossed with bluish-violet and greenish-blue; iris brown. *Young in first winter plumage:* Usually about as adults but in some individuals the gloss of upper plumage less distinct and averaging greener; also duller below. *Young in juvenal plumage:* Dull brownish or grayish-black above; duller below; wings and tail black with violet and greenish reflections; bill and feet grayish or grayish-black; iris bluish.

MEASUREMENTS. — Length 17.00 to 21.00 in.; spread 33.00 to 39.70; folded wing 10.80 to 13.00; tail 6.50 to 8.00; bill 1.80 to 2.60; tarsus 2.00 to 2.58. Weight about 1 lb. 4 oz. (B. H. Warren); very variable. Female averages somewhat smaller than male.

MOLTS. — Juvenal plumage, acquired by complete molt of grayish-brown nestling down, becomes fully developed soon after flight stage; first winter plumage produced by partial postjuvenal molt (July to September); juvenal wings (except wing-coverts) and tail retained; with full development of this plumage young become similar to adults; first nuptial plumage is merely worn first winter plumage and is virtually as adult, though the young may require another year to attain highest plumage with finer more purplish luster; adults have but one (complete) molt (late June to autumn).

FIELD MARKS. — Unnecessary. The Crow is known to everyone who goes into the field, but cannot be distinguished at sight from other forms of the species or the Fish Crow.

VOICE. — The so-called *caw* and a great variety of other notes, some musical (which see under Haunts and Habits); *Young:* a hoarse *car.*

BREEDING. — Usually, but not invariably, in woods. *Nest:* In deciduous or coniferous tree, rarely in bush where no trees grow; from 6 to 60 feet from ground; large, built of strong sticks and lined with shreds of grapevine or strips of cedar bark, bits of squash vine, fine roots, dry grass, seaweed, leaves, moss, straw, wool, hair, rags or some similar material, rough and straggly outwardly but well made and warmly lined. *Eggs:* 3 to 8, very rarely 9, usually 3 to 5 (in cases where the larger numbers are found they are supposed to have been produced by two females); 1.42 to 2.06 by 1.02 to 1.40 in.; commonly ovate, but very variable in shape, pale bluish-green to olive-green or olive-buff, very rarely pink or even white, rarely unmarked, but usually with irregularly shaped blotches of various browns, and shades of gray variously distributed, sometimes covered with small spots; figured in Bendire's "Life Histories of North American Birds," Vol. II, Plate IV, Figs. 8 to 12 and Plate V, Figs. 21, 22. *Dates:* Mid-March, South Carolina; March 27, District of Columbia; April 11, Pennsylvania; April 5 to June 13, Massachusetts; April 20 to May 25 (June 15), Maine. *Incubation:* Period variously given as from 15 to 18 days, probably by both sexes. One brood yearly; two are reared in South Carolina (A. T. Wayne).

RANGE. — Central and eastern temperate North America chiefly. Breeds from southwestern Mackenzie, southern Keewatin (south of Cape Eskimo), northern Ontario, southern Quebec and Newfoundland south to north central Texas and the Gulf coast east of Texas; (the southern crow has been separated as a subspecies and occupies the southeastern states except most of Florida, north to Maryland and southern Illinois); west to central Alberta, Minnesota, Nebraska, Kansas, central Oklahoma and northwestern Texas; in winter from the northern tier of states within its range in the United States, also southern Ontario and southern Quebec southward. Other races extend the range of the species.

Photograph by Cordelia J. Stanwood

FIG. 64. — FLEDGLING BLUE JAY
Page 375

Photograph by Miss Stanwood

FIG. 65. — YOUNG CROWS IN JUVENAL PLUMAGE
Page 392

DISTRIBUTION IN NEW ENGLAND. — Common migrant and permanent resident; leaves higher elevations in winter; only casual then in extreme northern parts of northern New England; usually most abundant in winter near sea-coast.

SEASON IN MASSACHUSETTS. — Permanent resident, except on higher elevations in western part; most common from April to November.

HAUNTS AND HABITS. The Crow "knows a good thing when he sees it." He seeks and finds for his home a land of plenty. Arctic regions with their "icy mountains" are not for him; he leaves them to the Raven, and inhabits temperate climes and fertile lands where the fruits of the earth are spread before him. He seeks the bounty of the fields. On September 23, 1913, while sitting on a moss-grown ledge near the brow of a precipitous side-hill just east of the village of Stowe, Vermont, I viewed a splendid panorama of mountain, valley and sky. Below me lay the village, nestling amid its environment of autumnal foliage like a gem in its setting or a bird on her nest. The neat well painted houses and well kept yards, the tall white church spire pointing toward the sky and the American flag flying from its staff on the cupola of the public hall typified much that is best in American village life. The eye roved to wide meadows stretching down the valley, clothed in plush-like green. There the winding course of the stream was marked by a double border of green shrubbery, with here and there a row of willows, and some scattering elms and maples glowing in the sunlight with the rich primal colors of the season. Then the eye, lifting, passed on over bordering fields to upland pastures with their soft and changing tints, interspersed with groups and groves of trees — the whole a great park laid out as if by the hand of a master. Beyond the pastures on either hand rose the hills, and in the background towered mighty Mount Mansfield, the giant of them all, its slopes darkened and blued by distance. Over the landscape flamed the red and gold of autumn, toned and darkened here and there by drifting shadows, and above all arched the blue dome with its fleecy clouds. The warmth and peace of summer brooded gently over all. Crows cawed in the valley, where substantial farm-houses and well filled barns attested the prosperity of the people. This is indeed a country of the blest. Such are the favorite haunts of the Crow in New England. Such fertile valleys are chosen by the wise old birds when in March they begin to push northward, and in autumn many Crows from the hills come down to them, some remaining all winter in mild seasons or as long as they can find food.

Unfortunately for the Crow he has a bad reputation, and it must be admitted that there is some reason for the low regard in which he is held among men. First he is black, the color of evil; then, he knows too much; his judgment of the range of a gun is too nearly correct. If Crows could be shot oftener they would be more popular. Henry Ward Beecher once remarked that if men wore feathers and wings a very few of them would be clever enough to be Crows. Also, as Dr. N. A. Cobb says, "The Crow rises too early." We have to get up very early in the morning to get ahead of the Crow. Most of us rarely see the sun rise, and while the sluggards still slumber, the early Crow is up to some abominable mischief in the back yard. It irritates us to have this disreputable fowl take such a mean advantage of us, especially as we know that it would not have happened had we been up and about, as we know we should have been. Then, according to human standards, the Crow is a thief and a robber. He steals eggs, chickens, corn; he robs song birds of their eggs and young, and so he is vilified and anathematized, pursued and destroyed, at every opportunity; but all to little purpose, for we may well believe that there are more Crows in the country now than there were when the Pilgrims landed on Plymouth Rock. To-day then, the Crow is the great American bird. Everybody knows him. How many people have ever seen the American Eagle except on the silver dollar? But who has not seen the Crow? If a person knows only four birds, one of them will be the Crow. The bird is well known because he is large, black, ubiquitous and noisy. He is well worth knowing. Each Crow is a character. There is more difference in Crows than appears as they fly over.

Mr. John A. Bryant of Kansas City, Missouri, believes that at least one crow knows a gun at sight. Mr. Bryant was able with a fishing-rod case in his hand to walk up under the tree in which this Crow sat; but when he undertook to approach the same bird with a gun in that hand he was unable to get within gunshot.[1] It would be unsafe, however, to infer too much from a single experiment of this kind.

Some individual Crows are superior in vocal powers, or in the imitative faculty, to most of their race. The Crow is not generally regarded as a song bird; although as a member of the order *Oscines* it is provided with the syrinx of a singer, it seems to lack a tuneful voice; yet some Crows, if not all, are capable of producing unusual, tuneful or pleasing sounds. As an example of the unusual let me refer to an individual that I heard early one morning on Cape Cod repeating for over an hour syllables like *clockity-clock, clockity-clock;* while as showing the musical attainments of the species mention may be made of a Crow that I saw on the banks of the Musketaquid, August 10, 1906, which uttered a series of exceedingly melodious, soft, cooing notes unlike any others within my experience. In the same locality on July 14 a young Crow remarked very plainly *aaaou, cou, cou, cou, aaaou, coucoo*. On October 20, 1903, I heard and saw a Crow give an excellent imitation of the whine of a dog. The bird then flew to another tree where it was joined by three more; but soon one saw me and all moved to a tree about a hundred yards from my position, where one of them repeated the same sound eight times in succession. I have heard from Crows a varied assortment of notes, some of which apparently were imitations, such as the cry of a child, the squawk of a hen, or the crow of a young rooster. The cooing notes mentioned above were similar to sounds uttered by the male in courtship. At that season, also, the male has a peculiar cry which may be an attempt at song and has been represented by the syllables *hollow-ollo-ollo*. The male pursues the female through the air in swift flight, and both fly erratically, rising abruptly, plunging downward, and at times turning almost complete somersaults as they go. The male now becomes very excitable. His behavior at this interesting period includes spreading the

---

[1] Burns, Frank L.: The American Crow, Bulletin No. 5, Wilson Ornithological Chapter of the Agassiz Association, 1895, p. 7.

tail, drooping the wings, strutting with head held high, and neck curved like that of a prancing horse. When the female responds to his advances, there is much lover-like contact of bills and more cooing. Often three Crows take part in this exercise. Mrs. Arthur Caswell of Athol, Massachusetts, informed me that three Crows near her home came to the branches of a large oak tree. First one and then another held its head down to have its feathers dressed by the others, and then they presented one another with little sticks, and touched their beaks together. Sometimes one bird apparently performs for the benefit of two others, sitting on a near-by perch while he bows, and sways back and forth on the limb; the others seem to be interested observers.

The eternal triangle seems to be common among Crows; the old saying that "two is company and three is a crowd" does not apply to them. I have noticed that sometimes when an incubating Crow is flushed from her nest, two other Crows appear and join in the outcry that she raises. I had always supposed that the third Crow was a male from some other nest, but in April, 1919, three Crows were seen indulging in courtship ceremonies in the Back Bay section of Boston and for a week or two all three were seen carrying sticks about, before they settled on a location for their nest; later they began to build in a tree on the mall on Commonwealth Avenue. Mr. Harry V. Long and others who saw them asserted that two of them assisted in building the nest, while the other kept watch. While the two were at work pecking tar or some similar substance from a roof, the other mounted guard on the chimney. The material taken from the roof was plastered on the nest by the other two who were often seen at the same time either in the nest or on it, engaged in building or lining it, while the other watched the proceeding from a branch above. When the two departed the third descended to the nest and arranged things to its own satisfaction. Finally only one of the Crows at a time was seen to be sitting upon the nest while the others "played around but were not so much in evidence." No one has been able to determine whether this indicated either polygamy or polyandry. The third Crow was a very interested spectator and a close companion of the other two. This companionship of three Crows about a nest has been noted by several observers, but its import remains to be determined. Mr. Frank Novak informs me that three Crows in Fairfield, Connecticut were seen feeding the young in one nest. Mr. Frank A. Burns records a case where two sets of eggs were found in the same nest. One set hatched in four days after the eggs were discovered and the other in seven. This nest was found by Mr. Stephen J. Adams in Cornish, Maine, and contained seven eggs. In another case where eight eggs were found, four of them were darker, larger and farther advanced in incubation than the other four.[1] Probably such cases are rare, and their causes are problematical. It seems remarkable that a bird so wary and so much persecuted by man as the Crow should choose a spot in the most densely populated residential part of the city of Boston to build its nest. Nevertheless there is good ground near by for foraging. The Charles River flows near on one side, and not far away there is the open land of the Public Gardens and the Common. "English" Sparrows and street pigeons

---

[1] Bulletin No. 5, Wilson Ornithological Chapter of the Agassiz Association, 1895, pp. 22, 23.

nest in the region in considerable numbers, and their eggs and young furnish the Crows an abundant supply of animal food during the spring and early summer. Crows soon learn where they are safe, and in the city no shooting is allowed. Several other instances where Crows have bred in cities are on record. When I first went to Puget Sound, Crows were never molested by the settlers, and they were more tame than street sparrows. They often alighted on heads of hogs engaged in rooting out clams; they tried, sometimes with success, to snatch a clam unearthed by the beasts, and were even seen (in the hope of securing a share) to alight occasionally on the back of a "klootchman" or squaw engaged in digging clams.

Crows take the best of care of their young and defend them valiantly against their enemies. One day while I was climbing to a Crow's nest the old birds clamoring overhead seemed to communicate their alarm to the young which, just as I reached the nest, flew out as one bird. They flew well and far, disappearing in the distant woods and thickets, but evidently all the time nearing the ground. My companions and myself started in pursuit, but we never found those youngsters. After we had hunted awhile, we heard one calling behind us. Going back we found that it was in the nest. Believing that it was unable to fly up there from the ground, we concluded that the parents must have carried it there, and we decided to leave it to their care. In some cases the young, when nearly fledged, climb out of the nest and perch on branches during the day. The parents attend them, guard them and feed them for a long time after they are fully fledged. After the young have left the nest, they keep their parents exceedingly busy for some time, as the condition of the stomach of a young Crow seems to approximate that of a bottomless pit. They require to be fed almost constantly. Two of my assistants once kept some young Crows in confinement which required at least half their own weight of food daily, and would eat even more if they could get it.

Young Crows make exceedingly interesting pets. In the brief intervals between "feeds" the juvenile Crow is like a child with nothing to do, and it is extremely liable to get into mischief. As soon as it has mastered the intricacies of flight, it is likely to seize and carry off many small articles, such as small tools, trinkets and jewelry, and hide them in places where they are seldom seen again by human eyes. If a young bird is watched, however, it may be caught in the act of recovering its treasures and hiding them elsewhere. I once watched one that buried a bright colored *Calosoma* beetle which he afterward exhumed and interred again in another place. Many of my correspondents have described mischievous habits of their Crow pets. Among others was the tale of a country grocer who, making his rounds, was surprised to find every paper package in his wagon torn open and all the eggs broken. As this occurred repeatedly at a particular place, he watched, and learned that as soon as his back was turned two tame Crows made free with the contents of the wagon. Another young Crow delighted in pilfering its master's pipes and hiding them in the woodpile. One day in want of a better occupation this bird pulled up the young plants in the garden beds and laid them all out carefully along the rows in excellent order. Another enjoyed backing a small child up against a fence while pecking at the buttons on its shoes; still another delighted to peck at the bare legs of children. One seemed to think it a great joke to wait at a gap in a fence until a little fox terrier came through the opening, when the expectant *Corvus* pecked the frisky pup strongly on the nose, and at once flapped up to the top of a grape arbor, dancing about as if in great ecstasy at the success of the joke. It followed its master when he was at work in the garden, picked up all the worms that were unearthed, dug a hole and buried them, but seemed not to understand why they were not there when he returned to the hole with more worms. One young pet Crow was extremely fond of eggs, and soon learned that when a hen cackled she was advertising her wares; so as fast as the eggs were laid, they were wafted away by the sable bird.

The imitative powers of pet Crows often lead them to attempt to reproduce the sound of the human voice. Some become expert enough to pronounce quite plainly a few words. One learned to call the cows, another the cat; short words such as "Fred," "father" and "mother"; such phrases as "come on Jack," "hello Joe," "Now you've done it" and "Ah go on" are pronounced easily. One imitated the bark of a dog, while another learned to laugh like a man and to simulate the clucking of a rooster when calling the members of his harem to a treat. When the hens came running at his call he seemed to enjoy it. Mr. James Knight, of Amesbury, Massachusetts, had a Crow that became quite proficient in the use of English. "Brother Tom" says Mr. Knight "sometimes overslept; when this happened our honored sire, standing beneath the window, would shout most emphatically *Tom get up*." The Crow soon learned to wake Thomas very early in the morning, as well as everyone else in the house, by shouting the well-known call with great emphasis. One day the boys had a big bonfire in the field. The Crow watched the exciting scene with great interest and soon joined in the hurrahs of his boyish companions. After that whenever the bird saw a cloud of smoke arising from the chimney, he saluted it with rousing cheers. Mr. Adelbert Temple of Hopkinton, Massachusetts, had a Crow that made friends with all its human companions, except a boy who had clipped its wings. After that it would have nothing to do with that boy. Mr. Temple says that if anyone threw water at the bird, it made sounds in simulation of an angry man. One day in winter Mr. Temple's son took the bird with him while he went fishing. The Crow watched the boy bait his hook and let it down through the hole in the ice; then as soon as the boy's back was turned, it took hold of the flag attached to the tilt as a signal and sprung the tilt, thus setting up the signal for a fish hooked; the bird continued to go from one tilt to another and spring it and then "laugh." The boy finally had to take the little rascal home. Wild Crows sometimes exhibit a faculty for imitation. Some of them learn to fly down and snatch fish and other creatures from the water as sea gulls do. And like gulls they carry shellfish up in the air and drop them on rocks or hard ground to break the shells.

I recall a single instance where a pair of Crows built their nest like those of gulls on the ground on the surface of a high island with precipitous sides. I found this nest and destroyed the young birds, as they were fed largely on the eggs and young of the sea

birds nesting on the island. The parents were too wary to come within gunshot. This island lies near the north end of Vancouver Island at the entrance of the Straits of Fuca.*
There were no trees or shrubs upon it and as the nearest island bearing trees was a mile away the Crows by nesting here gained a mile or more on other black marauders who came from other islands, whenever the sea birds were driven from their nests. Crows often nest near a heronry and ravage it when the owners of the nests are away.

Crows are helpful to those of their own kind but their altruism usually stops there. Mr. Freeman B. Currier tells me that one day a Crow in some way fell into the Merrimac River, off Newburyport, and its feathers having become soaked, it could not rise. Soon, however, the cries of the unfortunate bird brought assistance. A flock gathered, and after much cawing one bird flapped down to the surface, seized the half-submerged one in its claws, and flew toward shore, dragging the unfortunate along. As the strength of the first rescuer failed, another seized the bedraggled victim and so, one after another, they seized and dragged or carried shoreward their drowning comrade until it reached the land. There, after it had spread out its soaked pinions in the sun and had dried them, all flew away to the woods.

Though Crows frequently bathe in shallow water, they do so by wading in from the shore. They rarely attempt to alight upon the water or to swim unless forced to do so. The following incident shows, nevertheless, that there may be an occasional exception to the rule. In a recent letter Mr. R. M. Chase of Ithaca, New York, tells me as follows of an experience while duck shooting:

"We had arrived at the blind in the early morning and had watched the Crows from a near-by roost flying over the blind to the western shore of the lake. We remained in the blind all day without a shot at those which came within range. While looking out over the water for some bird which might prove a suitable target our attention was attracted to a bird flying very low over the surface and straight towards us. We were all certain it was a Crow until it suddenly stiffened its wings and dropped into the lake! About ten seconds elapsed before it took flight again and continued on its course coming directly for our blind as before. During the time the bird was in the water I did not take my eyes from it. As it drew nearer we all prepared to shoot, and not until it had flown directly over the stools and around one side of the blind did we realize that it was really a Crow and not a Scoter or a Cormorant or any of the many other things we had thought when we saw it drop into the water."

If a Crow badly wounded or disabled is found by his comrades, a company of his kind collects quickly and gathers overhead, apparently lamenting his fate. If there are many Crows in the neighborhood or if it is winter and a large flock is near, the whole concourse gathers above the stricken one with frightful clamor. Similar lamentations occur at times over a recent death of one of their number. When mobbing a fox, a hawk, an owl or an eagle they are exceedingly noisy, and their intermittent outbreaks of cawing over an owl sometimes last all day. The Horned Owl attacks them in the night, and they seem to

---

* The species in this case probably was the Northwest Crow (*Corvus caurinus*).

know that this bird is their greatest enemy, and to take every opportunity to retaliate if they find one dozing in daylight. There are tales of Crow trials followed by the execution of the condemned one. There may be a grain of truth in these relations. However that may be, there is at least one authentic account of the killing of a Crow by his companions. My good friend, Dr. T. Gilbert Pearson, president of the National Association of Audubon Societies, writes as follows regarding the incident:

"Especially do I recall one evening when, as I watched them coming to roost, I became conscious of an unusual commotion among a flock of eight. One evidently was in great disfavor with the others, for, with angry and excited cawings, they were striking at him in a most unfriendly manner. The strength of the persecuted bird was all but spent when I first sighted them, and when, perhaps two minutes later, the fleeing one sustained a particularly vicious onslaught, it began to fall. It did not descend gradually, like a bird injured while on the wing, but plunged downward like a falling rock a hundred feet or more into the top of a large pine-tree, and, bounding from limb to limb, struck the ground but a few yards from me. When I picked it up I found it to be quite dead."

It is a well-known fact that Crows when feeding on the ground usually, if not always, are protected by a sentinel posted in some elevated position near by. Mr. Bryant, in the bulletin quoted above, tells of leaving a string of fish submerged in the water of a creek and when he returned to them he found a Crow in a tree on the bank which gave warning to three more that, hidden under the bank, had devoured his fish.

In October before the frosts of autumn begin to form thin skims of ice around the shores of lakes in the northern woods, the Crows, which have been drifting down from the highlands into the valleys, form into great migrating flocks, not in any regular formation though occasionally columns or ring-shaped flocks are seen. More often the birds fly southward in irregular masses, usually in daylight, as they rarely move about at night. These great flocks continue to pour southward in November, leaving behind in New England only a remnant of the vast summer Crow population. In southern New England, however, many Crows remain through mild winters wherever food is plentiful. A piggery with its daily supply of garbage attracts a multitude. A corn-field from which not all the grain has been removed, the salt-marshes along the sea-coast, a crop of beechnuts or any large space of ground bare of snow will attract many winter Crows. At night these Crows assemble, sometimes from a distance of forty miles around, to a common roosting place. In New England, white pine groves are favorites for Crow roosts. Farther south deciduous trees may be chosen. In one of the New England roosts as many as 50,000 to 100,000 (estimated) Crows have gathered at night. In the Middle States the numbers of birds assembled in a roost is much larger, and the estimates reach hundreds of thousands. I have witnessed the assemblage of Crows in two large Crow roosts in Massachusetts, but those interested should read the account given by my friend, Samuel S. Rhoades, contributed to the American Naturalist in 1886, to get an adequate idea of the character of the great roosts of the Middle States and the numbers of their occupants. In recent years many Crow roosts have been broken up by gunners and the birds composing them have scattered to roost in smaller colonies from which persecution continually drives them; nevertheless some of the larger roosts still remain to be reckoned as among the most wonderful assemblies of birds to be seen now on the continent of North America. Occasionally during severe winters considerable numbers of Crows are found dead in the woods. Sometimes they are the victims of a disease resembling roup, but possibly in some cases some are starved and frozen — victims of strong attachment for their winter home. In hard winters only a lone Crow or none at all will be seen in localities where hundreds appear in milder seasons. Sometimes a single Crow in autumn, winter or early spring will join a flock of Starlings or grackles, flying and feeding amicably with them, as if desirous of their company or else finding safety in numbers. Crows swallow the hard parts of their food, and, after digestion has had its way, eject through the mouth such substances as hard seeds, fur, bones and teeth in the form of pellets, such as are regurgitated by birds of prey.

The food of the Crow consists of almost anything edible alive or dead which it can seize in bill or claws — all animals of every kind that it can catch and kill except some of the very small ones such as the smaller insects. Occasionally a Crow catches a full-grown, adult bird of some smaller species, but usually in such cases its victim is sickly or partially disabled. Mr. A. W. Beckford of Danvers, Massachusetts, tells of a Crow that chased a Starling in winter, following the bird in the open and chasing it around buildings. When at last the Starling, losing ground, plunged under some cakes of ice, the Crow found it, killed and ate it on the spot. Birds' eggs and young birds, mammals, reptiles, fishes, batrachians, insects, crustaceans, worms, etc., all pay tribute to the Crow. Dead animals of all sizes from the ox and the horse down furnish food for the sable bird. The greatest injury done directly to man through the Crow's choice of animal food consists in its destructiveness to poultry and their eggs and to young lambs.

Its vegetal food is confined largely to seeds, nuts, acorns, grains and fruit (both wild and cultivated) of nearly all native kinds. Corn is the principal vegetal food of the Crow. In farming regions it formed 38.42 per cent of all the food found in the stomachs of 1,340 adult Crows, according to the experts of the Biological Survey. A very full account of the food of the Crow may be found in Bulletin No. 6 of the Division of Ornithology and Mammalogy of the United States Department of Agriculture,[1] and in Bulletin No. 621 of the Biological Survey.[2] Considerable injury is done at times to fruit and vegetables, particularly to apples, muskmelons and watermelons.

Unfortunately there are many small insect pests of the farm that the Crow does not eat. It confines its insect diet chiefly to the larger species. Thus it is very useful at times, especially when numbers of certain caterpillars or grasshoppers attack crops or trees. Ordinarily its principal service is rendered in the destruction of grasshoppers, locusts and May beetles and their larvæ, the white grub. During the spring of 1865 Professor Samuel Aughey examined a number of Crow's stomachs during the locust in-

[1] Barrows, W. B., and Schwarz, E. A.: The Common Crow of the United States, 1895, pp. 23–87.
[2] Kalmbach, E. R.: The Crow and Its Relation to Man, 1918, pp. 9–71.

vasion in Nebraska and found them all partly filled with locusts.[1] Dr. N. A. Cobb gives some figures, worked out carefully by him, forming a very conservative estimate of the number of grasshoppers eaten by Crows in the Moss Vale district, New South Wales, Australia, during one month in 1894. The common crow of Australia is much like that of North America and has similar habits. During a great irruption of grasshoppers, enormous numbers of Crows gathered to feed upon them, and by stomach examinations Dr. Cobb found that 100 grasshoppers was about the average number contained in each stomach. He estimated that there were 250,000 Crows feeding in the district, and that in a month they consumed 750,000,000 grasshoppers, thus saving to the farmers over 2,000 tons of grass and other fodder.[2]

ECONOMIC STATUS. Ornithologists do not agree regarding the economic status of the Crow. He has many partisans and many opponents. Numerous controversies have arisen over the bird, but the general concensus of opinion seems to be that the Crow is at least a necessary evil. Its habits of eating eggs and young of other birds should not count too heavily against it, as the birds thus molested usually have an opportunity to raise young later in the season, when the young Crows have been reared, and natural enemies of birds are necessary to keep their numbers within bounds. Among the smaller birds such species as the Robin, Blue Jay and Bronzed Grackle suffer most. The reduction of the first brood of Robins may be a blessing to the grower of small fruits; Jays and grackles are themselves destroyers of the eggs and young of smaller birds and their numbers must be held in check. It should be borne in mind also that the Crow probably destroys the eggs of hawks and owls.

The following experience of the late Gardiner Hammond on Marthas Vineyard indicates that a successful attempt to exterminate the Crow might prove disastrous. Mr. Hammond owned great pastures where many sheep grazed. He told me once that he had offered a bounty of fifty cents each for Crows, as the birds had already killed about 200 of his newly born lambs, and that the native hunters under the stimulus of this bounty had killed nearly all the Crows about the Squibnocket region. Notwithstanding my objection he continued to offer the bounty, although he expressed some fear that the expense would leave him bankrupt. About three years later he hailed me one day to see if I could determine what had destroyed the grass in his pastures. The grass was dead, having been cut off at the roots by white grubs which had increased so rapidly after the destruction of the Crows that they had already ruined a large part of the pastures. The offer of a bounty was withdrawn and the pastures gradually recovered.

Perhaps the greatest visible damage by Crows results from their habit of pulling sprouting corn, but that may be prevented by tarring the seed before planting; there are various devices that usually will keep them away from corn-fields, and poultry may be safeguarded from their attacks by wire netting. They are a serious menace however to

---

[1] First annual report of the United States Entomological Commission, 1878, Appendix II, p. 36.

[2] Department of Agriculture, Sydney, New South Wales, Miscellaneous Publication No. 103. The Common Crow, 1896, pp. 10–12.

a game farm or game preserve and their numbers about estates devoted to such purposes must be reduced. We are not likely to exterminate the Crow, although by taking advantage of the bird's weaknesses many may be killed, and sometimes such killings are justifiable. Thoreau says "this bird sees the white man come and the Indian withdraw, but it withdraws not. Its untamed voice is still heard above the tinkling of the forge. It sees a race pass away but it passes not away. It remains to remind us of aboriginal nature."

Corvus ossifragus WILSON. Fish Crow.

Plate 59.

DESCRIPTION. — Similar to common Crow, but considerably smaller, bill relatively smaller and back without dull feather-tips seen in common Crow. *Adults (sexes alike)*: Black from tip of bill to ends of tail and claws, with gloss rather more bluish above than in common Crow and more greenish below; iris brown. *Young in juvenal plumage*: Similar to young of common Crow but smaller.

MEASUREMENTS. — Length 15.10 to 21.00 in.; spread 30.00 to 43.75; folded wing 9.75 to 13.50; tail 5.50 to 7.25; bill 1.62 to 1.90; tarsus 1.55 to 1.90. Weight 14 to 15½ oz. (B. H. Warren). Female smaller than male.

MOLTS. — Similar to those of common Crow.

FIELD MARKS. — Smaller than common Crow, but not surely distinguishable from it in the field, except (in winter or early spring) by voice.

VOICE. — A hoarse drawling nasal *car* almost exactly like the call of a young common Crow; "a querulous *maah, maah* or *whaw, whaw* varied occasionally to *aack, aack* or *waak, waak*" (C. Bendire).

BREEDING. — Usually in coastal regions or near some body of water. *Nest*: In tree, commonly in pine or other conifer from 15 to 50 feet up, but sometimes higher and frequently near top, similar to that of common Crow, usually with some pine needles in the structure. *Eggs*: 3 to 5; similar to those of common Crow; average smaller; 1.38 to 1.64 by 1.00 to 1.10 in.; figured in Bendire's "Life Histories of North American Birds," Vol. II, Plate IV, Figs. 16 and 17. *Dates*: April 30 to May 15, Florida; May 4 to 28, Virginia; May 15, New Jersey; May 5 to June 3, Connecticut. *Incubation*: Period 16 to 18 days; by both sexes. One brood yearly.

RANGE. — Carolinian and Austroriparian parts of Atlantic and Gulf coast regions. Resident and breeds from southern Connecticut, lower Hudson, Delaware, Susquehanna and Potomac valleys to Florida, Louisiana and southeastern Texas.

DISTRIBUTION IN NEW ENGLAND. — *Vermont*: Possibly may reach southern Vermont casually through Connecticut Valley but doubtfully recorded. *Massachusetts*: Casual or accidental in the Connecticut Valley and eastern Massachusetts; occasional spring migrant in southeastern Massachusetts; a few may remain in summer. *Rhode Island*: Casual in spring. *Connecticut*: Rare summer resident, usually along southwestern coast where occasional in winter; occasional along whole southern coast.

SEASON IN MASSACHUSETTS. — March 10 to July 16.

HAUNTS AND HABITS. The Fish Crow, a smaller species than the common Crow, resembling it very closely but having a rather weak, undeveloped voice, is rather closely restricted in its range to the seaboard, and the lower valleys of rivers. Its haunts and habits are similar to those of the common Crow, except that it is more strongly attracted by water, and that its food consists more largely of fishes and crustaceans. It is more destructive to the eggs of wild birds than is the common Crow, and less injurious to crops and poultry. Its flight is similar to that of other crows, except that it hovers, much like a gull, when it discovers food in the water below it. When, in early spring, a small Crow is seen which cries like a young one, the presumption is that it is a Fish Crow. Some Fish Crows breed here and there on Long Island and in southern Connecticut, and in early spring when the alewives begin to run up the streams of Plymouth and Barnstable Counties, Massachusetts, a small number of Fish Crows, migrating eastward, follow

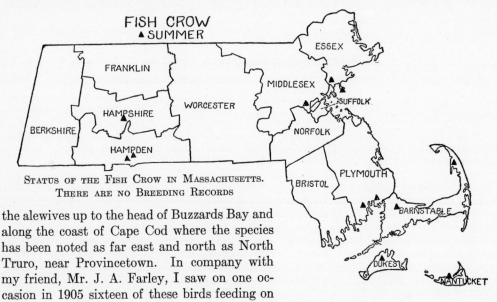

STATUS OF THE FISH CROW IN MASSACHUSETTS.
THERE ARE NO BREEDING RECORDS

the alewives up to the head of Buzzards Bay and along the coast of Cape Cod where the species has been noted as far east and north as North Truro, near Provincetown. In company with my friend, Mr. J. A. Farley, I saw on one occasion in 1905 sixteen of these birds feeding on tide flats at Wareham, and have seen them not infrequently there in spring, but I have never seen courting, pairing or breeding, though I have searched for their nests. Now and then one may stray north up the Connecticut Valley into Massachusetts. The species has been recorded north of Boston where it was seen in Cambridge by William Brewster, March 16, 1875.[1] It was reported also by Mr. Richards at Nahant.

ECONOMIC STATUS. The status of this species resembles that of the common Crow, except that it is seldom inimical to the interests of agriculture and is more destructive to the eggs of water-birds.

FAMILY **STURNIDÆ**. STARLINGS.

Number of species in North America 1; in Massachusetts 1.

This family is confined normally to the Old World, but has no aboriginal representatives in Australia or New Guinea. Birds of this group have 10 primaries, the first very short or spurious but not obsolete. The bill is shaped somewhat like those of our blackbirds and orioles, but is longer, and wider at base; it has a hard scale over each nostril.

[1] Bulletin of the Nuttall Ornithological Club, Vol. I, 1876, p. 19.

The wings are long, the tail short, the legs of medium length and the plumage of adults more or less metallic. The feathers of the head, neck and breast are long, narrow and pointed. Starlings are very adaptable birds, taking advantage of every opportunity to appropriate safe nesting places, procure food and increase their kind.

ECONOMIC STATUS. Birds of this family on cultivated lands are regarded as chiefly beneficial. Some of them, however,* when unduly numerous, are very destructive to grain, fruit and garden crops.

Stúrnus vulgáris LINNÆUS. Starling.

Other names: ENGLISH STARLING; EUROPEAN STARLING.

Introduced Species

Plate 62.

DESCRIPTION. — Bill nearly or quite as long as head, pointed, widened at base, rising high on forehead. Wings long, pointed, but not reaching end of tail which is short and nearly square or even; 1st primary spurious (very short and small); 2d and 3d longest. *Adult male in winter plumage:* Black or blackish, with small, buff feather-tips above, and whitish tips below, and with metallic reflections which are green and purple above and green on throat; wings and tail brownish-black or blackish, the feathers edged and tipped buff, and with more or less green and bluish-green gloss; most of breast bronze-green; abdomen black and bronze-green; flanks bluish-purple; regions of vent and under tail-coverts black with slight greenish gloss, and feather-margins of gray or pale buffy; axillars and wing linings brown with pale buff margins and tips; bill dusky brown or blackish, often with more or less yellow basally and becoming mostly yellow by January or February; iris dark brown; legs and feet reddish-brown. *Adult male in breeding plumage:* As in winter but spots both above and below nearly obsolete, and bill yellow, except extreme tip, which sometimes is blackish. *Adult female:* Similar to male winter and summer but duller; body feathers shorter, not so sharp pointed; iris brown with "narrow yellowish-white outer ring" (Witherby's Practical Handbook of British Birds). *Immature in first summer plumage:* As adults, but more spotted, particularly above. *Young in first winter plumage:* Nearly as adults but body feathers broader, less pointed and light tips larger and rounder, especially below, bird therefore appearing more spotted; chin white or whitish and forehead buffy; iris light brown; bill dusky yellowish-brown; legs and feet brownish. *Young in juvenal plumage:* Very different from adults; dark grayish-brown or dark olive-brown above, lightening below, with flecks of whitish on center of chin and throat, and abdomen streaked with grayish-white; some birds collected in Massachusetts show little white or whitish below, leaving bird practically uniform in color except for some whitish on chin and throat; wings and tail with lighter or dull buffy feather-edges; bill dusky brown; iris brown; legs and feet somewhat lighter than in adults.

MEASUREMENTS. — Length 7.50 to 8.50 in.; folded wing 5.00 to 5.10; spread about 15.50; tail 2.60 to .90; bill .95 to 1.00; tarsus 1.00 to 1.25; weight 2½ to 3½ oz. Female averages smaller than male.

MOLTS. — Juvenal plumage acquired by complete molt of grayish-white nestling down, and quite well developed as young leave nest; first winter plumage acquired by complete molt (July to September); individuals seen in August or September with brown heads and spotted bodies are molting young; first breeding plumage is result of wear during which many of the spots disappear and plumage then resembles that of adults, but is more spotted; second winter plumage is as adults; adults have a single complete molt (June or July to September), and then in winter plumage resemble the more heavily spotted young; breeding plumage acquired by fading and wear which, by wearing off tips of feathers and fading of spots, removes most of the spots and renders the rest inconspicuous.

FIELD MARKS. — Size, between Robin and Red-winged Blackbird or Catbird; about as heavy as Robin but *shorter*. *Adults in summer:* A black bird with short tail and yellow bill; iridescence of plumage seen at close range or in good light; light spots not noticeable at a distance. *Young in summer:* A rather dark, grayish-brown bird, like female Cowbird, but larger with longer, slimmer *dark* bill, and short tail. *Adults and young in winter:* Similar to summer plumage, but light spots more noticeable and bill showing little or no yellow, becoming more yellow as winter wanes; bustles about with a quick, nervous, erratic *walk* while looking for food on the ground.

VOICE. — *Male:* A high, clear, rather long-drawn, ascending whistle (F. M. Chapman); a whistle as if calling a dog, a harsh rasping cry unlike that of any native bird; many guttural notes and some chattering; imitates notes and songs of many other birds; flocks sometimes utter a chattering chorus. *Young:* A harsh grating call.

BREEDING. — Usually in cultivated lands, villages or cities, sometimes in woods. *Nest:* Commonly in holes at any convenient height from ground, such as hollow tree, woodpecker's nest, nesting box or even in holes in ground, rocks or cliffs; often in or on buildings, in cavities, on cornices, or even on a roof under eaves of dormer window; sometimes in barns, dove-cotes or even haystacks; untidy, built largely of grass or straw, occasionally with some twigs, seaweed, corn husks, etc.; lined sparingly with feathers (or sometimes, green leaves) or moss. *Eggs:* 5 to 7, rarely 8; averaging about 1.20 by .86 in.; pale blue, occasionally whitish, somewhat glossy; figured in Morris's "Natural History of the Nests and Eggs of British Birds," 1896, Vol. II, Plate XCVI, Fig. 1. *Dates:* May 15, New Jersey; early April to July, Massachusetts; breeding season begins from March 14 to early April; young sometimes raised in autumn; some have been found frozen in the nest in winter. *Incubation:* Period 11 to 14 days (various authors); by both sexes. One or two broods yearly; sometimes three.

RANGE. — Western and central Europe, north to Greenland (casually) and Spitzbergen (casually), south in winter to the Mediterranean and northern Africa. Range of introduced birds in North America from Wisconsin, southeastern Ontario, southern Quebec, New Brunswick and Nova Scotia, south to Tennessee and Georgia and casually northern Florida, Alabama, Louisiana and Texas. Recorded west also to Illinois. Breeds over the central and northern part of its range; in winter from southern Ontario southern Quebec and Nova Scotia southward.

DISTRIBUTION IN NEW ENGLAND. — Common, local, permanent resident except in extreme northern New Hampshire and northern and extreme eastern Maine; gradually increasing in northern New England; abundant locally in southern New England.

SEASON IN MASSACHUSETTS. — Permanent resident, in winter most numerous near coast.

HISTORY. In Europe the Starling has been a common and familiar bird from time immemorial, breeding largely in or about buildings or near them, feeding chiefly on grassy lands and among growing crops, and consorting with the cattle in pasture and paddock. Within the last century people who were fond of the bird began to introduce it into other countries, and so it came about that many attempts were made to acclimate it in North America. We shall never know how many unsuccessful efforts have been made to establish the species. The following introductions are on record:* Cincinnati, Ohio (1872–73); Quebec, Canada (1875); Worcester, Massachusetts (1884); Tenafly, New Jersey (1884); New York City (1877, 1887, 1890, 1891); Portland, Oregon (1889,

---

* In Auk, Vol. XLII, 1925, pp. 272, 273, Harrison F. Lewis speaks of the Starling taken in 1878 in *Labrador* (not Quebec) shown by Herr Cabanis and now in the Berlin Museum as the first known to have occurred on the North American continent. This may have been a stray from Europe, says Mr. Lewis, but it may have come from the reputed unsuccessful introduction of Starlings in 1875 in Quebec given on the authority of Kalmbach and Gabrielson in Bulletin No. 868. United States Department of Agriculture.

1892); Allegheny, Pennsylvania and Springfield, Massachusetts (1897); and Bay Ridge, New York, about 1900. The introductions in Central Park, New York City, undertaken by Mr. Eugene Scheifflin, are credited as the first to be successful. He liberated 80 birds March 16, 1890 and 40 more April 25, 1891. Some remained in the park and bred there, but a few appeared on Staten Island in 1891, and by 1896 they had increased in number and extended their breeding range to the borough of Brooklyn. About six years later they were first noted outside of Greater New York. After that their increase was more rapid, and by 1916 they were reported as breeding north to east central New York, southern Vermont and New Hampshire and west and south through New Jersey, eastern Pennsylvania and most of Maryland, reaching also the District of Columbia, and ranging in migration casually to Ohio, West Virginia and Georgia. Since 1920 the increase and spread of the species has been more rapid. It appears probable now that unless something develops to check the increase of the Starling, it will extend its range west to the Great Plains and even to the Pacific coast, north into the middle provinces of southern Canada and south to the Gulf States; though just how far south it will remain to breed is problematical, it is now known to nest in South Carolina. It may be many years before it passes the barrier of the Rocky Mountains, unless it is introduced on the Pacific coast. Its increase and distribution have not been so rapid as that of the so-called English Sparrow for two reasons: (1) it is not so prolific and (2) it does not travel on grain cars as did the Sparrow.

HAUNTS AND HABITS. The Starling is a trim and handsome bird. It haunts by preference grass fields, pastures and lawns, but it feeds more or less also among cultivated crops, fruit trees and to some extent in the woods. It has become somewhat of a parasite on man, depending much on his agricultural industries for its food supply and increasing to excessive numbers in a cultivated, fertile country. Therefore it haunts farms, villages and cities wherever grass grows, and is more rarely seen in unsettled regions. It seems particularly fond of lawns and pastures where the grass is short, the walking good and the ground easily gotten at. In pastures it follows the cattle or sheep, catching the insects that the animals stir up, or actually alighting on their backs in search of ticks or other insects. A flock of Starlings so occupied might be mistaken for Cowbirds as the adult males appear black at a distance thus resembling male Cowbirds, while the young Starlings are about the color of females and young of the Cowbird. Starlings, however, may be distinguished from Cowbirds at a considerable distance by their short tails and their quick, nervous, erratic walk. They zigzag about over lawns or pastures, stopping only long enough to pick up food or to fly away with it. In villages and cities where no shooting is allowed, Starlings feed largely on lawns and in parks where people are constantly passing; the birds seem to exhibit no fear of them, but let one stop to watch the birds and the moment they feel that they are under observation, they become restive and soon fly. In flight the Starling is spindle-shaped, the rather long bill and short tail giving it a somewhat similar shape at both ends. It moves through the air by alternately flapping and sailing on fixed wings, much in the manner of the Meadowlark which it somewhat resembles in shape. Its flight appears fluttering, slow and feeble, but it can attain great speed at need.

The song of the Starling, so far as I have heard it, seems to consist largely of imitations of the notes of other birds. It begins to sing in winter or even in autumn and continues throughout a great part of the year. Its vocal performances seem to reach their climax in early spring. While family cares take up its attention, its tuneful lays are more in abeyance, though even in the height of the breeding season it sings occasionally a "whisper song" (with bill closed) interspersed, as usual, with softly whistled imitations. Its own song, if such it can be called, contains many guttural, chattering and whistled notes, while it adds to its repertory, notes, songs or calls of the Wood Thrush, Robin, Bluebird, Chickadee, Tufted Titmouse, White-breasted Nuthatch, Red-breasted Nuthatch, Catbird, House Wren, Carolina Wren, Chestnut-sided Warbler, Barn Swallow, Purple Martin, Scarlet Tanager, Field Sparrow, English Sparrow, Crossbill, Goldfinch, Slate-colored Junco, Meadowlark, Bronzed Grackle, Baltimore Oriole, Red-winged Blackbird, Cowbird, Crow, Blue Jay, Red-headed Woodpecker, Kingfisher, Wood Pewee, Phœbe, Red-eyed Towhee, Red-shouldered Hawk, Bob-white, Guinea Fowl and Killdeer and rather imperfect imitations of the calls of both species of Cuckoo. The imitations of some performers are excellent, some of those of others are less so, but all are recognizable, even to the barking of a dog or the mewing of a cat.

Starlings readily adapt themselves to unpropitious circumstances. Often a church steeple is occupied by many for a breeding place, and during the winter hundreds may roost in its interior. The noise of church bells or chimes seem to disturb them very little. By prying off a plank of the floor above a chime of bells in a Long Island church-tower I was enabled to enter the chamber above, where about thirty nests of Starlings were occupied by young birds. Concealed in this dark chamber and watching the feeding of the young I noted that every 15 minutes when the chimes were rung some of the machinery struck the planks beneath my feet with a sound like that of a sledge-hammer. The birds did not seem to regard this or the tremendous sound of the clanging chimes as they rang in that confined chamber, but at each quarter-hour from daylight to dark every youngster in those nests stretched its neck up toward the zenith, opened its mouth to the fullest extent and cried for food. As the chimes were a "continuous performance" day and night their slumbers must have been somewhat intermittent.

Many Starlings' nests for the first brood are completed in April, and by early May the young are crying for food. The parents are very industrious and devoted. They search the grassy lands almost constantly for food, and carry great numbers of worms and insects to the young. By late May or early June many young of the first brood are out of the nest. These gather in small flocks which frequent pastures and other grass lands, and pay regular visits many times a day to cherry trees when the fruit begins to ripen. Few if any adults now flock with them in the daytime, but some roost with them at night. (Many are engaged with their second broods). The small flocks roost at night in trees or buildings or among the reeds in marshes. Second broods are commonly fledged in

July or August, and as summer wanes these flocks continue to increase.   By late August and early September they contain many adults and also many molting young, some of which have acquired winter plumage with the exception of their heads which are still brown.   At that time many roost nightly in large marshes, in river valleys or near the sea-shore.   I once visited a great marsh near the Hudson in New York State to see the Starlings come in.   As the sun set and the shades of evening began to fall, birds appeared, coming from every point of the compass in twos or threes or in small flocks.   All converged on the great marsh, plunging down into it and alighting on the reeds.   They continued to come in increasing numbers until thousands had assembled at the roosting place.   Now and then flocks rose, swept rapidly back and forth for a time, turning like a flash, all in exact concert, and then gradually settled again in the marsh.   This animated scene continued until night shut down.   Another type of roost, which attracts many thousands, consists of the rows of street trees in southern cities.   As autumn draws on, particularly if severe weather comes with it, many great flocks of Starlings depart from New England for the south.   The capital of the nation has become a popular resort for these birds, and another concourse assembles in Nashville, Tennessee.

In the autumn of 1925–26 I watched the gathering of the flocks in Washington. Before sunset small groups of Starlings appeared high in air.   Coming from several directions, they flew swiftly and erratically about, but soon some began to alight on the projections on the south side of several buildings on Pennsylvania Avenue, while others dropped into the tops of trees located along that thoroughfare or in various parks and squares.   There was considerable shifting about of small flocks, as the birds were restless; but their numbers on both buildings and trees rapidly increased as twilight advanced until all the upper parts of trees and higher ledges of buildings along the avenue for a considerable distance were well filled with them, and newcomers continued to crowd others off the buildings.   They forced the "English" Sparrows to occupy the lower limbs of the trees.   All this time, as it was a busy Saturday night, many cable cars and motor vehicles were passing noisily through the streets, the broad sidewalks were crowded and all the bustling activities of a great city went on, apparently unheeded by the birds.   The droppings that rained down upon passers-by, vehicles and sidewalks had already caused so much complaint that (so the evening papers stated) the fire department was to be called out to play on the birds and drive them away.

By November 10 many of the Starlings have left New England; but though large numbers migrate at the approach of winter, many remain in the north.   These roost mainly in buildings, though some occupy hollow trees and coniferous thickets.

Starlings are resourceful in discovering sheltered places in which to roost in winter. During an extremely cold snow-storm one was observed in a barn, sitting on the back of a cow, thus keeping his feet warm.   Now and then one may be seen in cold weather hopping about on one foot while keeping the other comfortable under the feathers.   Some probably roost in unused stovepipe holes in chimneys as they have been seen going into chimneys in winter. Others go down the chimneys of summer cottages, thus entering the rooms, and, unable to find the way out, die there.

In winter, Starlings gather wherever they can find food. They visit barn-yards, poultry-yards, garbage dumps, etc. Many are fed by humane people who put out food for birds in winter; but whenever the thermometer goes far below the zero mark with cold winds or storms, some are frozen, for, hardy and fit as they undoubtedly are, many of them cannot endure the extreme cold and privation of a very severe New England winter. During hard winters many reports of dead and dying Starlings are received. Mr. Carl E. Grant reported to Mr. Orrin C. Bourne, chief warden in charge of the protection of Fish and Game in Massachusetts, that after the severe weather of January, 1925, he found in an area of less than an acre in a pine grove near Wenham Lake about 500 dead Starlings and innumerable parts of others, which had been partly eaten. He counted 22 dead Starlings in a space less than two feet square where, apparently, they had crowded together for warmth. Probably the birds were roosting there in the protection of the pines when overtaken by a cold storm. At that season large numbers seek the milder climate and more available food supply of the seaboard of southern New England.

Apparently the Starling has not many effective enemies in Massachusetts. Cats get some of the young and a few adults. Hawks and shrikes also get a few, but Starlings have a habit of gathering in flocks and following a hawk, Crow, or shrike that has seized one of their number, attacking their enemy from above and sometimes even from below and making life very unpleasant for him. Sometimes when a hawk is the object of their attack, their offensive is strengthened by a reinforcement of Crows. Mr. A. W. Higgins tells of a flock of Starlings massed like a great ball that followed a large hawk and descended upon him *en masse*. The hawk appeared to be bewildered and helpless. I have seen a great flock of Starlings gather into a huge ball above a Goshawk, but they did not molest him.

In the matter of food the Starling is nearly omnivorous, though its food materials are not quite so varied as are those of the Blue Jay and the Crow. So far as I know it does not eat the seeds of trees. The animal food of adult Starlings in this country, as determined by experts of the Biological Survey after an examination of the stomach contents of 2,157 individuals, is set down as 57 per cent, while 43 per cent is tabulated as vegetal.[1] It is interesting to note that in England, where the Starling is native and is now much more abundant than in America, an exhaustive investigation by Dr. Walter E. Collinge, the eminent English economic ornithologist, shows that its animal food consitutes but 51 per cent of its yearly aliment, while its vegetal food has increased to 49 per cent. The difference is significant as will be shown hereinafter. Of the food of the Starling as determined in the United States, according to Kalmbach and Gabrielson, 41.55 per cent consists of insects, alive or dead. Beetles, including many weevils, destructive to clover, grass and strawberries, also May beetles and a small quantity of useful carabids are taken.

---

[1] Kalmbach, E. R., and Gabrielson, I. N.: United States Department of Agriculture, Bulletin No. 868, Economic Value of the Starling in the United States, 1921, page 15.

It takes fewer caterpillars, but consumes many of these during their season. It eats many bees, wasps and ants, few bugs, large numbers of millipeds and a goodly number of spiders most of which are fed to the young; also a small number of snails, a few beach fleas and sow bugs and more or less animal garbage, meat, fat and carrion, and to some extent the eggs and young of other birds. Starlings have even been known to kill young game birds. Mr. Perry S. Knowlton, of Essex, Massachusetts, says that he saw a small flock of Starlings attack five young pheasants "about as large as robins" and kill two of them. The Starlings struck the young birds with their bills, piercing the skull about at the ear where the blood oozed out. Its vegetal food consists largely of fruit, both culti-vated and wild; apples, pears, peaches, grapes, currants and other small fruits, including strawberries and practically all wild fruits that native birds eat. A flock of Starlings swings into a cherry tree, there is a rain of cherry stones and the flock is away again only to return later unless the flock is large enough to strip the whole tree at once. It takes practically all grains, including corn, and digs up the seed in planted or sowed fields. It takes the young sprouts of such garden vegetables as beans, peas, lettuce, onions, radishes, beets, carrots, muskmelons, squashes and tomatoes and young flowering plants as well. The food of nestling Starlings is nearly all animal, largely insects. The largest animal item consists of caterpillars, including many cutworms, and the largest vegetal item con-sists of cultivated cherries.

ECONOMIC STATUS. The Starling has damaged fruit and crops to such an extent and has molested native birds so frequently that it has acquired a bad reputation wherever it has become numerous in this country, and every state where it now breeds abundantly has removed from it the protection of the law. Nevertheless, Kalmbach and Gabrielson, of the Biological Survey, after a long investigation extending over at least ten years, assert that "most of the Starling's food habits have been demonstrated to be either bene-ficial to man or of a neutral character." [1] They say that "a thorough consideration of the evidence at hand indicates that, based on food habits, the adult Starling is the eco-nomic superior of the robin, catbird, flicker, red-winged blackbird or grackle. It is pri-marily a feeder on insects and wild fruit — less than 6 per cent of its yearly food being se-cured from cultivated crops." [2] My own investigation of the economic status of the Starling had left on my mind a somewhat different impression from that given by the above report, but as the inquiry undertaken by the Biological Survey was much more extensive and exhaustive than my own, their conclusions should be accepted. In con-sideration of the status of this bird in America, however, this question arises — what will happen if the Starling continues to increase until it becomes unduly numerous over large areas? In such a case there will be an over drain upon its normal food supply and it will turn more and more to crops and fruit. Kalmbach and Gabrielson quote the British Board of Agriculture to the effect that in agriculture and gardening the usefulness of the bird far outweighs the occasional harm done. On the other hand, Dr. Walter F. Collinge,

[1] Economic Value of the Starling in the United States, 1921, p. 59.
[2] Ibid., p. 58.

who has made extensive investigations of the food of the Starling in England, published an article in the Journal of the Ministry of Agriculture for March, 1921 (the year in which the report of Kalmbach and Gabrielson appeared), in which he showed that the Starling had increased unduly in England and that as hereinbefore stated vegetal matter forms 49 per cent of its food for the year — an increase of 6 per cent over that found by Kalmbach and Gabrielson as the vegetal content of the Starling's food in America, while its consumption of animal food is correspondingly less. It is a fair assumption that with such a change in the proportions of animal and vegetal food, the bird would destroy fewer insects and more crops, and we find this has actually occurred in England. Doctor Collinge now sets down the injuries to man's industries there by the Starling at 41 per cent, the benefits at only 36.5 per cent and regards as neutral 22.5 per cent. He points to excessive and progressive increase of the Starling in England and to the resulting damage to grain and fruit, and says that the percentage of cultivated roots and cereals is so high that the species must be condemned. I have published notes on extensive injury to fruit and crops by these birds in England.[1] Dr. Collinge says that from one of the most useful birds it has become one of the most injurious. It is notable that he attributes this change in its economic status to a recent great increase in its numbers, and that he predicted in 1919 that any further increase could be "fraught only with the most serious consequences." Such an undue accession of the Starling's numbers is what we have to fear in this country. The greatest damage results from the multitudes that flock together. In Switzerland when enormous flocks settle like black clouds on a vineyard, they have been known to pluck the entire crop of fruit in ten or fifteen minutes. In the south of France and in Italy crops of olives are taken in the same way. When attacking apples, pears, peaches and plums they ruin far more fruit, by pecking holes in it, than they can possibly eat. It should be said, however, that in continental Europe the opinions of ornithologists and foresters generally favor the Starling. Nevertheless, in countries where it has been introduced, the experience with it has not been reassuring. Not long after it was imported into New Zealand it became a pest, but now, it is regarded as beneficial. In Australia and Tasmania it is considered a pest and its faults are strongly condemned, as it commits great havoc on fruit and drives away native birds.

During the past ten years or more I have received many complaints of the Starling's combativeness in this country. It is well known that it drives out flickers and other birds that nest in tree-cavities provided that the entrances to the cavities are large enough for the Starling to enter. This may be prevented in building bird houses by narrowing the circular entrance hole to at most $1\frac{5}{8}$ inches. Flickers and martins, however, cannot be protected thus, though martins may sometimes enter such an entrance if a smaller hole be bored above it to admit light. Starlings have been known in many cases to destroy the eggs and young of other birds from the size of a sparrow to that of a Domestic Dove, and sometimes they drive Doves out of dovecotes, kill the young doves and occupy their nests. We can readily understand the Starling's motive for killing birds that occupy

---

[1] Circular No. 45, Massachusetts Department of Agriculture, 1920, pp. 5, 6.

holes which it covets for nesting purposes, but the slaying of young Robins is wanton slaughter.   Raids on the nests of other birds are described in the above mentioned papers of the Biological Survey and the Massachusetts Department of Agriculture.   The question often is asked : "If the Starling becomes unduly numerous in this country, what can be done to exterminate it?"   The answer is, "nothing."   The Starling is a strong, resolute, cautious and sagacious bird.   As soon as aggressive measures against it are taken, it becomes more shy than the Crow which in my opinion would be less difficult to exterminate than the Starling.   The bird is here to stay.   It has many friends.   We must make the best of it.   Where not too numerous it will be mainly beneficial, as it is a great destroyer of cutworms, weevils, grasshoppers and such destructive larvæ as those of the gipsy moth, the moth of the tent caterpillar, and the European corn-borer. If its numbers increase greatly we must expect great injury to newly-sown grain and also to fruit, and considerable damage to garden vegetables.   Also it will displace native birds to a degree by destroying their winter supply of wild fruit and by usurping their nesting places.   If it becomes unduly abundant and seriously harmful, we may hope that in time, like the formerly pestilential "English" Sparrow, it will be reduced by the forces of nature, or by some fortunate combination of circumstances to a condition of comparatively "innocuous desuetude."

FAMILY **ICTERIDÆ.**   BLACKBIRDS, ORIOLES, ETC.

Number of species in North America 19 ; in Massachusetts 9.

This is an American family, including the cowbirds, blackbirds, meadowlarks, orioles and grackles of North America and also the troupials, caciques and many other icterine species of Mexico and Central and South America.   Some birds of the group are chiefly terrestrial, but most of them are arboreal.   Members of this family apparently are related to the crows on the one hand and on the other they approach the finches, and naturally the group is regarded as intermediate between the two.   Their bills vary much in shape but are never conspicuously longer than the head, more or less conical, hard and pointed. The cutting edges of the mandibles have two angles as in the sparrows.   The Bobolink and the Cowbird very closely resemble sparrows.   The nostrils are never concealed by feathers and there are no prominent bristles at the corners of the mouth.   The wing is variable in shape.   The tail also is variable in shape as well as in size, but never conspicuously longer than the folded wing.   It is not notched or forked and usually is rounded. The tail-feathers are always twelve.   The tarsi are always scaled in front.   The plumage varies much, many of the species being dark, but in many others the males are bright colored.   Numbers of species, of which there are at least 130, largely South American, build elaborate arboreal nests ; others nest on or near the ground among reeds ; and members of one of our genera (*Molothrus*) deposit their eggs in the nests of other birds.

Dolichónyx oryzívorus (LINNÆUS). **Bobolink.**

Other names: REED-BIRD; RICE-BIRD.

Plate 60.

DESCRIPTION. — Bill rather short and conical like that of a sparrow; wings rather long and pointed, 1st and 2nd quills longest; tail rounded, rather short, when compared with wings, *its feathers stiffened and pointed*, resembling a woodpecker's tail; sexes much alike except in breeding season. *Adult male in breeding plumage:* Head, wings, tail and lower plumage black; a large buff patch on back of head and back and sides of neck, extending about half-way around base of neck; interscapulars streaked buff, black and ashy; rest of back, rump, upper tail-coverts and scapulars light ashy to ashy-white, usually whitish on scapulars and upper tail-coverts; greater wing-coverts and most of flight-feathers edged yellowish, most of which wears off in June or July leaving wing nearly black; tail-feathers narrowly edged buffy or ashy, more broadly so terminally on inner webs; feathers of flanks and under tail-coverts more or less distinctly margined and tipped buffy; bill horn-black, usually bluish below with black tip; iris brown, legs and feet brown or dusky brownish. *Adult male in winter plumage:* Similar to adult female in winter, but larger (and averaging slightly brighter); some adult males in this plumage show a few black feathers below, usually buff-tipped; bill clay colored or purplish; legs and feet lighter than in breeding plumage. *Adult female in breeding plumage:* Yellowish-brown or "light buffy-olive" above, and brownish-yellow or "light olive-buffy" below; often paler on throat and middle of abdomen; a broad central streak along top of head lighter than back, with two broad, blackish streaks finely marked with minute light streaks on either side; several blackish streaks composed of dark feather-centers extend down interscapulars; fewer and much shorter, narrower streaks over rump; wings and tail dusky, with conspicuous edgings of very light yellowish-olive or pale grayish-olive; sides of head and neck similar in color to lower plumage, with a narrow, blackish stripe running backward from eye; sides, flanks and under tail-coverts streaked with dusky; bill brown, darkening above toward tip, lighter below; iris, legs and feet brown. *Adult female in winter plumage:* Similar to breeding plumage but richer, especially below. *Young in first winter plumage:* As adult female, but usually yellower below, especially on throat and middle of belly. *Young in juvenal plumage:* Similar to adult winter female, but more buffy (not so yellowish), especially below (some juvenal birds, however, are quite yellow, while some have small dusky spots across upper breast); black stripes on head more mixed with buffy and not so clearly defined, and streaks on flanks obsolete; flight-feathers, except tertials, edged grayish-white around ends; "bill pinkish-buff, or clay color with dusky tip when older; feet clay color becoming deep Vandyke-brown" (J. Dwight).

MEASUREMENTS. — Length 6.30 to 8.00 in.; spread 10.25 to 12.50; folded wing 3.50 to 4.00; tail 2.60 to 3.15; bill .55 to .64; tarsus 1.00 to 1.10; weight $1\frac{1}{2}$ to $1\frac{7}{8}$ oz. (B. H. Warren). Female smaller than male.

MOLTS. — Buffy natal down succeeded in nestling (June) by juvenal plumage; first winter plumage acquired by partial postjuvenal molt (June and July) during which flight-feathers and tail-feathers are retained; prenuptial molt (probably February and March) probably complete, produces first nuptial plumage with its light feather-tips; light tips wear away so that in May on arrival in New England immature males are similar to adult males; immature females probably also have at least an incomplete prenuptial molt (late June, July and August); there is a complete molt of male in winter or very early spring in South America, probably females have similar molt, complete or incomplete, but no specimens indicating this examined; adult breeding plumage acquired by wear.

FIELD MARKS. — Bluebird size or a little larger; male in spring and summer unmistakable with coat on "wrong side up," the black chiefly below, the white and buff above, head and neck black with buff patch covering back of neck; in late summer and autumn resembles female. *Female and young:* Smaller sparrowlike birds like female Dickcissel, distinguished from latter by rounded tail of pointed feathers; (Dickcissel has slightly forked tail of rounded feathers) above streaked brown and yellowish-buff, below similar but nearly unstreaked.

VOICE. — Call notes sounding like *träck, träck,* or *tchäe, tchäe* or *killink, killink* (Bendire); a metallic *chuck* or *chenk* when alarmed for the safety of its young; song an indescribable bubbling medley from which the bird has received its name, often ending in *cheee* or *speee;* autumnal call note a single soft metallic *chink.*

BREEDING. — Chiefly in grass or clover fields and meadows, in grassy tracts along borders of streams, occasionally in lowland pastures. *Nest:* On ground, excellently concealed by tall grass or at the foot of a tuft of grass or small bush, usually in a depression of the soil, rarely above ground attached to grass stems, a structure sometimes frail, built of grasses, weed stems and rootlets and lined with finer similar material. *Eggs:* 4 to 7; .69 to .93 by .60 to .64 in.; usually ovate or short ovate; *extremely variable;* pearl-gray or ashy-blue to brownish-clay, drab or reddish-brown, variously spotted and blotched, usually heavily, with various browns, purple and lavender; darker markings often massed about large end and lighter ones more toward small end; figured in Bendire's "Life Histories of North American Birds," Vol. II, Plate VI, Figs. 1, 2. *Dates:* May 30 to June 5, Rhode Island; June 1 to 8, Massachusetts; June 6 to 15, Maine. *Incubation:* Period 10 days (F. L. Burns); by female. One brood yearly.

RANGE. — Chiefly eastern and central temperate North America, and much of South America. Breeds from southeastern British Columbia, central Alberta, central Saskatchewan, southern Manitoba, central Ontario, southern Quebec and Cape Breton Island south to northern Nevada, northern Utah, Colorado (probably), Nebraska, eastern Kansas, northern Missouri, central Illinois, southern Indiana, central Ohio, central West Virginia, northwestern Maryland, central Pennsylvania and central New Jersey, migrates south in autumn through eastern United States, West Indies, Yucatan and central America and northern South America; winters from Argentina to southern Brazil, Bolivia and Paraguay; casual in California, accidental in Bermuda and the Galapagos.

DISTRIBUTION IN NEW ENGLAND. — Common migrant and summer resident generally in open uplands as well as lowlands but chiefly at lower elevations; seldom seen in forested regions; quite local in northern Maine. Much less numerous along the New England seaboard than it was before the last quarter of the nineteenth century.

SEASON IN MASSACHUSETTS. — (April 22 and 27) May 1 to September 30.

HISTORY. Normally the Bobolink is a bird of the river valleys of eastern North America. When the country was forested, the bird must have been confined to grass lands in these valleys and to marshes along the coast, for there only could it have found its favorite foods — the seeds and insects of the grasses and weeds. In autumn it followed the Atlantic coast southward and fed largely on the seeds of wild rice, wild oats and other reeds. When the white man came, cleared the land and sowed grass and grain, the food supply of the bird was vastly augmented in the north, as well as the area suitable for its breeding purposes, and so it increased greatly in numbers and spread westward. It still follows, however, its old migration route down the Atlantic coast. While settlement and clearing went on in the north the same process continued in the south, but not so rapidly. However, the coastal regions and the river valleys soon were settled and here grain and rice were sown, the rice mostly in marshes along the coast, thus supplanting the native seeds and grasses, on which the Bobolink fed formerly, with a larger and more productive seed, and so increasing its food supply beyond anything known in aboriginal times. The rice-growing industry prospered and increased during the first half of the 19th century under the system of slavery, and with free labor during the latter part of the

PLATE 60

PLATE 60

COWBIRD
Page 421

RED–WINGED BLACKBIRD
Page 429

ADULT MALE IN BREEDING PLUMAGE

ADULT MALE

ADULT FEMALE

BOBOLINK
Page 413

IMMATURE MALE

ADULT MALE IN BREEDING
PLUMAGE

ADULT FEMALE

ADULT FEMALE

All about one-half scale.

century reached large dimensions. During all this time the rice-birds (chiefly Bobolinks) took a large toll of the crops — so large that in the report of the United States Department of Agriculture for 1886 the annual loss to the rice growers of the south caused by this bird was estimated at $2,000,000. This included the cost of hiring "bird-minders" to shoot or frighten away the birds, which was by far the greatest item, but without which the crop would have been so reduced by the birds that it would not have paid the cost of harvesting. With the rise of the rice industry in Louisiana, Arkansas and Texas, however, where rice is raised on dry land which can be flooded at need and where machinery can be used in rice culture, the rice industry on the Atlantic coast became unprofitable and rapidly dwindled to negligible proportions during the last years of the 19th century and the early years of the present century.

In 1912 Professor Chas. E. Chambliss, expert in charge of rice investigations for the United States Department of Agriculture, informed me that the farm value of the commercial rice crop of South Carolina in 1907 was but $552,000 and in 1909 $433,000. Later still, rice planting for the market became nearly negligible on the Atlantic coast, though it was revived during the World War by war prices. In the meantime an industry had arisen among the negroes, that of killing rice-birds for the market, which rapidly assumed large proportions during the months when the birds passed through South Carolina and Georgia. Before the Civil War the negroes were not allowed to have guns, but when they were freed some of them secured cheap guns, and most of their sons naturally took to hunting. In 1912 Mr. James H. Rice, then chief game warden of South Carolina, wrote to me that he had checked up the game shipped from Georgetown, South Carolina, in one year. The result was 60,000 dozen of rice-birds and about 20,000 dozen of Carolina Rails and Virginia Rails, but at the time of writing (1912) the number shipped had fallen off greatly on account of the reduced number of the birds. He also stated that these birds were not shot to protect the rice, as they were not killed until they had grown fat on rice and until they would bring a good price in the market. I decided then to go to South Carolina and witness the killing and marketing of the birds. It was evident that no bird raising, like the Bobolink, but one brood a year of from five to seven young, could stand such a drain on its numbers as must have resulted, provided other markets had been taking their share. Early in September, 1912, I left Boston for Georgetown, South Carolina, and remained until after the fifteenth in the coastal region of the state. I found that the negroes used two methods of taking the birds: (1) hunting with a gun by daylight, (2) hunting at night with torches, when the men poled skiffs along the irrigation ditches and picked the dazzled birds off the reeds where they roost, or else threshed them off into the boat with branches cut for the purpose. This could be done on dark nights. The following quotation from my report of the trip will give an idea of the conditions there at that time regarding the Bobolink:

"On my arrival at the rice fields, colored gunners were seen in all directions, and the popping of guns was continual. All the shooting appeared to be done by creeping up to birds when they were sitting on stubble or on the heaped-up rice, selecting a time when a large number flocked together. One of the negroes said that he often frightened up the birds in the rice fields and shot into the flocks as they flew, but I saw nothing like this. One man with a full bag told me that he had 8 dozen birds at noon and that he killed 16 dozen the day before. Another stated that he had six dozen so far, and shot about 12 or 13 dozen daily on an average, but that formerly he used to get 14 or 15 dozen, or even more, when the birds were numerous. He said it was not unusual formerly to kill 20 to 30 dozen at night, and sometimes even 40 dozen, but all the negroes that I talked with agreed that they were getting very few at night now. Some said that nights must be dark for successful hunting. They said that they received 20 cents a dozen now for 'shoot' birds and 25 to 30 cents for 'ketch' birds. One gunner said that when he could not get 25 cents a dozen he would knock off.

"Canals bordered on both sides by dikes enter the rice fields from the river. Here and there on the dikes are patches of small cane, and the banks are lined with flags, reeds, rushes and other water plants. Ditches run around each field about a rod from the dike. A negro shoots sometimes from the cover of vegetation on the dike, but usually approaches the birds crouchingly over the marshes. Some use muzzle-loading guns, others breech-loaders, buying their shells loaded. At noon a dozen men and boys were counting up their forenoon's bag on a dike, and if their count can be relied upon, they had about 1000 birds. Every man but one that I saw had a gun and was shooting birds. This one was carrying a tin pail and was a rice harvester. He said that rice harvesting paid better than shooting rice-birds. Sometimes he said the gunners did not get any rice-birds at all. He said he never had had a gun or shot birds in his life. Another stated that he had been shooting since he was ten years old. He shoots ducks in the rivers, birds in the marsh, and anything that can be sold or used for food. The man who did not shoot had a long whip with a short, wooden handle and a lash about 15 feet long made of old rope. He said that this would scare the birds more than a gun. He picked it up, and, whirling the long lash around his head, yelled with full volume of his lungs and cracked the whip; it sounded somewhat like a rifle shot. Mr. Donaldson stated that when the birds get accustomed to the sound of the shotguns, the crack of the whip, being an unusual sound, frightens them more than the gun.

"My inquiries at the markets of Georgetown, regarding the shipments of bobolinks, corroborated the statement made by Mr. Rice to the effect that the traffic had fallen off greatly. Those markets which formerly furnished the greater part of the supply were doing very little business. On the Back River, however, a firm was found which had established quarters in a scow, roofed over, in which about 14 women and children were engaged in picking the birds, and here the hunters came in with their 'game.' Each negro 'picker' plucked the feathers from the birds and arranged them, when plucked, in rows of a dozen each, when they were packed in small baskets by the white men having charge of the business. . . .

"The people shipping bobolinks were very chary about volunteering any information, and it was impossible to get any statistics of the number of birds shipped. Every one agreed, however, that there were not nearly so many birds as formerly. Nevertheless, the quantity of birds shipped must have been large, as numbers of gunners were coming every morning with them and the pickers were very busy." [1]

It was evident to me that the Bobolinks were not killed to protect the rice at that time as most of the rice was already cut. They were killed for the twenty-five cents a dozen received by the shooters, and marketed for the seventy-five cents to one dollar per dozen that the marketmen received. In the height of their abundance the birds were shipped in quantity to the great markets in New York, Philadelphia, Paris, etc., and were eaten mainly by wealthy or spendthrift epicures. Since that time the marketing of small birds and wild game in this country has been prohibited by law, and this drain on the numbers of the Bobolink has been mostly done away with. Doubtless some are still shot and more frightened away to protect the rice fields. The Biological Survey which now has charge of the protection of migratory birds has now forbidden the killing of these birds for game in some of the Middle States, where the only excuse for shooting them was that gunners desired the privilege. It seems to be generally agreed that the species has decreased much in numbers along the Atlantic Coast within the past fifty years. No other result could have been expected. In New England the greatest reduction in numbers has occurred in the coastal region. On Cape Cod and Nantucket where the species was once abundant it is rarely seen now, but of late it is said to be increasing in some of the hill towns of western Massachusetts. An inquiry was made in 1923 by the National Association of Audubon Societies to determine the status of the Bobolink at that time, and Dr. Pearson, president of the organization, permitted me to examine the great number of letters received from various parts of the country. This correspondence convinced me that while the Bobolink had been decreasing along the eastern seaboard it had continued to increase and spread in the west where it has followed grain raising. It may be found to-day west of the Cascade Mountains in British Columbia. It has spread into regions in western states where formerly it was unknown, and this westward movement may have had something to do with its decrease in the northeast.

HAUNTS AND HABITS. The Bobolink is a distinctive bird; he is unlike all the rest. If there exists anywhere on earth another bird like it, I have yet to see it. His song is entirely his own. I have never yet heard the Mockingbird, the Catbird, the Starling or the Blue Jay even try to imitate it. His finest livery and his sweetest music are reserved for northern fields and for a brief period only. He is at his best in New England in May and early June. As I have written elsewhere —

"The Bobolink is the harlequin of the spring meadows. He is a happy-go-lucky fellow, with his suit on wrong side up, the black below and the white above; a reckless, rollicking sort of a fowl, throwing care to the winds, and always bent on a lark. His spirits are of the effervescent kind, and his music bubbles irrepressibly forth at such a rate that half a dozen notes seem to be crowding upon the heels of every one uttered.

---

[1] Report of State Ornithologist for 1912. Annual Report of the Massachusetts State Board of Agriculture, 1913, pp. 220–223.

Indeed, this is about the only bird that completely baffles the latter-day 'interpreters' of bird music. His notes tumble out with such headlong rapidity, in an apparent effort to jump over each other, that it is next to impossible for the scribe to set them down in the proper sequence of musical notation. Nevertheless, this harum-scarum expression of irrepressible joy is of the most pleasing character, and ranks among the finest music of the fields." [1]

About the second week in May the male Bobolinks usually arrive in some numbers in New England, and they continue to come all through the month. They have run the gauntlet of the guns in the south both going and coming, and they are now among friends. Care and caution they throw to the winds and usher in the day with a revel of flight and song. A little later when the females arrive the merry fellows seem to go mad with joy in pursuit of their fleeing inamoratas. They chase their prospective mates about the fields, pouring forth a perfect torrent of song. Dr. C. W. Townsend gives the following account of the behavior of the wooing male. "The courtship song of this bird bubbles over with joy and merriment. Not only from the air but from the tops of trees and from the ground the song is given, but its ardor almost always carries the bird through the air. Especially is this the case when the courting season is in full sway. When the birds first come, before the arrival of the females, they often sing in trees, sometimes as many as a dozen together, making a splendid chorus. One may see a male courting a female on the ground. He spreads his tail and forcibly drags it like a Pigeon. He erects his buff nape feathers, points his bill downward and partly opens his wings, gurgling meanwhile a few of his song notes." [2]

My old friend, the late Edward A. Samuels, has written thus of the nesting: "When the birds are mated, usually early in June, they commence the structure in which their family is to be reared. Selecting a thick tussock of grass in a field or meadow, through which, or near which, a brook prattles of cool and delicious draughts and sweet and refreshing baths, beneath the bending and concealing leaves, they entwine fine grasses and rootlets into a loose and not deeply hollowed nest, which they line with softer pieces of the same material.

"The position is so well chosen that, nine times out of ten, if you walk the meadow over again and again, knowing it to be there, you will not discover the nest; the male bird flies over your head, chiding and complaining at your presence, and his mate skurrying off through the thick grass, rises away from the nest, that you may not discover its locality." [3]

The female takes entire charge of the eggs, while the male enjoys himself, but he is likely to be near enough to give the alarm when an enemy appears and to draw the attention of the intruder to himself at some spot distant from the nest. Samuels says: "As soon as the young birds are hatched, the father, hitherto full of song and merriment,

[1] Useful Birds and their Protection, 1913, p. 322.
[2] Supplement to the Birds of Essex County, Massachusetts, 1920, p. 128.
[3] Birds of New England, 1870, p. 337.

becomes more quiet, spending a great part of his time in family cares. The young birds are fed on grasshoppers, crickets, and various other insects; and this food is the chief sustenance of the parents as well, at this period, for the seeds of the wild grasses are not yet ripened. . . . "When the young birds leave the nest, the parents provide for them for a few days, and then turn them away to shift for themselves; this is in about the middle of July. The old birds then pass a comparatively idle season, — roaming through the country, recuperating from the cares of parentage, and exchanging their nuptial dress for one more in accordance with their matured, respectable, old folks' condition; the male assumes the sober, and lately more sober, attire of his mate, and dropping his song, contents himself with repeating her simple '*chink.*'" [1]

By the middle of July most of them have left the higher lands and after that date their songs are rarely heard. By the last of July most of the males have assumed their modest autumnal garb and both old and young have assembled in flocks. In August they begin to move slowly southward, frequenting river marshes, coastal lands and grain-fields, taking toll of the seeds as they go. By the middle of August they are abundant in the marshes of southern New Jersey, Delaware and Pennsylvania, where thousands formerly were shot by gunners, and by the second week of September their flocks have assembled in the rice fields of South Carolina. The migration story of the Bobolinks is one of the most interesting that can be told regarding the movements of any New England bird. Let Dr. Frank M. Chapman tell it, for he does it briefly and well.

"Where, now, does the Bobolink winter? Not with the Red-winged Blackbirds in the South Atlantic and Gulf states, or even in the West Indies or Central America, nor yet in northern South America, but far south of the Amazon in the great campos or prairies of southwestern Brazil and the marshes of La Plata. From British Columbia to Argentina, 6,800 miles in as straight a line as one can lay a ruler on the chart. But, however, it may be with the Crow, 'as the Bobolink flies' is not always the straightest line. Let us see, therefore, what route or routes the Bobolink follows.

"At once we make an interesting discovery. Whether a Bobolink spends his summer in Massachusetts or British Columbia, he leaves the United States through Florida. If Bobolinks are found in Texas or Mexico, they are merely birds which have lost their way. The port of departure as well as of entry is the Florida peninsula, or, at least, the waters that bound it.

"But it may well be asked, why do not the Bobolinks of the western United States migrate southward with other western birds into Mexico over the all-land route?

"To which it may be answered, that the Bobolink is not truly a western bird. We have seen that he probably has settled in the far West in only recent years. So, in returning to his winter quarters, he retraces his steps, as it were, going back over the same country through which his ancestors gradually extended their range westward. Thus the Bobolink gives us an indication of how birds learn to travel regularly, season after season, between their winter and summer resorts. The route is learned little by little, as the

---

[1] Birds of New England, 1870, p. 338.

birds gradually widen their range, and the birds go back by the way they came. **This** habit appears to be inherited, to be passed on from generation to generation, and when we remember that birds have been migrating for thousands of years, it gives us some clue to the manner in which such a great journey as the Bobolink's may have been developed.

"After leaving Florida, the Bobolink Grand Trunk Line appears to have three branches. One leads to Yucatan and thence southward along the eastern coast of Central America; one crosses over Cuba to Jamaica, and one goes eastward to Porto Rico and thence southward through the Lesser Antilles.

"The Jamaica route is apparently the most popular. Gosse, in his 'Birds of Jamaica,' tells us that vast numbers of Bobolinks arrive in that island in October and remain until early November. Fresh from the rice fields of our southern states, they are extremely fat and are known as 'Butter-birds,' many being killed for food.

"From Jamaica, Bobolink must cross 400 miles of open sea to reach northern South America, — a journey which he doubtless makes in one night's flight; and, having reached the mainland, he probably follows along the eastern slope of the Andes to the treeless region toward which he has been travelling for at least three months.

"Here Bobolink passes the next five months, with no family cares and nothing to do but eat and be merry. He spends, therefore, almost twice as much time in his winter home as in his summer one.

"Just when the northward journey is begun, no one seems to know. Probably late in March, for Gosse writes that Bobolinks reach Jamaica in April; about the twenty-sixth of that month they arrive in northern Florida, and, during the first week in May, reach their particular meadow or pasture in the Middle and New England states, with as much regularity as though they had travelled eight instead of eight thousand miles since leaving it." [1]

In its spring flight northward the Bobolink travels mostly at night, but in passing south it moves largely by day, at least so far as the Atlantic seaboard of the United States is used as its highway.

The food of the Bobolink on its breeding grounds consists chiefly of insects, which comprise from about 70 per cent to over 90 per cent of its sustenance in May, June and July. Of the vast quantity of insects consumed by the bird less than 3 per cent, on the average, are beneficial species. In May it takes a small and fast dwindling per cent of grain, and in July an increasing amount, which rises in August to about 35 per cent, but decreases rapidly until at the end of September it is only about 3 per cent. Its consumption of weed seeds averages about 8 per cent in May, June and July, but increases rapidly in August until at the end of September it reaches over 90 per cent; by that time most of the Bobolinks have left New England. In its movement southward down the Atlantic seaboard, the bird feeds principally on the seeds of weeds and other wild plants, until it reaches South Carolina and Georgia, where rice is raised, when its chief food is the rice in the fields.

[1] Bird-Lore, Vol XI, 1909, pp. 137, 138.

ECONOMIC STATUS. There is no doubt regarding the economic value of the Bobolink in New England. Here it is one of the most beneficial birds. Caterpillars (particularly cutworms and army worms) weevils and grasshoppers form a large part of its food while with us. It eats some beneficial hymenopterous parasites but very few useful predaceous beetles.[1]

The grain that it takes in New England is negligible, as it gets most of its vegetal food while here from weed seeds. Even in the south, where it undoubtedly has been a great pest on the rice plantations, it destroys many insects and weed seeds. Probably its chief mischief on the Atlantic coast is done now to patches of rice owned by small farmers who are raising rice on the uplands, mostly for home use. There have been no reports of any great damage done by the bird in the rice fields of Arkansas and Texas, but if the species continues to increase in the west, it may in time find a food supply there.

Molóthrus áter ater (BODDAERT). Cowbird.

Other names: COW BLACKBIRD; COW BUNTING; LAZY BIRD.

Plate 60.

DESCRIPTION. — Bill much shorter than head, stout, conical, sparrow-like; wings long and pointed, first three primaries forming the tip; tail shorter than folded wing and nearly even or square at tip; legs and feet rather stout and fitted for walking, hind toe not raised. *Adult male:* Head, neck and a little of upper breast deep, warm brown, somewhat variable; elsewhere glossy, greenish-black with more or less purple and violet reflections on upper back; bill, legs and feet black; iris brown. *Adult female:* Brownish-gray or grayish-brown above, with faint greenish gloss, the feathers with darker centers and still darker or black shaft-streaks; below lighter brownish-gray or brown, usually more or less streaked darker, becoming much lighter on throat; bill brownish-black, lighter below; iris brown; legs and feet lighter than in male. *Young in first winter plumage:* Virtually as adults, but some young males retain some grayish-brown feathers through the winter. *Young male in juvenal plumage:* Similar to female but feathers edged gray, chin white or yellowish; elsewhere below dull white becoming buffy on throat; breast and flanks streaked with brown (some males, however, show faint buffy feather-edges). *Young female in juvenal plumage:* Similar to young male but lighter, especially below.

MEASUREMENTS. — Length 7.00 to 8.25 in.; spread 11.70 to 13.75; folded wing 3.75 to 4.60; tail 2.70 to 3.35; bill .61 to .72; tarsus .98 to 1.12. Weight 1½ to 1¾ oz. (B. H. Warren). Female smaller than male.

MOLTS. — Juvenal plumage acquired by complete postnatal molt of olive-gray down; molt nearly completed when young are fully fledged; first winter plumage acquired by complete (?) postjuvenal molt (August to November); this plumage is practically as adult; a few male birds still retain a few brown feathers; first breeding plumage is merely worn first winter plumage; after a postnuptial molt (August to October) all immature birds apparently become as adults; adults have one complete molt (postnuptial, August to October), and breeding plumage is the result of wear.

FIELD MARKS. — Bluebird size or larger; adult male the only adult bird of New England that is black with brown head. *Female and young:* Grayish-brown like young Starlings, but smaller, with shorter bill and longer tail.

VOICE. — *Male:* Call note prolonged high-pitched whistle, *phee de de;* "a feeble squeak" (Ralph Hoffmann); "a shrill *cluck see*" (H. Nehrling); "a guttural *quieack*," a low *cook-oo'*, various guttural

[1] Beal, F. E. L.: Bulletin No. 13, United States Department of Agriculture, Division of Biological Survey, 1900, pp. 19, 20.

sounds; a chattering note, a low *chuck chuck* or *gluck gluck* pleasing and liquid, uttered when courting (C. W. Townsend). *Young:* Feeding cry *"peer perr"* (O. W. Knight).

BREEDING. — Anywhere where the nests of other birds may be found, but apparently prefers open country. *Nest:* That of any bird smaller (usually) than itself. *Eggs:* Number for a set not definitely known; .70 to 1.00 by .60 to .70 in.; usually short or rounded ovate; white or whitish, speckled thickly (sometimes blotched) with various browns and neutral tints; figured by Bendire, Vol. II, Plate VI, Figs. 3 to 6. *Dates:* May 9 to June 14, Connecticut; May 15 to July 1, Massachusetts. *Incubation:* Period variable, about 10 to 12 days; by other species.

RANGE. — Eastern North America. Breeds from southern Ontario, southern Quebec, New Brunswick and Nova Scotia south to central Texas, northern Louisiana, Tennessee and Virginia. South in winter from southern Iowa, southern Illinois, southern Indiana, southern Ohio, southern New York and Massachusetts (casually farther north) to Florida, Alabama, and central Mexico (Michoacan); accidental in the Bermuda Islands.*

DISTRIBUTION IN NEW ENGLAND. — *Maine:* Common migrant and common to rare summer resident *New Hampshire:* Common migrant; less common to rare summer resident, chiefly on lower lands; casual in winter. *Vermont:* Rather uncommon migrant and uncommon to occasional summer resident, chiefly in lowlands; casual in winter. *Massachusetts:* Common migrant and summer resident; casual in winter except in southeastern part, where irregularly abundant locally. *Rhode Island and Connecticut:* Common migrant and summer resident; rather rare and irregular winter resident, chiefly coastwise.

SEASON IN MASSACHUSETTS. — March 1 to November 25 (winter).

HAUNTS AND HABITS. Cowbirds are free lovers. They are neither polygamous nor polyandrous — just promiscuous. They have no demesne and no domicile; they are entirely unattached. Their courting is brief and to the point. In this pleasant pastime the male usually takes the lead. He erects his feathers until he is all "puffed up" and struts with spread tail, and wings drooping or partly extended, in the meantime making the most farcical attempts at song. At times he opens and closes his wings in his excitement and stretches up his neck to its full length with bill pointing upward. One spring day I observed a male on the ridge-pole of a house on Marthas Vineyard, attitudinizing for the benefit of his consorts. His attempts at song were peculiar and probably unusual. With each swelling of his throat he produced a soft rather musical sound in two syllables like that of the cuckoo of Europe, but with the accent on the last syllable thus — *cook-oo'*, but several seconds elapsed between the calls. At times a male performs before several females, at other times males are in the majority. Sometimes a popular female will have three or four males in attendance. There seems to be little jealousy, and few combats occur between either males or females; the courtship is a happy-go-lucky affair. It is "off with the old love and on with the new," and the results of this brief union of congenial natures are surreptitiously deposited, not on the nearest available doorstep — but in the nests of other birds which are relied upon as good foster-parents to rear the foundlings, while the care-free Cowbirds wander at their own sweet will with nothing to do but "eat, drink and be merry." The saddest part of the life-history of the Cowbird is that the introduction of its egg or eggs into the nests of smaller birds usually dooms the eggs or young of their foster-parents. Apparently in most cases the birds so imposed upon do

---

* The northwestern part of this breeding range is occupied by a western race (*molothrus ater artemesiæ*) not yet, 1926, recognized by the A. O. U.

Photograph by Daniel D. McDavid

Fig. 66. — Nest of Phœbe with Three Eggs of Cowbird
Courtesy of Eugene W. Schmidt
Pages 339 and 422

Photograph by Mr. McDavid

Fig. 67. — Nest and Eggs of Red-winged Blackbird
Courtesy of Mr. Schmidt
Page 430

not seem to realize the danger that threatens their own brood through the introduction of the interloper; though now and then a Cowbird's egg is found broken beneath the nest of another bird.

In a recent letter Dr. Herbert Friedmann who has made an intensive study of the Cowbird and written a monograph upon the species relates the following experience: "On May 19, 1921, at Ithaca, N. Y., I found a Robin's nest with four eggs. As I had made considerable noise in tramping through the bushes I went back about 20 feet and hid in a clump of bushes, remaining still so that the birds might return. I had been there but half a minute when a female Cowbird that I had not noticed before, lit on the nest, looked around a little, and then settled on it. She shifted her position three times, a little bit each time, and then settled down in the same way that a Robin does on the nest. She had been on the nest just a few seconds when one of the old Robins came back, saw her, and began its distress call and drove her off. The other Robin, two Catbirds, three Yellow Warblers, and one Blackpoll Warbler joined in the chase after the female Cowbird, each calling its loudest, while the Cowbird flew off giving an excited series of chucks, a sort of *chuck-a-tuck-a-chuck-a-tuck* given fairly rapidly. I looked in the nest and saw where there had been only four Robin's eggs before, the four Robin's eggs and also one egg of the Cowbird.

"About a minute and a half later one of the Robins came back, looked in the nest, gave two syllables of its distress call and then drove its bill through the Cowbird's egg, and with a jerk of its head, threw the egg out. It then called a few times more in loud strident tones, and settled on its eggs.

"Although there were two male Cowbirds in the near vicinity, neither of them appeared during the fracas, and both were silent for about 10 minutes after it was over, when one of them was heard squeaking.

"This took place at 7.30 A.M.

"Experiments were made to see whether the Robin distinguished strange eggs from her own by differences in color or size or both and it was found that color was the chief factor. Chipping Sparrow's eggs, which are even smaller than Cowbird's eggs, were accepted by the Robin, while larger eggs, more nearly approximating in size those of its own but not as similar in color, were rejected."

Occasionally a warbler or some other small bird will build a new nest on top of the Cowbird's egg, thus burying it for good and all. In some cases nests three stories in height have been thus built, each of the upper stories with one or more cowbird's eggs buried beneath it. If the Cowbird cannot wait until there are eggs in the nest which she has chosen, and therefore deposits her egg first, or if several Cowbirds' eggs are deposited in the same nest, the owner may desert it. But many birds having one or more Cowbird's eggs thus foisted upon them proceed to incubate it or them with their own. The Cowbird commonly deposits but one egg in a place, and in most cases that is left in the nest of some bird which already has one or two eggs of its own. A pregnant Cowbird, desiring to be rid of an egg, sneaks quietly through orchards, woods or thickets searching for an unguarded nest in which to deposit her leavings. This must be done surreptitiously in the absence of the owners, as they would make it very unpleasant for this unattached female should they discover her in the act. She is not always able to find an unoccupied and unwatched domicile at the right moment, and sometimes is obliged to deposit her treasure on the ground. If she is successful, however, in her quest she may even go so far as to peck small holes in the eggs of the rightful occupant, thus insuring them against hatching. John Burroughs remarks that when a Cowbird finds more than two eggs already in a nest where she wishes to deposit, she removes one. ("Birds and Bees," 1887, p. 30). As "Uncle John" has gone to his reward we must take it for granted that he saw the act. Nevertheless, probably every American ornithologist, who has studied the Cowbird, knows that this is not always the case, for as many as seven Cowbirds' eggs have been found in the same nest. (See Fig. 66, where three are shown in a Phœbe's nest). Once in the nest, the Cowbird's egg, being usually larger than those of the bird chosen to incubate it, gets more heat from her body than the other smaller eggs; therefore it often hatches first. The young bird being larger than the other occupants of the nest reaches higher and gets most of the food, so that while he or she waxes fat and lusty, the legitimate nestlings remain weak and stunted, and usually either die in the nest or are thrown or crowded out alive by the young Cowbird. Cases where any of the "rightful heirs" survive are rare indeed. The Cowbird now has the nest to itself and all food brought by its foster-parents goes into its capacious maw, which seems to be ever ready for more. In about seven days the youngster is strong enough to climb out of the nest, and in a few days more essays its first flight; but its faithful foster-parents guard and feed it for many days thereafter. It is a common sight to see a young Cowbird tended and fed by a little warbler so much smaller than the great clumsy foundling that in feeding it the little bird seems almost in danger of being swallowed alive. The number of species imposed on by the Cowbird considerably exceeds one hundred,* ranging in size from the Blue-gray Gnatcatcher to the Mourning Dove. It seems to make little difference to the Cowbird where the nest is built in which her eggs are left, but nests on the ground or in the lower branches of trees are commonly chosen. Domiciles in hollow trees are entered freely and even the redoubtable Kingbird occasionally is victimized. As soon as the young Cowbird has learned to feed itself, it seeks others of its kind or is sought by them, for Cowbirds are always gregarious and flock more or less the year round.

There are observations on record which may incline some people to the belief that female Cowbirds take an active interest in the fate of their eggs and young. The late Mason A. Walton, the "Gloucester Hermit," published in Forest and Stream for March, 1892, and also in his book [1] an account of his experience with a female Cowbird, which, as he believed, visited from time to time the nest in which her egg was laid, and finally fed and cared for her young one. From my acquaintance with Mr. Walton I am inclined

---

* Dr. Friedmann informs me that the Cowbird (including its western subspecies, *obscurus* and *artimesiæ*) is known to have victimized 190 species.

[1] A Hermit's Wild Friends. 1903, pp. 211–214.

to believe that his observations were reported accurately, but that his deductions from those observations often were unwarranted by the facts. He "believed" that this Cowbird made frequent visits to the "Yellow Birds" nest in which her egg was deposited but did not say that he saw this. However he wrote that he saw her feeding her own young and assisting the male "Yellow Bird" in feeding it, but he had no way of identifying the feeding Cowbird with the bird that laid the egg and no way of proving that the bird doing the feeding at different times was always the same individual. Mr. Ira N. Gabrielson observed a female Cowbird which apparently was alarmed by his intrusion at a nest of a Red-eyed Vireo, containing three Cowbirds' eggs,[1] but he had no evidence that this particular Cowbird laid any of those eggs.

Mr. Laurence B. Fletcher, however, trapped a female Cowbird with a young one, saw the female feed it, banded both birds and saw the two together afterward, the same adult still feeding the young. The adult, which was decorated with Biological Survey band #64782, continued to feed the banded fledgling and no other, although there were other young Cowbirds near.[2] This is a careful observation but it offers no proof that that particular fledgling was the progeny of that particular female. (Birds sometimes feed fledglings of another species). It shows, however, that the adult cared for one particular young, which may have been her own. It will be difficult to secure absolute proof that any Cowbird ever recognizes or cares for its own young, but the observation of Mr. Fletcher has shown that a Cowbird may show maternal consideration for a young bird of its own species. Whether the mother Cowbird ever follows the fortunes of her own offspring may be determined eventually by bird banders' methods. During the summer, Cowbirds gather about pasturing cattle and search for the insects stirred up by the beasts, or, as the cows lie tranquilly chewing their cud, the birds may be seen walking about upon their backs, engaged in ridding them of flies and other pests, or merely resting quietly there in perfect security. In September the flocks begin to move southward; they often associate with other blackbirds and with Starlings, and at times the mixed flocks are enormous, but so far as I have observed in New England Cowbirds usually roost by themselves; often they choose thick coniferous trees or other thickets in the shelter of which they pass the night in great numbers. Another favorite roosting place is in the grass and reeds far out on wide meadows. These moving flocks drift southward until November when most of the Cowbirds have reached their wintering grounds. During mild winters considerable flocks remain on Marthas Vineyard and Cape Cod and near other coasts of southern New England. Generally some of these birds remain wherever they can find food.

The origin of the parasitic habit of Cowbirds is unknown. In the old days many flocks followed the bison herds in their annual migrations north and south over the Great Plains of the west where the birds were known to the pioneers as buffalo birds. The theory has been advanced that this following of the buffalo may have originated the habit of laying in the nests of other birds, as the buffalo birds could not stay long enough

---

[1] Auk, Vol. XXXVIII, 1921, pp. 459–460.
[2] Bulletin of the Northeastern Bird Banding Association, Vol. I, 1925, pp. 22–23.

in one place to rear families of their own. This theory, however, must rest on the assumption that all other Cowbirds which have similar habits (some of which are natives of South or Central America) must have originated on the plains of North America.

The food of the Cowbird has been investigated by the Biological Survey. In a collection of 544 stomachs examined by experts, the animal food was 22.3 per cent of the contents, the vegetal 77.7 per cent. The animal food consisted almost entirely of insects and spiders with a few snails. The insects included ants, wasps, flies, leafhoppers, beetles, including injurious curculios, more grasshoppers than most other birds take and caterpillars, including destructive army worms. Grain, chiefly oats (evidently mostly waste grain), was taken largely early in the year, and a small amount of corn, but the chief vegetal food consists of weed seeds of which great quantities are eaten. The amount of fruit eaten is insignificant, mostly wild berries.[1]

ECONOMIC STATUS. Professor Beal said that the Cowbird must be rated high in the economic scale on account of its food habits; that in most cases the birds destroyed by young Cowbirds which usurp their places in the nest are much smaller than the interloper and so their feeding has less effect. Probably a young Cowbird must be fed by the foster-parents quite as many insects as their own progeny would have consumed, and in some cases more than one young Cowbird is reared in a nest. Says Professor Beal: "The question is a purely economic one and until it can be shown that the young birds sacrificed for the Cowbirds have more economic value than the parasite, judgment must be suspended." Professor Barrows, on the other hand, believed it "one of the few species of native birds which might well be exterminated if possible."

Xanthocéphalus xanthocephalus (BONAPARTE). Yellow-headed Blackbird.

DESCRIPTION. — Bill about as long as head, stout at base, its outlines nearly straight; wings pointed and ample; tail very slightly rounded; feet formed for perching and walking; claws very long and much curved. *Adult male in breeding plumage:* Black including narrow space around eye, extending also to and around base of bill. Rest of head, neck and most of breast rich yellow varying from lemon-yellow to near orange or rarely pinkish-saffron, some feathers about vent usually yellow; parts of feathers of greater wing-coverts and all primary coverts white, forming a large white patch on fore-wing; bill bluish-black; iris brown; legs, feet and claws black. *Adult male in winter plumage:* Similar, but top of head and nape obscured or concealed by dusky tips. *Adult female in breeding plumage:* Dark, dusky grayish-brown; wings without white; stripe above eye, cheeks, chin and throat whitish, dull yellow or yellowish, passing into light yellow on upper breast, rest of breast streaked with white; bill dark horn to black; iris brown; legs and feet blackish or black. *Adult female in winter plumage:* Similar to female in breeding plumage, but markings on side of head often more buffy, chin and throat usually duller, yellow on upper breast deeper, and stripes below it less distinct; bill dusky brownish above, paler below. *Immature male in first breeding plumage:* Similar to young male in winter but yellows purer,

YELLOW-HEADED BLACKBIRD,
ADULT MALE

[1] Beal, F. E. L.: Bulletin No. 13, United States Department of Agriculture, Division of Biological Survey, 1900, pp. 24–28.

top of head blacker and primary coverts without white tips (Ridgway). *Young male in first winter plumage:* Similar to female in winter, but larger and generally darker, especially so about head, where both yellow and dark markings are deeper and yellows richer; no white on breast, but primary coverts tipped white. *Young female in first winter plumage:* Similar to adult female. *Young male changing to first winter plumage in July:* Head and neck dull cinnamon-buff, paler on chin and throat; a central stripe of dusky on top of head; rest of plumage dusky, the feathers margined more or less tawny, especially wing-coverts and tertials; breast unstreaked or streaked dull whitish, middle line of abdomen and leg-feathering whitish. *Young in juvenal plumage:* Variable; from cinnamon-buff, to clay color, much paler or even dull whitish below, and more or less dappled with dusky above; a pale whitish or buffy-cinnamon wing-bar formed by broad, light tips of greater coverts; sometimes another wing-bar formed by tips of lesser coverts; bill brownish, legs and feet flesh color.

MEASUREMENTS. — Length 8.70 to 11.10 in.; spread 13.98 to 17.00; folded wing 4.40 to 5.80; tail 3.35 to 4.85; bill .75 to 1.00; tarsus 1.25 to 1.30. Female much smaller than male.

MOLTS. — Juvenal plumage acquired by complete molt in nestling; first winter plumage acquired by incomplete molt beginning in July (tail, flight-feathers and primary coverts retained: Chapman); apparently this plumage is retained until the following May when partial molt occurs; in ensuing autumn young birds become as adults in winter plumage; adults have complete postnuptial molt (June and July).

FIELD MARKS. — *Male:* Size of Robin or larger; a black bird with yellow head and neck and white patch in fore wing. *Female:* Similar but smaller, duller and paler. *Young:* Resemble female; upper head not yellow but dark brown.

VOICE. — Song, "laborious, whistling, squeaky, chuckling" (N. S. Goss). "It's notes are harsh and rasping;" call notes "a shrill *chäck, chäck*" (C. Bendire).

BREEDING. — In marshes and swamps. *Nest:* In cattail flags, reeds or wild rice, 6 inches to 3 feet above water; composed of blades of grass and sedges, large and bulky but well made. *Eggs:* 2 to 5, usually 4; .91 to 1.14 by .65 to .78 in.; from ovate to elongate ovate or even elliptical ovate; from grayish-white to greenish or pale greenish-white, profusely spotted and blotched with reddish-brown and other browns, drab and gray, some have also fine hair-like dark lines; figured in Bendire's "Life Histories of North American Birds," Vol. II, Plate VI, Figs. 10 to 12. *Dates:* May 15 to June 7, northern United States; July 1, northern Saskatchewan. *Incubation:* Period about 14 days (C. Bendire); chiefly or wholly by female. One brood yearly.

RANGE. — Western North America; north to the borders of Hudsonian Zone. Breeds from south central British Columbia, southwestern Mackenzie, northern Saskatchewan, northern Manitoba and northern Wisconsin south to southern California, Arizona, New Mexico, south central Mexico and east to eastern Wisconsin, northwestern Indiana, and eastern Illinois; south in winter from southwestern California, southern Arizona, southern Texas and southwestern Louisiana to south central Mexico; casual or accidental in Ontario, Quebec, New York, Vermont, Maine, Massachusetts, Connecticut, Pennsylvania, West Virginia, New Jersey, Maryland, District of Columbia, Georgia, South Carolina, and Florida; accidental in Greenland, Cuba, Alaska and Barbadoes.

DISTRIBUTION IN NEW ENGLAND. — A casual straggler in migration. Records: *Maine:* Metinic Island, August 17, 1882, bird taken by Fred Rackliff;[1] Monhegan Island, September 11, 1925, adult female taken.[2] *Vermont:* Windsor, August 27, 1916, male seen at close range by Henry S. Wardner and Mrs. Wardner.[3] *Massachusetts:* Watertown, October 15, 1869, one in immature plumage taken by Frank Sawyer;[4] Eastham, September 10, 1877, two taken by a Mr. Loud;[5] Chatham (Monomoy

---

[1] Norton, A. H.: Auk, Vol. XI, 1894, pp. 78–79.
[2] Taylor, Warner: Auk, Vol. XLIII, 1926, p. 241.
[3] Kennard, F. H.: Auk, Vol. XL, 1923, pp. 695–696.
[4] Maynard, C. J.: Naturalists Guide, 1870, p. 122.
[5] Allen, J. A.: Bulletin of the Essex Institute, Vol. X, 1878, p. 18.

Island), September 8, 1897, female taken by W. B. Revere;[1] Ipswich, September 17, 1917, "I had under observation for about half an hour, a Yellow-headed Blackbird (*Xanthocephalus xanthocephalus*). It was in the plumage of a female." Francis Beach White, Concord, N. H.[2] *Connecticut:* New Haven (?), 1878 (?), a female formerly in collection of Dr. W. H. Hotchkiss and now in collection of L. B. Bishop (without label; but Dr. Hotchkiss informed Dr. Bishop that all of these birds were taken near New Haven, chiefly during the spring of 1878); Hartford, July 1884, one (a supposed female) shot in a flock of Red-wings (W. E. Treat: Auk, Vol. IV, 1887, p. 256); Stamford, July, 1888, female shot (E. K. Colbron: Ornithologist and Oölogist, Vol. XIII, 1888, p. 189).[3]

SEASON IN MASSACHUSETTS. — Casual straggler in September and October.

HAUNTS AND HABITS. As the large, handsome Yellow-headed Blackbird is a mere straggler in New England, little space can be allotted to it here. Probably, however, it will be seen and taken many times in the future. The Vermont record being that of the first specimen reported for that state would hardly have been mentioned here, were it not for the fact that intelligent observers saw the unmistakable birds and had ample opportunity to observe them for several minutes. Soon after the females arrive on their western breeding grounds in spring, the males begin their wooing. Dr. Alexander Wetmore thus describes one of their mating displays: "In the most common display the male started towards the female from a distance of 30 or 40 feet with a loud rattling of his wings as a preliminary. The head was bent down, the feet lowered and the tail dropped while he flew slowly toward his mate. The wings were brought down with a slow swinging motion and were not closed at all so that the white markings on the coverts were fully displayed, the whole performance being reminiscent of a similar wing display of the Mocking-bird."[4] Professor F. E. L. Beal says of this bird: "Its breeding habits are much like those of the redwing, but it is usually less abundant than that bird. It is gregarious and resorts to marshes to build its nest, which is very similar to that of the redwing, and similarly placed. Although it breeds in marshes, it does not by any means confine itself to them in its search for food, but forages far afield, visiting corncribs, grainfields, and barnyards. The writer's first experience with the yellow-headed blackbird was on the prairies of Nebraska, where flocks visited the railway then in process of construction, running about among the feet of the mules and horses in search of grubs and worms exposed by the plow and scraper, and all the time uttering their striking guttural notes (almost precisely like those of a brood of suckling pigs). In their habit of visiting barnyards and hog pastures they resemble cowbirds much more than redwings. When the breeding season is over they often visit grainfields in large flocks, and become the cause of much complaint by Western farmers."[5]

Dr. Chapman says of the bird's song:

"If result were commensurate with effort, the Yellow-head would be a world-famed songster; but something besides unbounded ambition and limitless muscular exertion

[1] Bishop, L. B.: Auk, Vol. XVIII, 1901, p. 195.
[2] Auk, Vol. XXXV, 1918, p. 224.
[3] Sage, Bishop and Bliss: Birds of Connecticut, 1913, p. 112.
[4] Auk, Vol. XXXVII, 1920, p. 403.
[5] Division of Biological Survey, Bulletin No. 13, 1900, p. 30.

is required to produce music. In vain the Yellow-head expands his lungs and throws out his chest, his wide-spread tail testifying to the earnestness of his endeavor; sound he produces in volume, but surely such a series of strained, harsh calls, whistles, like escaping steam, grunts, groans and pig-like squeals never before did duty as a song! In his youth he does far better, the note of the young bird being a wooden-rolling call as different from the voice of the parent as is that of a young Baltimore Oriole." [1] A life history of this species is given in the second volume of Major Bendire's "Life Histories of North American Birds." The food of the Yellow-headed Blackbird has not been the subject of exhaustive investigation. The bird is a potent destroyer of harmful insects and weed seeds, but unfortunately the proportion of grain that it takes appears to be considerably larger than that taken by the Red-winged Blackbird.

ECONOMIC STATUS. Not fully determined. The bird is of no importance in New England.

Agelaíus phœníceus phœniceus (LINNÆUS). Red-winged Blackbird.

Other names: SWAMP BLACKBIRD; MARSH BLACKBIRD; RED-WING.

Plate 60.

DESCRIPTION. — Formed much like Yellow-headed Blackbird, but shorter, smaller, feet relatively longer, claws relatively shorter and tail much more rounded; nostrils small, overhung by a pliable scale. *Adult male in breeding plumage:* Black from head to tail and bill to nail (except fore wing) with slight greenish gloss; lesser wing-coverts red varying from scarlet vermilion to deep orange, middle wing-coverts forming a buffy or buffy-whitish border to the red "epaulets"; iris brown. *Adult male in winter plumage:* Similar, but buff of wing-coverts deeper and some rusty margins on back and scapulars. *Adult female in breeding plumage:* Unlike male; above, dusky or brownish-black varied with streaks and edgings of buffy-grayish, pale buffy, grayish and rusty; more or less distinct light streak along middle top of head, another lighter one over eye; dusky flight-feathers and tail-feathers all edged with the lighter colors; often brownish or red margins or both ornament lesser wing-coverts; lower jaw and lower plumage white (lower jaw, chin and throat sometimes buffy or pink), streaked with dusky; under tail-coverts dusky, margined whitish; chin and throat sometimes unmarked; bill dusky usually paler below; iris brown; legs and feet dark horn to dusky, but not black. *Adult female in winter plumage:* Similar but lighter, markings above more buffy and rusty, and below more buffy. *Immature male in first breeding plumage:* Similar to adult male in winter plumage, but dull brownish-black, with some pale grayish spots and pale narrow feather-edges; the bright wing-patch usually orange, spotted and barred with black; wings and tail worn and faded. *Young male in first winter plumage:* Dull greenish-black; plumage veiled and streaked with buffy, and reddish-brown edgings nearly obsolete on flight-feathers and tail-feathers, and lighter below; wing-patch orpiment orange, flecked and barred with black, but varying according to molt (some have little orange or none on wing); bill and feet black. *Young in juvenal plumage (sexes alike):* Much like adult female but light tint of sides of head, chin and throat more yellowish, ground color below more yellowish or pinkish-buff; dark streaks usually narrower and light edges of flight-feathers buffy-brown or buffy; bill and feet olive-brown.

MEASUREMENTS. — Length 7.50 to 9.50 in.; spread 12.00 to 14.50; folded wing 4.75 to 5.00; tail 2.65 to 3.71; bill .72 to .90; tarsus .85 to 1.20. Weight 2½ to 3 oz. Female smaller than male.

---

[1] Chapman, F. M.: Camps and Cruises of an Ornithologist, 1908, pp. 318, 319.

Molts. — Juvenal plumage, acquired by complete molt (usually completed in June), succeeds mouse-gray natal down; first winter plumage acquired by complete postjuvenal molt (beginning August or later); this plumage at first resembles juvenal plumage, but reddish wing-patch appears sooner or later in male, sometimes not until spring, and as the light edges wear away in winter and spring he bears more resemblance to adult male; first breeding plumage acquired by wear, after first postnuptial molt young males are as winter adults; adult breeding plumage acquired by wear in second spring. Adults have but one complete (postnuptial) molt (August and September); breeding plumage acquired by wear which abrades light edges.

Field Marks. — Size between Robin and Bluebird. Male unmistakable; black with red epaulets, but often when wings are closed only buffy or whitish lower edges of the scarlet wing-patch can be seen. *Female and young:* Smaller, mottled and striped above and below with dusky and whitish or dusky and buffy.

Voice. — Song: *cónkareé, ókaleé, quóng-ker-eé* or some similar sound represents it fairly well; some birds follow it with a brief jingle like a part of the Bobolink's song; alarm note: a long shrill whistle; call note a harsh *chuck* or *tcheck* often accompanied by a jetting of the tail.

Breeding. — Often in communities, in swamps, marshes or meadows, sometimes in upland grassy fields. *Nest:* Usually in reeds, flags, rushes or grass (often in a tussock) above the mud or water or in bushes near or overhanging water; rarely as high as 10 to 15 feet, very rarely 30 to 40 feet; more rarely on ground in grass. *Eggs:* 2 to 5; .81 to 1.10 by .62 to .75 in.; usually ovate; pale bluish-green, sometimes clouded with smoke gray; markings exceedingly variable, spots, blotches and erratic lines or scrawls of black and various shades of brown and purplish, usually most numerous about large end; figured in Bendire's "Life Histories of North American Birds," Vol. II, Plate VI, Figs. 13 to 15. *Dates:* April 25, South Carolina, to May 8, Pennsylvania; May 10 to June 18, Massachusetts; June 1 to July 1, Maine. *Incubation:* Period variously given, 10 to 15 days; by female. One brood yearly. Various authors say two broods may occur occasionally, but I have seen no conclusive evidence.

Range. — Eastern United States and southeastern Canadian Provinces. Breeds from southern Ontario, southern Quebec and Nova Scotia south to east central Texas, northern Louisiana, northern Alabama, and North Carolina; west to central Ontario, central Wisconsin, Iowa, Missouri and eastern Oklahoma; south in winter from Arkansas, Illinois, southern Indiana, southern New York, southern Massachusetts and southern New Hampshire to the Gulf coast and northern Florida.

Distribution in New England. — Common to abundant migrant and summer resident, though rather local in summer in Maine, New Hampshire (accidental in winter) and higher parts of western Massachusetts; local and irregular winter resident in southeastern Massachusetts, Rhode Island and Connecticut, chiefly coastwise.

Season in Massachusetts. — (February 22) March 6 to November 20 (November 28) (winter).

Haunts and Habits. The Red-wing is a typical marsh blackbird. It loves the marsh and waterside and seldom nests far from water. Its very notes carry a suggestion of boggy ooze, and its *chuck*, like that of other blackbirds, is frog-like. It has a strong predilection for the oozy slough and the "floating island," where the treacherous soggy turf gives beneath the incautious footstep and precipitates the adventurer into the dark and watery depths below. Nevertheless Red-wings sometimes choose other places for nesting. We may find an isolated pair, here and there, nesting on some beach ridge among the dunes by the sea, and where their favorite marshes have been filled or drained, or are insufficient in area for their numbers, they sometimes build on the ground in a hayfield, as they did on Staten Island when I was there, and still do in New Jersey. I have but one record of such a nesting in Massachusetts, which was reported by Mrs.

Lucinda Vincent at Chilmark on Marthas Vineyard. The nest was on the ground in a dry spot on the meadow, but less than a foot from the bank of a lily pond. If, however, the drainage of swamps and marshes in Massachusetts continues as it has begun, these blackbirds will have to change their nesting habits or go elsewhere. Although these birds nest near water they are not by any means confined to its vicinity. They may go half a mile from their nests to an orchard to secure an abundance of caterpillars for their young, while in migration they often swarm on the upland and in the corn-fields. From late February to late March, according to the season, Red-wings appear in the Middle States, moving up a little later from the south in enormous flocks. If the season is early, the advance guard (very few in number) reaches southern New England about the 22nd of February. When the main flight arrives here, from the middle of March to the first part of April, the flocks have become much smaller, as many have fallen out of the ranks on the way. Sometimes in their early northward movement, they meet a blizzard from the frozen north, and then some of them turn and drift before the storm toward the shores of Long Island Sound or the sand dunes of Cape Cod. The early flights consist of males alone; the females follow later. The males are now perfecting their bright nuptial dress and are full of vigor and song, and when a flock alights on some lone tree, blackening it with their sable plumage, the air is resonant with blackbird music. We have it on the authority of Alexander Wilson, that the combined singing of a great flock has been heard at a distance of two miles, but Wilson's hearing was exceptionally keen. The spring movement of the flocks seems orderly and directed as if at the command of a leader. If there really is a leader, when he turns, all the rest turn at the same instant. They choose certain trees about some swamp or body of water which they use regularly as stopping places and from which they sing for about ten to fifteen minutes at a time even while the swamps are still ice-bound. Some small flocks increase in numbers as the days go by until they number hundreds (including Cowbirds and Starlings), but after the females appear they begin to scatter and mate. Now the males actively pursue the females, or perching before them they raise the fore part of the wings well out from the shoulders, bowing with lowered head to show the beauties of their epaulets, spreading their shining black tails, and pouring forth their finest music. Their song does not sound very fascinating to our ear, but it seems to be effective with the gentler sex, as some males secure two or three mates, all living happily together with nests near one another in the same bog or meadow. While their modest consorts attend to their wifely duties, the brilliant male stands guard over his numerous progeny. Perched high on the top of some tree or bush he watches for intruders. Let a crow appear and the blackbird is after him. He will chase a Marsh Hawk, a Bittern or even an Osprey in his anxiety to protect those dependent upon him, and sometimes his mates lend a hand in driving the enemy from the field. At sight of a man approaching he becomes hysterical, and goes out to meet him, fluttering overhead and uttering blackbird maledictions or lamentations as long as the intruder remains in the vicinity of his charges. Some of the males are devoted to their offspring and assist in feeding them. Others seem to leave this **duty** mostly to their mates.   The males are not all polygamists, as some, apparently less vigorous or less willing to accept the responsibility which devolves on the father of several families, have but one mate.   It may be that polygamy results from a disparity of the sexes.

The young often leave the nest before they are able to fly, and climb about among the reeds or bushes, moving actively from place to place.   Where blackbirds nest in large colonies, the marsh soon becomes alive with moving young.   Some fall into the water, but usually get out again unless snapped up by frogs, fish or turtles.   Blackbirds have their full share of enemies and many of the eggs and young fall victims to them before the flocks gather for the fall migration.   This gathering begins in July.   Dr. T. Gilbert Pearson describes their autumnal movements well as follows : "After the nesting season when the young are able to fly with their parents the Red-wings collect in flocks and wander about the country in search of food.   As cold weather approaches the birds from the prairies and marsh-lands throughout the northern states and southern Canada begin to move southward.   At this time they may be seen in flocks numbering tens of thousands, and they present a marvelous spectacle as they fly with all the precision of perfectly trained soldiers.   I have seen fully thirty thousand of them while in full flight suddenly turn to the right or the left or at the same instant swoop downward as if they were all driven by common impulse.   They perform many wonderful feats of flight when on the wing.   Sometimes a long billow of moving birds will pass across the fields, the ends of the flying regiment alternately sinking and rising, or even appearing to tumble about like a sheet of paper in a high wind.   In the southern states these great flocks may be seen at almost any time during the winter months.

"In feeding on the ground they progress slowly across the country in a given direction. The birds at the back rise in a continuous cloud, and flying over their feeding friends, alight in the van of the army.   Thus, like a vast wide black hoop, they roll across the peanut or millet fields, until reaching a thicket or wood, they all take wing with a rush, and pass on to the next open field to continue the remarkable performance." [1]

Most of the Red-wings have left New England by the end of October, but now and then some appear locally in Eastern Massachusetts until about the last week in November, and in mild winters a considerable number remain on Cape Cod.   In some winters flocks of 75 to 100 birds are seen there.   Very likely some of those that attempt to winter there in severe seasons succumb to the effects of cold and privation.   I have given elsewhere a brief summary of the food of this bird which follows :

"Although the Red-wings almost invariably breed in the swamp or marsh, they have a partiality for open fields and plowed lands; and most of the Blackbirds that nest in the smaller swamps adjacent to farm lands get a large share of their food from the farmer's fields.   They forage about the fields and meadows when they first come north in spring. Later, they follow the plow, picking up grubs, worms and caterpillars; and should there be an outbreak of cankerworms in the orchard, the Blackbirds will fly at least half a

---

[1] National Association of Audubon Societies, Educational Leaflet No. 25.

mile to get cankerworms for their young. Wilson estimated that the Red-wings of the United States would in four months destroy sixteen thousand, two hundred million larvæ.

"They eat the caterpillars of the gipsy moth, the forest tent caterpillar, and other hairy larvæ. They are among the most destructive birds to weevils, click beetles, and wireworms. Grasshoppers, ants, bugs and flies form a portion of the Red-wings' food. They eat comparatively little grain in Massachusetts, although they get some from newly sown fields in spring, as well as from the autumn harvest; but they feed very largely on the seeds of weeds and wild rice in the fall. In the south they join with the Bobolink in devastating the rice fields, and in the west they are often so numerous as to destroy the grain in the fields; but here the good they do far outweighs the injury, and for this reason they are protected by law." [1]

ECONOMIC STATUS. The chief injury done by Red-wings in New England is the destruction of seed corn, especially sweet corn. Growers in Connecticut suffer considerable loss from this bird. This loss, however, has been emphasized and increased greatly in recent years by hordes of Starlings which join with the blackbirds. Otherwise the Red-wing is distinctly a beneficial bird in this region. In the south where it assembles in much greater numbers, it sometimes destroys large crops of grain. On the other hand it does comparatively little damage in the rice fields as its greatest numbers appear after the grain has been harvested. It feeds on the rice scattered on the ground and thus benefits the planters by destroying the "volunteer" or red rice which if allowed to grow, reduces the value of the crop. It also attacks the fall army worm which in company with other birds it eats in such enormous numbers as to stop some destructive invasions of the insect.

Agelaius phœniceus fórtis RIDGWAY. Thick-billed Red-wing.

Other names: RED-WING, NORTHERN RED-WING.

DESCRIPTION. — Similar to Red-winged Blackbird except that it averages decidedly larger and that the bill often is relatively shorter and thicker.

MEASUREMENTS. — Length from about 9.00 to 10.00 in.; spread up to 15.25; folded wing 4.50 to 5.20; tail 2.80 to 4.10; bill, length .68 to 1.06, depth at base .45 to .53. Female smaller than male.

MOLTS, FIELD MARKS, VOICE AND BREEDING. — Similar to those of Red-winged Blackbird; not distinguishable from latter in field.

RANGE. — Interior of North America. Breeds from central Mackenzie and northern Manitoba south to southeastern British Columbia, southeastern Idaho, Wyoming, Colorado, northwestern Texas, Nebraska, Minnesota and northern Michigan; winters mostly in southern part of its breeding range and south to Texas, New Mexico, Louisiana and Alabama; occasional in autumn or winter east to Ohio, New York and Connecticut.

DISTRIBUTION IN NEW ENGLAND. — A straggler in Connecticut. Records: *Connecticut:* North Haven, "Dec. 25, 1901, one adult male, Jan. 10, 1902, young male and young female, Nov. 11, 1903, young male. Quinnipiac Marshes, (Ludington and Louis B. Bishop, now in collection of L. B. B.)." [2]

---

[1] Useful Birds and Their Protection, 1913, pp. 319, 320.
[2] Sage, Bishop and Bliss: Birds of Connecticut, 1913, p. 113.

HAUNTS AND HABITS. The Thick-billed Red-wing, a geographic race, has a life history similar to that of the common Red-wing; probably its food habits differ somewhat in the northern part of its range, but descriptions of the habits of the Red-wing in the west do not differentiate between the two races. They are essentially alike. Probably the present form occurs in New England more often than the few records given indicate; the difference between the two races is chiefly one of size, as the shape of the bill is more or less variable in both. It is quite possible that many of the individuals seen here in November and in winter are of this race. I have seen a number of specimens taken in this region that have thicker bills than some taken in the range of the Thick-billed Red-wing, and as the measurements of the two forms overlap, the difficulty of distinguishing one from the other is evident, but such adult males as I have seen from the northern range have little or no pale edging to the scarlet wing-patch.

ECONOMIC STATUS. Similar to that of Red-winged Blackbird.

Sturnélla mágna magna (LINNÆUS). Meadowlark.

Other names: MARSH QUAIL; OLD-FIELD LARK.

Plate 61.

DESCRIPTION. — Bill a little longer than head, nearly straight, tapering and pointed in profile, but when seen from above less tapering and tip somewhat rounded; resembles bill of Starling; ridge extends back into feathers of forehead; wing short, rounded but ample with long secondaries and tertials; tail quite short and somewhat graduated, its feathers rather pointed; feet very large, stout, with long toes; hind toe especially large and long with great claw about twice as long as middle claw. *Adult male in breeding plumage:* Prevailing aspect blackish above, mixed with light brownish-gray; feathers of back and rump, with dark or blackish centers and light edges; tertials and secondaries barred in herring-bone fashion with black, but these feathers like primaries have light edges; central stripe of dull buffy or dull buffy-white on top of head, separating two broad stripes of black; broad stripe running from nostril over eye, lemon-yellow before and over eye, changing to buffy-white behind eye; narrow stripe below it (behind eye) black or blackish; rest of sides of head grayish-white with slight grayish streaks in ear region; sides of neck whitish, tinged buffy and streaked black; back of neck more buffy, also streaked black; middle tail-feathers brownish-gray with black centers and barred with black in herring-bone pattern, all marked similarly except three outer tail-feathers which are chiefly white; below largely lemon-yellow; broad black crescent on upper breast, extending upward on either side and merging with black spot below angle of jaw; sides of breast, sides and flanks whitish (the two latter tinged buffy), streaked black; under tail-coverts and leg-feathering similarly colored and streaked; bill dusky or black above, pale grayish-blue below; iris brown; legs and feet pale pinkish-gray. *Adult male in winter plumage:* Similar but much browner above with less black; whitish stripe on top of head, flanks, under tail-coverts, etc., more buffy, and black crescent more or less veiled by yellowish tips. *Adult female in breeding plumage:* Similar to adult male, but much smaller, somewhat duller, dark stripes on top of head less distinct and more streaked with brown, and black crescent relatively smaller. *Adult female in winter plumage:* Similar to breeding plumage, but browner above, and white parts more buffy. *Immature in first breeding plumage:* Similar to adults, but faded and worn to brown and whitish above, bright yellow and black below. *Young in first winter plumage:* Like adults in winter plumage, but black crescent below veiled at first by yellow feather-tips; these wear away in winter when young become almost like winter adults. *Young in juvenal plumage:* Similar to adult female in winter plumage but still more brown above and no black cravat; yellow below much duller or buffy and many blackish spots on upper breast.

PLATE 61

PLATE 61

ORCHARD ORIOLE
Page 438

BALTIMORE ORIOLE
Page 442

ADULT MALE IN BREEDING
PLUMAGE

ADULT MALE IN BREEDING
PLUMAGE

YOUNG MALE IN FIRST
WINTER PLUMAGE

ADULT FEMALE

ADULT FEMALE

MEADOWLARK
Page 434

ADULT MALE IN BREEDING PLUMAGE

All about one-half scale.

Louis Agassiz Fuertes

MEASUREMENTS. — Length 8.98 to 11.00 in.; spread 13.50 to 17.00; folded wing 4.15 to 5.15; tail 2.48 to 3.50; bill 1.26 to 1.49; tarsus 1.24 to 1.70. Weight about 4 to 5 oz. Female much smaller than male.

MOLTS. — Juvenal plumage follows natal down by complete postnatal molt, and becomes fully developed in July or shortly after young leave nest; first winter plumage acquired by complete post-juvenal molt (August to October); first breeding plumage acquired by wear; in second winter plumage young birds become as adults; adults have one complete postnuptial molt annually; breeding plumage acquired by wear.

FIELD MARKS. — Size somewhat larger than Robin with longer straight tapering bill and very short rounded tail. *Adults:* Brown birds with yellow breast crossed by broad V-shaped black cravat; on ground or in flight, which alternates fluttering with sailing, often show white on each side of tail; when on ground usually keep back toward watcher, not often showing bright yellow breast or black cravat; short tail when spread to show white is then best mark; feed on ground where they *walk*, but male often sings from tree-tops. *Young:* similar but duller and browner, black cravat wanting, or more or less veiled.

VOICE. — Calls: A rather guttural chatter, a long drawn shrill whistle, a note somewhat like that of Nighthawk. Song: Plaintive, variable; a common song is rendered like *Hee-héé-héé-héé-thée-hea* (Bendire); or *heetar-su-e-oo;* sometimes translated as *spring-o'-the-yeéar;* more or less varied as *seel-yah seel-yah; seel-yah-see-e* and *ah-tick-seel-yah* (Thoreau); a rare song, usually given in flight, is such as might be expected from a giant glorified Bobolink but not so hurried as Bobolink music.

BREEDING. — In open country and grassy lands. *Nest:* On ground, in grass, usually in depression, and well concealed, often arched over, built of grasses, weeds, etc., and lined with similar but finer material; sometimes a covered grassy tunnel leads to it; rarely one has two entrances. *Eggs:* 3 to 7 (very rarely 8), usually 5; .85 to 1.21 by .72 to .89 in.; short ovate to elongate ovate; white, rarely pinkish or greenish, more or less spotted (very rarely unspotted), blotched and speckled all over with different shades of brown and purple or lavender, often clustered more about large end than elsewhere; figured in Bendire's "Life Histories of North American Birds," Vol. II, Plate VI, Figs. 20 and 21. *Dates:* May 5, Virginia; May 9, Pennsylvania; May 6, Rhode Island; May 11 to June 28, Massachusetts; early June to July 22, Maine. *Incubation:* Period 15 to 17 days (Burns); by female chiefly, male assists. One brood yearly; possibly two at times in the south.

RANGE. — Eastern North America, north to Canadian Zone and James Bay. Breeds chiefly in Transition and Upper Austral life-zones from central eastern Minnesota, northern Wisconsin, northern Michigan, southeastern Ontario, southern Quebec, and New Brunswick south to central Texas, southwestern Missouri, northern Arkansas (probably), central Illinois, central western Tennessee, western North Carolina, and southern Virginia, and west to southwestern Minnesota, western Nebraska, central Kansas, central Oklahoma and northwestern Texas; south in winter from southern Wisconsin, southern Michigan, southern Ontario, southern New York, and southern Maine to southern South Carolina, Alabama, Louisiana and southeastern Texas; casual northeast to Nova Scotia and Prince Edward Island.

DISTRIBUTION IN NEW ENGLAND. — *Maine:* Uncommon to rare migrant and uncommon local summer resident; rare in winter along the seaboard, recently increasing. *New Hampshire:* Uncommon to common migrant and summer resident in lowlands; very local in northern part, rare in winter on seaboard. *Vermont:* Common migrant and common local summer resident in lowlands; rare and irregular in winter; *Massachusetts, Rhode Island and Connecticut:* Common migrant and common summer resident; rather rare, irregular winter resident in interior but more common on seaboard.

SEASON IN MASSACHUSETTS. — Permanent resident but most common inland from March to October.

HAUNTS AND HABITS. The Meadowlark is a bird of the fields. There it greets the spring while the meadows are still brown. Often it mounts to the top of some tall tree on a grassy hilltop and with brilliant yellow breast turned to the rising sun welcomes with song the coming day.　As Mrs. Mabel Osgood Wright well says, its lay "has a breezy sound, as fresh and wild as if the wind were blowing through a flute."　The male is a persistent singer and continues to sing more or less from March to November.　The Meadowlark is not a lark; it is a meadow starling.　The name of the genus *Sturnella* is an irregular diminutive of *Sturnus*, the Starling, and one can see at a glance that the bird bears a close superficial resemblance in form to a Starling, and its flight is similar to that of the latter.　Our Meadow Starling in New England is rather a shy bird and keeps to the open lands where it can command a wide view and perceive from afar the approach of an enemy.　Along the seaboard it frequents meadows and salt marshes and there it is known as the Marsh Quail, and though protected by law it sometimes is the victim of youthful gunners.

About the second week in March the flight of Meadowlarks reaches southern New England.　It continues into April.　More and more birds come from the south until the fields of southern New England are sparingly populated with them.　Here their courtship begins in late April or early May and nest building quickly follows.　Dr. T. Gilbert Pearson tells of the nesting:

"If you want to find a Meadowlark's nest you must look for it on the ground.　It is usually made entirely of dead grasses, although at times a thin lining of horsehair is added.　Most of the nests I examined possessed a dome-shaped roof of grass, thus allowing inspection from one side only.　This snug little house is hid under the edge of a clump of grass or weeds.　Sometimes one finds it in a field of corn, or concealed by a stump around which grass is growing, or elsewhere protected by an overhanging grassy clod left unbroken at the spring plowing.

"It is something of an adventure to find one of these stationary cradles built for the comfort of the wee Larks to come.　Usually it is discovered quite by accident as one pursues his way across a meadow or field.　So closely do the colors of the feathers on the head and back of the bird resemble its surroundings that if it could restrain its fear one might pass within a foot of the spot with small chance of discovering the secret.　The bird seems to be conscious of this fact, and often will permit one almost to step on it before fluttering away.　One day, after a forenoon spent in a marsh with two other bird-lovers, we came out on a dry meadowland for lunch.　After spending half an hour lunching and lounging on the ground we rose to go, when suddenly up flew a Meadowlark from her nest with its five speckled eggs not over twelve feet from where our lunch had been spread.　There she had been sitting all that time, and probably would not have moved when she did had I not stepped within a foot of her hiding-place.　It is a very discouraging task to attempt to find a Meadowlark's nest by watching the birds go to it, for the reason that when one of them wishes to approach the spot, it alights on the ground many yards away and walks quietly through the grass to its destination.　Ordinarily it leaves its home in the same careful manner.　Certain well-defined paths of travel may often be noted radiating from the nest." [1]

---

[1] National Association of Audubon Societies, Educational Leaflet No. 3.

While the female takes all pains to conceal the location of the nest the male also plays his part in the deception. Mrs. Wheelock tells of a male that persistently carried butter-flies and dragon flies to a point 100 yards from the nest as if he were feeding his mate or young there. While the female is incubating, the male sings to her as she sits on the nest. At that time the listener may hear, rarely, the jingling flight-song, as the bird flies high, pouring forth a bubbling medley not unlike that of the Bobolink, but louder and not so hurried. I have heard this song but once, but Mr. W. Glenn Boyle of Gill, Massachusetts, tells me that it is not uncommonly heard in the part of the Connecticut Valley where he lives. The young remain in the nest for ten days or two weeks, and then wander about in the grass until their wings grow strong, attended by their solicitous parents. Dr. Pearson says:

"Late in the summer the birds assemble and in more or less straggling companies go foraging about over the fields. Sometimes one may find only half a dozen together, but in crossing meadows I have at times seen fifty or a hundred at a time. They do not fly in compact flocks like Blackbirds, nor do all the members of a company spring into the air at once as is the custom with Quails. Their flight is leisurely and rather slow, which renders them an easy mark for the amateur gunner." [1]

When the frosts begin to nip the meadow grasses, the Meadowlarks gather in small flocks each containing several families, and fly southward or toward the sea-coast. A few may winter regularly for a series of winters in the interior of the New England states, until some very severe season destroys most of them. This occurs not infrequently. Along the coast many winter in flocks about the salt-marshes and old fields, but even there exceptionally severe seasons kill many of them, as in the winter of 1917–18, when they were nearly wiped out along the coast of Massachusetts. They cannot stand high winds accompanied by very severe cold and heavy snowfalls, and even though well fed many perish. Dr. C. W. Townsend shows in the following words how they find shelter in violent snowstorms: "On February 13, 1916, as I was walking over the marsh in a driving snowstorm on snowshoes, a Meadowlark whirled out of the snow within three inches of the tip of one of my shoes. He had been snugly settled in a cavity in the grass and had been nearly or entirely snowed in. In another part of the marsh, about a mile away, on the same day another Meadowlark suddenly emerged from the snow leaving a small round hole of exit. Into this I could insert my hand as into a cavity." [2] The majority, however, go south only to run the gauntlet of the guns. In the southern states they assemble in great flocks of a thousand or more and many fall victims to gunners.

In the year 1906 I wrote as follows of the food of the Meadowlark and see no reason to change the statement now: "The Meadowlark is now quite generally protected by law at all times, and no bird more fully deserves such protection. It is practically harm-less, and takes nothing that is of any use to man except a few small grains and seeds.

---

[1] Pearson, T. Gilbert: National Association of Audubon Societies, Educational Leaflet No. 3.
[2] Supplement to the Birds of Essex County, Massachusetts, 1920, p. 131.

On the other hand, it is one of the most useful birds of the fields, perhaps the most valuable. In summer almost ninety-nine per cent of its food consists of insects and allied forms. It eats about all the principal pests of the fields, and is particularly destructive to cutworms, hairy ground caterpillars and grasshoppers. In summer it gets but few seeds, but in fall and winter it takes many weed seeds. It visits weedy cornfields and gardens in search of ragweed and other seeds, of which it devours enormous quantities, which make up about one-third of the food for the year. Even in winter it prefers insects when it can get them. Mr. C. W. Nash says, in his "Birds of Ontario," that several specimens shot in winter contained only insects, taken about market gardens. Professor Beal says that even in December and January the insect components of the food are thirty-nine and twenty-four per cent, respectively; and in March, when insects are still hard to obtain, the quantity rises to seventy-three per cent. Professor Beal makes an ingenious and very moderate estimate, from which he concludes that twenty-five dollars' worth of hay is saved annually in an ordinary township by Meadowlarks, through their destruction of grasshoppers, and he values hay at only ten dollars per ton. When we consider that grasshoppers, green grasshoppers, locusts and crickets all together form twenty-nine per cent of the food of this bird for the year, and that it is almost entirely insectivorous by preference, and when we consider also the additional injury that must occur were the insects and their progeny allowed to increase through a lack of Meadowlarks, the value of the bird becomes evident." [1]

ECONOMIC STATUS. Although the Meadowlark is a useful bird everywhere, it does considerable injury to corn and other grains in the south where in winter great numbers feed on the grain.

Ícterus spúrius (LINNÆUS). Orchard Oriole.

Plate 61.

DESCRIPTION. — Bill shorter than head, pointed, tapering, slightly down-curved; tail shorter than folded wing, much rounded. *Adult male in breeding plumage:* Head, neck, middle of upper breast, back, wings (except lesser and middle coverts) and tail black; greater wing-coverts and flight-feathers edged very pale chestnut or whitish; rest of plumage, above and below, rich, dark chestnut, deepening on breast, some specimens lighter, probably faded; bill black or bluish-black above, pale bluish sometimes along edges and at least basally so below; iris brown; legs and feet bluish to bluish-black. *Adult male in winter plumage:* Similar to male in breeding plumage, but black and chestnut plumage of body and head more or less veiled, the black with buffy-grayish, light olive or chestnut feather margins, and the chestnut of lower plumage with indistinct yellowish margins or tips. *Adult female:* Above, including tail, yellowish-olive, dulling and graying on back and scapulars; wing grayish-dusky with two white bars (one at ends of middle coverts the other at ends of greater coverts), each wing-feather with brownish-gray edging and tipping; below light olive-yellow. *Young male in first breeding plumage:* Similar to adult female, but chin and throat black; some show slight markings of black and chestnut elsewhere. *Young in first winter plumage:* Similar to adult female but male larger and back browner. *Young in juvenal plumage (sexes alike):* Similar to adult female but more brownish above and lighter wing-markings tinged buff.

---

[1] Useful Birds and their Protection, 1913, pp. 318–319.

MEASUREMENTS. — Length 6.00 to 7.25 in.; spread 9.15 to 10.25; folded wing 2.75 to 3.25; tail 2.65 to 3.25; bill .60 to .80; tarsus .65 to .88. Female smaller than male.

MOLTS. — Juvenal plumage resembles first winter plumage, but browner above and paler below; young male in first winter plumage (acquired by molt of body feathers and wing-coverts in July) indistinguishable from young female in first winter plumage; and differs only slightly from adult female in summer; in first nuptial plumage, acquired by partial molt in spring, male has throat black, but, as a rule, is otherwise like female; amount of black in throat varies; sometimes much restricted, sometimes spreads somewhat down breast; such highly developed birds usually have traces of chestnut below; postnuptial (fall) molt apparently occurs after bird has left for the south when it passes into winter plumage which, as Dwight has said, resembles that of adult; there is no spring molt and adult chestnut and black breeding plumage is acquired by wearing off of buffy tips which fringe winter plumage.[1]

FIELD MARKS. — About Bluebird size. *Adult male:* Black head and neck, wings, back and tail, one white wing-bar; elsewhere deep chestnut. *Adult female and young:* Yellowish-olive above, olive-yellow below; wings dusky with two white wing-bars; much like female and young of Baltimore Oriole, thus difficult to distinguish in field, but female Orchard Oriole is more greenish above; immature male like female, but throat black; some immature males have patches of black and chestnut on body and head.

VOICE. — Call note: Suggests the *chuck* of a blackbird, also a loud rattling call *tarrrrrrr* (H. Nehrling). Song: Different from that of Baltimore Oriole — a "definite outburst of musical notes; also a chatter resembling that of Cowbird" (Ralph Hoffmann); "like glorified song of Purple Finch"; the full song is given with great abandon "especially on the wing"; have tried to express his song by the words, *Look here, what cheer, what cheer, whip yo, what cheer, wee yo*, sometimes ending in *sit-e-wee*, "occasionally a rattle is introduced" (C. W. Townsend); fledgling "a whinnying noise" (Mrs. J. E. Carth).

BREEDING. — Usually in orchards and gardens, on farm lands, or among shade trees or timber along streams. *Nest:* In a fruit or other deciduous tree or shrub, more rarely in coniferous tree, usually from 7 to 20 feet from ground; sometimes resting among forked twigs, but some are suspended from forked end of limb (sometimes from two); a rather short purse-shaped structure, well woven. In the south composed chiefly of grasses or "Spanish moss," unlined or little lined with soft materials. In the north often made of green grasses lined usually with plant-down. *Eggs:* 4 to 6; .71 to .88 by .56 to .60 in.; mostly ovate; usually bluish-white marked with blotches, spots and scrawling lines of various browns, purples and lavender; markings usually clustered more about large end; figured in Bendire's "Life Histories of North American Birds," Vol. II, Plate VII, Figs. 3 to 5. *Dates:* May 27, Alabama; May 9 to 31, South Carolina; May 28 to June 25, Massachusetts. *Incubation:* Period about 14 days; chiefly by female. One brood yearly in the north, possibly two sometimes in the south.

RANGE. — United States east of the Rocky Mountains, southeastern Canada, middle America and northern South America. Breeds from northern North Dakota, Minnesota, Wisconsin, north central Michigan, southeastern Ontario, central New York, southern Vermont and southern New Hampshire and (casually) Maine; south to northern Florida and the Gulf coast, southeastern Texas, Vera Cruz, Chiapas and Oaxaca, Mexico, and west to western North Dakota, western South Dakota, eastern Colorado, western Oklahoma, western Texas, northwestern Durango and Jalisco, Mexico; winters from southern Mexico and Central America to Colombia; occasional during migration in southern Florida and Cuba; casual to southern New Brunswick, Nova Scotia, Maine, northern Vermont, eastern Wyoming, central Colorado and central southern New Mexico.

DISTRIBUTION IN NEW ENGLAND. — *Maine:* Accidental visitor. Knight gives three records of specimens taken in Maine [2] near Auburn, near Calais, Thomaston. Westbrook, May 21, 1922, young male seen within 6 feet of open window for 20 minutes by Mrs. Fabius M. Ray.[3] Lewiston, summers of

---

[1] Chapman, Frank M.: Handbook of Birds of Eastern North America, 1914, p. 364.
[2] Knight, O. W.: The Birds of Maine, 1908, p. 350.
[3] Ray, Mrs. Fabius M.: *in litt.*

1924 and 1926, pair bred; nest found in 1924 by Clarence Farrar.[1] *New Hampshire:* Accidental visitor. Rollinsford, about 1880, adult male taken by George H. Yeaton.[2] Spofford, no date, male seen at Spofford Lake.[3] *Vermont:* Very rare summer resident or visitor, in southern parts mostly. Brattleboro, prior to 1907, young found once by Mrs. Elizabeth B. Davenport.[4] Hartland, June 4, 1907, pair seen by Mrs. J. G. Underwood.[5] Hartland, May 14, 1908, pair seen by Mrs. E. D. Morgan.[6] Middlebury, June 1, 1883, two males, one adult, one immature, taken by F. H. Knowlton, and in Middlebury College collection.[7] *Massachusetts:* Rare local summer resident chiefly along seaboard and in river valleys. *Rhode Island:* Rare summer resident. *Connecticut:* Uncommon to common summer resident.

SEASON IN MASSACHUSETTS. — (May 1) May 7 to September 28.

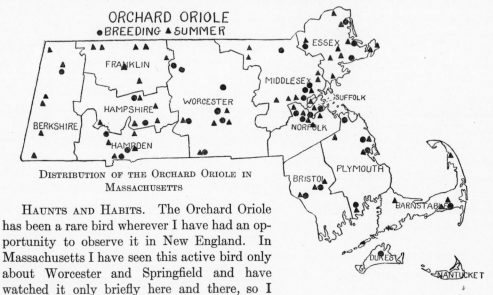

DISTRIBUTION OF THE ORCHARD ORIOLE IN MASSACHUSETTS

HAUNTS AND HABITS. The Orchard Oriole has been a rare bird wherever I have had an opportunity to observe it in New England. In Massachusetts I have seen this active bird only about Worcester and Springfield and have watched it only briefly here and there, so I know little about its habits in the northeastern states. I can do no better than to quote a part of Audubon's life history of the bird, which is more nearly complete than any other that has come to my notice: "The migration of the Orchard Oriole from south to north is performed by day, and singly, as is that of its relative the Baltimore Oriole, the males appearing a week or ten days sooner than the females. Their flight is lower than that of the Baltimore, and considerably shorter in its continuance, the Orchard Oriole alighting more frequently on the tops of the trees, to rest or to feed. They exhibit a greater repetition of motions of the wings, although sliding through the air for a few yards only at a time, and whilst about to alight, as well as afterwards, perform strong and well marked jettings of the tail. This the Baltimore seldom does. No sooner have they reached the portion of the country in which they intend to remain dur-

[1] Miller, Miss Carrie E.: *in litt.*
[2] Yeaton, George H.: *in litt.*
[3] Davenport, Mrs. Elizabeth B.: *in litt.*
[4] Vermont Bird Club, Bulletin No. 2, 1907, p. 9.
[5] Underwood, Mrs. J. G.: *in litt.*
[6] Morgan, Mrs. E. D.: *in litt.*
[7] Knowlton, F. H.: Auk, Vol. I, 1884, p. 390.

ing the time of raising their young, than these birds exhibit all the liveliness and vivacity belonging to their nature. The male is seen rising in the air for ten or twenty yards in an indirect manner, jerking his tail and body, flapping his wings, and singing with remarkable impetuosity, as if under the influence of haste, and anxious to return to the tree from which he has departed. He accordingly descends with the same motions of the body and tail, repeating his pleasant song as he alights. These gambols and carollings are performed frequently during the day, the intervals being employed in ascending or descending along the branches and twigs of different trees, in search of insects or larvæ. In doing this, they rise on their legs, seldom without jetting the tail, stretch their neck, seize the prey, and emit a single note, which is sweet and mellow, although in power much inferior to that of the Baltimore. At other times, it is seen bending its body downwards, in a curved posture, with head greatly inclined upwards, to peep at the under parts of the leaves, so as not to suffer any grub to escape its vigilance. It now alights on the ground, where it has spied a crawling insect, and again flies towards the blossoms, in which many are lurking, and devours hundreds of them each day, thus contributing to secure to the farmer the hope which he has of the productiveness of his orchard.

"The arrival of the females is marked with all due regard, and the males immediately use every effort in their power to procure from them a return of attention. Their singings and tricks are performed with redoubled ardour, until they are paired, when nidification is attended to with the utmost activity. They resort to the meadows, or search along the fences for the finest, longest, and toughest grasses they can find, and having previously fixed on a spot either on an Apple Tree, or amidst the drooping branches of the Weeping Willow, they begin by attaching the grass firmly and neatly to the twigs more immediately around the chosen place. The filaments are twisted, passed over and under, and interwoven in such a manner as almost to defy the eye of man to follow their windings. All this is done by the bill of the bird, in the manner used by the Baltimore Oriole. The nest is of a hemispherical form, and is supported by the margin only. It seldom exceeds three or four inches in depth, is open almost to the full extent of its largest diameter at the top or entrance, and finished on all sides, as well as within, with the long slender grasses already mentioned. Some of these go round the nest several times, as if coarsely woven together. This is the manner in which the nest is constructed in Louisiana; in the middle districts it is usually lined with soft and warm materials. . . . The young follow the parents for several weeks, and many birds congregate towards autumn, but the males soon separate from the females, and set out by themselves as they arrived in spring.

"The sociality of the Orchard Oriole is quite remarkable, and in this respect that bird differs widely from the Baltimore, which will not suffer any other bird of its species to build a nest, or to remain within a considerable distance from the spot which it has selected for its own; whereas many nests of the species now before you may be observed in the same garden or orchard, and often within a few yards of the house. I have counted as many as nine of these nests on a few acres of ground, and the different pairs to which they belonged lived in great harmony.

"Although the food of the Orchard Oriole consists principally of insects of various kinds, it is not composed exclusively of them. They are fond of different sorts of fruits and berries. Figs are also much relished by them, as well as mulberries and strawberries, but not to such a degree as to draw the attention of the gardener or husbandman towards their depredations." [1]

All authorities agree that the food of the Orchard Oriole consists chiefly of insects. It takes a few useful parasitic wasps and quantities of insect pests. Professor S. A. Forbes shot two of these birds in an infested orchard, and found that 97 per cent of their stomach contents consisted of cankerworms and other caterpillars and the rest of ants.[2] The bird consumes quantities of grasshoppers and locusts; it takes many plant lice, scale insects, leaf-mining beetles, rose beetles and other injurious beetles (including the cotton boll weevil), rose slugs, cabbage worms and other caterpillars.

ECONOMIC STATUS. The only injury to man's property recorded of this bird is some slight eating of the stamens of fruit blossoms and some pilfering of small fruits such as strawberries, raspberries and grapes. Normally its fruit supply comes from wild fruits, but where these are not abundant this oriole sometimes when numerous does considerable damage to grapes in vineyards. It is generally regarded, however, as a very beneficial bird.

Icterus gálbula (LINNÆUS). Baltimore Oriole.

Other names: ORIOLE; GOLDEN ROBIN; FIRE-HANG-BIRD.

Plate 61.

DESCRIPTION. — Form like that of Orchard Oriole but larger and male much more brightly colored. *Adult male in breeding plumage:* Head, neck, back, scapulars and middle of upper breast black; rest of under plumage, rump, upper tail-coverts and lesser and middle wing-coverts orange-yellow to bright rich orange (in high plumage, near flame scarlet on breast and rump); wings and exposed part of tail largely black; flight-feathers all outwardly edged lighter or white, these edges sometimes worn away except on tertials and ends of greater coverts where broadly white; concealed base of tail and ends of all tail-feathers yellow or orange (the two middle feathers merely tipped thus), the yellow ends increasing in length toward outer feather where they occupy nearly half or more of the exposed surface; bill black or blackish above, pale grayish-blue on sides and below; iris orange to brown; legs and feet light to dark plumbeous-blue. *Adult male in winter plumage:* Similar, but scapulars and back with feather-margins of yellow or orange; orange of rump and upper tail-coverts obscured somewhat by olive tips, and white edges of wing-feathers broader. *Adult female in breeding plumage:* Variable; usually saffron-olive above, commonly more or less indistinctly spotted with black or blackish; wings dusky with two white bars and grayish feather-edges; rump and upper tail-coverts dull yellowish-olive, sometimes dull orange; tail similar but duller, more olive; below dull orange-yellow often, but not always, with more or less black on throat, and sometimes black elsewhere; old females sometimes black and yellow like immature or faded males. *Adult female in winter plumage:* Similar but back more tinged with gray. *Immature male in first breeding plumage:* Similar to adult male but somewhat duller, the primaries not black, but faded to brown and much worn; rump and under plumage usually yellow. *Young in first winter plumage:* Variable, similar to adult female and not always to be distinguished from those with no black on throat, but

---

[1] Audubon, John James: Ornithological Biography, Vol. I, 1832, pp. 222, 223.
[2] Illinois State Laboratory of Natural History, Bulletin No. 6, 1883, p. 14.

young male usually browner above. *Young in juvenal plumage (sexes alike):* Similar to adult female but paler and grayer above and usually paler or more whitish below; chin grayish-white, light wing markings more buffy; skins examined showed no black spots above.

MEASUREMENTS. — Length 7.00 to 8.15 in.; spread 11.15 to 12.50; folded wing 3.42 to 4.00; tail 2.65 to 3.55; bill .70 to .85; tarsus .80 to .90. Weight of female 1½ oz. Female smaller than male.

MOLTS. — Juvenal plumage acquired by complete postnatal molt of natal down beginning in nestling; first winter plumage acquired by partial molt (July and August) including body plumage and wing-coverts, flight-feathers and tail being retained; first breeding plumage acquired by partial or nearly complete molt (April and May) which does not involve primaries or their coverts or secondaries; tertials are renewed in some cases, also tail; young male is still distinguishable from adult male by worn brown wings and duller plumage and does not become as adult winter male until complete postnuptial molt (August and September), and does not acquire adult breeding plumage until the next spring; adults have one molt (complete postnuptial, August and early September); breeding plumage is believed to be acquired by wear, which abrades pale and dull feather-tips of winter so that colors become brighter and more uniform.

FIELD MARKS. — Somewhat larger than Bluebird. *Adult male:* Black head, neck, back, wings and tail; one white wing-bar; breast, rump and terminal parts of outer tail-feathers orange-yellow or orange. *Female and young:* Olive above; more yellow on rump and below (sometimes some black about head, neck and back); wings dusky with *two white bars;* practically indistinguishable in the field from female Orchard Oriole but larger; somewhat similar to female Scarlet Tanager but latter has no wing-bars.

VOICE. — Alarm note: A long rattling chatter. Call notes: Clear short whistles. Song: A succession of clear, wild, rounded notes easily imitated by whistling, but difficult to describe; many variations; one bird had several songs on the key of C apparently; imitations of bugle calls; Call of young from nest: *teé-dee-dee, teé-dee-dee* (Hoffmann); call of young after leaving nest, *he-he-häe* (Bendire); young then very noisy.

BREEDING. — Chiefly on farm lands or along highways; nest in orchard or shade tree, very often in a street elm, rarely in edge of woods. *Nest:* A neatly-woven, pensile, purse-shaped structure, often inaccessible if hung from tips of lofty elm branches; from 9 (very rarely lower) to 90 feet from ground; usually open at top and sheltered by leaves above it; occasionally roofed over, with entrance hole on one side; woven of vegetal fibers and lined with hair, tree moss, plant down or similar soft warm material or cotton string, yarn, rags and other discarded materials of human use. *Eggs:* 4 to 6; .82 to 1.02 by .59 to .66 in.; elongate ovate to ovate; grayish-white with streaks, blotches and irregular lines and scrawls of various browns and black, and (sparingly) marks of lavender and pearl-gray; these usually cluster most about large end; figured in Bendire's "Life Histories of North American Birds," Vol. II, Plate VII, Figs. 6 to 9. *Dates:* May 15, Virginia; May 23 to June 24, Connecticut; May 24 to July 4, Massachusetts. *Incubation:* Period 14 days; by female chiefly. One brood yearly.

RANGE. — Temperate eastern North America to northern South America. Breeds from central Alberta, central Saskatchewan, southern Manitoba, southern Ontario, southern Quebec, southern New Brunswick and Nova Scotia south to southeastern Texas, southern Louisiana, central Alabama, central Georgia and central South Carolina, and west to eastern Montana, western South Dakota, eastern Colorado and northwestern Texas; migrates south through eastern Mexico and southeastern United States. Winters from southern Mexico through Central America to Colombia; accidental in northern Manitoba (York Factory), Cuba and Bermuda Islands.

DISTRIBUTION IN NEW ENGLAND. — Common migrant and summer resident, generally rare in dense forests of northern Maine and on higher elevations of Vermont and New Hampshire, though its nesting area seems to be coincident with the distribution of elm trees rather than a question of altitude; a few winter records in Massachusetts and one in Vermont.

SEASON IN MASSACHUSETTS. — (April 22, 23, 26) May 1 to September 25 (October 8, 22; November 13, 15, 18, 19, 23; winter). *Recent unusual records:* Cohasset, December 25, 1917, bird seen by Dr.

John B. May; December 21, 1920, bird seen by Dr. May and nearly caught by him, eating partly frozen grapes; Watertown, January 3, 1901, male seen by Miss Adelaide Stockwell, had been feeding at one place for a week but disappeared after the next storm; Fitchburg, December 19, 1925, bird trapped by Fred H. Dillon, probably an escaped cage bird, soon died; Osterville, April 5 and 21, male seen *singing* by Harris C. Lovell.

HAUNTS AND HABITS.   There is an interesting bit of history or tradition connected with the naming of the Baltimore Oriole which Mrs. Mabel Osgood Wright mentions in "Birdcraft."   The story goes that George Calvert, the first Baron Baltimore, who in 1632 wrote the Charter of settlement of the lands known today as the states of Delaware and Maryland, becoming worn and discouraged by his various trials and the rigors of climate that beset his Newfoundland colony, visited the Virginia settlement.   Around the shores of the Chesapeake he found the woods teeming with birds.   The brightest among them were flocks of Orioles, and he was so cheered by their song and beauty that he took their colors, orange and black, for his coat of arms.   When, later, Linnæus first saw the skins of the Golden Robin or Fire-hang-bird of our fathers, he named it the Baltimore Oriole, as it wore the colors of Lord Baltimore.

The coming of the Baltimore Oriole to the north is always an event to be welcomed with joy.   The winter now is past, April showers have fallen and May is here.   Again we see the annual "miracle" of the spring awakening.   Where but a few weeks since the "white death" covered all and the brook was fettered by the "great frost," now a velvety carpet of tender grasses and green mosses clothes the earth.   Dandelions, cowslips and violets are in bloom, and the stream prattles noisily over its stony bed.   The wonderful old earth, swinging the northern hemisphere again toward the sun, responds as ever to his cheering warmth and clothes herself in beauty.   A thousand orchards are in bloom, and among their tinted blossoms the resplendent orioles with songs of joy weave in and out.   Ever in New England this beautiful, elegantly formed bird is associated with blooming apple orchards, and with peach and cherry blossoms.   The bird is supposed to take the nectar from the blooms.   It certainly eats the petals of some and takes insects from others, but we cannot say that it gathers no nectar.

Orioles are almost always here about the 10th of May though some arrive earlier, and they continue to come and pass for two or three weeks.   The males usually precede the females by several days, but when their modest consorts arrive, the ardent birds soon begin their wooing.   In displaying his charms before the object of his affections the male sits upon a limb near her, and raising to full height bows low with spread tail and partly-raised wings, thus displaying to her admiring eyes first his orange breast, then his black front and finally in bright sunlight the full glory of his black, white and orange upper plumage, uttering, the while, his most supplicating and seductive notes.   A pair once mated appear to be very affectionate and constant during the season.   The males rarely assist the females in nest building, but most of them keep close to their consorts while nest construction is going on, cheer them with song and evidently take much interest in the proceeding.   Some males bring nesting material, but so far as I have observed the female alone builds the nest.* In fashioning her swinging domicile she displays more skill in weaving than does any other bird of New England. She first hangs long strands over the twigs which support the nest, fastening them in place until she has a hanging framework, then she loops and weaves them together, frequently hanging back downward on the suspended fabric while she works. The happy bird while building sometimes chatters or sings a bit while in the nest.

The material normally used for the framework is vegetal fiber, gathered chiefly from dried or decaying stalks of plants of the previous year; fibers of tree bark also are used by some females. Birds building (as most of them now do) near the habitations of men use also string, yarn, horsehair, strands of hemp or flax and other similar materials gleaned from door-yards, farm-yards or roadsides. The birds usually select white or light grayish tints, similar in color to the natural materials used for ages by their forbears; but I have seen one nest chiefly composed outwardly of jet black hair from the manes and tails of horses. This nest, placed low down in a pear tree, was very conspicuous among the green leaves. The nest of this oriole, whatever its color, usually is more conspicuous than that of the Orchard Oriole which is built largely of green grasses which, shaded by the leaves, retain for a long time some resemblance to their primal tints and so are easily concealed amid the foliage. Many attempts have been made by putting out brightly colored yarns in conspicuous places to induce the Baltimore bird to build a nest of the gayest hues, but usually with little success. Apparently they prefer white yarn or twine to any of the brighter colors. Mrs. Bertha G. Sloan of Fitchburg, Massachusetts, described to me an experiment of this kind where white, green and pink twine was used. When there was no white to be had, the birds pecked at the colored twine, but never used it, and when the nest was completed it was almost entirely white. One bird took a little green and red twine, but never while the white was in sight. A detailed account of the experiment is given in "Country Life" for April, 1909 by Dr. Craig S. Thoms. Mrs. William F. Eldredge of Rockport, Massachusetts, says that the Orioles about her home carried off untwisted rope strands, white string and a little blue worsted, but rejected all other colors. The late Frank E. Peck, formerly one of the assessors of Wareham, Massachusetts, wrote out for me the following story of an event that happened in his boyhood and made a very strong impression on his youthful mind:

"I was amusing myself with my playthings on the grass in front of an old farmhouse, which was my abiding-place at the time. There were some half dozen giant elm trees standing at the edge of the lawn just where it sloped sharply to the highway. These elms, as I learned later, had for many years been the favorite nesting place of what the people thereabout called "firehang-birds." There were several nests in the trees that season. I used to lie on my back looking up in the trees watching the bright coated visitors. I had among my playthings some silver shoe and knee buckles, formerly worn by my grandfather, and which my grandmother had tied to as many ribbons, and I was permitted to carry out of doors, providing I was careful not to lose any of them. On

---

* Some nest building activities of the male have been reported.

this day in particular I noticed that one of the largest and brightest of the red birds seemed to be more tame than usual, and each time that he came down from the tree he would light nearer and nearer to where my buckles were lying. Finally he swooped down upon the articles, and seizing the brightest buckle in the lot attempted to fly up into the tree. Of course I protested but he got away with my treasure, and took it to and wove it into his nest in such a way that when the wind blew in a certain direction we could see the buckle glisten. The buckle remained attached to the nest until a heavy gale of wind broke away the nest, and it came tumbling down into the yard. Our hired man found it and restored it to me."

The completion of the external part of the nest occupies two to six days. While the female is incubating the male wanders back and forth in the immediate neighborhood, singing and calling to her, and she sometimes answers from the nest as if to assure him that all is well. While she seems to perform most of the labor of incubation, the male in some cases relieves her, taking her place upon the nest, and usually he does his full share of brooding and feeding the young. Miss Jean Martin of Hillsdale, Michigan, tells, as follows, how a bereaved and crippled bird took full charge of an orphaned brood:

"For several summers, a pair of Baltimore Orioles had nested in an apple tree near my study window.

"Last summer, when the nest was full of young ones, the mother bird was killed, and the father bird had a broken wing. When I discovered this tragedy, the father was carrying food to his family.

"There was a grape-vine growing under the tree, untrimmed and lawless. Some wayward branches had caught hold of the lowest apple boughs, and a pole, leaning against the trellis, formed a continuous roadway from nest to ground. Down this road the poor bird would hop, and forage for food. He never went far from the grape-vine, and kept a sharp lookout for enemies. After filling his mouth with food, he would commence his tedious journey up the grape-vine, one hop at a time, — and thus cared for his family until they reached the flying age and were able to care for themselves." [1] Would any human father under similar circumstances have done as well?

The male is a valiant and swift defender of his brood and at times will join neighboring birds in defense of their young. The common chipmunk, like all squirrels, will take now and then both eggs and young birds. Mrs. Wright tells how a Baltimore Oriole came to the rescue of a young Catbird which had been dragged from its nest by a chipmunk and how the oriole finally destroyed the squirrel's eyes with two strokes of his sharp, pointed bill. The unfortunate squirrel fell to the ground and was put out of its misery while the victorious bird "flew off as if nothing had happened."

Mr. F. E. Campbell tells me that he saw nine Bronzed Grackles attack a pair of "orioles," but after two minutes of swift action the Grackles retired from the combat, leaving the "orioles" the victors. As has been hereinbefore stated, even the redoubtable King-bird meets his match in the Baltimore Oriole. The female is even more devoted to her

[1] Martin, Jean: Bird-Lore, Vol. XI, 1909, p. 129.

treasures than the male, and Mr. Robert Ridgway tells of one that entered the nest while the limb to which it was attached was cut from the tree, and remained in it until nest, limb and all had been taken into a house. Both birds exhibit an attachment to the nesting site and return to it year after year. Occasionally such a nest of the preceding year is repaired in spring and used again, but commonly a new nest is fashioned each year, and so lasting and durable are these fabrics that one may see nests of three successive years upon the same tree, if not on the same branch. Sometimes material is taken from an old nest and incorporated in a new one.

The male sings loudly and cheerfully through May and June or until the young have left the nest which in most cases occurs in late June, and soon thereafter the melodies of the male are hushed. Now, with few exceptions, the Baltimore Orioles leave the scene of their nativity, and in early July the broods with their parents betake themselves to the woods, pastures and thickets where wild berries are ripening; now the swamps and thickets resound with the cries of the feeding young, and there most of them remain until late August. In some localities, even in city streets, a number of them remain at this season, molting, shy and silent, keeping largely in the tops of tall elms and maples where they escape notice. The males usually have a second song period when from about the middle of August to its last week they reappear in their former haunts in winter plumage, singing more or less. Occasionally a young male will attempt a snatch of song at this time. Early in September most of them disappear on their southward way, and by the end of September the species has left New England. The most remarkable fact in regard to this bird that winters south into South America is that straggling individuals have been seen or taken in New England in October, November, December and January and also in March and April. Young Baltimore Orioles brought up by hand become perfect pets. A physician in Southboro, Massachusetts, had such a bird that went away with the family on their summer vacations in Maine. It was given its liberty. Such a bird might be lost. Probably nearly all orioles remaining here in winter succumb to starvation and cold. Such a one which was captured soon died while another seen in January was evidently very weak. The following is appended from one of my former works:

"The clear, wild calls of this bird are as well known as its musical song. The song, however, varies so much in tone and rhythm that no pen can ever adequately describe its many variations. Nearly every male has a distinctive song of its own. When we have once learned to recognize the song of a certain individual bird, we are able to note his arrival annually. An Oriole with a peculiar song nested near my home in Worcester for four consecutive years. Only last year I heard a new bird-note in Andover, and found that the bird was a Baltimore Oriole, singing a song unlike that of any bird of any species that I had ever heard before. . . . The Oriole itself, however, is not always guiltless in respect to other birds. Occasionally it destroys other nests, either to get material for building its own, or out of pure mischief. Mr. Mosher observed a male Oriole attempting to drive another away from its nest. The stranger would make a rush at the nest, and then the owner would grapple with him. This running fight was kept up for fully three hours. In the meantime the rogue Oriole went to a Redstart's nest, threw out the eggs, and threw down the nest. The next day an Oriole, probably the same bird, was seen to throw out an egg from a Red-eyed Vireo's nest, when he was set upon and driven away by the owners. Three other instances have been reported to me by trustworthy observers who have seen Orioles in the act of destroying the nests or eggs of other birds; but, so far as I know, few writers have recorded such habits, and they are probably exceptional. Indeed, the Oriole's bad habits seem to be few. It occasionally helps itself to green peas; but Dr. Harris tells us, in his work on insects injurious to vegetation, that this Oriole splits open the green pods for the sake of the weevil grubs contained in the peas, thereby greatly helping to prevent the spread of these noxious insects. Nuttall says that it takes the saccharine nectar from fruit blossoms. It eats cherries, but seems to prefer Juneberries and mulberries. Professor Beal says that several Orioles that were shot in cherry trees had no cherries in their stomachs, but some seeds of *Rubus* and Juneberries. John Burroughs told me years ago that it was very destructive to ripe grapes at his place on the Hudson River, but I have never heard of it injuring grapes in Massachusetts; it usually leaves us before most grapes are ripe.

"Having catalogued the sins of this bird, let us see what its good qualities are. Professor Beal finds that eighty-three and four-tenths per cent of the Oriole's food consists of animal matter, caterpillars forming thirty-four per cent of the whole. Evidently the Oriole is one of the first among the birds known to destroy hairy caterpillars, and for this alone it may be ranked as one of the chief friends of the orchardist and forester. The tussock, gipsy, brown-tail, tent, and forest caterpillars, the fall webworm, and even the spiny caterpillar of the mourning cloak butterfly — all are greedily eaten by the Baltimore; and it does not usually swallow many, but merely kills them and eats a small portion of the inner parts. It thus destroys many more than would be needed to satisfy its appetite were they swallowed whole, while at the same time no recognizable portion of the caterpillar can be found in the bird's stomach. This is a habit about which, like many others, we can learn only by observation. Mr. Nash received a number of reports from correspondents in 1900 regarding the clearance of tent caterpillars from trees by these birds. They were watched day after day, and in the end cleared the orchards of the pests. An Oriole was seen to finish one nest of small caterpillars and begin on another while the observer was eating his breakfast. Young Orioles are fed very largely on injurious moths and caterpillars. The Baltimore Oriole is worth its weight in gold for its services in destroying both gipsy and brown-tail moths. The bird is particularly fond of snap beetles or click beetles, the parents of the destructive wireworms. Professor Beal says that more than five hundred species of these beetles are found in North America, and their larvæ are exceedingly injurious to a great variety of plants, particularly to corn, grass, and garden crops. As they attack the roots or work within the stalks, they are very difficult to control. Many birds eat either the beetles or larvæ. The very injurious May beetles and other leaf-eating beetles are taken by the Oriole, among them the striped squash beetle or cucumber beetle, one of the most destructive pests of the garden. Bagworms, curculios, wasps, bugs, plant lice, scale insects, March flies, and crane flies are among the insects eaten by this bird.

" The following, from Mr. [A. H.] Kirkland's notes, made at Malden in 1896, shows that this bird is of value in woodlands, for the observations were made in the woods:

" 'A sawfly (probably *Selandria*) is at present one of the insects most commonly devoured by the Baltimore Oriole. These birds are very abundant around the experiment station, and I have repeatedly seen them feeding upon these sawflies, even as early as 4.30 one bright morning. By six or seven o'clock these birds are well at work, feeding around the building. I have seen them eat cankerworms, and, what was more interesting, devour a large Tortricid larva, which rolls the leaves of the white oak. This larva rolls the leaf around itself, thus forming a kind of cylinder, within which it feeds. The Orioles put their bills into one end of the cylinder without tearing the leaf, and pull out the larva.' " [1]

Mrs. Jean E. Carth reports that she watched two adults and three young at a distance of about 10 feet which fed for fifteen minutes on the blossoms and tiny pods of scarlet runner beans.

ECONOMIC STATUS. The Baltimore Oriole is one of our most useful birds; innumerable instances of its valuable services to the farmer and orchardist have been observed. It has but one serious fault. In migration it punctures many grapes in the vineyards of several states from New York to Nebraska and for this fault hundreds of orioles are shot year after year. Some people believe that the orioles pick the grapes for the purpose of attracting insects on which to feed, but it seems probable that the birds actually drink grape juice.

Icterus búllocki (SWAINSON). Bullock's Oriole.

DESCRIPTION. — Much like Baltimore Oriole in shape and color, but somewhat larger, tail less rounded and colors differently disposed. *Adult male in breeding plumage:* Space before eye, and top of head, except forehead, black which extends over nape, back of neck, upper back, scapulars, most of lesser wing-coverts and flight-feathers; two middle tail-feathers black, the next pair mostly so; exposed parts of greater and middle wing-coverts white (forming a large white patch on wing) and edges and tips of flight-feathers white (white on primaries and outer secondaries very narrow); rest of plumage chiefly orange or orange-yellow; outer tail-feathers becoming dusky or blackish at tips; rump and upper tail-coverts sometimes tinged with olive; bill black above, bluish on lower edge of upper mandible and below; iris brown; legs and feet bluish or leaden. *Adult male in winter plumage:* Similar, but black feathers of back and scapulars with grayish margins, feathers of rump and tail-coverts with grayish tips, and feathers of lower plumage tipped whitish. *Adult female:* Similar to adult female Baltimore Oriole, and, like her, with two white wing-bars, but olive-gray above and a tendency to whitish below, sometimes with more or less black on throat. *Immature male:* Similar to adult female but chin and middle line of throat black, and more buffy below. *Young in juvenal plumage:* Similar to adult female, but throat all yellowish, and generally more buffy which shows especially in lighter wing-markings and below.

[1] Useful Birds and Their Protection, 1913, pp. 224–228.

MEASUREMENTS. — Length 7.50 to 8.60 in.; spread 11.25 to 13.50; folded wing 3.80 to 4.15; tail 3.10 to 3.70; bill .75 to .82; tarsus .85 to .90. Female smaller than male.

MOLTS. — Similar to those of Baltimore Oriole.

FIELD MARKS. — Size larger than Bluebird or Baltimore Oriole. *Adult male:* Similar to Baltimore Oriole in color, but forehead and sides of head and neck orange, and large white patch on fore wing. Female similar to female Baltimore Oriole but grayer above, except on tail, which is yellowish; more whitish below.

BULLOCK'S ORIOLE, ADULT MALE

VOICE. — Call notes similar to those of Baltimore Oriole but song not so pleasing (C. Bendire).

BREEDING. — Usually in sparse or open woods or in open country where there are scattered trees; not in forests or on high mountains. *Nest:* Similar to that of Baltimore Oriole; sometimes roofed over with entrance in one side. *Eggs:* 3 to 6; virtually indistinguishable from those of Baltimore Oriole but averaging a little larger; figured in Bendire's "Life Histories of North American Birds," Vol. II, Plate VII, Figs. 10 to 13. *Dates:* May 15 to June 12, southern California to northern Oregon. *Incubation:* Period 14 days (Bendire); about 15 days (O. W. Knight); chiefly by female. One brood yearly.

RANGE. — Western North America. Breeds from the transition Zone in southern British Columbia, southern Alberta and southern Saskatchewan south to northern Lower California, Sonora, northern Durango, Coahuila and southern Texas; from the Pacific coast to central North Dakota, eastern South Dakota, central Nebraska, western Kansas, western Oklahoma and central Texas. It winters in Mexico north to Durango, and south to Colima, Michoacan, Guerrero and Puebla; accidental in New York and Maine.

DISTRIBUTION IN NEW ENGLAND. — Accidental straggler. Record: *Maine:* Sorrento, about Nov. 15, 1889, specimen shot and in collection of Manly Hardy.[1]

HAUNTS AND HABITS. Bullock's Oriole is a mere accidental straggler in New England. I have had no opportunity to see it alive except very briefly in southern British Columbia. It resembles the Baltimore Oriole in voice, color and habits, and frequents similar open country. Undoubtedly it is a beneficial bird. It is the chief oriole of the western United States, where it takes the place of the Baltimore. An account of its nesting habits is given in the second volume of Bendire's "Life Histories of North American Birds." Dr. Coues gives an excellent account in his "Birds of the Northwest."

Eúphagus carolínus (MÜLLER). Rusty Blackbird.

Other names: RUSTY GRACKLE; THRUSH BLACKBIRD.

Plate 62.

DESCRIPTION. — Ridge of bill more curved toward tip than in orioles, and not quite so long as head; shaped somewhat like that of Robin; wings pointed, longer when folded than tail; tail rounded. Whole form decidely thrush-like. *Adult male in breeding plumage:* Black with slight bluish-green and violet

[1] Brewster, William: Auk, Vol. VII, 1890, p. 92.

gloss; bill, legs and feet black; iris yellow, pale straw or yellowish-white. *Adult male in winter plumage:* Similar, but black more or less obscured by rusty brown feather-ends of upper plumage except on sides of head, which with lower plumage (except abdomen) are obscured by a paler shade of brown. *Adult female in breeding plumage:* Dull slate, darkening a little above, where slightly glossed with bluish-green; bill, legs and feet as in male; iris pale yellow. *Adult female in winter plumage:* Obscured more or less with rich rusty brown above and with paler brown below; tertials and greater wing-coverts more or less margined with same; greenish reflections on wings and tail; light buffy stripe over eye. *Young in first winter plumage:* Like adults and practically indistinguishable from them. *Young in juvenal plumage:* Dark sooty-brown or clove-brown, slightly slaty on back; greenish reflections on wings and tail and brownish edgings on tertials.

MEASUREMENTS. — Length 8.20 to 9.75 in.; spread 13.00 to 15.00; folded wing 4.12 to 4.80; tail 3.24 to 4.03; bill .75 to .95; tarsus 1.22 to 1.30; weight 2 to 2⅔ oz. (B. H. Warren). Female smaller than male.

MOLTS. — Juvenal plumage acquired in June by complete molt, following dark natal down; first winter plumage acquired by complete postjuvenal molt (July to September); "first nuptial plumage acquired by wear" (Jonathan Dwight, Jr.); in first winter and first breeding plumages male and female young closely resemble adults of their respective sexes; adults have but one molt annually, postnuptial (July to September), and breeding plumage, according to Dwight, results from wearing away of light feather-tips of winter plumage.

FIELD MARKS. — Size, smaller than Robin, of similar shape; near size of Red-winged Blackbird; when perched, jets tail like Red-wing. *Male:* In spring a black or very dark bird with a nearly white, light yellow or straw eye and shaped much like Robin; bill and feet black. In autumn, body and head veiled with rusty. *Female:* In spring, slaty; *Female and young:* In autumn a broad light stripe over eye, and more veiled with rusty than males; this distinguishes them from young of Bronzed or Purple Grackles which are sooty and larger with heavier bill.

VOICE. — A *chuck* resembling the spring call of the wood frog; alarm note *cheek-che-weeck* (N. S. Goss); or *check che weecha, turulee turulee, turulee* (C. Bendire); also a *chip. Female:* A chattering cry like that of the female Red-wing when disturbed at nest (E. A. Samuels); their creaky chorus is like the sound of a lot of little ungreased wheels revolving rapidly (J. A. Farley).

BREEDING. — Usually in swamps or along the near-by borders of lakes and streams. *Nest:* In thickets of conifers, in swamps or in bushy thickets growing in or near water, rarely on top of a stump or brush pile in water, or in a tree fallen into water; from 1 to 10 feet above ground or water; built first of sticks, mosses and lichens; then a cap of wet decaying leaf-mold which dries hard; lined with grasses and vegetal fibers. *Eggs:* 4 or 5; .91 to 1.05 by .70 to .79 in.; usually ovate; light bluish-green, blotched and spotted with shades of chocolate and lighter reddish-brown and paler shades of drab and gray; markings sometimes heaviest and thickest near large end, very variable; figured in Bendire's "Life Histories of North American Birds," Vol. II, Plate VII, Figs. 14 to 16. *Dates:* From May 5, northern Vermont to June 19, Maine. *Incubation:* Period about 14 days (Bendire); by female. One brood yearly.

RANGE. — Northern and eastern North America. Breeds in Alaska to Bering Sea and the Arctic Ocean and in Canada, north to tree limit from northern Mackenzie, northern Manitoba, northern Ontario, northern Ungava (Quebec) and northern Labrador south to central British Columbia, central Alberta, central Saskatchewan and south central Manitoba, and casually to southern Wisconsin, south central Ontario, northern New York, northern Vermont, northern New Hampshire, Maine, New Brunswick and Nova Scotia; south in winter from Nebraska, Iowa, northern Illinois, Indiana, southern Michigan, southern Ohio, southern New York, Massachusetts and southeastern Maine (accidental) to the Gulf coast from eastern Texas to northern Florida; in migration west to the Dakotas, Kansas, Oklahoma and Texas, and casually to southern British Columbia, eastern Montana and central Colorado; accidental in Lower California, California and Greenland.

DISTRIBUTION IN NEW ENGLAND. — *Maine:* Common migrant and rather rare summer resident in northern parts; accidental in winter * *New Hampshire and Vermont:* Common migrant, rare summer resident in northern part. *Massachusetts:* Common migrant, casual in winter. *Rhode Island:* Common migrant, winters rarely. *Connecticut:* Common migrant, rare in winter.

SEASON IN MASSACHUSETTS. — March 7 to May 8 (May 14, 17 and 30) (August) September 11 to November 22 (winter).

HAUNTS AND HABITS.   The Rusty Blackbird is not so widely known in New England as other blackbirds, as it breeds only in rather inaccessible places in the northern parts of the region, and generally is rather shy, when, as a migrant, it passes through on its migrations.   It is most common in Massachusetts in late March and early April and again in late September and early October.   It is the most nearly aquatic of our blackbirds, and in spring it frequents lowlands, swamps, woodland pools and the margins of ponds and streams.   When it first appears in small groups or flocks, its *chuck* so nearly resembles that of the wood frogs which frequent its favorite woodland pools that it is rather difficult to tell at a distance whether the frogs or the birds are responsible for the noisy chorus; but when the blackbirds begin to sing, their notes at once distinguish them, not only from frogs, but from all other birds.   Their chorus then is a mixture of chuckling and shrill squeals or whistles unlike any other sound in nature.   When once heard it will always thereafter be recognized.   In spring they like to feed in shallow water where they find insect larvæ and probably some small crustaceans or other forms of life.   At times they may be seen wading quite deeply in the water and plunging in not only their bills but their whole heads in the manner of the Solitary Sandpiper and very likely finding similar food.   If disturbed they usually fly up into a tree all together and all facing the same way, and after some preliminary chucks and tail-flirts give the listener one of their free concerts.   In autumn they are not so closely confined to the water, and they often frequent weedy gardens and corn-fields where they walk quietly about, turning over dead leaves, etc.   They flock at times with other blackbirds or Starlings.

I have never seen these birds on their nesting grounds.   Dr. C. W. Townsend says that their courtship display "is produced with apparent great effort, wide-open bill and spread tail, resulting in a series of squeaking notes suggestive of an unoiled windmill — *wat-cheé e.*"   This note represents very well its usual song, and, he says, "at times a sweet lower note, often double, is heard."   The male is said to produce also a soft, low song, but this I have never heard.   My friend, Mr. F. H. Kennard, who has had more experience with the species on its breeding grounds than any one with whom I am acquainted, writes as follows of its nesting habits in Northern Vermont and Maine:

"The female usually starts incubation with the laying of the first egg, particularly in the early spring, when the weather is cold, and sits pretty close, flying off only upon one's near approach.   Particularly shy birds may, when disturbed, disappear without uttering a note, but the great majority that I have observed will remain in the vicinity of the nest, uttering their loud 'chips' of alarm, becoming more and more distressed, when disturbed,

* Machias, January 28, 1925, F. W. Kilburn *in litt.*

as incubation progresses, until after the hatching they are particularly vociferous.   During incubation the male is very assiduous in his attentions to the female, feeding her frequently, and seldom flies far from the nesting locality.   The female at this season is usually seldom in evidence, but by watching the male, one can soon determine by his actions the approximate locality of the nest.   He has the very conspicuous habit of sitting on the top of some tall dead stub or tree, often with a nice fat grub in his bill and calling to the female.   This call note is a two-syllabled 'conk-ee,' very similar to the three-syllabled 'conk-a-ree' of the Redwing, but clearer and more musical, and usually distinguishable from the notes of the other blackbirds.

"If disturbed by the proximity of watchers, he may delay for a while, uttering an occasional 'chip' of alarm, but sooner or later he will fly close to the nest or to the top of some nearby stub, when the female will fly out to him, and with low 'chucks' and much fluttering of wings, partake of the delicious morsel he has brought her.   The knowledge of this habit, acquired during our second trip, greatly simplified our hunts during succeeding seasons.

"It has so happened that I have never been able, from personal observation, to check up the exact time of incubation, but Bendire states it to be 'about two weeks' and Dr. Bergtold states that it is '14 days.'

"The young, when hatched, are covered with a long, thin, fuscous natal down; and fed by both parents, at frequent intervals, develop rapidly, as such young birds do.   The nest is kept clean, and I saw the female frequently drop a white fecal sac in the nearby brook, as she flew away from feeding her charges.   By the fifth day, the primary quills and other wing feathers are well under way, while the growths along the remaining feather tracts are starting; and slight slits begin to show between their eyelids.   By the tenth day the young are well covered with feathers, through which some of their natal down still protrudes, and their eyes are nearly but not quite wide open.

"A tragedy occurred to the only brood I was able to watch, for on the tenth day after hatching, one of the young was found in the water, about ten feet from the nest, dead and partially eaten.   Whether he deliberately climbed from the nest, and later fell into the water, or was taken by some animal, will never be known, but the next day the three remaining young all climbed out into the adjoining bushes, it seemed to me, ahead of schedule time, for their eyes were hardly open, and they were still unable to fly.

"They remained in the immediate vicinity of the nest for the next two days, climbing and hopping from bush to bush, with both parents in close attendance, till on the thirteenth day, they had learned the use of their wings; and in the evening the last one was seen to fly across the stream, followed by its mother, and to disappear in the swamp beyond.

"The actions of the male, of this particular brood, were peculiar, for, after being very attentive to the female during incubation, he spent his days, as soon as the young had hatched, away from the locality, never helping the female in any way with her duties, except in the evenings, when returning with some other Rusties, that he had apparently been spending the day with somewhere, he would help feed the young, and spend the night in the vicinity.

"As soon, however, as the young climbed out of the nest, he resumed his share of the parental duties throughout the day. Perhaps under normal conditions, he would have been taking care of the young of a first brood, while the female took care of a second."[1]

Professor Beal has given a tabulation of the food of this blackbird as revealed by the examination of 132 stomachs of the species by the Biological Survey. This cannot be considered an exhaustive investigation. None of the birds was taken on its breeding-grounds and only the months of March, April, October and November, when the birds were migrating, were fairly represented, but for these months the percentage of animal food was very high including some injurious insects and many aquatic ones. Crustaceans, snails and small fishes constituted about 7 per cent of the food. The vegetal food was chiefly grain and weed seeds with a very small amount of fruit, chiefly wild fruit and a little mast.[2]

ECONOMIC STATUS. As this species does not breed in agricultural regions, it is of value to agriculture only in migration and in winter, and it cannot be said that its economic status has as yet been determined. As it destroys a considerable number of insect pests, and as no great complaints of its depredations on grain have been reported, the protection accorded it now by law seems wise.

Quiscalus quiscula quiscula (LINNÆUS). Purple Grackle.

Other names: CROW BLACKBIRD; CROW-BILLED BLACKBIRD.

Plate 62.

DESCRIPTION. — Much larger and stouter than Rusty Blackbird; bill usually relatively longer, heavier and more crow-like, but very variable in shape; wings less acute; tail long (but seldom longer than folded wing), considerably graduated; outer tail-feathers often appearing upturned as if tail were wrong side up; legs and feet stout and crow-like. *Adult male:* Head, neck and upper breast varying from metallic reddish-violet to golden green; prevailing color of back and scapulars varying from bronzy-purple or polished bronze to metallic olive-green or bottle green, always more or less broken by bars (mostly concealed, except on scapulars) of metallic green, blue, bronze or purple (or all these tints); rump varying in color from purplish-bronze to violet, color usually more or less broken by admixture of other metallic hues; prevailing color of wings violet or purple (primaries, primary-coverts and alula usually more bluish, sometimes bluish-green); lesser and middle coverts usually banded, more or less conspicuously, with purple, blue, green, golden, etc.; tail dark purple, violet, blue, or green, or (in worn or faded plumage) black, glossed with one of these colors; lower plumage (posterior to upper breast) metallic purple, violet, blue, green, etc., varying in different parts, sometimes mixed with golden-bronze; bill, legs and feet black; iris pale yellow or yellowish-white; . . . *Adult female:* Decidedly smaller than male and much duller, metallic hues more subdued, sometimes very faint (Adapted from Ridgway).[3] *Young in first winter plumage:* Similar to adults, and practically indistinguishable from them. *Young in juvenal plumage:* Dark clove or sooty-brown, tail darker with some purplish gloss; usually a little lighter below and sometimes indistinctly streaked there; iris, bill and feet brown.

[1] Auk, Vol. XXXVII, 1920, pp. 420, 421.

[2] Bulletin No. 13, United States Department of Agriculture, Division of Biological Survey, 1900, pp. 46–49.

[3] Bulletin No. 50, United States National Museum; Birds of North and Middle America, 1902, Part II, pp. 215–216.

MEASUREMENTS. — Length 11.00 to 13.50 in.; spread 17.00 to 18.50; folded wing 4.73 to 6.05; tail 4.50 to 6.00; bill 1.08 to 1.35; tarsus 1.25 to 1.45. Weight of one male 4 oz. (B. H. Warren). Female considerably smaller than male.

MOLTS. — Juvenal plumage succeeds pale sepia-brown down in nestling by postnatal molt (May); first winter plumage acquired by complete postjuvenal molt (June to August), when young bird becomes practically as adult; first breeding plumage acquired by wear; adults have annually a complete post-nuptial molt (August to October); breeding plumage acquired by wear.

FIELD MARKS. — *Adult male:* Size larger than Robin; appears black at a distance; flies slowly and steadily (not rising and falling in flight as other blackbirds do) with sides of graduated tail often upturned or middle feathers depressed; on close approach or in bright sunlight shows purple and bronze reflections; typical birds never have a bright, pure, bronzy back like that of typical Bronzed Grackles, and the colors of the head are not so different from those of the body as in the latter, but in southern New England there are many intermediates between this race and the next which in the field it is impossible to place with certainty. *Female:* Similar to male but duller and smaller. On the ground both sexes walk like other blackbirds.

VOICE. — A *chuck* like that of other blackbirds, but somewhat louder, more metallic and resonant than that of the Red-wing; song of a flock has been compared to creaking of swinging signs, rusty hinges of iron gates and creaking of un-oiled wheelbarrow or cart wheels.

BREEDING. — Usually in or near swamps, but often on farm lands. *Nest:* In bushes or trees often coniferous; from 4 to 60 feet high (usually up to 20 feet); rarely in barns or church steeples; sometimes in interstices in the outside of an Osprey's nest, sometimes in cavities of trees, in hollow stubs or even in bird houses; made of grass, weed-stalks, seaweed, etc., sometimes reinforced with mud and lined with finer, similar materials; feathers, string and rags sometimes used. *Eggs:* 4 to 6, very rarely 7; 1.01 to 1.29 by .81 to .91 in.; usually ovate; commonly pale greenish-white varying to light reddish-brown, usually sparsely marked with blotches, dashes and scrawls of various shades of dark brown and sometimes also with lavender, sometimes profusely marked; figured in Bendire's "Life Histories of North American Birds," Vol. II, Plate VII, Figs. 21 to 23. *Dates:* April 17, Virginia; April 25 to June 8, Connecticut; May 5, Massachusetts. *Incubation:* Period 14 days (Burns); 14 to 15 days (B. H. Warren); probably wholly by female.

RANGE. — Chiefly east of the Alleghenies in Atlantic district of United States from southern New England to Florida. Breeds from northeastern Pennsylvania, southeastern New York, southern Connecticut and southern Rhode Island south to central Mississippi, central Alabama, and northern South Carolina, and west to central Pennsylvania, western Maryland, eastern West Virginia, southeastern Kentucky, central Tennessee and northern Mississippi; south in winter from New Jersey to southern Alabama, and southern South Carolina.

DISTRIBUTION IN NEW ENGLAND. — *New Hampshire:* Casual visitor in southern part: One record: Tilton, September 13, 1902,[1] two birds taken by Ned Dearborn. *Vermont:* Accidental visitor in southern part. *Massachusetts:* Casual migrant and summer resident, chiefly in southern part; occurs in summer north at least to Cambridge, Worcester and probably to Amherst, but is not recorded in Berkshire County, though probably occurs there. *Connecticut and Rhode Island:* Not uncommon migrant and common summer resident, chiefly in southern parts; accidental in winter.

SEASON IN MASSACHUSETTS. — March 4 to November 22.

HAUNTS AND HABITS. Most of the grackles breeding in Massachusetts are referable not to this race but to the Bronzed Grackle, the next race described. Nevertheless some nearly typical examples of the present race breed in southern and southeastern Massachusetts. According to Brewster some are found in the Cambridge region and several

---

[1] Dearborn, Ned: The Birds of Durham and Vicinity, 1902, p. 110.

specimens of the species that I examined in Worcester during the latter part of the last century (before this race had been recognized) probably were closer to *quiscula* than to *æneus*. Birds from Springfield recently examined were intermediate between the two. Southern Massachusetts is on the border line between the normal habitats of the two races where probably they interbreed and where many intermediates between the two may be found. The above remarks are to explain the close relationship between these two races of the species in Massachusetts and to show why their haunts and habits here are practically identical, as they often roost, flock and probably breed together. As *æneus* is by far the most abundant of the two in the greater part of Massachusetts, the habits of both grackles are described under that race.

Quiscalus quiscula æneus RIDGWAY. Bronzed Grackle.

Other names: CROW BLACKBIRD; CROW-BILLED BLACKBIRD.

Plate 62.

DESCRIPTION. — Similar to Purple Grackle in form but differing in the uniform golden or brassy color of entire body (except upper breast) and the unbarred bronze or purplish-bronze wing-coverts; size about the same. *Adult male:* Head, neck and upper breast varying from greenish blue to purple, neck and chest sometimes brassy green; rest of plumage perfectly uniform bronze or brassy-olive, more purplish on wings and tail; lesser wing-coverts uniform brassy-olive or bronze, and neither these nor middle coverts marked with bars of other metallic tints; . . . *Adult female:* Similar to male but decidedly smaller and much duller (Adapted from Ridgway).[1] *Young in first winter plumage:* Virtually as adults. *Young in juvenal plumage:* Like young of Purple Grackle.

MEASUREMENTS AND MOLTS. — Virtually the same as in Purple Grackle, but this bird *averages* a little larger, and molts, especially those of young, come later, juvenal plumage being assumed in May and June. *Weight:* Male, from about 4 to 5 oz.; female 3¼ to 4 oz.

FIELD MARKS. — Same as in Purple Grackle except that the back is plain bronze and unmarked.

VOICE. — Same as in Purple Grackle or a trifle more resonant; a "split whistle" (Thoreau); also a scream much like that of Common Tern (C. W. Townsend).

BREEDING. — Chiefly in groves of large coniferous trees, such as are found in parks and cemeteries; also in open and swampy woods and in reedy marshes. *Nest:* Sometimes almost on ground among reeds in marsh, but usually high in coniferous or deciduous trees; sometimes in an old hole used for nests by woodpeckers or in other tree-cavities, in a barn or shed or other building, or even on a stump standing in water. Similar to that of Purple Grackle. *Eggs:* Indistinguishable from those of Purple Grackle but averaging a little larger; figured in Bendire's "Life Histories of North American Birds," Vol. II, Plate VII, Figs. 26, 27. *Dates:* April 19 to May 15, Indiana; May 2 to June 1, Massachusetts; May 27 to June 21, Maine. *Incubation:* Period 14 days; by female. One brood yearly.

RANGE. — Central and eastern North America east of the Rocky Mountains. Breeds from Great Slave Lake in southern Mackenzie, northern Manitoba, northern Ontario, central Quebec and Newfoundland south to central southern Texas, northern Louisiana, western Tennessee, central Kentucky, central West Virginia, southwestern Pennsylvania, southwestern and central New York, northern Connecticut and northern Rhode Island. Not known to breed east of the Alleghenies south of New England, but breeds west to the base of the Rocky Mountains in western Alberta, Montana, Wyoming and central Colorado; south in winter from Nebraska, Iowa, southern Michigan, Illinois, southern Ontario, southern New York, Massachusetts, New Hampshire and Maine, chiefly west of the Alleghenies

[1] Bulletin No. 50, United States National Museum; Birds of North and Middle America, Land Birds, Part II, 1902, p. 219.

to the Gulf coast; in migration or in winter casual on the seaboard of the south Atlantic states from Maryland to southern South Carolina.

DISTRIBUTION IN NEW ENGLAND. — *Maine:* Common migrant and local summer resident; accidental in winter in coastal region. *New Hampshire:* Common migrant and local summer resident; casual in winter. *Vermont:* Common migrant and common local summer resident. *Massachusetts:* Common to abundant migrant, common summer resident and rare or casual winter resident. *Rhode Island and Connecticut:* Common to abundant migrant, common summer resident in northern parts and casual or accidental winter resident.

SEASON IN MASSACHUSETTS. — February 23, March 4 to November 22 (winter).

HAUNTS AND HABITS. As winter nears its end grackles begin to move up the Atlantic coast from the south. They are land birds and follow the coast, but occasionally a few probably are blown out over the sea. Mr. F. F. Burr of Augusta, Maine, informs me that in early March, 1913, while coming north from Florida on the Clyde liner *Lenape*, several grackles came aboard off the Virginia coast, and being treated kindly by the passengers remained aboard the vessel all the way to New York, when they disappeared. Some day in March or early April when the brown earth has partly emerged from the receding snows of winter and while snowdrifts still linger in shady places, we may see a flock of blackbirds whirl into the top of some tall, lone, leafless tree. They may be too distant to identify by sight, but soon the twanging of their "loose-strung harps" floats down the wind and then we know that they are grackles. If in northern New England the singers presumably are Bronzed Grackles; if in extreme southern New England some of them are likely to be of the purple race. Both are known to the people as crow blackbirds. Evidently the grackles believe that they can sing, and they apply themselves to song with enthusiasm, industry and perseverance, but from our point of view their performance is not harmonious music. The outpourings of a flock of these birds have been likened to a "wheelbarrow chorus," but the sound might be better represented by a number of iron gates swinging, creaking and clanging on rusty un-oiled hinges. Musical or not it is one of the sounds of nature which is worth the hearing.

Later in the season you may see one or a pair in the back yard or on the lawn. The male is trim and handsome. As his iridescent plumage flashes in the sun he appears as a creature cast in polished bronze and blued steel. He walks with head held nearly level, taking not short, quick, nervous steps like the Starling, but longer, more labored strides. With each step his head is pushed forward and one shoulder is raised a trifle, and as he walks, his long tail swings a little from side to side. In the mating season he carries the tail rather high, and in flight, which is rather heavy, the upturning of the outer tail-feathers is very noticeable. Dr. Townsend gives the following account of the display of the male:

"The courtship of the Bronzed Grackle is not inspiring. The male puffs out his feathers to twice his natural size, partly opens his wings, spreads his tail and, if he is on the ground, drags it rigidly as he walks. At the same time he sings his song — such as it is — with great vigor and abandon. That this vocal performance should be classed as a song from a scientific point of view there is no doubt, but such it would not seem to the ordinary observer.   It is harsh and disagreeable, a squeaking, saw-filing explosion of notes.   It varies considerably and sometimes suggests the sound of a jet of escaping steam.   I have written it down *er wheet, dam that*, but my interpretation may have been influenced by my mental attitude induced by the performance.

"During the period of courtship the male in flight depresses the central feathers of its tail forming a V-shaped keel.   I was at first inclined to think that this was of use in flight like a rudder, but I am inclined to think that it is in the nature of courtship display, for this arrangement of tail feathers is not seen when a bird is actively engaged in flight for the purpose of obtaining food.   Under these circumstances the tail is spread in the ordinary manner." [1]   Sometimes two males, rivals for the favors of some female, fight fiercely in the air and when, later, a nesting colony has been established there are frequent battles.   Grackles are devoted to their young and rally to their defense in case of danger.   Mr. Hoyes Lloyd writes that when some young grackles were picked up and put in boxes for safe keeping the parents actually attacked and struck people who came near them.

Normally our crow blackbirds are birds of the marsh and water-side in forested regions.   As settlements and clearings took the place, in part, of the primeval forests, these birds found a new food supply in the corn crop of the settlers, and multiplied exceedingly. In colonial days crow blackbirds were known far and wide as maize thieves; bounties were paid for their heads, and in some Cape Cod towns a young man was forbidden by law to marry until he had turned in to the town clerk a certain quota of blackbirds' heads. The war against the birds was so successful that in 1749 locusts, cutworms and other grass-destroying pests so completely ruined the grass crop of the New England states that the farmers were obliged to send to England and Pennsylvania to obtain hay enough to feed their cattle through the winter.   The Swedish traveler Kalm tells us that after this occurrence the people "abated" their enmity against the "maize thieves" as they thought that they had observed the birds feeding on the pests which destroyed their crops. Owing to the widespread sentiment for the protection of the birds we have now again an excessive multiplication of grackles in New England with accompanying complaints of serious damage to the corn crop.

The grackle is a wise bird and like the Crow, the Blue Jay and the Starling, soon recognizes a place of safety.   It has learned to come into villages and cities and to nest in trees in parks and cemeteries and in grounds of the larger estates, where it prefers the white pine as a nesting tree.   A few Bronzed Grackles came into the Boston Public Garden before the year 1900, and then they began to breed there regularly and in some numbers, and although their favorite pine trees are not grown in the garden they have continued to nest there, meantime waging war on the "English" Sparrows which are now reduced to minimum numbers.   Thus far, also, the Grackles have held their own with the Starlings.

Grackles are extremely interesting birds; they rank high in intelligence.   They are excellent judges of the extent of the danger zone surrounding the man with a gun.   They

---

[1] Townsend, Charles W.: Supplement to the Birds of Essex County, Massachusetts, 1920, pp. 133,134.

destroy the eggs and young of other birds, and not only do they take young birds from the nests but they catch, kill and eat them after the little things are fledged and able to fly, and at times they kill adult birds. This has been observed repeatedly. I saw a Bronzed Grackle on Boston Common with a full-grown dead "English" Sparrow which it tried to carry away, as I thought, in its claws, but it dropped the smaller bird after flying up a few feet from the ground. In a letter received from Dr. John W. Dewis he says that he and others saw a flock of these sparrows on the wing, pursuing and apparently attacking a Bronzed Grackle, also in flight and carrying a live sparrow in its bill. When a few feet from the ground the grackle dropped his prey which was fluttering, and squatted over it, threatening the sparrows which soon gave up the fight. The grackle then pecked out the eyes of its victim, disemboweled it, ate the muscle from its right breast and left it. The bird proved to be a full-fledged "English" Sparrow. Major Mark Robinson wrote to me that he saw a pair of grackles attempt to rob the nest of a Red-winged Blackbird. The male Red-wing sat on the nest, covering it with his wings, while the female fought the robbers until other Red-wings came to her assistance and drove off the grackles, when the male Red-wing left his charges and attacked the enemy furiously. As a water bird the grackle is by no means a failure. It is fond of the water and bathes in it even in a Massachusetts winter. It walks about in shallow water with tail elevated to keep it dry. It often catches small fish by dipping down like a gull or a tern, though I have never seen one go entirely under water. Several observers have seen grackles take dry, hard pieces of stale bread and soak them in water until softened.

Grackles are scavengers to some extent, especially in cold weather, when they visit garbage cans and dumps where they pick up almost anything eatable. Mr. F. E. Campbell informs me that near Humarock Beach he saw one fly across the river with about two-thirds of an ice cream cone in its bill. The bird, he says, appeared as if its head was in the cornucopia.

Like crows, grackles are more or less omnivorous. Professor Beal lists their food as 30.3 per cent animal and 69.7 per cent vegetal. Besides insects they eat spiders, myriapods, crawfish, worms, sowbugs, hair snakes, snails, clams, fish, frogs, salamanders, lizards, small snakes, birds' eggs, birds and mice. They destroy enormous numbers of insect pests such as May beetles and white grubs, curculios and many other beetles, grasshoppers and locusts, caterpillars, including tent caterpillars, cutworms, army worms and brown-tail and gipsy caterpillars, bugs and ants. Among the vegetal food we can list all common grains, most wild and cultivated fruits grown in New England that are eaten by man and a few that are not, acorns, beech-nuts, chestnuts and the seeds of many noxious weeds, small bulbs, plant galls, grass and leaves. In spring a large part of their food consists of noxious insects, and when feeding the young the destruction of insects increases rapidly, as the young are fed a considerably larger proportion of insects than that taken by the adults. The adults are so fond of insects that they sometimes clumsily pursue them in the air and occasionally catch one, though they are not fitted to do the work of flycatchers; but in autumn when grain, fruit, nuts and seeds begin to develop, this species turns largely to vegetal food. Before the end of August, grackles assemble in flocks and these flocks increase in size until some contain thousands of birds. When such flocks roost in thickly settled localities they become a nuisance because of their noise and droppings. They sometimes ruin many early apples and pears pecking them as Starlings do, and eating only a little from each fruit. Such vast bodies of birds can do immense damage to corn-fields, and they attack the corn when it is in the milk. As they move south the flocks grow to enormous size. The most remarkable assemblage of these birds that I have seen is described in the following words:

"A great flight of these birds passed over Concord on October 28, 1904. From my post of observation, on a hilltop, an army of birds could be seen extending across the sky from one horizon to the other. As one of my companions remarked, it was a great 'rainbow of birds;' as they passed overhead, the line appeared to be about three rods wide and about one hundred feet above the hilltop. This column of birds appeared as perfect in form as a platoon. The individual birds were not flying in the direction in which the column extended, but diagonally across it; and when one considers the difficulty of keeping a platoon of men in line when marching shoulder to shoulder, the precision with which this host of birds kept their line across the sky seems marvelous. As the line passed overhead, it extended nearly east and west. The birds seemed to be flying in a course considerably west of south, and thus the whole column was gradually drifting southwest. As the left of the line passed over the Concord meadows, its end was seen in the distance, but the other end of this mighty army extended beyond the western horizon. The flight was watched until it was nearly out of sight, and then followed with a glass until it disappeared in the distance. It never faltered, broke, or wavered, but kept straight on into the gathering gloom of night. The whole array presented no such appearance as the unformed flocks ordinarily seen earlier in the season, but was a finer formation than I have ever seen elsewhere, among either land birds or water-fowl. It seemed to be a migration of all the Crow Blackbirds in the region, and there appeared to be a few Rusty Blackbirds with them. After that date I saw but one Crow Blackbird. It was impossible to estimate the number of birds in this flight. My companions believed there were 'millions.'" [1]

Others have reported flocks in New England containing 15,000 (estimated) or more birds. By the first of November most of the grackles have left New England for the south. A few flocks remain later in the southern parts, and occasional stragglers often spend the winter here. My farthest north winter record is City Point near Belfast, Maine, where the species passed the winter of 1924–25.[2]

ECONOMIC STATUS. There is much difference of opinion among ornithologists regarding the place of the crow blackbird in the economic scale. Let us then take the conclusions of the two men, who having examined 2,346 stomachs of these birds for the Biological Survey, have made the most exhaustive investigation of the food of grackles ever attempted. Professor Barrows opines that the crow blackbird is a serious foe to

---

[1] Useful Birds and Their Protection, 1913, pp. 314, 315.   [2] Newell, B. H.: *in litt.*, March 13, 1925.

the farmer, whenever it occurs in large numbers, but that "taken all in all the facts seem to show conclusively that the Bronzed Grackle is a valuable bird; which does considerably more good than harm. . . . The good done is widely distributed, the harm is often concentrated on a few acres." [1] Professor Beal says that these birds do a good share of the work of keeping insect life down to a proper level and are, therefore, most emphatically useful birds, but he says that when overcrowded, their numbers should be reduced. [2] Regarding the economic status of the Purple Grackle which is not common enough anywhere in New England to be much of an economic factor, the reader is referred to the report of Dr. B. H. Warren on the food of the bird. [3] Dr. Warren was the first to make any extended examination of its food.   He examined the stomach contents of about 700 crow blackbirds in Pennsylvania.   He tells of the food contents of 31 birds, shot in a corn-field, — 19 contained only cutworms, five contained chiefly beetles and seven showed some corn, with a large excess of insects.   October is the only month recorded by him when corn formed a large part of the food eaten.   Although the bird takes more or less corn it is an efficient enemy of the pernicious corn-borer.

[1] Barrows, W. B.: Michigan Bird Life, 1912, p. 460.
[2] Beal, F. E. L.: United States Department of Agriculture, Division of Biological Survey, Bulletin No. 13, 1900, p. 69.
[3] Birds of Pennsylvania, 1890, p. 221.